CW01034231

BRITISH RAILWAYS
ENGINEERING
1948–80

BRITISH RAILWAYS ENGINEERING 1948–80

by

John Johnson and Robert A. Long

Editor in Chief
Roland C. Bond, FEng, FICE, FIMechE
Sometime Chief Mechanical Engineer of British Railways

Foreword by Sir Peter Parker

MECHANICAL ENGINEERING PUBLICATIONS LTD
LONDON

FIRST PUBLISHED 1981
Reprinted 1982

ISBN 0 85298 446 4

Photoset in Great Britain by
Rowland Phototypesetting Ltd, Bury St Edmunds, Suffolk
and printed by St Edmundsbury Press
Bury St Edmunds, Suffolk

Contents

Foreword

by SIR PETER PARKER MVO
Chairman, British Railways Board

THIS is a remarkable book. Written by two retired railway officers, who have been guided by Roland Bond, that doyen of retired railway engineers, and a distinguished advisory panel, helped by the serving Chief Engineers and their staff, it was originally intended to be the story of the Engineer, but with the spirit of compromise so necessary in engineering, it has become the definitive and factual history of the Engineer's work, of railway engineering, from Nationalization in 1948 to the present day. With accuracy and readable ease and simplicity, it tells the story of an engineering revolution, of a period where the whole basis of railway engineering, in all its forms, was changed with its inevitable effect on the lives of men and women at every level throughout the business.

The story has been told before that, when the first production diesel main-line locomotives entered service in 1958 there was no new diesel locomotive maintenance depot, there were no electricians, and there was no artisan training school. On the other hand, there were plenty of boilermakers and steam fitters and steam drivers and firemen and there were engineers in charge. Men rose to the occasion to learn, to train, to organize as never before, to master a technological change so quick and unique to their experience and above all to handle the associated human problems which, if not thoroughly and fairly faced, could have checked progress and success. Within five years, the task had been completed, the total abolition of steam traction in this particular area. While this was going on, electrification at 25 kV was being introduced in part of the NE London Suburban area, affecting many of the same staff and managers. To electrify at high voltage posed many problems but the decision to do so was well taken. It was not immediately successful but within a matter of months, it was the effective precursor of the system of overhead electrification which, without doubt, will be extended in the hard driving years to come. Bridges will be altered or renewed, tunnel clearances increased, track relaid, modernized, and simplified, new signalling systems introduced of great sophistication and reliability. A challenge as great as faced the railway engineers all over the country in the period covered by the authors.

It is sometimes forgotten that we have been – indeed are – dependent on the expert knowledge of private industry, in many branches of railway engineering. And, of course, the converse must apply. There have been techniques of which our engineers had but little initial knowledge and experience but it is also fair to say the Manufacturers have gained their practical experience through this association with British Railways. Some of the service engineers who worked so closely with us in the early days, made their career with us; others, more senior, joined and enriched us with their particular knowledge of engineering and business in the private sector.

The High Speed Train has revolutionized the passenger business to the North East and the West and the electrically driven APT will do so under the wires to the north. I am dedicated, indeed committed to the policy of high-voltage, high-speed, high-efficiency electrification to replace diesel traction on main lines. It is the only way to run a first-rate railway: I intend to overcome the obstacles standing in our way and proceed, neither slowly nor with hesitation, but with vigour, determination, and speed to set the seal on the great work that our engineers have accomplished in recent years.

The task fills me with enthusiasm: it drives us on and we are building for the future, not only of the railway industry, but of mass high-speed transport. In every engineering department, we are creating, training, and developing engineering talent as never before. Some may say that they are a different breed, more academic, less practical but they are good and they will have to be good to accept the challenge to create, to develop, and then to extend the lifework of those who engineered 'the revolution' covered in the pages of this book.

Authors' Preface

THE title of this book needs some explanation. It relates to engineering in British Railways (sometimes abbreviated to BR) and no attempt has been made to consider the notable contributions to the development of railways by the engineers of London Transport. Furthermore, although some attention is paid to the manufacturing activities of British Railways itself, it has been impracticable to deal at any length with the vast contribution made by the railway manufacturing industry generally, without which the modernization and re-equipment of the railways would inevitably have been a much slower process.

Neither does the story confine itself to the years from 1948 to 1980. We have had good reason to discuss many aspects of engineering development which occurred before the creation of British Railways as a single entity. Not only did many of the engineers who have made their contribution to more recent railway technology gain their experience with the privately owned companies, but the engineering initiatives of those companies helped to shape today's railways. Indeed, such is the technical longevity of railway equipment that the engineer of 1980 is involved not only with modern technology but also with the maintenance of fixed works dating back to the middle of the nineteenth century, signalling installations more than a hundred years old and rolling stock built before nationalization in 1948.

We have not set out to write an engineering textbook or to capture the romance of railway engineering, which is closely associated with the design and performance of the steam locomotive. Our aim has been to record in as non-technical language as possible, and in the space available to us, the main railway engineering developments during years which were unique in the nature of the challenges which were presented, and in the opportunities offered. The story unfolds within the wider framework of transport policy in Britain, as external factors have influenced – and continue to influence – the shape of railway engineering development. Without an appreciation of this wider background it is not possible to understand why certain engineering decisions were taken at critical periods in the history of British Railways.

made by the officers of the British Railways Board must be the first to be acknowledged. It is not only the engineering departments which have assisted our work, as we have had considerable help from several of the Board's departments and subsidiaries. The Director of Public Affairs has been particularly helpful in the provision of photographs. The engineers have, however, borne the main weight of our inquiries at both Head-quarters and Regional levels. We would particularly acknowledge, there-fore, the assistance received from M. C. Purbrick, Chief Civil Engineer, K. Taylor, Chief Mechanical and Electrical Engineer, A. A. Cardani, Chief Signal and Telecommunications Engineer, and Dr K. H. Spring, followed by Dr A. H. Wickens, Director of Research. They and their officers, in particular F. G. Clements, N. Howard, and C. M. S. Maguire, have answered many questions and provided much information. Our thanks are also due to I. M. Campbell, Member of the Board responsible for Engineering and Research, who became Chief Executive (Railways) and then Vice-Chairman.

A number of officers who have retired from British Railways have also helped us to reconstruct earlier situations and we are most grateful to Dr M. R. Bonavia, E. Claxton, C. W. Edwards, A. I. Emerson, G. F. Fiennes, Dr Sydney Jones, John Ratter, E. C. Lyon, H. Wilcock, and the late Sir Allan Quartermaine.

Finally, we are grateful to R. C. Bond, A. H. Cantrell, E. G. Brentnall, A. H. Emerson, and T. C. B. Miller who, as fellow members of the Advisory Panel on the preparation of this book under the Chairmanship of E. L. Dellow of MEP Ltd, have been so helpful in many ways.

Postscript

It was with deep regret that we heard shortly before this book was published, of the sudden death of Roland Bond. During the first twenty years of the period under review he held a succession of very senior engineering posts – Chief Officer (Locomotive Construction and Main-tenance), Chief Mechanical Engineer, Technical Adviser, and General Manager, Workshops – at Railway Executive, BTC and BRB Head-quarters. In doing so, he made a very significant contribution towards the modernization and re-equipment of British Railways and the organizational developments which were necessary to meet the changing circumstances.

He was a dedicated railwayman and his Presidency of the Institution of Mechanical Engineers in 1963 and his election as a Fellow of Engineering are a measure of his stature as an engineer.

Over the past four years he has given us the benefit of his wide experience, as Editor in Chief. We are grateful to him and are sad that he did not live to see the publication of the results of his guidance.

Introduction

by ROLAND C. BOND

THE purpose of this book is to record, and comment as objectively as possible, upon the achievements of the engineering and research departments of British Railways during the first thirty years since they were brought under national ownership on January 1 1948. The period covered by this review has seen changes and innovations in railway technology more fundamental and far reaching in character than any previous similar span of years, even in the early days of railways.

For nearly 150 years the railways developed steam locomotives to a high degree of perfection; tracks became stronger and signalling very much more sophisticated with the use of electric track circuits. The reader will find that with the introduction of diesel and electric traction many developments in all fields of railway technology appeared, and any account of the work undertaken by the Engineering Departments would be incomplete without some explanation and comment on the broad political and organizational backgrounds against which it was carried out. This the authors have provided with penetrating insight.

Most of the members of the Railway Executive were not unfamiliar with the problems involved in welding four proud companies into one organization, as they were enjoined to do by the 1947 Transport Act. They would remember, may even have taken part in, the inter-company rivalries arising from the 1923 amalgamations. Thus, they were well prepared to resolve and settle the conflicting interests which would inevitably arise.

Clearly the work ahead demanded firm central direction. It was indeed fortunate that the Railway Executive was organized on functional lines. The two engineering Members were, in effect, chief departmental officers to whom certain corporate responsibilities were added. They exercised unchallenged authority from top to bottom over their departments at Headquarters and in the Railway Regions. Without this, progress to the desired objectives would inevitably have been slower and less certain.

To a greater extent than in many other branches of the profession railway engineers are required to live, day in, day out, with their own creations. They specify, design, and often manufacture and build the structures and moving and fixed equipment which together constitute a railway system, for the operation and maintenance of which they are held responsible. One hears criticisms from time to time that railway engineers tend to be unduly conservative in their outlook, but let it never be forgotten that they are the custodians of the safety of the travelling public and all who use and work upon the railways. There is no one to whom they can pass the buck if things go wrong.

The original proposal that this book should be written arose from discussions among members of the Railway Division Committee of the Institution of Mechanical Engineers, and since no individual could possibly possess all the necessary technical knowledge or know the entire story from personal experience, an Advisory Panel, consisting of representatives of all the railway engineering disciplines, was set up to provide information and guidance to the authors.

Many engineers who have been involved in the development of railway engineering have written of their experiences. It is difficult, however, to be personally associated with the making of history and, at the same time, to write objectively about the experience. That is why the two authors who were invited to write this book are not engineers. Both were, however, intimately involved in the development of British Railways since nationalization in senior appointments and worked closely with their engineering colleagues.

I have regarded my task as Editor as being to ensure, as far as possible, complete accuracy as to facts and I have had the closest possible co-operation throughout from both authors in accepting any suggestions which I felt it necessary to make. Opinions expressed and conclusions drawn are theirs alone.

The authors in their Preface have mentioned the work of the Advisory Panel, and I should finally like to add my tribute to the help and support which my fellow members have given throughout.

CHAPTER ONE

End of an Era
1923 to 1947

T HERE has always been a sense of massive continuity about railways. Their great appetite for capital investment, the rugged longevity of their equipment, the bold confidence of their early building, and the statutory structure within which they function have all contributed to an aura of enduring inevitability. Indeed, is there not a grandly assertive ring in the very use of the term 'permanent way'?

Any record of engineering development within British Railways since 1948 cannot ignore the unique manner in which earlier experience shaped the more recent story of railways in Great Britain. Much of the engineering effort within these later years has been concerned with overcoming problems which have arisen from early policies. The nature of these problems will unfold as the following narrative evolves but some knowledge of the last twenty-five years of private ownership of railways in Britain forms an essential introduction to the chronicle of engineering activity since nationalization. This was not only a period which included much brilliant engineering innovation, many serious economic problems, and the grave results of wartime deprivation. These were also the years when so many of the engineers who would make their impact after 1948 were already at work and gaining the experience which would prepare them for their later responsibilities.

By 1921 the dominance of railways in the British transport scene had passed high noon. In the August of that year the Railways Act received the Royal Assent. Recognizing the fact that some of the weaker railway companies needed the financial support of their stronger neighbours, the Act created four major groups out of 123 separate railways. On the first day of January, 1923, four new companies were to operate the main lines of the country for exactly a quarter of a century. Ranking them in order of size they were the London, Midland and Scottish (LMS), London and North Eastern (LNER), Great Western (GWR), and the Southern (SR). The LMS alone was Britain's largest commercial enterprise.

Maybe, the country was too occupied with its post-war problems in the 1920s to realize that the early splutterings on its roads of vehicles fuelled by cheap and plentiful petroleum would rise to a volume which would soon challenge the very assumptions of railway continuity on which the 1921 Act was based. Also, this development would lead to technological advances in all forms of transport which would gather enormous pace within the half-century to come. Within the railways themselves the steam locomotive was about to enter its golden era of the 1930s, which was also to be the decade of a revolution in railway signalling technology, a number of early diesel traction experiments, and the expansion of suburban electric services South of London.

In effect, the 1921 legislation was the first stage in the painful process of adjustment in the relationship between British railways and the State since the pinnacle of the railway age, which coincided with the beginning of the First World War. The nineteenth-century railway enjoyed such a technological superiority over other forms of inland transport that it was difficult to think of any future situation when it would not be necessary in the public interest to curb its dominating enterprise within a framework of statutory restriction and obligation. This supremacy diminished with the advance of the internal combustion engine on the roads and, later, with the coming of powered flight. Public opinion, however, has always been very reluctant to recognize the fact that the railway may no longer be the most suitable means of fulfilling all the obligations expected from a nationwide transport system. Consequently, the right balance between the scale of railway activity and what society expects from its railways has been fought out in the cockpit of British national politics over five decades. This is not the place to consider how the problem has been tackled in Britain and elsewhere. It is sufficient to say, at the risk of understatement, that since the 1920s the British railway engineer has worked in ever-changing situations which have been unique in the nature of the challenge presented and the opportunity offered.

With the benefit of being able to look back through half a century it is all too easy to say that railway affairs should have been ordered differently in the 1920s and 1930s. More rail services could well have been closed: there should have been a greater rationalization of freight depots: competing routes should have been reduced: the demise of the steam locomotive foreseen. At the same time, it must be remembered that the Government had itself rejected the conception of a single railway management which would have had the incentive to rationalize its activities. Instead, it was decided to preserve the spur of competition between companies which had, therefore, good reason to suck business from each other by extending their tentacles. Later, the four group Companies were allowed to diversify their activities into road transport and so participate as major operators in a wider world of transport which embraced rail, road, shipping, port, and airline interests.

Meanwhile, two massive obstacles to change remained. One was the framework of statutory obligation and regulation. The other was the inability to attract investment funds to the railways. Profits were at a very low level due to a combination of low economic activity and a standard system of passenger fares and freight rates throughout the country.

Although the worsening financial position of the four Companies during the inter-war years began a period of serious under-investment in the railways of Britain which was to last until the 1960s, there were several valuable lessons learned by the engineers during this period which were to serve them well in later years. The first was a highly developed skill in achieving an objective with the use of minimum resources. There may well be differing views on the technical aspects of the Southern Railway electrification schemes but none can doubt the scale of the benefit in relation to the investment input. The second was the effect of rivalry between the Companies. Handicapped by inflexible pricing policies, competition concentrated on the quality of service given to the customer and on standards of engineering excellence. Never, since the races between London and Scotland in 1895, had railway rivalry been so publicly relished, or fanned by the media, as when the GWR 4–6–0 *Caerphilly Castle* and LNER 4–6–2 *Flying Scotsman* rested alongside each other at the Wembley Exhibition in 1924, both claiming to be Britain's most powerful express passenger locomotive. Or again, when the LMS and LNER urged their main-line locomotives to ever higher levels of performance, culminating in those epic non-stop runs between London, Glasgow, and Edinburgh on the West Coast route and *Mallard*'s world speed record for steam of 126 miles/h, achieved in 1938 south of Grantham on the East Coast route. The third lesson was that of the value of the practical co-operation which developed between the engineers in the four Companies, in spite of the rivalries which existed.

The exchange of ideas occurred not only within the professional Institutions. It came about also through the movement of individual engineers between companies, of which the appointment of W. A. Stanier to the LMS from the GWR, O. V. S. Bulleid to the SR from the LNER and A. F. Bound to the LMS from the LNER were outstanding examples. It emerged again at the meetings of the associations formed by the chief civil and mechanical engineers of the groups. The First World War had already brought the engineers from the pre-group Companies very close together: so close, in fact, that standard locomotive designs were prepared in anticipation of a post-war nationalization that never materialized.

It could well be said that the typical British compromise course between maintaining the status quo, which would have brought financial disaster to some companies, and unification into one system was what the country wanted in the period between the two world wars. It was a stage on the road to later nationalization but preserved a spirit of individualism in engineering design when technological horizons were expanding.

Within the mechanical field the activities of the electrical engineer and the road motor engineer were rapidly developing within the main line

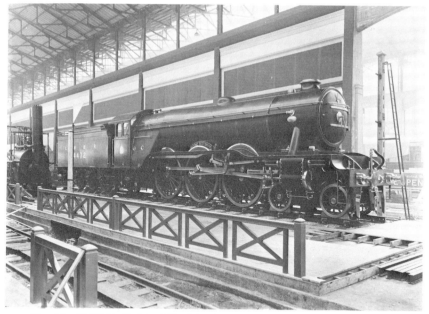

Fig. 1.1   LNER Pacific No. 4472 *Flying Scotsman* at the British Empire Exhibition, Wembley in 1924 (NRM)

Companies. Indeed, until the process of diversification was put into reverse in the 1960s, the railways were to become the biggest road transport operators in the country. Also, the signal engineer was beginning to challenge his organizational sponsorship by the civil engineer as signalling became more sophisticated. In engineering terms the atmosphere was stimulating but in the background lurked the restricting knowledge that the Companies were not producing the net revenue expected and the annual shareholders' meetings could be very difficult experiences for the company directors. It is to the everlasting credit of the Boards, managers, engineers, and all grades of staff that engineering standards were maintained in years when the railways were unable to meet fully their obligations to shareholders and temporary wages cuts had to be made. It would have been so easy during these financially depressing years for maintenance to have deteriorated to the extent experienced more recently, and so sadly, in North America. A more serious threat to these high standards of maintenance was to become a reality during the Second World War. It was to arise again, only to be rejected, in the 1960s. These stories are for later telling.

What were the engineering experiences of the four group Companies which prepared the railways for the second half of this century, and moulded the attitudes of the engineers who were to shoulder the responsibilities of that later period? A railway begins with its infrastructure but the civil engineering task has never excited the popular imagination as has the story of locomotion. The main reason is that few civil engineers between the two wars ever had the opportunity to build the kind of structure by which the Stephensons, father and son, or Isambard Kingdom Brunel so perfectly expressed the confidence of their age. The later civil engineers have had to shoulder the less exciting task of maintaining, or replacing, over 100 000 structures erected mainly in the nineteenth century and inherited by the four group Companies in 1923 as a virtually completed national railway network. The effort put into railway building had been prodigious and the results dwarfed the creative wonders of earlier ages. During the peak years of the mid-1840s about a million men were involved, directly or indirectly, in railway construction. Between 1830 and 1860 an average of 1000 bridges were built in Britain by railway engineers every year. By 1860 the great builders like the Stephensons, Brunel, and Joseph Locke had left the scene but most of their great monuments remain in useful service cared for by their successors after more than a century has passed.

Also, the less centralized nature of civil engineering design has allowed much of the work to proceed at lower organizational levels than has ever been the case with the servicing and maintenance of mechanical equipment. Mechanical engineering design has always been a more centralized function. Indeed, the LNER found it necessary to create the position of Chief Civil Engineer only following the special need for co-ordination under Second World War conditions. The occupant of the post was never in the position of, for example, John Miller, Engineer of the North Eastern Area of the LNER at York from 1925 to 1937. Miller will be long remem-

Fig. 1.2 Brunel's bridge across the Tamar at Saltash, photographed on the centenary of its opening in May, 1859. Carrying today's heavier loads, the bridge is still in use (BRB)

bered for his inspiring contribution in such areas as standards of design and support for bold signalling developments.

That there was a need for co-operation between the civil engineers from the different railways was recognized by the existence of the Railway Engineers Association. With the sturdy independence of their forebears these engineers allowed their General Managers only to take note of their minutes but that was the limit of vertical integration permitted. The most important of the decisions made by the Association was when they agreed on a standard rail section, but it was of particular interest that there were, in effect, two standards. One was of 95 lb a yard applying to three companies while the Great Western used both 95 lb and 97½ lb as standards. Again, the Great Western used a different method of fastening chair to sleeper, preferring bolts through the sleeper to the large coach screws used by the other main-line railways. A revealing aspect of a recent conversation between the authors and the late Sir Allan Quartermaine, the Chief Engineer of the Great Western at the time of nationalization, was that he had no cause to question the reasons for other companies not conforming to GWR practice.

These permanent-way differences provided only one example of how the Great Western had preserved its identity. It tended to stamp its pattern after 1923 on the companies with which it was amalgamated to an extent never experienced on the other three groups and this was due to its dominating position in the new partnership. There was none of the watchful competition as on the LMS between London and North Western and Midland practices or on the LNER between North Eastern and Great Northern engineers. As early as June 1923, F. T. Bowler, Permanent Way Assistant to the Chief Civil Engineer of the Great Western gave the first of two lectures to the South Wales Section of the Permanent Way Institution. The title was 'GWR Standard Permanent Way Practice' and the lectures were '. . . primarily intended for the guidance of those who have recently joined the Great Western Railway Group and are more or less unfamiliar with its practice . . .' In effect, a detailed code of practice was being laid down for those who had just come under the protective umbrella of Paddington.

Apart from the new family of marshalling yards built in the 1930s, of which the Up Yard at Whitemoor on the LNER was the first, the civil engineering effort between the wars was mainly concerned with the complete renewal of some 23000 miles of track, the re-building of 350 passenger stations, and a number of electrification schemes. Electrification was mainly on the SR suburban services but the Manchester–Sheffield–Wath scheme of the LNER and the five-year programme in the London area supported by Government funds began in the later 1930s. During the national economic blizzard of that time the return on capital invested in the railways was sinking almost to half the figure of 4·7 per cent, which Parliament had considered to be a reasonable rate. In these circumstances many developments, including new stations and signal boxes, had to wait over a quarter of a century for the modernization funds of the 1950s and 1960s. Many of the new bridges that were later to figure in the civil engineering programmes owed their existence, rather ironically, to major investment in road building developments.

The civil engineer was particularly concerned with the more efficient maintenance of the existing permanent way and works. In this area the introduction of a limited number of high-speed trains in the mid-1930s brought its own problems. They demanded more lateral support in the current form of track laid with 95 lb a yard bull-head rails. This led to experiments with flat-bottom rails, initially of 110 lb a yard section. The rail profile attributed to C. B. Vignoles in 1837 and used on a world-wide scale had now returned to the land of its birth. Also, the advent of the Coronation Scot between London and Glasgow in 1937 required the re-alignment of many miles of track on the West Coast main line of the LMS.

Steel sleepers were used in the years between the wars, though on a relatively small scale, and have never been laid to any great extent in Britain. Concrete sleepers were also introduced during the same period although the first really large-scale installations were not introduced until 1946. Track-laying machinery for renewals was in its infancy. Measured shovel packing was introduced on LMS tracks, so assisting maintenance by allowing more accurate measurement of the amount of chippings

Fig. 1.3 Paddington Station in 1980. The modern lines of a Mark III carriage blend harmoniously with the details of a train shed built in 1854 by Isambard Kingdom Brunel, with ornamentation by Matthew Digby Wyatt (From the collection of Bernard Kaukas)

required under the sleepers. The big programmes for the continuous welding of rails appeared after 1948 but welded rails in relatively short sections had been in use for many years, particularly in special locations such as tunnels and under bridges. In the *Railway Gazette* dated 21 July 1939, A. H. Cantrell of the Southern Railway gave the first explanation of the behaviour of long welded rails, which did much to overcome apprehension regarding their propensity to buckle on expansion in very hot weather. Much new knowledge was also gained from research into such diverse subjects as soil mechanics and protective coatings.

Although the era of the four group Companies was associated with competition, experiment, and evolution, the financial resources were never available for innovation on a large scale. The civil engineer was not accustomed to seeking financial approval for large schemes. He was more likely to be given an objective and then be expected to achieve it within a prescribed financial limit. Thus, when the Great Western decided to accelerate The Bristolian, which involved the raising of speed limits in several places, the two District Engineers involved were each told what had to be done. They were also told that each would be allowed to spend up to £5000 on the work. With objective and resources fixed, only ingenuity could get the required result!

Every effort was made to avoid capital expenditure in every area of engineering, particularly on the LNER which was financially so dependent on the depressed heavy industries of North East England. One of the reasons for contracting with the Pullman Car Company to provide their luxury services on the East Coast route was to avoid the extensive building of new restaurant cars. Also, the LNER introduced some complicated operating regulations to avoid new signalling investment on a large scale, including the well-known one which required the clearance of two block sections ahead of the high-speed trains introduced during the 1930s between London, Scotland, and the West Riding of Yorkshire.

The same period was, however, an age of extraordinary vitality in railway signal engineering even if the results were limited in application. Before the amalgamations in 1923, railway signalling had barely emerged from the purely mechanical age. York Locomotive Yard signal box with 295 levers in one row remained the supreme example of the manual operation of points and signals but illuminated signal box diagrams had been in use for some years. Also, experience of three-position semaphore and power signalling had been brought together in the new installation on the Eastern side at London Victoria in 1918.

In 1915, A. F. Bound of the Great Central had caused some stir among his contemporaries by advocating the replacement of the block system of signalling by continuous track circuiting. This could have been taken as another example of the brash Great Central kicking over the traces but, after the formation of the LNER, Bound was to introduce three-aspect colour-light signalling between Marylebone and Neasden Junction in

Fig. 1.4 Crewe South Junction, with signal box and gantry typical of the equipment inherited by the main-line companies in 1923 (NRM)

1923, only three years after the first use in Britain of the daylight colour-light on the Liverpool Overhead Railway.

Bound left the LNER to become Chief Signal Engineer of the LMS. He was always an advocate of speed signalling, as distinct from purely route signalling, and installed Britain's only speed signalling scheme at Mirfield in 1932. His great contribution to railway signalling had been to change from an emphasis placed solely on keeping trains physically apart to combining this objective with that of ensuring that trains were kept on the move. This was achieved by giving drivers a more comprehensive indication of the state of the line ahead of their trains. Two-aspect signalling had now been developed to the four-aspect stage. The Southern had been the first railway in the world to adopt four-aspect colour-light signalling, when it was introduced in 1926 between Holborn Viaduct and Elephant and Castle in the London area.

Meanwhile, another great signal engineer was placing emphasis on continuous track circuits and relay interlocking, which would later lead to substantial reductions in the number of signal boxes required. In theory, it was now possible to think of a railway controlled from one location only. A. E. Tattersall has been termed 'the father of modern railway signalling' and was certainly responsible for giving the main impetus to miniaturization in signalling along with signal box concentration.

In the early 1930s, Tattersall was responsible for introducing the first relay interlocking scheme of its size in the world with continuous track circuits. It covered 25 miles of multiple track between York and Northallerton with the central area controlled from the route relay interlocking at Thirsk, where the operation of only one panel switch could set up a complete route. Backed by his chief, John Miller (on the LNER the Signal Engineer at York was responsible to the Area Civil Engineer), he soon brought in the new Leeds West and Hull Paragon schemes. On the very day when the Second World War began (3 September 1939) Tattersall achieved another world 'first' in the signal box at Northallerton, where the route set up for every train was indicated by a visual display in lights.

Modern marshalling yard design was pioneered on the LNER at Whitemoor near March with power-operated points, track circuit protection, hydraulic wagon retarders in the Up Yard and eddy current retarders in the Down Yard. Toton Down Yard on the LMS followed, but the automatic regulation of the wagon retarding force was to be a post-war development. Marshalling yards are unique as meeting points for the mechanical, civil, signalling, and electrical engineers, who share the responsibility in a comparatively small area for producing and maintaining a multi-disciplinary tool of railway operation.

Automatic train control made limited progress within the four Companies as a whole. The Great Western system was extended and the LMS installed the Hudd system on the London–Shoeburyness line. The LNER were beginning to introduce the Hudd system between Edinburgh and

Glasgow in 1939 but the Southern had decided to concentrate on multiple-aspect colour-light signalling rather than automatic train control systems. Further developments had to await the later unification of the railways, but the signal engineer had achieved enough in other fields greatly to improve safety in operation while at the same time increasing line capacity.

The mechanical engineers of the four Companies had more scope for developing their equipment than the civil engineers although change was not as revolutionary as that experienced in signal engineering. Apart from the remarkable development of electrification on the Southern suburban services (where A. D. Jones and A. Raworth had played a prominent role), the planning of two electrification schemes by H. W. H. Richards on the LNER, some early work on diesel traction, and functional carriage design, efforts were directed primarily to improving the performance of the steam locomotive. The extent of the effort is appreciated when any comparison is made between the relatively unsophisticated locomotives of 1923 and the machines of the later 1930s when steam performance had reached its peak.

At the time of amalgamation Great Western practice dominated the locomotive scene. G. J. Churchward had embodied in the Swindon-built product not only his own experimental work but also the best ideas that he could garner from Europe and America. C. B. Collett inherited from him the most highly standardized and efficient locomotive fleet in Britain. The great Churchward tradition was perpetuated by Collett, whose products were soon to have an influence on both LMS and LNER designs after running over the tracks of the two northern companies. The Great Western enjoyed a sense of effortless superiority in locomotive matters. This was due mainly to Churchward's contribution but also to the fact that the amalgamations of 1923 strengthened the corporate unity of the GWR. The other groups had the problem of reconciling the policies of proud and powerful partners.

In the case of the LMS, George Hughes was appointed as the Company's first Chief Mechanical Engineer. Although his background was with the Lancashire and Yorkshire Railway he made sincere attempts to decide on the best features of the pre-grouping locomotive designs which he had inherited and he generally favoured Midland Railway practice. It was typical of the man that the type of whistle to be chosen as the new standard emerged from a competitive test of company whistles. It was also typical of the period that the winner of the open-air contest, being a Caledonian product, so offended certain sensitive Midland ears that it was not introduced for another decade.

In 1925 Hughes was succeeded by Sir Henry Fowler, a Midland man who made no secret of his preference for Midland products. The Midland policy of small engines was, however, not consistent with the need to run fast and heavy West Coast expresses, or heavy coal trains between Toton and Brent, with an eye to the need for maximum economy in manpower. So the 4–6–0 Royal Scot and the Garratt designs emerged to meet the operating needs of the time. The *Royal Scot* was remarkable in that it incorporated not only good features from the locomotives of the LMS pre-grouping companies but also the results of the trials with the GWR Castle class along with some ideas from the Southern 4–6–0 *Lord Nelson*, the drawings of which had been made available to the LMS. Piecemeal development on these lines could have had disastrous results: in the event the outcome was very successful and some of the engineers associated with this locomotive were to play a significant part in locomotive design after the LMS ceased to exist.

Fowler was succeeded by E. H. J. Lemon and he was in turn succeeded by W. A. Stanier from the GWR. During the next twelve years Stanier transformed the face of mechanical engineering on the LMS. With his Swindon background he was not concerned with pre-grouping rivalries on the LMS except to end them. The Caledonian whistle now became a standard fitting on LMS locomotives! Standardization, simplification, and good organization were the objectives in the Stanier era.

The LNER had only one Chief Mechanical Engineer between the wars – Sir Nigel Gresley. He was, therefore, in a position to exert the greatest influence of any holder of the post on the practice of his Company. Although he introduced considerable standardization within the different classes of large locomotive which he introduced, the LNER was noted for its proliferation of locomotive classes. For one thing, the financial situation of the company precluded large building programmes. At the same time, Gresley did not reject the products of his pre-grouping predecessors if they worked efficiently and sometimes perpetuated their designs in LNER building programmes.

On the Southern Railway R. E. L. Maunsell of the South Eastern and Chatham had been appointed Chief Mechanical Engineer. He had been quick to realize the significance of Churchward's work and recruited key men from Swindon to the cosmopolitan team of senior engineers at his former headquarters in Ashford. Southern development in steam locomotive design was on a relatively modest scale between the wars as the company's resources were being so heavily committed to the electrification of the suburban passenger services. The name of Maunsell will, however, always be remembered for his two express passenger designs: the 4–6–0 Lord Nelson class and the very successful 4–4–0 Schools. With the coming of O. V. S. Bulleid from the LNER as successor to Maunsell in 1937 steam on the Southern was to achieve new performance standards. Revolutionary designs of locomotive appeared and carriages took on a new, functional, look. Bulleid now had both the authority and rather more financial backing for introducing his ideas than he had enjoyed on the LNER as Gresley's deputy.

Before discussing Bulleid's work – much of which took place during

Fig. 1.5   The earliest known photograph of a locomotive. Crampton's *Folkstone* (sic) of 1851 looks strangely out of date when compared with the great civil engineering works of the same decade which are still in use today (BRB)

the Second World War – it would be convenient at this stage to chronicle the relationship between the Companies and the electrification of railways. Reference has already been made to the Southern policy of suburban electrification and this Company, under the skilful leadership of its General Manager, Sir Herbert Walker, was the only group to carry out a consistent programme of electrification.

The competition of the electric tramways south of the River Thames had stimulated electrification in this area before the amalgamations of 1923. Other pre-grouping Companies had developed separate pockets of electric rail services in other parts of England. The most determined approach was that of the North Eastern Railway. Its Chief Mechanical Engineer, Sir Vincent Raven, not only electrified the local passenger services on Tyneside but introduced Britain's first electric freight service on the heavy coal-carrying line between Shildon and Newport. It is also very probable that the North Eastern's main line between York and Newcastle would have been electrified if war had not broken out in 1914 and been followed by industrial recession in the North East. This proposal was not revived after the 1923 amalgamations when some consideration was given to the Taunton-Penzance section of the GWR and the LNER trans-Pennine route between Manchester and Sheffield.

On the Lancashire and Yorkshire Railway Sir John Aspinall had been responsible for the electrification of the Liverpool–Southport and Manchester–Bury passenger services while on the Midland Railway James Dalziel, working under Sir Henry Fowler, brought into service electric trains on the Lancaster–Morecambe–Heysham section. On the London and North Western lines Cortez Leigh undertook the schemes which reached out from London to Watford and Richmond, but the company's ideas for electric underground services in Birmingham and Manchester were without result.

Apart from the Shildon–Newport line all the electrification schemes introduced before the great developments on the Southern in the 1930s were confined to relatively short distance passenger services. They were motivated by a mixture of engineering initiative and commercial necessity. Britain not only had a great natural asset in suitable locomotive coal but exported it to less favoured countries. There was not, therefore, the same incentive at national level to develop main-line electrification policies as existed in several European states. The Government did take some interest, however, in the standardization of electrification systems and in the matter of main-line electrification. In the 1920s the Kennedy and Pringle Committees considered the alternative standard systems which should be adopted in Britain and these will be referred to again in Chapter Seven. One of the systems recommended was used by the LMS and LNER when they electrified their joint passenger service between Manchester and Altrincham.

In 1931 a committee under the chairmanship of Lord Weir reported on the 'economic and other aspects of the electrification of the railway systems in Great Britain with particular reference to main-line working'. The findings were very favourable to the case for main-line electrification: indeed, they referred to the relatively modest outlay in relation to the spending on roads at that time! The omens for the modernization of motive power on British main lines seemed favourable.

The reality was different. The attitude of the Companies was well

Fig. 1.6   Gresley's P1 Class of locomotives was restricted to two. They were designed to haul 100-wagon coal trains between Peterborough and London, so improving productivity in freight movement. An auxiliary booster engine fitted to the trailing wheels allowed this locomotive to develop a maximum tractive power of 47 000 lb

summarized by Lord Stamp, Chairman of the LMS Board, when he
addressed the Company's shareholders in 1935 in the following terms:

> Close consideration has recently been given to . . . the general question of
> main-line electrification. Although our inquiries are not complete, there does
> not appear to be any likelihood of any further large-scale outlay in the im-
> mediate future. We have a statutory obligation to show annually to the Railway
> Rates Tribunal that our affairs have been conducted with efficiency and
> economy, quite apart from the Board's obligation to you in this respect, and any
> new outlay for electrification or anything else must comply with that test. If any
> new work is unlikely in due course to pay its way, clearly the burden will fall on
> railway users generally, or the proprietors or employees, or partly one or
> another. Such outlay differs from the competitive expenditure on public roads
> for motor traction, which causes a charge on the rates, whether the expenditure
> is commercially justified or not. Those who talk glibly on the subject without
> knowledge of the facts may not bother much about this aspect, but we have to
> do so. The merits and amenities of electricity have to be weighed against the
> merits of other forms of tractive power, with due regard to the risk involved in
> new outlay on fixed plant in the present still indefinite position of the finance of
> the public roads.

In his speech Stamp rightly outlined the statutory and economic
verities of the situation. At the same time, the railway engineer would
have listened in vain for any sign of enthusiasm for the electrification of
the Company's main lines. A pointed reference was made to the funding
of roads on a non-commercial basis but no clear hint given that the LMS
would welcome similar treatment. Viscount Churchill, Chairman of the
GWR, had been rather more definite. Writing to the Minister of Transport
as Chairman of the Railway Companies Association, which represented
the owners of all the Companies, he implied that the Companies would
want to know what investment resources would be made available from
the Government before showing greater interest in the proposals. The
Government was not responsive.

The outcome must have been very disappointing to the advocates of
main-line electrification, particularly to H. W. H. Richards who, as Chief
Electrical Engineer of the LNER, had given great assistance in the preparation of the Weir report. Under the Railways (Agreement) Act of 1935
the Government decided to give some financial assistance towards
electrification in order to stimulate a very sluggish economy. It was some
consolation to Richards that his Company was to benefit from two projects. One was the main-line scheme linking Manchester, Sheffield, and
the colliery area of Wath-on-Dearne. The other was the suburban passenger service between London (Liverpool Street) and Shenfield. Neither
scheme would have been contemplated if Government funds had not
been made available.

There was clearly a degree of ambivalence in the attitude of the Companies to electrification. In pre-grouping days, the engineering urge to
experiment and the commercial competition from the electric tramways

provided the motivation to electrify. Only the North Eastern came close to the objective of main-line electrification. The Great Eastern and Great Northern produced prototype tank locomotives with the aim of showing that steam traction could equal electrification in suburban working, but these were desperate measures by Companies which were well aware that they could not financially service the investment in electric traction.

The situation of the four group Companies was different. The Government showed its interest in electrification by the appointment of committees to consider the standardization of systems and application to main-line working. The Companies were interested but not prepared to worsen their already low return on capital. The promise of financial support from Government necessary to bridge the gap did not materialize until 1935 and was limited to the creation of further pockets of electrification: not to a nationwide main-line plan. It was linked more to national economic reflation than to the conclusions of the Weir Report.

The attitude of the Southern to electrification was more positive than the almost aloof approach of the other Companies. By 1930 the Southern had 857 miles of track electrified and was able to claim 'the world's greatest suburban electrification'. The commuter characteristics of the Southern network clearly had a strong bearing on the situation but another feature played its part. The three other Companies seem to have regarded electrification as a means of improving train working efficiency and reducing costs. The Southern also thought in these terms. In addition, their management saw the positive revenue-earning potential of electric services which does not appear to have figured in the main-line passenger service calculations of the other Companies. This positive marketing drive gave a great impetus to progressive electrification investment on the Southern.

It will have already been appreciated that the years following the creation of the four amalgamated group Companies in 1923 had been characterized by both co-operation and conflict. These years began with the organizational problems of bringing together the attitudes of over a hundred companies and were later to be clouded by financial problems. It was also a time which was rich in engineering experience. It said much for the spirit of enterprise within the four Companies that this period produced the world's fastest steam trains, the longest regular non-stop runs, new frontiers in railway signalling, the commissioning of a joint LMS/LNER Locomotive Testing Station at Rugby, and much experimental work which had brought the steam locomotive to a peak of performance which it proved difficult to exceed in later years. Taking into consideration speed, comfort, and frequency, the British passenger train service had every claim to be considered the best in the world. The same could not be said for the freight service. It was within neither the political nor the financial capacity of the Companies to take over and re-equip the wagons in private ownership. Much of the rail freight traffic was still being carried in vehicles and operating conditions associated more with the nineteenth than with the twentieth century.

The next stage in progress towards railway unification in Britain occurred on 3 September 1939, when the darkness of war descended on Europe. The four Companies, along with the London Passenger Transport Board, were now managed as one system by the Railway Executive Committee under the chairmanship of Sir Ralph Wedgwood, Chief General Manager of the LNER. The transition from peace to war was remarkably smooth but the belief that war fell upon an unprepared nation is not easily shaken. There had been some preparations made by the railways during a period of over two years and the Railway Executive Committee itself was appointed in September 1938. Also, some Government work had been undertaken in railway workshops before 1939.

From 1940 until mid-1942 all available men and machines were involved in the production of war materials, leaving a much reduced part of the Companies' workshop facilities serving railway activities on a make-do-and-mend basis. The railway shops produced aircraft, artillery, tanks, boats, high explosive bombs, and much highly specialized equipment. The skills of the railway engineers were, therefore, during this period stretched well beyond the boundaries of railway production: this was to prepare them for the application of new technologies from the automotive and aircraft industries to future railway products. It was also to stretch them in the physical sense as they had, at the same time, not only to manufacture the means to fight a war but also to keep in working order the transport system which was the very lifeblood of wartime existence. In fact, the increasing importance of the transport effort to the outcome of the war was later to result in a reversal of policy regarding railway workshops. By mid-1942 Government work was moved elsewhere and the shops were exerting most of their effort in making and repairing locomotives and wagons in order to keep the expanding Allied armies on the move.

Fig. 1.7   The Southern Railway progressively developed their electrified system. These vehicles were built in 1937 for the London (Waterloo)–Portsmouth service (BRB)

The war took its toll of the railways not only through the diversion of design and construction capacity to the machinery of war. The Companies released over 109000 of their staff, including many to the Transportation Companies of the Royal Engineers: these Companies were recruited entirely from railwaymen. Some of the most senior of engineers were released, including W. A. Stanier, Chief Mechanical Engineer of the LMS, and R. A. Riddles, at that time Mechanical and Electrical Engineer of the LMS in Scotland and who will figure later in the story. The strain on the engineers who remained in railway service was very severe. They had to cope with their normal task, supplemented in many cases by ordnance responsibilities, as well as keeping in running order a railway which was a prime target for enemy attack and burdened by over half a million special trains during the period of the war.

It was with great enthusiasm, therefore, that the railway engineer responded to the mood of the nation when it began to think of its future in a post-war world. While the epic Beveridge report on Social Insurance was being written, including the words 'The object of government in peace and war is . . . the happiness of the common man', the railways were developing their post-war philosophies, both individually and corporately. The corporate effort was to be shaped later by the Railway Companies Association mainly into political areas concerning the future ownership of the railways, but the individual Companies were more involved in preparing plans of a physical nature which directly involved the engineers. The LNER, for example, started its planning in earnest in 1942. It assessed its role within the future transport markets, developed the case for freight traffic concentration, and specified the actual locations of its colour-light signalling, electrification, and station reconstruction proposals. In the following year the Railway Companies Association set up its Policy Committee to guide the rehabilitation and modernization of the Companies as a whole.

By 1945, when peace was restored, Britain was to be more interested in its wider social problems than the need to restore its railways to pre-war efficiency levels and most of the ideas that came out of that brave new railway thinking were to gather dust for many years. Indeed, those European railway systems which suffered such savage destruction of way, works, and rolling stock had to be reconstructed urgently as a national priority, so giving them a modernization lead of several years over anything possible in Britain. The British railway system had been severely run down, rather than destroyed, by the Second World War and could still be kept working, although at an unacceptably low level of efficiency. Another reason for taking little recuperative action was that a change of ownership seemed to be in the air, and organizational uncertainty is always a reason for postponing decisions. Meanwhile, the railways were to remain under the control of the Railway Executive Committee until the question of ownership was settled, and the Companies were never again to return to their pre-war standing.

By the end of the war and the beginning of what were to be three twilight years, many of the personalities responsible for the developments in the golden 1930s were no longer in their seats. At Swindon, C. B. Collett had given way to F. W. Hawksworth but the Churchward tradition remained virtually intact. W. A. Stanier had been knighted in recognition of his wartime work and had retired from railway service with his mark clearly made both in locomotive performance and the standardization of types. He was succeeded by C. E. Fairburn, who died soon after taking office but not before he had made some significant contributions to diesel traction. These included the introduction of the shunting locomotive which was to become the basis of the later standard British Railways design. The last Chief Mechanical Engineer of the LMS was H. G. Ivatt, who will be remembered as the man who proudly drove out of the Derby shops Britain's first diesel main-line locomotive, No. 10000, shortly before the Companies themselves came to the end of the line at midnight on 31 December 1947.

Sir Nigel Gresley of the LNER had died in 1941 after making a great contribution to locomotive and carriage development with his famous Pacifics hauling what his Company termed, 'High Speed Trains' (at not quite the speeds of the later HST!), the application of the principle of articulation to coaching stock and his never-ceasing enthusiasm for new ideas in the pursuit of excellence. He was succeeded by Edward Thompson, who took an early opportunity to reject some of Gresley's favoured features, particularly the conjugated valve gear on the three-cylinder locomotives, in the interests of efficient servicing and maintenance. Thompson was followed by A. H. Peppercorn who wisely pursued a course almost mid-way between those adopted by his two predecessors.

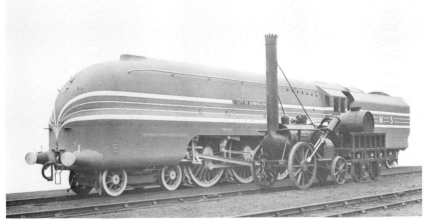

Fig. 1.8   The development of the steam locomotive from 1825 to 1937. Stephenson's *Rocket* alongside Stanier's *City of Birmingham* of the Princess Coronation Class (BRB)

The one Chief Mechanical Engineer at the helm throughout the war was O. V. S. Bulleid of the Southern. He had formerly been Gresley's assistant at Doncaster. Wartime problems did not prevent Bulleid producing his highly original 4–6–2 designs which were intended to raise steam performance standards close to those of the Southern electric services, so making the best use of the line capacity available. The Bulleid Pacifics were magnificent machines when in peak condition, but presented maintenance problems at a time when skilled artisans were becoming hard to find on railways. It speaks well for his reputation on the Southern – and his personality – when it is remembered that the Company's Board was persuaded to approve the building of five locomotives of the revolutionary Leader class.

Bulleid showed a great individuality throughout the generally uninspiring three short years which were left to the Companies between the end of the war and approaching nationalization. It was, however, a period more suited to rehabilitation than to the flowering of engineering genius. There was much postponed repair work to be done. Continued food rationing emphasized the austerity of the times and many commodities essential to railway reconstruction were also to be rationed for some years. Speeds were low and the days of the High Speed Trains seemed far away. Standards of maintenance were such that, in the case of expresses leaving one of London's main-line terminals, the most roadworthy locomotive had to be allocated to the first train in the series, so hoping to reduce the domino effect of any failure on the following trains. Locomotive building programmes were determined by the tonnage of steel which the railways could squeeze out of the Government in a given year. The fatigue of war had also brought its human reaction and national morale was a post-war casualty.

The impact on railway engineering had been to swing the emphasis away from sophistication to simplicity. The GWR class 2310 0–6–0 freight locomotives (the 'Dean goods') had preceded the time even of the great Churchward by being designed in 1883. Some had seen service overseas in two world wars and were still to be at work well into the 1950s. Meanwhile, clever devices like the firebox thermic syphon had been tried and discarded. On the other hand, the 2–8–0 freight locomotives brought over from the USA during the war had shown the value of drop grates, hopper ashpans, and self-cleaning smokeboxes in reducing servicing time. Servicing and maintenance simplicity were now assuming greater importance than the performance of the locomotive in terms of thermal efficiency.

The Companies now generally supported their engineers' efforts to reduce the costs of servicing and maintenance. Their individual character as Companies continued to have some influence during their inevitable progress towards unification. The GWR and LMS had carried standardization to greater lengths than the LNER and SR. The LNER had retained its basically federal type of organization which had preserved considerable autonomy to its three Areas. The SR had concentrated much of its resources into its electrified passenger services but Bulleid had tried to bring out in dramatic fashion the untapped potential which he believed steam to possess. He alone had introduced no less than 170 Pacifics of a new design at a time when the other Companies were content to modify designs which had their origins in an earlier decade. The proposed Gresley 4–8–2, the Stanier streamlined 4–6–4, and the Hawksworth 4–6–2 had never reached the stage of working drawings. Bulleid certainly seemed to be on collision course with current thinking in railway mechanical circles.

There had been experimental applications of the internal combustion engine to rail traction in Britain since the early 1900s and the diesel was now well established in shunting duties. Both the LMS and SR had ordered main-line diesel locomotives. The diesel railcar was in service, particularly on the GWR, which had ordered two gas-turbine locomotives. In signal engineering, only one speed signalling scheme was in use but route relay interlocking was well advanced. The civil engineer who had, during the nineteenth century, filled the land with great works which had reduced the pyramids of Egypt to comparative insignificance, was now engaged on the less dramatic task of re-thinking the materials for construction and the design of permanent way. Although great organizational changes were imminent and there were many arrears of maintenance to be overtaken, the engineering outlook was filled with promise.

Fig. 1.9   Diesel shunting locomotive of 200 h.p. introduced by the LMS in 1932 (NRM)

Fig. 1.10　The gas turbine locomotives ordered by the Great Western Railway were delivered after the Company ceased to exist.

The stage was now being set for the Companies to pass from the overall control of the Railway Executive Committee to ownership by the nation from the beginning of 1948. For the engineers who were to shape the future course of technological development in British Railways the Company years had been exciting in achievement, even if confined in scale by the increasing financial constraints of the 1930s. The organizational future was uncertain. A few did not wish to take part in it and withdrew. Many, however, had lived with the 1923 amalgamations and were well prepared for the challenge of unification.

Perhaps none were more aware of what change would mean than the mechanical engineers. Some belonged to the Churchward, Gresley, Bulleid tradition, believing that it would be through ever-increasing ingenuity in design that the locomotive would rise to increasing heights of performance. Others were inclined to the Stanier, Thompson, Riddles opinion that it would be through simplification in design and good organization for maintenance that progress would be made. The outcome was to be a close-run thing. It was also inevitable.

CHAPTER TWO

Nationalization: The British Transport Commission and the Railway Executive 1948 to 1953

T HE great events of history are ever shaped by the coming together of intention and opportunity. The intention to nationalize railways had long been latent in Britain and was given some substance in 1844, when what is remembered as Gladstone's Cheap Trains Act gave powers to the State to purchase all railways built subsequent to enactment. These provisions for public ownership were never exercised. Again, Winston Churchill's often-quoted announcement to the Dundee Chamber of Commerce in 1918 that the Government had decided to nationalize the railways indicated the mood of the time. Less reference is made to the experience of the next year or two of Government control over the railways, which caused him later to explain his changed views.

The Railways Act of 1921 continued private ownership, although it moved some way towards unification by creating four major groups out of over a hundred companies. The State continued, however, to concern itself very closely with the regulation of railways, particularly in matters associated with safety in operation, the obligation to carry, and the imposition of standard rates and fares.

It is important to contrast the attitudes to State intervention in Britain with those in mainland Europe as the differences help to explain the unique character of railway engineering experience in Britain. On the mainland, Governments took a more positive role not only in providing some of the investment capital which flowed so strongly from private sources in Britain but also in the planned development of the railway networks themselves. As a consequence, they became more clearly identified with the ownership – and the success – of their railways than ever was the case in Britain. The development of railways in Britain was viewed with surprise and disapproval by most European visitors. The French historian Halévy referred to 'this system or rather want of system' after examining the unco-ordinated growth of the intertwining rail networks of Britain. This lack of co-ordination will later be seen to have been the root cause of many of the organizational problems which have tormented the railways of Britain as they faced the contraction of their route system in the twentieth century, following the rapid growth of mechanized road transport.

If railway nationalization was an ever-latent intention in Britain, the opportunity was to be very clear in 1945. A Labour Government had, for the first time in Britain, come to power with an overall majority large enough to introduce controversial legislation. The Labour Party's manifesto prepared for the general election included a pledge to nationalize inland transport, basing its argument mainly on the theme that competition between different forms of transport was wasteful.

The attitude of the four Companies did not reflect the enthusiasm of the electorate, although they were not entirely of one mind on the matter except in their determination to get the best possible settlement terms for the shareholders. The LNER, for example, was aware of its financial weakness and would have been willing to sell its track and structures to the Government. The proceeds would then have been used to renovate the system generally and the Company would have paid a rental to the Government for the use of the track and structures. It is of interest that this concept of separating the ownership of the infrastructure from that of other railway equipment has been advocated on more than one occasion since the LNER made its original proposals, and is likely to continue to be proposed in some form both in Britain and in the wider European context. The ownership of its track by the railway has always complicated comparisons with other forms of transport where vehicle and track are in separate ownership. On the other hand, it would be a retrograde step if separate ownership were to weaken the relationship between the signal and civil engineers, on the one hand, and the mechanical engineers and operators, on the other.

In the event, the LNER did not get the support of the other Companies to its proposal – known rather aptly as the 'Landlord and Tenant' scheme – but worked with them through the Railway Companies Association to make the best of what increasingly appeared to be an inevitable change of ownership. The Association itself was to disappear following nationalization, but it enshrined opinions that would be heard of again, and influence the organizational development of railways in a later decade when public ownership would have lost some of its appeal in the minds of the electorate.

So the intention to nationalize railways and the political opportunity provided in 1945 were consummated in the Transport Act of 1947. This Act began a chain of legislative conflict regarding both the role and the organizational structure of railways in Britain which was to last over two decades and inevitably influence the course of railway engineering development. The legislation was intended to integrate the major elements of public freight and passenger transport under a body to be known as the British Transport Commission and to encourage each form of transport to specialize on the types of service to which it was most suited. The essential unity of the undertaking was made clear in Section 3 (4) of the Act, which stated:

> All the business carried on by the Commission, whether or not arising from undertakings or parts of undertakings vested in them by or under any provision of this Act, shall form one undertaking, and the Commission shall so conduct that undertaking and, subject to the provisions of this Act, levy such fares, rates, tolls, dues and other charges, as to secure that the revenue of the Commission is not less than sufficient for making provision for the meeting of charges properly chargeable to revenue, taking one year with another.

In addition to emphasizing the unity of the undertaking, Section 5 of the Act went on to refer to the public authorities known as Executives which would assist the Commission in the discharge of its functions. In case of any doubt existing about the relationship between Commission and Executive, Section 5 (4) read:

> Each Executive shall, as agents for the Commission, exercise such functions of the Commission as are for the time being delegated to them by or under a scheme made by the Commission and approved by the Minister.

By any standard, the relationship between the Commission and the Railway Executive was characterized by a liberal interpretation of what was meant by delegation. Dr Bonavia, in his book *The Organisation of British Railways* (1971) has described the problems in the relationship between the two bodies: it is sufficient here to refer to those attitudes which had some bearing on the engineering story.

To some extent the relationship was pre-ordained by decisions reflected in the Act. The Commission was committed to Executives reflecting composition by form of transport and not by function, e.g., engineering, operations, commercial. This gave each Executive a strong incentive to look inwards rather than outwards towards the horizon of integration. Again, the Members of the Executives were appointed by the Minister of Transport and the Commission was not in a position to ensure that the Members selected were strongly motivated by the objective of integration. Indeed, in conversation with one of the authors in 1968, Lord Hurcomb – the Commission's first Chairman – unhesitatingly stated that the main weakness of the 1947 Act was that the Commission did not appoint the Members of its Executives.

In addition to any statutory provisions bearing on relationships, there were differences of interpretation. It was clear that the Commission represented the owners of the nation's inland transport systems and should, therefore, direct the progress of the whole undertaking, leaving the management of the services provided to the Executives.

Beyond that point opinions differed. The Railway Executive was in no doubt that it had been set up as the management of a unified railway system, where the prime objective was to provide Britain with the most efficient service possible. It considered integration between the different forms of transport as of less importance than the integration of different railway practices and an early return to pre-war operational standards. In this matter, its attitude was little different from that of the Road Transport (later Road Haulage) Executive. The Railway Executive saw the Commission as a supervisory body, somewhat akin to the Company Board of Directors of pre-nationalization days. It considered that the Commission should think about road/rail integration policies for putting into practice when the work of forging four railways into one system had been completed.

The Commission saw things in a different light. It wished to be in partnership with the Railway Executive and share the decision making in this – by far the largest – section of its undertaking. It was true that there were certain tasks reserved to the Commission, including the very important one of designing the future charges schemes for customers, but it knew that it was being excluded from important policy decisions, including some in the engineering field.

It is easy to over-estimate what course would have been followed in the five years following nationalization if statutory requirements and relationships had been different. There could have been more determined moves towards road/rail integration if the Executives had been created on different principles or the main effort directed towards joint rail/road managements on a regional basis throughout the country. Maybe, the direct appointment to senior posts in its agencies by the Commission itself would have had some effect. It is of great importance, however, to remember that there was at this time very little room for manoeuvre in the short term within the railway. Pricing and the framework of public obligation were still statutorily fixed, investment was at a minimal level, and the obstacles to integration were not only at Executive level. Experiments with traffic integration, as in East Anglia, showed that grass-roots attitudes proved difficult to reconcile with the arguments advanced in favour of it at national level, particularly when jobs were at stake. It is of interest to recall that integration between Executives made some progress in the road motor field, although in small pockets and helped by the personal efforts of the engineers involved.

The Commission required the co-operation of the Executives in the development of the new passenger and freight charging schemes which were intended to be the main instruments for achieving road/rail integration. The Railway Executive was not alone among the Executives in its initial reaction to the task of achieving integration. It was more interested in standardizing practices and making progress with technological evolution. The Commission, however, pressed the matter strongly as it wished to change the practice by which the railway averaged its costs in the absence of a satisfactory means of knowing the relative profitability of its different passenger and freight services. The Commission needed to know the relative costs of performing similar services on rail, road, and inland waterway as a contribution to determining where the advantage of one form of transport was to be found. The prices charged could then be designed to encourage traffic to be carried in the most economic manner.

The work was carried out by a group known as the Traffic Costing Service, which included experts from different types of transport and departmental backgrounds, including engineers. New legislation was later to remove the need for the common pricing schemes but the Traffic Costing approach, developed over the years, was to become established railway practice in decision-making processes and to make its influence felt even outside Britain. Unfortunately, it did not become a common financial language early enough to link the Commission and the Railway Executive in the decisions taken during the first three years of nationalization.

The Railway Executive certainly set about its task with great energy. From the beginning it constituted itself a functional, or departmental, type of organization. The decision was a sensible one as the task was daunting and demanded strength at the top. Not only had the systems of four proud companies to be unified as a national network, but parts had to be hived off to other Executives. These included the major docks, the hotels, the canals, and some of the lines in the territory of the London Transport Executive. Railway regions had to be created and some strong views were expressed as the original proposal of five was increased to eight, before finally emerging as six, Regions, each under a Chief Regional Officer.

There was no statutory basis for the Executive's functional organization, although it is understood that the Cabinet of the day gave the matter some consideration. Its functional character was emphasized by the appointment of its Members. With the exception of the Chairman (Sir Eustace Missenden, formerly General Manager of the Southern Railway), the Deputy Chairman (Sir William Slim, a distinguished soldier), and W. P. Allen (formerly General Secretary of a trade union) all were former railway departmental officers. Two were engineers.

R. A. Riddles was appointed as the Member responsible for Mechanical Engineering, Electrical Engineering, Road Motor Engineering, and Scientific Research. He was formerly a Vice-President of the LMS and had been with railways since he joined the London and North Western Company at Crewe in 1909. He had been Principal Assistant to the Chief Mechanical Engineer and later Mechanical Engineer for the LMS in Scotland. In any position held he had shown a practical grasp of the situation and a marked ability to achieve the results required of him. He was, therefore, an obvious choice for the wartime task of Deputy Director General, Royal Engineer Equipment at the Ministry of Supply, where both his engineering experience and personal qualities were responsible for directing the production of a wide range of equipment, including the Bailey bridges and the Mulberry harbour. Included in the railway tools of war were the 2–8–0 and 2–10–0 freight locomotives, which were to become a familiar sight both in Britain and overseas. In 1943 he returned to the LMS as Chief Stores Superintendent and later became a Vice President with responsibility for engineering matters. His long experience of workshop procedures and close association with Stanier had convinced him of the importance of simplification in design and the efficient organization of maintenance procedures. On grounds of both experience and seniority (as a Vice President his ranking was now higher than that of any Chief Mechanical Engineer, including his former chief, H. G. Ivatt) he was clearly high on the list for appointment as a Member of the Railway Executive.

The choice of the Member responsible for Civil Engineering, Signal and Telegraph Engineering, and Architecture fell upon J. C. L. (later Sir Landale) Train, formerly Chief Engineer of the LNER. It is known that this was one of the cases where the person originally selected (Quartermaine of the Great Western) declined the appointment. Attitudes to nationalization and the conditions of service offered by the Executive caused some of the very senior men to prefer to remain in their present positions or look elsewhere for their future. Train was, therefore, somewhat at a disadvantage compared with Riddles in the personal authority which he was able to establish.

The task inherited by Train was also very different from that of Riddles. Civil engineering had never been as centralized as some aspects of mechanical engineering. Also, the two Members in charge of engineering had different backgrounds. Riddles had come from the functional

Fig. 2.1 The 2–8–0 'Austerity' freight locomotive designed under the direction of R. A. Riddles when at the Ministry of Supply during the Second World War (BRB)

organization of the LMS. It was to be expected that he would create a team which would take upon itself the responsibility for forging unification policies. Train, on the other hand, had come from the LNER which had always had a federal structure where three Divisional General Managers enjoyed very considerable territorial autonomy. For both personal and organizational reasons, Train elected to lead with a very light rein.

At Executive headquarters four Chief Officers reported direct to Riddles. It had been decided to separate mechanical engineering from electrical engineering, mainly because the railways were not large manufacturers of heavy electrical machinery as they were of mechanical equipment. In the Regions, on the other hand, they were to be combined on the grounds that the two aspects of power engineering were converging so rapidly. The division between locomotives, on the one hand, and carriages and wagons on the other, was, however, instituted at both headquarters and regional levels. The actual introduction of the division in the Regions was postponed until the time when the respective Chief Mechanical Engineers of the former Companies retired from railway service. At both levels it was also the policy to have a separate Motive Power Department, which would provide engine crews as well as being responsible for servicing and running repairs. The Motive Power task was joint in that it reported both to the Member for Mechanical Engineering and to the Member for Operations. An outline of the organizational relationships is shown in Fig. 2.2.

R. C. Bond was appointed Chief Officer (Locomotive Construction and Maintenance) from his former position as Deputy to Ivatt, Chief Mechanical Engineer on the LMS. E. Pugson, who had been Ivatt's Assistant for Carriage and Wagon matters became Chief Officer (Carriage and Wagon Construction and Maintenance), and H. Rudgard, also from the LMS, became Chief Officer (Motive Power).

The only Chief Officer on the staff of Riddles who did not come from the LMS was C. M. Cock who became responsible for Electrical Engineering after being Chief Electrical Engineer on the SR. Below the Chief Officers were the Executive Officers and of these two reported directly to Riddles. One was A. E. C. Dent from the GWR and the other E. S. Cox from the LMS. They were responsible for Road Motor Engineering and Design respectively. Riddles had taken the wise decision to leave the locomotive and rolling stock design offices with the Regions but to ensure that their work was co-ordinated by Cox. Both Bond in his book *A Lifetime with Locomotives* and Cox in *Locomotive Panorama* have chronicled the period in considerable detail.

T. M. Herbert, Director of Research and also from the LMS, completed the list of officers reporting direct to Riddles. The heavy LMS component in his organization was very evident, not least to Riddles himself. Given equal ability with other contenders for the posts, the choice was sensible. The men concerned had similar backgrounds and had worked closely

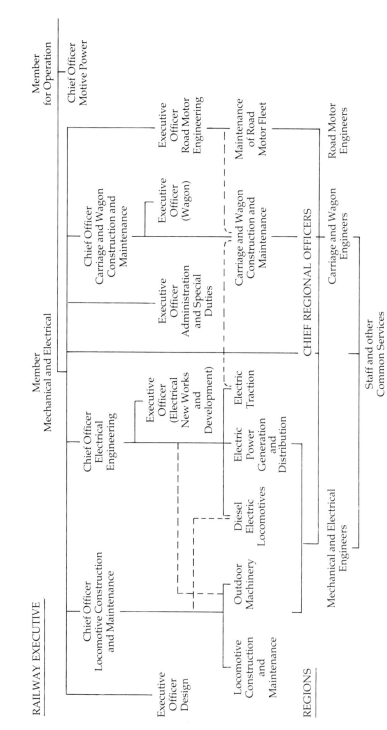

Fig. 2.2　Mechanical and Electrical Engineering Organization: Railway Executive Headquarters and Regions

with each other, as well as with Riddles himself. In short, they were a team that needed little training in working together. It is significant that Riddles consulted the four Chief Mechanical Engineers of the former Companies regarding the appointments. They raised no objections as they recognized the logic of the situation and appreciated the magnitude of the task which he faced.

The position was very different on the civil engineering side. Train was particularly sensitive to the interests of the engineers from Companies other than the LNER. He appointed Arthur Dean from the SR as Chief Officer (Civil Engineering) and H. H. Dyer from the LMS as Chief Officer (Signalling and Telecommunications). Train himself chaired the main committees, but listened very carefully to the views of the Regional engineers, in whose departments so much of the expertise on civil and signal engineering existed. Three of these Regional engineers were to enjoy the distinction of becoming President of the Institution of Civil Engineers. V. A. M. Robertson of the Southern Region became, in 1949, the first engineer in railway service to hold this position while in office (Robert Stephenson was not on the staff of a railway). A. S. (later Sir Allan) Quartermaine, of the Western Region was appointed to the office in 1951, and W. K. Wallace became President in 1955, some three years after his retirement from the London Midland Region.

There was no neat geographical pattern available for the Regional organization throughout Britain. It was very evident that the aim of unification would not easily have been achieved if the four networks of the former Companies had remained intact. These networks had developed as overlays, or spider-like webs, seeking to capture from each other every possible passenger and ton of freight. Perhaps the best-known example of these maverick activities was the extension of the Great Central Railway to London in 1897, which added a fifth route to the four already existing between London and Merseyside. Even after amalgamation GWR, LMS, and LNER competed vigorously for traffic between these centres.

In view of the intertwined nature of the British railway network, a compromise solution was inevitable. In commercial terms, unification meant the creation of clearly defined geographical areas of responsibility where a manager could be identified with the interests of customers in his area. In operating terms, unification was particularly concerned with the movement of trains, which often penetrated several geographical areas in the course of one journey. Civil and signal engineering had similar linear complications but could more easily be managed on an area basis than operational management. Mechanical engineering involved the management of major workshops as well as a large number of maintenance depots, which were usually associated with the main operating centres.

For the next twenty years the organization at local level of the engineering departments was to be swayed by the conflicting claims on organizational patterns of the commercial and operating departments as British Railways at regional level tried to escape from the legacy of its nineteenth-century route structure.

The six Regions were designated Eastern, London Midland, North Eastern, Scottish, Southern, and Western: the Railway Executive was always careful to address them in this alphabetical order! They were designed with regard to the geographical areas dominated by the former Companies but special instructions had to be issued regarding the management of what were termed 'Penetrating lines'. These were the lines geographically within one Region but, in operational aspects, the responsibility of another.

The one exception to the general approach to area organization was the Scottish Region, which comprised the former LMS and LNER lines in Scotland. This avoided the problem of penetrating lines and gave the Region a sense of stability, which has explained the noticeable initiative it has always shown in organizational development within British Railways.

With the Headquarters organization established and the Regions taking on the day-to-day running of the railway from the former Company organizations, the Members of the Railway Executive began their main task of the unification of design and technical standards. There was another task, which involved decisions on the future volume and quality of service, but this was an area that impinged on the work of the Commission. As such, it will be considered later. It is sufficient to say at this stage that the Railway Executive, in control of by far the biggest of the Commission's group of assets, considered itself sufficiently adult to handle its problems without parental help.

Perhaps the biggest single task was that falling on Riddles. He had to weld together the mechanical and electrical engineering practices of four Chief Mechanical Engineers and two formerly independent Chief Electrical Engineers. In particular, he had to develop the best design, manufacturing, and maintenance standards, bearing in mind that each had an effect on the others. There were three elements in his approach. First, he had to examine what had been done within the four Companies. Second, standard designs and practices had to be established. Third, and not easiest, he had to convince his Regional officers that these standards should be accepted because they were the best. It says much for the patience and organizational skill of Riddles and his team that they were to achieve so much success in such a short time.

During the first year and a half of the Executive's life all the Chief Mechanical Engineers of the former Companies were still in office. Of these, Ivatt appears to have had most influence on the views of Riddles: this was understandable in view of their former associations. It would cause no surprise to state that Bulleid, then in his sixty-sixth year but still bubbling with a zest for innovation, was the most dynamic of his contemporaries. Also, Bulleid's flair for experimentation was poles apart from the emphasis so firmly placed by Riddles on the need for simplicity in design. Both men believed that the steam locomotive had not yet reached its peak of potential performance but Bulleid sought to design in ever-higher power output, while Riddles sought to design out those features which increased servicing and maintenance costs. It was fortunate for the Railway Executive (soon abbreviated to RE) that Riddles believed in persuasion while Bulleid maintained that deep sense of loyalty which had been so prominent in his association with Gresley on the LNER.

Riddles had eighteen months to wait before being in a position to bring new blood into the top positions in the different Regions. The first of the Chief Mechanical Engineers of a former Company to retire was Bulleid who, in September 1949 became Consulting Mechanical Engineer to the Irish Transport Company (CIE). He was succeeded on the Southern Region as Mechanical and Electrical Engineer by S. B. Warder and as Carriage and Wagon Engineer by F. Munns. Both had a Southern background, although the latter was trained in the Derby tradition. Warder was an electrical engineer, but R. A. Smeddle was appointed as his deputy and brought his former LNER experience with him from Darlington. Later, when Warder took over the Headquarters responsibility for electrical engineering from Cock, he was replaced by H. H. Swift whose background was associated with the LNER. These appointments had the effect of ensuring that the infusion of other Company practices was not long in making itself felt on the Southern.

All eyes were turned towards the Western Region when Hawksworth retired some three months after Bulleid at the end of 1949. He was only the sixth CME of the Great Western since the great Daniel Gooch had been appointed in the time of Brunel. In the event, both K. J. Cook and H. Randle, who were appointed to the posts of Mechanical and Electrical Engineer and Carriage and Wagon Engineer respectively, maintained the tradition of Swindon trained men. At the time of nationalization A. H. Peppercorn, CME of the LNER, had continued to take the mechanical and electrical engineering responsibility for both the Eastern and the North Eastern Regions. He also retired at the end of 1949, and another former LNER man, J. F. Harrison, took on the position of Mechanical and Electrical Engineer at Doncaster. A. E. Robson, from the former LMS, was, however, appointed to the post of Carriage and Wagon Engineer.

The major switching of the senior engineers between Regions was, however, to follow Ivatt's retirement from the London Midland Region in 1951. Harrison and Randle now moved across to Derby from Doncaster and Swindon, respectively. Cook left Swindon and replaced Harrison in charge of the Eastern and North Eastern Regions. The Western Region now had two vacancies. That of Mechanical and Electrical Engineer was occupied by Smeddle, whose background was with the LNER but who had more recently been working on the Southern Region. Some of the

Swindon tradition was retained on the Western Region by the appointment of C. T. Roberts to succeed Randle as Carriage and Wagon Engineer.

With the task in the Scottish Region shared between M. S. Hatchell (formerly with Southern and London Midland experience) and James Blair (formerly LNER) as Mechanical and Electrical and Carriage and Wagon Engineers respectively, the Regional organizations were responding by 1952 to their new leadership. Believing in the organic character of organizational change, Riddles had waited not only for each of the former Chief Mechanical Engineers to retire before separating the mechanical and electrical engineering work from the carriage and wagon engineering task in the Regions concerned, but had progressively developed the process of the inter-Regional penetration of engineering practices. The speed with which the changes took place, once the organizational outlines were settled – and the main posts filled – was typical of Riddles himself. With the earlier bastions of company tradition now mainly occupied by men from other backgrounds, the obstacles to the introduction of standard practices were being eroded.

The method adopted in the achievement of technical unification began with the procedure of policy making committees. This was the ideal use of this type of procedure as there were many practices to be examined and recommendations made. In a later decade, when weaker central management found decision making difficult, the committees deteriorated into a means of achieving corporate management in British Railways, but in the early days of the RE they were very efficient in achieving their purpose in the mechanical engineering function.

This purpose was to bring out all the different practices adopted in a particular activity, expose them to critical examination, and then make recommendations. If these recommendations were acceptable to Riddles, then they would be adopted and the committee disbanded, unless it had further work to do. While the Regions carried the main burden of the day-to-day running of the railway, they also were the repositories of most of the engineering design resources inherited from the Companies and some of the developments approved by those Companies were still in production. The main-line diesels ordered by the LMS and SR and the gas-turbine locomotives approved by the GWR were built, but the LNER's proposal to introduce main-line diesels onto the East Coast Main Line had no outcome. Bulleid's Leader class 0–6–6–0 mixed-traffic locomotive and prototype double-deck carriage had still to be tested on the track. The opinions expressed on future development at many of the meetings were pungent. Not only had the Regional representatives on the committees some pointed comments to make to their colleagues: they had an even more demanding task in reporting back from the meetings to their Regional chiefs.

On the civil engineering side the same procedures were followed. A. S. Quartermaine, Chief Engineer of the Great Western Railway, resigned shortly after guiding his department into the new Western Region. He had no wish either to be associated with the RE or to remain at Paddington under the salary scales and conditions associated with nationalization. On the London Midland and Southern Regions W. K. Wallace and V. A. M. Robertson remained in their respective chairs, so Train faced men who were both formidable in character and distinguished in their professional achievements.

In his book *Memoirs of a Railway Engineer* (Mechanical Engineering Publications Ltd, 1979), E. J. Larkin, who acted as chairman of a number of the policy-making committees, has described the care which went into the preparation of the remits to the committees. An extract from a letter received by Larkin from Riddles at the time of the latter's retirement in 1953 gives a clue to the purpose behind the elaborate committee structure:

> The fact that you, an expert in the particular subjects which you are investigating, are enabled to draw on the experience of all Regions and make a recommendation as to the right policy to adopt, had short-circuited by many months, if not years, the policy of standardization and of using the best practice immediately, rather than adopting one of dictatorship through trial and error.

On the civil engineering side, the switching of senior engineers between Regions was less evident than in the case of the mechanical engineers. Wallace retired from the London Midland Region at the end of August 1948 and was followed by J. Briggs from the same Region. Briggs was succeeded in 1951 by J. Taylor Thompson from the North Eastern Region, who was himself succeeded by Dean from Railway Executive Headquarters, but with a Southern background. Robertson was succeeded on the Southern Region by F. E. Campion, his former Assistant, in March 1950. Campion was also succeeded by his former Assistant, A. H. Cantrell. Quartermaine retired from the Western Region late in 1951, and his title 'Chief Engineer' disappeared with him from the British Railways directory. His position was occupied by M. G. R. Smith, another Great Western engineer. In the Scottish Region, W. Y. Sandeman, previously with the LNER, was replaced when he retired at the end of 1951 by a former LMS engineer, I. R. Frazer.

Although the committee procedures in civil and signal engineering were similar to those in mechanical and electrical engineering, the personal involvement of Train was in lower key than that of Riddles and the Regional contribution correspondingly greater. For example, the Railway Engineers Committee of the former Companies was succeeded by a Civil Engineers Committee under the Chairmanship of W. K. Wallace.

The Regional engineers – and this applied on both mechanical and civil sides – nominated their representatives to each of the Policy Committees and the functional Member selected the Chairman. Some of the bodies completed their work quickly and were then disbanded. Others, including the Carriage Standards Committee, the Wagon Standards Committee, and the Locomotive Testing Committee endured for the life of the Executive itself. The value of the work lay not only in the recommendations made, but also in the process of technical consultation between Executive and Regions – and between the Regions themselves – being seen to be at work. Although the Members of the Executive exercised much patience in the early stages, they showed considerable skill in determining the constitution of the committees, and the RE itself began to force the pace. One feature favourable to the procedure was that the committees were wisely linked as far as possible with the practices of the Railway Executive Committee, which had taken over the running of the railways under wartime conditions. It was under these wartime conditions that railway engineers had been conditioned to think in terms of a common objective. Indeed, it was from such circumstances that some proposed standard locomotive designs had appeared after the First World War, although no locomotives were actually built.

The RE's spirited drive towards technical unification was not, however, without its critics at both Commission and Regional levels. The Commission was inclined to the view that the Executive should have given more thought to the railway of the future before standardizing existing practices. For example, it would have preferred that a thorough study should have been carried out into future traction policy before standardizing steam locomotive designs. On the other hand, the Regions thought that unification was being pressed too far and that Regional individualism was being stifled. For the Western Region, as territorial successor to the GWR where it had been the practice to enforce corporate unity since 1835, it was particularly difficult to accept direction from above. There always seemed to be a wisp of steam hanging around the safety valves of co-operation whenever Paddington or Swindon was involved and there was little doubt that, given the chance, the Western Region would have seceded from the new transport commonwealth.

The Regions also took exception to the functional character of the RE's method of working. Instructions went to engineer from engineer and the Chief Regional Officers initially had little more than a co-ordinating role. The Members of the Executive normally took the entire responsibility for decisions taken within their particular function and any form of collegiate policy making was rare. This was also a matter of some concern to the Commission, which looked for corporate railway views rather than those of the separate functions.

To be fair to the Executive, it considered its functional approach to be the fastest method by which it could reduce costs and improve the quality of railway service. Some cost reductions certainly resulted from the standardization of practices and the sharing of resources between Regions. The improvement of service quality was an even greater priority. At the beginning of 1948 16·6 per cent of the wagon fleet and

Fig. 2.3 The LNER alone could never fulfil its ambition to build a new marshalling yard at Temple Mills in East London. The scheme was authorized during the time of the Railway Executive. Here a rake of mineral wagons passes through the primary retarders (BRB)

14·45 per cent of the carriages were under or awaiting repair. In the case of locomotives over 7 per cent were under or awaiting repair at main works alone, in addition to those in the same situation at running depots throughout the country. Policy decisions could not change these statistics overnight, and the situation had to be improved at a time when so many essential materials were in very short supply.

Even if the results could hardly be discerned in the short term, there were very sound reasons for technical standardization being at the heart of the Executive's policy making. Until 1892 there was no standard gauge track network throughout Britain and although through working between the four group Companies had been standardized by the 1920s to the extent that the vacuum brake was used, there were significant groups of services using the air brake in 1948. Also, at the time of nationalization it was GWR practice to operate its brake system on 25 inches of vacuum while the other three Companies operated on 21 inches. This caused certain difficulties when used in conjunction, as well as effectively preventing the cost and other benefits attainable by using identical equipment. Similarly, LNER and SR used the buckeye coupler for coaching stock, while LMS and GWR used the screw coupling. Costly provision had to be made to enable buckeye and screw fitted vehicles to be coupled together.

Riddles himself was in no doubt that the time had arrived to alter the immovable attitudes of the former Companies which had proved an obstacle to standardization. In an article contributed to *Modern Transport* after two years of nationalization he wrote:

> Technical standardization has been widely sought on British Railways since the 1860s, and each successive amalgamation has widened the field of application. Moreover, in railway experience it cannot be said that standardization has prevented progress. . . . On the technical side one of the virtues of nationalization was to remove all remaining barriers.

There were a number of voices, particularly in the Regions and amongst the general public, which said that the Executive – and Riddles in particular – was over-zealous in removing the barriers to standardization. The most fascinating example of the RE approach arose in the case of locomotive design, and it is in this area that controversy continues to rage. The Locomotive Standards Committee was set up almost within the first week of nationalization coming into effect – on 8 January 1948 – which shows the importance attached to the subject. The work of this Committee will be discussed in a later chapter and only the policy implications are for consideration at this stage.

Riddles was of the opinion from the beginning that the designs of one of the former Companies could not become the future standard for steam locomotives. It would have been a logical approach and, after some furious protestations from the adherents to the causes of the three unsuccessful Companies, would probably have been generally accepted. Riddles argued that since the products of each of the Companies had reached a high state of development, no one set of Company designs towered head and shoulders above the others. Doubtless, he and his team considered that the rather obvious decision to follow LMS practice was politically inappropriate. It was evident that the LMS designs, taken as a whole, were more suitable as BR standard types than their rivals. Perhaps the LMS locomotives did not show particular advantages over the others but the Company had made considerable progress with its own standardization policy. In addition the LMS locomotive enjoyed wide route availability throughout British Railways due to the many restrictions with which the LMS network was saddled. The GWR also had gone a long way towards a standardized fleet but the slightly more generous dimensions of their locomotives would not have allowed them to meet the route availability requirements throughout Britain on the scale required.

Although the decision proved to be a costly one, it is understandable that, in the atmosphere of the time, Riddles and his LMS dominated team did not decide to standardize on LMS designs, at least until impartial testing had been concluded. A series of interchange trials were begun in April 1948, with fourteen different locomotive types over all Regions in order to report on the possibility of selecting, in each traffic category, the best existing ex-Company type as a future standard. The trials will be described in Chapter 5. Here it is necessary only to note the careful evaluation of results, the wide publicity given to what many enthusiasts treated as a latter-day gladiatorial contest, and the main conclusions.

These conclusions were far from sensational and took much of the heat out of the controversy. It was evident, for example, that a properly designed locomotive could work satisfactorily throughout the country: it was not necessary to design specific types for certain routes. Also, the findings suggested that the relatively small gap in performance standards between the complicated locomotive and the simpler machine did not justify the higher servicing and maintenance costs of the former.

The tests served to confirm the views of the design team at Executive Headquarters and produced much useful material. At the same time, they produced no evidence to destroy the case that could be made for standardizing on the former LMS designs, possibly altered in minor ways to make the decision more palatable and to take account of the results of the tests. Neither did the tests establish that any particular Company's designs in specific groups showed outstanding results in terms of all-round performance. If the results had proved positive in this matter it would have been possible to decide that one Company's designs would be the standard for, say, express passenger duties and another's for heavy freight workings. This was a course which would, however, have perpetuated a multiplicity of types and have denied the railway the benefits of standardization.

In the short term there was no practicable alternative to continue building former Company types in order to maintain the locomotive fleet up to date. To take care of the longer term Riddles decided, from a number of alternative options, to create a new series of British Railways standard locomotives. It was one of the most controversial decisions in the history of railways in Britain. On the one hand, the modern designs of steam locomotive available at the time were thoroughly competent, and a great advance over what had been inherited by the Companies in 1923. Electrification schemes suspended in 1939 were being brought to completion, diesel shunters and railcars had been in use for some time, main-line diesels were already in experimental service, and two gas-turbine locomotives would soon be running on the Western Region. To many it did not seem to be an appropriate time to go back to the drawing board and design a new generation of steam locomotives. Nevertheless, with the experience gained over a period of sixteen years of the success of Stanier's policy of introducing a completely new series of steam loco-motives on the LMS, it is understandable that Riddles and his team were strongly predisposed to tackle their own problems in broadly the same way.

It must also be added that the outlook for capital investment in British

Railways looked grim. For this reason the prospects for main-line electrification were remote. There was also some uncertainty with regard to supplies of oil for traction. Only in 1947, and at the request of the Government, the Companies had embarked on an urgent programme to introduce oil firing on steam locomotives with the aim of conserving coal. The scheme involved the conversion of 1217 locomotives and the provision of full-scale fuelling installations. After only a few months, during which 93 locomotives were converted, the project was abandoned. The Government was reminded by the Comptroller and Auditor General of the high outflow of dollars required to purchase the oil. When the memory of this wasted investment in the use of oil for traction was so fresh in the minds of railway engineers, it was understandable that there was some concern at the prospect of diesel traction on a large scale.

Riddles concluded, therefore, that there would still be steam locomotives in Britain, burning British coal, in thirty years time, and that a time scale of this order justified another generation of steam locomotives. If so, he intended to ensure that this new generation would embody the best of former Company practice, which would be enhanced by lessons from the tests and the work of the design teams. Another reason probably had some influence in making his decision. He remembered his wartime experience at the Ministry of Supply, where a group of individuals from different backgrounds had been transformed into a dedicated team when harnessed to the task of jointly producing some urgently required item of equipment. He had good reason to believe that a common design venture would create a sense of unity between the Regional design teams which had become steeped in the traditions of their parent Companies. Also, it must be said that Riddles, although personally more interested in standardization than in the process of design itself, had strong motivation to produce the most efficient steam locomotive fleet that could be accommodated within the British loading gauge.

A variety of reasons, therefore, led to the development of the British Railways standard locomotives. The designs themselves will be considered in Chapter Five. Here it is only necessary to say, as part of the Railway Executive narrative, that building began in 1950 and ended in 1960 when 2–10–0 No. 92220 *Evening Star* steamed out of Swindon Works resplendent in the former Great Western livery. While it could still be debated whether all of the new designs were necessary, it cannot be denied that the locomotives were generally efficient and at least two types were of outstanding quality.

More important than the locomotives produced was the effect of the Riddles policy in harnessing Regional engineers to British Railways objectives. Not only were individual types of locomotive allocated to the main workshops in the different Regions but standard components were manufactured in the same way, so increasing inter-Regional dependence and maximizing mass production. The whole process was furthered by the transfer of mechanical engineers between Regions, so mingling the traditions of the former Companies.

Even so, the standard locomotives had a mixed reception. The Eastern Division of the Eastern Region put forward some persuasive arguments to ensure that the first of the new locomotives arrived in East Anglia and soon proved that it could use them very efficiently. Their initial complaint was the minor one that their Class 7 Pacifics had not been named, as suggested, after East Anglian rivers! At the other extreme, there were pockets of resistance to anything produced to a Railway Executive standard. There were the occasional posturings to show that former Company locomotives could perform better than the new ones, including one exhilarating run on a special train conveying many of the Commission's senior officers to a conference at Oxford, when resort was made rather slyly to double heading! On the whole, however, the standard locomotives were well received.

In the case of carriages the former Companies had been in the habit of agreeing to differ in many aspects of design and construction. They had, however, worked together towards the objective of a common profile for adoption throughout the whole of Britain. The results were re-examined soon after nationalization by the Carriage Standards Committee. From this work emerged the standard carriage, known as 'Mark 1' and to emerge in twelve different body styles. The decision to include in the design the buckeye coupler and Pullman gangway favoured former LNER and SR practice. The steel shell owed much to the later carriage bodies used by the LMS and SR. The fact that welding was widely used recognized the work which Bulleid had carried out on welding techniques over the years. The result of this widespread welding was a very high safety standard with minimum weight. The design of the bogies fitted to the Mark 1 carriages was the result of fully instrumented tests carried out over the former Great Central main line and generally favoured GWR practice. The standard carriage was, therefore, rather more mixed in its parentage than the series of standard locomotives, which strongly favoured LMS forebears.

There were four main committees concerned with carriages, namely Carriage Standards, Carriage Production, Power Brake, and Train Lighting. Besides these committees, which continued throughout the lifetime of the Executive, there was an 'Ad hoc' Committee on Interior Decoration, which included the Architect as well as engineering, operating, and commercial representatives.

As in the case of locomotives, carriages to former Company designs were produced within the allocation of steel made available to British Railways and until the new jigs were ready for the standard designs. The most publicized of these Company designs were two that came from the fertile mind of O. V. S. Bulleid. These were the double-deck commuter carriage and the 'Tavern' car. The former just failed to overcome the

Fig. 2.4   A complete passenger train, as designed by the Riddles team. A standard Class 7
Pacific hauls a train of Mark 1 carriages (Fox Photos Ltd)

loading gauge restrictions and operating problems on the Southern
Region although it was a brave attempt to ease the condition of the
commuter. The latter, intended to simulate the interior of an English inn,
fell foul of public taste which did not take to the idea of riding the rails in a
timbered tap room. Short of refreshment cars, but sensitive to public
opinion, the RE allocated the Tavern cars around the country. The oppro-
brium was thereby spread more thinly and the Regions involved did not
take long to find alternative ways of providing refreshment facilities.

The wagon problem inherited by the RE was serious. Section 29 of the
Transport Act of 1947 provided for the Commission to take into ownership some 540000 wagons of several hundred designs. These wagons in
private ownership were in addition to those taken over from the Companies and were mostly of low carrying capacity with loose couplings,
grease-lubricated axle-boxes, and brakes operated only by hand. They
had effectively restricted freight train running speeds and braking performance from the early days of railways in Britain as they had undergone
little basic change in design for a century. During the 1920s two Royal
Commissions had reported adversely on both the design and the condition of these wagons. The railway companies were not, however, in a
position to compel the owners to carry out the recommendation that this
decrepit fleet should be replaced by new 20-ton wagons.

Many of the wagons owned by the Companies were little better than
those in private ownership. There was, however, little incentive to
modernize the Company fleets as long as the relics of Victorian coal
trading practices had to be accommodated within their general operating

patterns. These operating practices were, with the exception of the fast freight trains, more appropriate to an age when the wagon was as important as a means of low cost storage as it was for carriage.

In 1948, the RE recognized the urgent need to increase wagon carrying capacity, generally up-date the whole fleet to twentieth-century standards and introduce more fast freight trains controlled by the automatic continuous brake. These objectives required very substantial investment and this was not available, although the post-war Government had been rather more favourable to wagon building than to other forms of railway investment. Given such limited investment resources, there were severe limits on what could be achieved by the engineers. It was first necessary to ensure that the new high-capacity wagons could be accommodated at the thousands of terminals throughout Britain and this required the reconstruction on a large scale of colliery screens and other handling equipment which was not railway owned. The National Coal Board, which now was responsible for the nationalized coal industry, also had an interest in the more efficient carriage of coal by rail. At the same time it had its own investment priorities and had to pay regard to the preferences of its many customers whose pattern of trading depended on storing coal at low cost in railway wagons. It was, therefore, a commercial responsibility at Executive and Regional levels to revolutionize the attitude of the

Fig. 2.5   Double-deck commuter carriage on the London (Charing Cross)–Dartford service in 1948 (BRB)

Fig. 2.6   The type of wagon which has severely affected the efficiency of freight
movement on British Railways (NRM)

customer to the wagon. Revolutionary solutions were not, however, available and changes could be achieved only by persuasion and pricing incentives, which were still firmly within the slow-moving machinery of statutory control. It seemed that the long-cherished ambition of the engineers to produce and maintain a modern wagon fleet would not be achieved for many years.

Meanwhile, an inter-departmental Ideal Stocks Committee was established in order to determine the different types of wagon which would be needed on the railway of the future. As would be expected, the underlying objectives of the work were to eliminate the grease-lubricated axlebox, to introduce higher capacity wagons, and to increase progressively the proportion of the fleet fitted with the continuous brake. A separate body which was more heavily weighted with engineers – the Wagon Standards Committee – had the task of standardizing the components of the designs which were recommended by the Ideal Stocks Committee.

Riddles was particularly interested in the standardization of the manufacturing and maintenance practices in the different Regional workshops. This was necessary not only in the interests of overall efficiency, but also to provide for the new standard locomotives and rolling stock so that interchangeable parts could be manufactured to the same standards of tolerance. The requirements of efficient workshop performance were responsible to a large extent for the deliberate avoidance of anything which could be construed as startlingly original or untried in the British Railways standard rolling stock designs. It has been said that these designs represented yesterday's answers to today's questions.

Nobody was more conscious of this criticism than Riddles himself. He said in his Presidential Address to the Institution of Locomotive Engineers on 16 November 1950:

> . . . we have preferred to start with something based on well tried experience. I feel that to have gathered together the best of that experience is a step forward in itself, and is a well founded base from which to reach out into the future. I look forward eagerly to the development of all the good ideas we can get hold of in the years to come.

At another point in the same address Riddles reminded his audience that the cost of a corridor carriage in Britain was about one-fifth or one-sixth of that in North America. The fairness of the comparison may be argued, but it is the comment itself that puts emphasis behind the attitude of the day. This was still the Britain of austerity where the essentials of everyday life were strictly rationed. The railway workshops were short of materials and staff were leaving for the higher wages of private industry. It was a time when it was important to achieve the maximum output with minimum resources, and Riddles thought more of the efficiency of the workshops than what posterity would think of his ingenuity in technical innovation. This 'value for money' approach accorded with the spirit of the age in Britain and was by no means alien to engineers who had worked under the financial disciplines of the former Companies.

Turning from mechanical engineering activities to the fields of civil, signal, and telecommunications engineering, the 1948 report of the British Transport Commission made the organizational situation clear when it said in Paragraph 269:

> The functions assumed by the headquarters organization are not those that would be undertaken by a Chief Civil and Signal and Telecommunications Engineer for the whole of the railways, but are limited in the main to issuing directions and exercising control in matters of general policy such as uniformity of practices, standardization of methods and equipment, and the general planning of programmes and budgeting of expenditure. There is no encroachment upon the administrative responsibilities of the Regional Engineers who are left to carry out, without interference, the actual work that requires to be done in the Regions.
>
> The decision to separate in the Regions the civil engineering and signal and telecommunications functions was carried into effect and new S & T Engineers were appointed as necessary. The division of responsibility was defined in some detail as between the Civil and the S & T Engineers and between them and the Mechanical and Electrical Engineers and is in course of being implemented.

It was first necessary for the team working under Train to design a standard procedure for the preparation and submission of annual programmes for way and works. This was arranged in two parts. The first was the Railway Executive programme which included permanent way and bridge renewals along with other major works. The second was the annual maintenance programme. The RE rightly regarded one of its priority tasks to be to make good the large amount of arrears in permanent way renewals that had accumulated during the war years.

A working party on capital investment, which had been appointed by the Government, made its views clear that supplies of materials for the permanent way should be 'reduced to current needs, about the same as pre-war, without overtaking arrears.' This meant that the arrears authorized by the former Companies were now cancelled, and the prospects for return to pre-war track standards receded into the future. In the case of structures it appeared that it would be possible to overtake maintenance arrears within some four to five years.

Flat-bottomed track was adopted as standard for British Railways in 1949. National currency exchange restrictions hampered the mechanization of track maintenance. The first 'Matisa' automatic tamping machine had been ordered shortly before nationalization, but twelve more machines were now urgently needed to assist in overcoming the shortage in railway manpower which had been depleted by the demands of military conscription then in force and the gearing-up of the export industries. The import of both tamping and ballast cleaning machines was delayed by currency difficulties. Track-laying equipment did not represent the same problem, as British machines had been available since the 1930s.

On the signal and telecommunications side, progress was also hampered by shortages of manpower and investment capital. The S & T engineers concentrated their energies, therefore, in establishing standards which could be applied throughout British Railways when the resources necessary for development became available. The list was a long one but by the time that development became a reality in the mid-1950s the application of the standards was to be seriously challenged due to structural re-organization within the railways arising from events which will be described later.

1949 brought further change in the civil and signalling fields following the organizational emphasis of 1948. There was still no improvement possible in the pace of track renewal, but the decision was now taken to overcome the currency restrictions by purchasing track maintenance machines manufactured in Britain under licence. It was also the year in which the RE appointed a Chief Architect (Dr F. Curtis) to advise on general design, so taking the first step towards the architect becoming separated from the department of the civil engineer. 1949 will be remembered as a turning point in another relationship: this time between the operator and the signal engineer. It happened at Doncaster, where the LNER had approved a re-signalling scheme. Tattersall, who will be remembered for his earlier schemes at Thirsk, Hull, and Leeds, proposed concentrating the work on one signal box. The operators, however, were successful in their demand for two boxes. They argued that one box would not permit adequate visual supervision of so large an area. So the signal box at either end of Doncaster station remained a reminder of the operator's reluctance to place his full confidence in the new signalling technology. There is now one box at Doncaster, which with only six more boxes, will control nearly 400 miles of the East Coast Main Line from London to the other side of Edinburgh.

Several major programmes of new works inherited by the RE, but authorized by the former Companies, were now re-examined. Amongst the schemes adopted were the LNER proposals to electrify the Liverpool Street–Shenfield suburban passenger services and all services between Manchester, Sheffield, and Wath. Associated with the latter scheme was a new, three miles long, double-track tunnel at Woodhead to replace the two single-track tunnels which had figured so prominently – and notoriously – in the history of the railway navvies in the nineteenth century. The LMS scheme for mechanizing and re-modelling the Up Yard at Toton and the SR proposals for installing colour-light signalling from Battersea Park and from Bricklayers Arms Junction to Coulsdon North were also confirmed.

The completion of the Liverpool Street–Shenfield electrification within two years of nationalization gave a great boost to railway morale in those grey days of austerity. Within six weeks after the full service was introduced passenger journeys had risen by 58 per cent over those of the former steam service. The results showed what could be achieved when a railway service was given new traction, new civil engineering works, and new signalling. It looked to railway engineers that dawn was beginning to break after a very long night.

The success of the Liverpool Street scheme breathed new life into the early planning stages of the electrification of the London, Tilbury, and Southend line. It also had the effect of quickening the interest in electrification throughout British Railways and did not escape the notice of the Commission. Both Riddles and Cock were disappointed that the only electrification schemes with which progress was being made had been authorized in the 1930s. As Chief Officer (Electrical Engineering) Cock's commitment to electric traction was manifest. The attitude of Riddles needs more clarification.

Riddles had shown evidence of an interest in electrical engineering in his early days at Crewe. It is also evident that he considered electric traction as the ideal form of motive power on railways, although he thought main-line electrification far enough away to justify the propagation of new standard steam locomotive designs. At the current pace of

Fig. 2.7   Multiple unit three-car sets assembled in the new Ilford Carriage Sheds await the opening of the Liverpool Street–Shenfield electric service on 26 September 1949 (BRB)

electrification it would have taken over half a century to have changed more than 50 per cent of the total train miles on British Railways over to electric traction. It is, therefore, to the credit of Riddles that he gave his support to the Lancaster–Morecambe–Heysham branch line being turned into a test bed for the development of 50 cycle a.c. traction before he visited Annecy in 1951 to see the substantial progress which had been made by the French National Railways (SNCF) in this field. On this visit he was accompanied by S. B. Warder, who had succeeded Cock, and both men returned with the conviction that what they had seen would prove a spur to main-line electrification in Britain.

At the same time, Riddles was firmly of the opinion that steam should continue as the principal form of traction on main lines and on the suburban services until replaced by electrification. Diesels would take over shunting duties but were not serious contenders in other fields. As Member of the RE with functional responsibility for mechanical engineering he had little difficulty in taking the Executive with him in the matter. He advanced three main reasons for his opinion. First, investment resources available to British Railways were strictly limited and it was possible to buy about five steam units for one diesel of equivalent power. Second, oil supplies were subject to strategic and foreign currency objections, as had been so evident in 1947. Third, the basically reliable steam locomotive had advantages over main-line diesel electrics, five of which were undergoing their early trials in Britain. They had by no means yet proved themselves. There was also another reason for not welcoming diesels on the heavily loaded expresses. At that time, twin units were needed to equal the haulage capacity of the most powerful steam passenger locomotives, and this would require some trains to be reduced by one carriage to avoid handling problems at stations. In the circumstances of the time, when main-line services were very heavily loaded, this criticism had some substance.

All these diesel drawbacks had some validity in 1948, although they were to diminish during the coming years. Indeed, J. S. Tritton in his Presidential Address to the Institution of Locomotive Engineers on 17 December 1947 had referred to the diesel/steam capital cost ratio as 1·6/1·0. Admittedly, he was thinking of North American experience with long production runs but the ratio was very far removed from the 5/1 figure quoted by Riddles in his Presidential Address to the same body some three years later.

Furthermore, there were compensating savings in servicing costs and availability which should have been assessed alongside the disparity in capital costs. The RE had good reason, however, to be concerned about oil supplies, because the Companies in their last year of life had been let down on this score by the Government. At the same time, the Executive seemed to have little concern over oil supplies for diesel shunting activities and its road transport competitors were making increased use of oil with little regard to the future. It is evident that the Executive did not consult the British Transport Commission on the latter body's views on the use of oil by its Executives.

The reality was that the relationship between the Commission and the Railway Executive was far from close. The Chairman of the Commission, Sir Cyril (later Lord) Hurcomb, tended to avoid the formal communication of the Commission's views. In its turn, the Executive thought it sufficient to keep the Commission in touch with railway activities by sending it carefully edited versions of its minutes. The Commission must have been irritated when J. C. L. Train, in an address to the Permanent Way Institution during the first fortnight of nationalization, said that the main task of the Commission was to control finance while the Executive was responsible not only for general management but also for 'much of the work of the private railway directors'. From the Executive's point of view this was one interpretation of its delegated powers described as 'functions relating to activities of the former Railway Companies'. Less emphasis was placed on the formidable powers reserved to the Commission, including that of giving directions to the Executive as its agent.

The Commission was spurred to take some action after noting the celerity with which the Executive was tackling the standardization of steam locomotives without appearing to have evaluated its future traction policy. In April 1948 – the same month in which the locomotive interchange trials were begun – Hurcomb wrote to Missenden expressing his dissatisfaction with the rate of progress in assessing the merits of different forms of traction. He added that this matter was 'probably the most important long term problem facing railways today.'

The reaction of the Executive to this prod from the Commission was one of grudging co-operation. Over eight months later – on 20 December 1948 – a Committee was set up under the chairmanship of J. L. Harrington, Chief Officer (Administration) at RE Headquarters. It reported at the end of 1951. The principal recommendations of the report were:

1. A scheme for the electrification of the former Great Northern main line from London (King's Cross) to at least Grantham should be planned and costed. Subject to a satisfactory outcome, the scheme should proceed.

2. A detailed investigation should be made of a scheme for the employment of a fleet of 2000 h.p. single-unit diesels in order to provide a relatively large scale test of diesel traction for main-line duties. (There was a similarity between this proposal and the scheme for twenty-five main-line diesels authorized by the LNER Board of Directors in 1947.)

3. The detailed investigation of a scheme for the placing into service of a fleet of modern diesel railcars.

Riddles had been invited to be represented on the Harrington Committee but he declined, preferring to leave himself free to comment after publication of the recommendations. Bond and Cox found much to criticize in the findings of the Committee and reported accordingly to Riddles, who then circulated his own views to the other Members of the Executive. He went to some length to emphasize that motive power policy must be founded on coal, rather than oil. He also laid particular stress on the improvement that steam could offer over the levels of current performance. Steam was, in his opinion, economical and adequate in every way for working the traffic of British Railways until such time as it was displaced by electrification.

By January 1952, the Commission had received the views which it had asked for in April 1948. Within that period the Executive had held the interchange trials of former Company locomotives, designed the standard British Railways steam locomotives and seen some of them enter service. Furthermore, the 'detailed investigations' recommended in the Harrington report would have taken another year or two to complete and the mid-1950s would have arrived before any practical results could have emerged.

While the report was following its tortuous course, the Bond/Cox partnership at RE Headquarters in conjunction with the Regional design offices and workshops had produced modern steam locomotives which, Riddles expected, would bridge the gap until electric traction made them redundant. He never committed to paper his deep concern that any intermediate diesel stage would inevitably postpone electrification. The same underlying feeling was later to emerge when one of the Regions regarded an allocation of high powered diesels as the kiss of death to its electrification ambitions.

One extraordinary feature of the traction comparisons which were made in the Harrington report was the crude nature of the financial figures. With the benefit of thirty years of increasing refinement of financial information the data made available at that time would appear to confuse rather than clarify. The arguments were supported by some cost comparisons, but no attempt was made to relate costs to different manning assumptions or levels of utilization. If the work of traffic costing had been more advanced at this stage, meaningful comparisons of both cost and net revenue for different forms of traction would have been possible. The different cost and revenue elements were fully taken into account in later work.

The Executive, however, had little need for complicated figuring in deciding on its traction policy. Neither did it see any role for the Commission in the matter. Until electrification was practicable it considered that modern steam locomotives should haul the trains. Shunting would, however, become a task for the diesel. Experimentation with diesel mainline locomotives and railcars would continue. The Commission could, in the Executive's opinion, better occupy itself with other than purely railway problems.

How should posterity judge the Executive's handling of its most important policy decisions? The organization and staff work at its headquarters was superbly handled, although the decision to separate locomotive and carriage and wagon responsibilities at Regional level could be challenged in view of the resulting duplication of facilities at ground level. Neither can there be any faulting of the pace at which unification proceeded, except by those at Regional level who thought it was too fast. After the reluctance to standardize on LMS locomotive designs for good political reasons, the interchange trials failed to throw up any ex-Company designs of marked overall superiority. Another opportunity now presented itself to use the LMS designs but Riddles opted for the new British Railways standards. With hindsight, he would have been wise to have confined the new designs to the British Railways Class 7 express passenger 4–6–2 and the heavy freight 2–10–0 in order to fill two gaps in the then existing range of modern designs. The LMS locomotive types could then have succeeded other former Company types when they needed replacement. A package of twelve new designs was over-ambitious.

Contrary to a widely held view, Riddles was no more dedicated to the design of steam locomotives than to the other mechanical engineering aspects of his task and it is a flight of fancy to portray him as burning to create a whole series of locomotive designs which would leave a mark on the history of locomotion. Although his attitude to main-line diesels was understandable, he would have been well advised to have hedged his bets on future developments by taking a closer interest in main-line diesels. With the knowledge gained from at least three visits to the USA of senior railway officers, all of whom had seen for themselves the rapid and successful progress being made with the replacement of steam by diesel locomotives, it would have been wise for the Railway Executive to have ordered for trial a substantial number of diesels. This would have been concurrent with the building of steam locomotives. For example, a scheme where diesels could have taken over a whole group of steam workings would have provided more practical experience than could be gained from five diesel units in their individual workings. It was probably an error of judgement on the part of the Executive when it decided not to adopt the LNER proposal to replace thirty-two Pacifics on East Coast Main Line services by twenty-five diesels.

Although there is no doubt that Riddles firmly decided the traction policy of the Railway Executive – and made the fact clearly known in any contacts with the Commission – he fully supported area schemes for diesel multiple-units to take over local passenger services. F. A. Pope became a Member of the Commission in 1951. He and Riddles, both former London and North Western men, had known each other for many years and had worked closely together as Vice-Presidents of the LMS. Pope had previously been Chairman of the Ulster Transport Authority, on whose railways diesel railcars were operating very successfully.

By 1952 the Commission had given its approval to the construction of the diesel sets for use in the West Riding of Yorkshire and Cumberland. It

Fig. 2.8   One of the first diesel sets ordered by the Railway Executive running
on the Keswick branch in 1955 (BRB)

also announced the intention to introduce further sets, not only for local workings, but also to provide fast services between neighbouring cities. The Railway Executive was, however, to be dissolved long before the first of the new Derby built diesel multiple units made its trial run between London (Marylebone) and Beaconsfield on 29 April 1954.

By 1952 there were other developments to be noted in traction policy. Some encouraging information was being received from the Lancaster–Morecambe–Heysham line, where the experimental 50 cycles a.c. scheme had been introduced. Also, the Commission's report for 1952 announced that studies were being made regarding the conversion of 'an important length of main line exclusively to diesel traction'. Some questions, both technical and economic, remained to be solved following the introduction of the two gas-turbine locomotives. Full electrical operation had begun on the first section of the Manchester–Sheffield–Wath electrification. The conventional steam locomotive did not merit a mention, but this was 1952. For the Railway Executive it was its last year of existence.

The Commission's annual report for 1948 embodied, with virtually no alteration, the whole of the report submitted to it by the Railway Executive. Indeed, the Executive had to be restrained from publishing its own report. By 1952, it was significant that the Commission's report included the question of railway motive power within its first chapter and excluded

Fig. 2.9   Displaced by electrification from its banking duties west of Wath in February, 1952, the most powerful steam locomotive ever built for a British railway, Garratt No. 69999, heads a Manchester–Sheffield freight train. Later it took over further banking work on the Lickey Incline (B. K. B. Green)

the topic from the section given over to the affairs of the Railway Executive. It was an indication of the maturing relationship between the Commission and its agent. Relations had not been good between the two bodies but by 1952 were improving, although the Commission still received edited versions of the Executive's minutes.

The relationship between the Executive and the Regions was also showing some signs of mellowing. There was still a feeling in the Regions that too much decision taking was centralized and that the committee procedure was sucking authority from their engineers to the centre. The attendance of the Chief Regional Officers at meetings of the Executive at two-weekly intervals since July 1948, had not dispelled these Regional views but by 1951 the Executive was beginning to slacken the reins.

In the wider scene, continuing national economic problems were causing disillusion with post-war Britain. The promised vision of public ownership seemed to be turning into an impossible dream. The Railway Executive had, however, made a massive contribution to the unification of the railway systems of Britain and had many achievements to claim for its efforts. At the same time, several streams seemed to be combining to put pressure on a dam which would not be long in breaking.

CHAPTER THREE

The Abolition of the Railway Executive and Subsequent Patterns of Organization

I N Britain 1951 was to prove to be a year of both change and opportunity. The results were particularly unsettling for the British Transport Commission. By the end of that year the Commission could be seen to be moving closer to the achievement of its objectives. It had completed the acquisition of the road haulage fleets and the national network of road services was taking shape. The new data on the comparative costs of the different types of service provided by road and rail were being fed into the new pricing proposals, which would be the basis of integration policies. The Railway Executive had made considerable progress in unifying the railway system, and the first of the new standard locomotives were coming out of the workshops. The quality of the service given to the public was a marked improvement on the standards of 1948 and many of the named expresses of the pre-war years, along with some new names, had appeared in the timetables.

Sir Eustace Missenden retired in 1951 and was succeeded as Chairman of the Railway Executive by John (later Sir John) Elliot. With some of the earlier tensions lessened, the Commission and the Railway Executive were now working more closely with each other. The Executive was also beginning to devolve further authority to the Regions. It now involved the Chief Regional Officers in its regular meetings, although it had asked them to desist from holding their own formal meetings. The Railway and Road Haulage Executives were jointly examining the amalgamation of their respective road collection and delivery fleets as a further stage in the process of integration. Although several years would still be needed to achieve the Act's objectives, the scene was set for the machinery created by the Transport Act of 1947 to move into higher gear.

Unfortunately for the Commission, public attitudes were also changing and were no longer behind the great experiment of 1947. After many years of austerity there was a widespread wish to see some material reward for sacrifices made in the national interest. The Festival of Britain, which was celebrated throughout the country in 1951, acted as a catalyst. Just as the Great Exhibition of 1851 had focused the energies of Victorian

Britain on its surging industrial potential, this Festival helped to make people aware of the new opportunities around them. Conceived by a Labour Government as a booster of national morale, the event was followed by the General Election of October, 1951 and a landslide victory for the Conservatives.

The new Government was soon to announce its views on the future of transport in Britain. The Commission also put forward its own views, but was not consulted by the Minister of Transport before the White Paper was issued in May 1952. It was only after the Bill was published in the July of the same year that the Commission was invited to put forward any opinion, but it was made clear that no fundamental policy changes could be considered. The Commission's case was put before the public in its Annual Report for 1952.

The new Government rejected the principles implicit in the 1947 Act, which was regarded as an abhorrent symbol of the triumph of public planning over private enterprise. Even more odious to some Government supporters was the belief that the Railway Executive had destroyed the individualism and boldness of the former Companies. This view was somewhat distorted by nostalgic comparisons between the Companies in the 1930s and the Executive in the late 1940s after the years of war and under-investment. The public were more aware of the fact that the high speeds of the pre-war days had not been restored by 1951 than that net ton miles per total engine hour were 30 per cent higher in 1951 than in 1938. These attitudes were fostered by those who disliked the results of unification and some of the voices came from within British Railways itself.

In spite of the nostalgia among many Government supporters for the days of the former Companies, there would have been no buyers for the railway system if de-nationalization had been seriously contemplated. Indeed, it did not prove possible to dispose of all the recently nationalized road haulage fleets, which was one of the objectives of the legislation about to be enacted. There were to be two main targets for the legislators. One was to eliminate the objective of integration of inland transport and replace it by competition. The other was to decentralize railway administration and abolish the Railway Executive. It was also intended to introduce the spirit of competition into the decentralized railway by encouraging '. . . healthy rivalry between areas . . .'. These were the principles enshrined in the Transport Act of 1953.

The Railway Executive was replaced by six area authorities to run British Railways under the general policy direction of the Commission, to which certain functions affecting the system as a whole were reserved. If the original proposals to appoint only part-time Members to the Commission had been adopted, Britain would virtually have had six separate regional railways. The intention was clearly to allow a very large measure of auto-nomy to the new area authorities. Indeed, during the latter part of the

1950s, considerable management effort was put into what turned out to be abortive attempts to produce separate financial accounts for the six areas.

It was conceded by the Government that such a dramatic, and fundamental, switch in policy direction could not take place overnight. The Act received the Royal Assent in May 1953 and the Railway Executive was abolished with effect from 1 October of the same year. The railways were then run under an interim organization within the Commission, which moved from the upper floors of the London Transport offices at 55 Broadway to the former Railway Executive's accommodation at 222 Marylebone Road. F. A. Pope and J. C. L. Train were the two Members of the Commission who inherited the main responsibility for the running of British Railways. Train was now functionally in charge of the railway engineering activities. The five Chief Officers reporting to him were responsible respectively for civil engineering (John Ratter), mechanical engineering (R. C. Bond), carriage and wagon engineering (A. E. Robson), electrical engineering (S. B. Warder), and signal and telecommunications engineering (J. H. Fraser). T. M. Herbert, formerly Director of Research at the Railway Executive now became directly responsible to C. C. Inglis, Chief Research Officer at the Commission. The Chief Regional Officers were re-designated as Chief Regional Managers and attended the regular meetings of the Commission.

Sir Brian (later Lord) Robertson, the new Chairman of the Commission, was unable to give full-time attention to his new task until the end of 1953. By April 1954 he was in a position to submit to the Minister of Transport the Commission's proposals for re-organizing the railways. Parliament approved the proposals, and they came into effect in January 1955. So ended over twelve months of the interim organization of what was still the largest single undertaking in the world, with over 870,000 employees and capital valued at a figure approaching £6000 million at 1979 price levels.

The effects of both the reversal of the course of transport policy in Britain and the organizational upheaval were seriously to check the course of railway development. It had taken over three years from the new Government's attitude, which caused the Railway Executive to lose some of its authority, to the introduction of the scheme for the re-organization of the railways. This period of organizational disarray alone was only a few months shorter than the time which had been allowed under the 1947 Act for carrying out the most fundamental change in Britain's transport history. In his Presidential Address to the Chartered Institute of Transport in November 1977, T. L. Beagley, a former Deputy Secretary in the Department of Transport, said, in referring to the 1947 legislation 'Such a major re-organization of the system needed ten–twenty years to show its real value and, with the major changes of the 1953 Act, it was not given time to prove itself.' There would be general agreement that changes were necessary but that they should have been more evolutionary in character.

And what of the personalities? Lord Hurcomb had been an able Chairman of the Commission. He will be remembered particularly for his quiet domination of the Commission's affairs, his intimate knowledge of the ways of Government and a will to be seen to be carrying out the spirit as well as the letter of the 1947 Act. He did, however, find it difficult to accept at face value any opinion in a field outside his knowledge. For this reason his relationship with engineers was not an easy one, as his considerable intellect had not been applied in technological areas. R. A. Riddles, although not insensitive to political atmosphere, was an outspoken engineer of the intuitive school and made little attempt to hide his opinion of the Commission. It was understandable, therefore, that he relinquished his railway career when the Railway Executive came to an end and became the chairman of an engineering company. J. C. L. Train was the only Member of the Railway Executive to become one of the fifteen Members of the new Commission. Sir John Elliot became Chairman of the London Transport Executive, but had already left his mark on the improved relationship which had developed between the Commission and the RE.

Lord Robertson, as would be expected of a former military Commander-in-Chief, tackled the structure of the new organization in a very determined manner and was to gain, during nearly eight years in office, the respect of all with whom he came in contact. His lucid mind had no difficulty in grasping the complications of the new organization, which is more than could be said of many of those who had to work within it. The headquarters organization introduced at the beginning of 1955 was inflexible and inimical to the taking of quick decisions.

As all the Executives, apart from that responsible for London Transport, had been abolished from 1 October 1953, some of their work had to be taken on at the headquarters of the Commission. These headquarters consisted of the Commission itself, including its Committees and Sub-Commissions, and an administrative group called the General Staff. In addition, a Railways Division was established: this consisted of a Central Staff for British Railways, the British Railways Committees and the General Managers' Committee (the Chief Regional Officers in RE days became Chief Regional Managers in 1953 under the interim organization and General Managers in 1955). The Committees of the Commission were policy-forming bodies covering all forms of transport responsible for presenting matters in such a way that the Commission could concentrate on reaching a decision. The railway engineering departments were particularly involved in the Works and Equipment and Technical Development and Research Committees. Mention should also be made of the Railways Sub-Commission which was concerned with co-ordination between Regions, standards of performance, and guiding the work of the British Railways Committees.

During the interim organization in 1953 and 1954 it was only to be

Fig. 3.1   The third stage of the Manchester–Sheffield–Wath electrification was completed during the period of the Commission's Interim Organization. CC locomotive No. 27000 heads the inaugural train as it enters Manchester London Road (now Piccadilly) Station on 14 September 1954 (A. H. Emerson)

expected that there would be many conflicts between the headquarters and regional levels as the Regions took advantage of their new freedom. These conflicts did not disappear with the coming of the new statutory organization in 1955 but their delaying effect on the taking of system-wide decisions was partially obscured by the tortuous channels which had to be followed at Headquarters. The 1953 Act had not only substituted competition for integration and decentralization for centralization: it had also introduced the opportunity to revolutionize the whole freight charging system. The retention of a charges structure devised under the 1921 Act was a major cause of the financial losses which were being incurred by British Railways from 1952. It seemed that the burden of organizational change was more than the Commission could be expected to bear over so short a period of time while the fundamental changes in commercial practice were still to come. These days were certainly not conducive to the taking of long-term engineering policy decisions, even if the investment resources had been available. Indeed, it was the beginning of an era when the spectre of financial deficit would pre-occupy both British Railways and the Government.

Although the Commission had to cope with mounting problems after 1953, there was no requiem for the former Railway Executive. This was unjust as it had applied great energy to its many tasks, and achieved much within its short life in the face of the resource constraints of post-war Britain. Perhaps, its fault lay in over-achievement rather than in faltering in its objectives. Certainly, it was over-ambitious in its standardization policy for steam locomotives and it under-estimated the potential of diesel traction on main lines. In the circumstances of the time it had opted for solid development rather than the brilliant experimental work which is associated with individualism. It never produced much evidence of rethinking the role of railways within the inland transport system, although branch line closures proceeded on a modest scale and services were withdrawn from some 1770 route miles during its span of life. It attempted no rationalization of Britain's excessive and inter-twined route system, but re-routed freight traffic on the most efficient routes as an early stage in the process.

With the Executive abolished and much of the decision-taking now decentralized, the Regions naturally reacted against the process of unification, which they believed had gone too far and too fast. It is of interest, therefore, that a manager who would soon be in charge of a Region himself said on 2 February 1959, when commenting on the Members of the Executive:

> They were mostly men of great strength of character, great expertise, undeviating departmental loyalties and they took, believe it or not, many corporate decisions. Working directly down through departmental officers in the Regions they made in unifying a first class start.
> When it was clear that the Railway Executive had achieved its prime objects much of the central authority was devolved.

The occasion was a meeting of the Institute of Transport and the speaker was G. F. Fiennes, author of *I Tried to Run a Railway*.

Now that the dust is long settled, there is no doubt that the mood of the nation in the early 1950s demanded change and that no exemption could be claimed for the transport industry. At the same time, it was to be deplored that a vindictive element motivated some areas of the 1953 legislation which, although so politically charged, lacked the acumen to realize that the pendulum inevitably reacts to a particularly violent swing. Although the 1953 Act planted some of the seeds that would flower later in the development of bi-partisan transport policies, it represented at the time a return to the British predilection to tackle transport problems in part rather than as a whole. A leader in *The Times* on 6 November 1952 was headed 'Third Thoughts' and dryly commented 'It is rare, if not unprecedented, for a Government to present a proposed Bill in three widely differing forms before the second reading is reached. . . . The best carvers, it has been remarked, pay some attention to the bone structure when they dismember a chicken.' This uncertainty in Government attitudes towards the role of railways in Britain was to affect their progress for many years, and its impact on engineering development is part of this narrative.

Under the 1955 organization the Members of the British Transport Commission did not have the functional responsibilities which were such a feature of the Railway Executive. Departmental responsibility was now with the Regional General Managers, but the Commission headquarters retained direct control in certain areas known as the Reserved Subjects. The Reserved Subjects affecting the engineering departments were:

1. The standards and codes of practice to be observed in the design, manufacture, and maintenance of locomotives, carriages, wagons, and general engineering plant and equipment.

2. Preparation and submission of annual building programmes for locomotives and rolling stock.

3. Allocation and overall planning of the work to be done in the main railway workshops.

4. Examination of new works schemes submitted to the Commission for approval.

5. Examination of Regional budgets for maintenance.

6. Inspection of materials and allocation of materials to Regions.

7. Co-ordination of research and development.

8. Central negotiations with national bodies.

9. Staff questions – in a professional advisory capacity and planning the training of men for the higher posts.

Apart from the functions reserved for decision at Commission headquarters the six Area Boards had a considerable range of responsibilities and a Member of the Commission acted as Chairman of each Board. The Boards delegated day-to-day management of the railway to their General Managers.

Although the engineers at Commission headquarters continued the practice of chairing the departmental committees, their position was very different from that existing under the functional organization of the RE. At best, the relationship between the headquarters and regional levels was an uneasy one. Although the former Company Chief Mechanical Engineers had now retired, their successors saw opportunities for regional autonomy in the new situation. The headquarters engineers were naturally reluctant to forgo the unifying effect of central control. Although the Commission itself was eager to encourage co-operation in the best interests of the railway system as a whole, there was now a marked tendency to favour debate rather than decision. Unfortunately, the new statutory organization, which had replaced the interim organization in January 1955, did little to clarify the situation and created a hierarchical framework which accentuated the letter rather than the spirit of the organizational linkages. The Minister of Transport was not very enlightening in explaining the 1955 organization. He explained that the Commission was a policy-forming body. The six Area Boards were also policy-forming at Area level, but certain matters requiring general treatment were to be 'focused' at Commission headquarters. The Area Boards were likened by him to the Boards of Directors of the former railway Companies. Little was said about the Boards in their role as area authorities for all the Commission's transport activities, and they confined their activities almost exclusively to railways.

From January 1955 the engineering officers at Commission headquarters were members of the British Railways Central Staff and, therefore, part of the British Railways Division. In addition, there was a Technical Adviser on the Commission's General Staff. John Ratter, a railway civil engineer, occupied this position, which was responsible for co-ordinating technical opinion and advice in respect of all the Commission's activities. Only the Chief Research Officer reported directly to the Technical Adviser, but the engineering officers on the British Railways Central Staff worked very closely with him. With the exception of C. W. King, who took over the civil engineering responsibility from Ratter, the engineers on the Central Staff were those involved in the interim organization of 1953, i.e., R. C. Bond, A. E. Robson, S. B. Warder, and J. H. Fraser.

Although explained in a document known as the 'Grey Book', and communicated throughout the Commission's activities with the help of conferences and visual aids, the organizational structure of 1955 was elegant rather than practical. Major policy decisions on any system-wide issue had to be the product of seven opinions, six of which were those of the Regional General Managers. As would be expected, the process was slow when unity was essential and fragmented in other situations. It was natural that every opportunity was taken to bypass the procedure in the interests of quick decision-making. For example, the Regions involved were to develop the Trans-Pennine diesel multiple unit trains without design approval from Commission Headquarters. It was argued that the trains would operate only within the Regions concerned and, therefore, there was no violation of the design function reserved at headquarters level. The proliferation of types of diesel multiple units on British Railways was later to create many problems for both engineers and operators.

The engineering departments were by no means alone in having to deal with the growth of local individualism at the expense of central standardization. Indeed, with the help of the list of Reserved Subjects, they enjoyed more disciplined procedures than the Commercial Department, which had to struggle for several years to find a national identity. One argument often used by the Regions in support of their different policies was related to their size as railway management units. As a Region could be larger than the national railway system in a country the size of Holland, it was claimed that there was room for six different railway attitudes in Britain. It could also be argued that the high degree of devolution in railway policy making which featured so strongly in Britain during the 1950s and early 1960s created lively initiatives and much innovation. Whether or not it was the right course to adopt in the engineering departments at a time when the Commission was under-

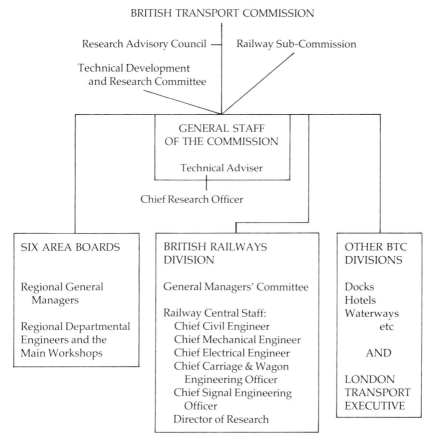

Fig. 3.2   The Statutory Organization introduced on 1 January 1955, showing the
railway engineering relationships

going such massive structural changes of a fundamental character is quite
another matter.

It is of particular interest that the Commission encouraged further
devolution than was required by the statutory framework. By 1956, for
example, the Area Boards had more powers delegated to them in the
approval of works and equipment schemes. In the same year there was a
move in the Eastern Region towards the decentralization of traffic
management. By 1957 the Region was divided into three lines – Great
Eastern, Great Northern, and London, Tilbury, and Southend – each
under a Line Traffic Manager. The engineering departments remained at
regional headquarters. There is no doubt that line management had a
dynamic effect on local decision making in the traffic departments, but it
did not have wide application throughout British Railways.

While decentralization on a line basis was not geographically suited to
the situations in all Regions, the encouragement of local traffic manage-

ment was widespread and not without its effect on the other departments. For one thing, it gave support to the view that improved traffic management would so revitalize the unprofitable activities of British Railways that the problem they presented would be reduced in scale. This had the effect of postponing some of the inevitable decisions to be taken on the rationalization of the system, with results which were soon to accelerate the pace of traction modernization, as will become apparent later in the story. Also, the emphasis on an integrated form of local management, while hardly affecting the civil and signal engineers, altered the situation of the mechanical and electrical engineers. Instead of being directly responsible to the Mechanical and Electrical Engineer at Regional headquarters, they reported to the local manager, maintaining only a professional link at Regional level. At a later date, the principles of local traffic management were modified, but the introduction of the system showed how far the Commission was willing to go in fulfilling the spirit of devolution enshrined in the 1953 Act.

While the years of re-organization were consuming so much time and energy in the 1950s, the engineers continued with their task of improving the physical condition of the railway. The carriage building programme had again been curtailed in 1952 due to steel being in short supply. This resulted in additional, and substantial, repair work on existing vehicles, too many of which were now up to fifty years old. The first section of the Manchester–Sheffield–Wath electrification was working well and some major re-signalling schemes had been introduced, including that at Euston. Large-scale trials of the proposed new system of automatic train control had been carried out on the East Coast Main Line between King's Cross and Grantham. The West Riding of Yorkshire diesel multiple unit scheme was being introduced and more diesel shunting locomotives were being delivered along with useful additions to the freight wagon fleet. The two gas turbine locomotives and the 'Fell' diesel were in trial running alongside the other five main-line diesels and an increasing number of standard steam locomotives which were coming into service.

Planning work was now in hand on the London, Tilbury, and Southend electrification and approval had been given to the extension of the Southern Electrics to the Kent coast. Particular attention was now being given to the problems arising from inductive interference experienced with adjacent telecommunications circuits following experience gained on the 50-cycle a.c. traction installation on the Lancaster–Morecambe–Heysham line.

Track renewals were still being hampered by staff and equipment shortages but use was now being made of Italian labour and mechanization was developing. The Southern Region was carrying out studies and trials for the application of work study and incentive principles to track maintenance and, later, to most civil engineering work. Speed restrictions on the main lines had been reduced and maximum speeds of 85 miles/h were now allowed on some lines. The crossing gates at Warthill in Yorkshire had been replaced by the first pole barriers, carrier current telephone circuits were being extended, and the largest automatic train describer installation in the world had been introduced between Liverpool Street and Romford.

It appeared that British Railways was making technical progress in a number of areas. The rate of progress over the system as a whole was not, however, on a scale which would result in a modern railway within the foreseeable future. The Commission could see no halting the decline in the financial situation of British Railways unless more positive efforts were made to modernize its equipment. The railway share of both passenger and freight markets was declining while the promise of reforms in railway charging practice extended under the 1953 Act would do little to improve finances, at least for some years. Robertson emphasized the need for a change in attitude towards railway investment when discussing the Commission's financial position with the Minister of Transport. The response was sufficiently encouraging to result in the appointment of a committee of Chief Officers to prepare proposals for re-investment. The Railway Executive had put together a railway modernization plan in its latter days, but the document never saw the light of day. Now, the need for putting proposals forward for approval was urgent as the atmosphere favourable to modernization could disappear as rapidly as it had emerged.

The nature of the modernization proposals form the subject of Chapter Four. Here it is necessary only to place them within the context of events in the mid-1950s. The British Railways Modernization Plan was developed while the statutory reorganization required by the 1953 Act was being shaped. The new organization came into effect on 1 January 1955 and the Modernization Plan was announced in the same month. The 1953 Act had revolutionized the organization of British Railways but had not dealt with the more fundamental matter of the role of railways within a competitive transport system. The railways were certainly to gain more commercial freedoms, but investment was now to flow back into them before the effects of organizational and commercial changes could have had time to take effect.

Hindsight is an inexhaustible commodity but not reserved for the exclusive use of the economic historian. With such fundamental changes being made in the rules of the transport game, it could have been expected that the dust of change arising from the 1953 legislation should have settled – and a survey made of the future need for road and rail resources – before embarking on large scale re-investment in railways. It now seems amazing that the first nation-wide investment proposals since the railway age began had to coincide with the first major change in the regulatory framework of railways and a complete upheaval in the Commission's organizational structure, without the three aspects being purposefully related to each other. Although the sequential ordering of events was to cause some problems at a later date, the Commission could not have tolerated any postponement of re-investment in their ailing railway until the Government had decided what kind of railway it wanted.

From the mid-1950s the financial situation of the Commission began to worsen. The new competitive structure of the transport industry, years of under-investment, postponement of price increases at Government request, and recession in the heavy industries had contributed to the position. Changes in the regulatory structure and the Modernization Plan had arrived too late to make their most effective impact, while the results of both the new commercial freedom and flow of investment could not appear for some years.

With its proposals for price increases blocked in 1956 and better service quality needed before more traffic could be attracted to rail, the Commission could only look for cost savings in order to improve net revenue. There were two main sources available. One lay in the withdrawal on a substantial scale of unprofitable passenger services. Any rationalization of freight or passenger services through the use of the pricing mechanism would have taken too long to produce results in the near future. The other practicable course was drastically to reduce the costs of operating the railway.

The Commission had been withdrawing unremunerative passenger services at a modest rate. Now they went to some trouble to prepare the Central Transport Users' Consultative Committee for the large number of proposals for closing branch lines that would soon be entering the consultative machinery. Then, after the decks had been cleared for what looked like being very drastic action, and with a suddenness that surprised even the Commission's own spokesmen before the Committee, there was a switch in policy. Apparently, the experience of line traffic management in the Eastern Region and the support given by the Trade Unions to the application of Work Study methods, along with the imminence of diesel railcars in substantial numbers, had brought a new confidence in the possibility of revitalizing the fortunes of loss making services. Admittedly, the dramatic increase in traffic generated by the early diesel railcars would have had the effect of strengthening the opposition to service withdrawals, at least until the diesel solution had been given a reasonable trial. Although the Commission assembled very detailed data on unremunerative passenger services and some line closures were made (including, in 1959, the former Midland and Great Northern Joint Line with a staff of 1500) the proposals assembled were not put into effect until the 1960s.

The Commission chose the course of reducing operating costs in its bid to reverse the decline in its financial position and this solution affected particularly the mechanical engineers. The main financial prize was, it was thought, to be won by a rapid acceleration in the process of replacing steam by diesel traction. Electrification, however desirable in many ways, was going to take too long to generate increased net revenue. The policy of a three-year trial period for new diesel locomotive types, which had been recommended by the responsible engineers, was abruptly abandoned and the burden fell upon the mechanical engineers to get rid of steam at the earliest possible date. That is why the 18000 steam locomotives possessed by the Commission in 1955 dwindled within the next thirteen years to the three narrow-gauge veterans running through the Vale of Rheidol in Wales. It was not an experience that the engineers would have chosen themselves as the most effective way to achieve the desired financial objective.

Following the Government's decision to support the Modernization Plan there was a quickening of interest in all areas of engineering. The engineering committees of the Railway Executive era had continued without radical change. In addition there was now the Technical Development and Research Committee, which helped to guide the progress of the Plan. It also helped to generate new thinking on railway technology and operational methods. One of its members, H. P. Barker (a gas and electrical engineer, who was Managing Director of Parkinson and Cowan Ltd and a part-time Member of the Commission) was mainly responsible for the concept of the Freightliner train. This involved the transfer of containers to and from a fixed formation train instead of switching wagons between trains. It emphasized the importance of the train, rather than the wagon, as the unit of rail freight movement, thereby initiating what could claim to be the most significant rail freight development of the century. The container had a long history on railways in Britain as a means of facilitating inter-modal transfers: now, it had a further role of reducing local rail movements and the work of the marshalling yard. This emphasis on the train as the unit was given additional thrust by 'merry-go-round' coal trains running in a continuous circuit between colliery and electricity generating station. These developments resulted in a fundamental re-thinking of attitudes to the policy of building large mechanized marshalling yards, which were such a feature of investment plans in the 1950s.

Also, a Design Panel was instituted in 1956, so beginning the uneasy, but stimulating, relationship between engineer and industrial designer. The industrial designer now played a major role in the interior decor and layout of carriages, as well as all aspects of non-technical design throughout the activities of the Commission. Besides acting as a corrective to centrifugal tendencies in the devolved type of railway organization in the post-1953 situation through the creation of a corporate identity, the Panel has made a notable contribution as a world leader in industrial design.

Although the Modernization Plan absorbed so much engineering effort during the later 1950s, some of the earlier work came to fruition during

Fig. 3.3   The 'Merry go round' coal train gave additional emphasis to the importance of the train, rather than the wagon, as the unit of rail freight movement (BRB)

this period. Measures to develop the performance of the steam loco-motive continued. In March 1956, the decision was made to adopt the 25 kV 50-cycle a.c. system of electrification and later in the same year the Minister of Transport approved the British Railways system of automatic train control: also, disc brakes were used for the first time on British Railways passenger carriages. During this time great strides were made in track design and methods of renewal. Continuous welded rails on concrete sleepers became standard for main lines and, in later years, on other lines.

Changes were also taking place within the engineering departments, particularly in mechanical engineering. The Motive Power Department, which had been jointly responsible in Railway Executive days to the mechanical engineering and operating functions, now reported only to the Operating Department. The Chief Mechanical Engineer had already joined forces with the Chief Electrical Engineer, as well as taking over the Carriage and Wagon Engineer, but the control of outdoor carriage and wagon maintenance passed to the Operating Department.

In 1958, Sir Landale Train retired and was replaced as a Member of the Commission by John Ratter. Bond took on the position of Technical Adviser and was in turn succeeded by J. F. Harrison who, although coming from the position of Mechanical and Electrical Engineer on the London Midland Region, was from the Gresley-trained school of the LNER.

Towards the end of the 1950s the Government and the Commission were running out of patience with each other. The Commission was now receiving investment funds on a scale never experienced before, it had been granted the commercial freedoms which its predecessors had sought in 1938 and it had been massively re-organized from top to bottom. The Government thought that these measures had been given a year or two to show results, but had failed to do so. They had showed similar impatience in 1951 with the integration proposals introduced in 1948. The Commission had not welcomed the re-organization, and was finding that the commercial freedoms were now inadequate and had come too late to be really effective. Also, it needed several years to reap any measurable benefits from the Modernization Plan.

   The outcome of some rather sharp exchanges between Government and Commission was a Parliamentary Select Committee, which reported in 1960, four years after an earlier Select Committee had put forward its views. Both Committees had some sympathy for the Commission's point of view, and that of 1960 referred to specific support payments for 'social services' as an alternative to general deficit financing. The Minister of Transport (Ernest Marples MP), however, ignored this advice and set up a Special Advisory Group headed by Sir Ivan Stedeford, Chairman of Tube Investments, to report directly to him on the Commission's affairs. The papers produced by this Group remained as confidential material within the Government's archives. This secrecy, and the apparent slight to the Select Committee procedure were sensitive issues within the British Parliament. For example, Aubrey Jones MP, a former Conservative Minister of Supply, said in the House of Commons on 30 January 1961:

> The statement of 10th March announcing the establishment of the Committee contained a very strong hint as to the findings which it should reach. However independent-minded the members of the Committee might have been, it is very difficult to believe that that hint did not keep on entangling their discussions. Next, the Committee was invited to do its job in a hurry in order to catch the legislative Session. It did the job in six months, an interval of time which could not possibly have allowed much opportunity to do all the cross-examination necessary in an analysis of this kind. . . . Finally, when the Government put forward their proposals in the House we were not allowed to know what the Committee recommended. The world is allowed to infer that what is proposed arises directly from the Committee Report. I do not know, but it is at least a fair possibility that the Government have run away from some of the Committee's recommendations and that some, if not all, of the members of the Committee think that some of the decisions are downright erroneous.

   Even these comments did not bring forth any indication of what had been said by Stedeford and his colleagues. It was generally understood, however, that they were much more critical of the Commission's organization than anything published by either of the Parliamentary Select Committees. The progress of the Modernization Plan itself was now at risk and the electrification of the London–Birmingham–Manchester–Liverpool lines was close to being halted until a more detailed case could be prepared.

This was the beginning of a very difficult period for the engineers on British Railways. The Stedeford Group seems to have thought that engineering considerations had too much influence within the Commission. If so, it was hardly accurate as a comment and certainly unfair. It was true that the engineers were now pushing ahead with modernization and gave every appearance of taking the initiative. On the other hand, the commercial department had still to gain the degree of freedom from statutory regulation which would lead to its marketing thrust re-shaping the activities of the railway. Neither had the operating department, with the notable exceptions of the Southern Electrics and the interval service patterns developed on the Eastern Region in the 1950s, been fully seized with the productivity potential of the new equipment now available. Again, the headlong rush into dieselization had not been on the advice of the engineers and mainly because the Commission considered the rapid elimination of steam traction as the most appropriate method of improving its finances. The enhanced reputation of the engineer which was associated with the Modernization Plan was to suffer some reverse during the 1960s when changes of a very different character were to overtake the British railway system.

The Railway Executive had been abolished in 1953. In 1960, it was evident that the British Transport Commission was soon to suffer the same fate and be replaced by a body to be known as the British Railways Board. From a statement made by the Prime Minister in the House of Commons on 10 March 1960 it was expected that the Government would prescribe a further dosage of decentralization and turn the Regions into almost autonomous subsidiaries of the Board. Work which had been carried out by the Commission on the problem of area financing had not, however, produced very promising results. Even so, the Government held fast to its belief in the decentralization of management as a remedy for railway ills when it said in its White Paper 'Re-organization of the Nationalized Transport Undertakings' in December 1960:

> The British Railways Board will assume the responsibility for running the railways as an effective national system. . . . The Board will, however, perform only those central functions which are essential to the running of the railways as a single entity: all other functions will be the responsibility of the Regional Railway Boards. Notably, the British Railways Board will be responsible for such matters as national staff and wage negotiations, overall control over finance and investment, policies for safety, training, and research, and the determination of the future size and shape of the railway system. . . .
>
> Regional Railway Boards, which will replace the present Area Boards, will be fully responsible for the management and operation of their regional railway systems. Each will be autonomous in all matters which concern its region alone. They will thus continue the process of devolution of authority and decentraliza-

tion of management. Each Regional Railway Board will maintain a regional trading account as a means of assisting it to secure the highest level of efficiency and economy of operation. . . .

The Transport Act of 1962 implemented the views expressed in the White Paper and came into force on 1 September 1963. As the British Railways Board appointments were made towards the end of 1962, there was a short period when Commission and Board existed together. The Chairman of the new Board was Dr Richard Beeching, formerly Technical Director of Imperial Chemical Industries and a member of the Stedeford Group. His very close partnership with the Minister of Transport (Ernest Marples MP) was to be the most effective in the history of railways in Britain up to that time. Both men were dedicated to ending the financial losses of British Railways. The Minister showed little concern with social implications and the Chairman, although recognizing them, considered them outside his province. Beeching knew what was expected of him, and let nothing divert his attention from the task of restoring profitability to the railways of Britain. This single-minded approach was a great source of strength, as if he had allowed himself to realize that many of the railway's problems were soon to beset the world's public passenger transport networks, he could well have lost the incentive to act quickly.

Beeching's four years as Chairman were to see more changes in the activities and physical network of the railways of Britain than at any other time since their creation. To some extent this was due to the personality and unswerving logic of the man himself, supported by his personal friendship with the Minister of Transport. Beeching was also fortunate in inheriting a great deal of preparatory work on the profitability of the different railway activities, which formed the basic material for his diagnosis of the problem. Again, there was now general agreement within the country that the railway could not continue in its current form and this had been given expression within the 1962 Act. British Railways had now been separated from the other activities under the British Transport Commission and given a much simpler organization. Even more important, all regulatory control over rail freight had now been abolished, leaving the railway free to decide its charges for the traffic it selected to carry. The Act statutorily excluded the railway from its common carrier obligation inherited from canal and turnpike trust in the nineteenth century. Although the impact was by now mainly psychological in value, the fact that the railway had broken away from the inhibitions of the past, both by statute and in the eyes of the public, meant that railway attitudes could now catch up with the physical modernization of the previous decade.

As under the 1953 legislation, it was fortunate that some guidance was given to the engineers on the functions reserved to the British Railways Board. In a written answer to a Parliamentary Question in the House of

Commons on 11 April 1963, the Minister of Transport said that these functions would include:

> The design, procurement, allocation, and overall control of rolling stock and ships.
>   Standards of design and maintenance of track and structures, buildings, and signal and electric traction equipment.
>   The control of railway workshops.

At the same time, the Minister made it clear that there was to be a return to a functional organization at Board Headquarters. This ended the General Staff concept of the Commission and represented a return to one of the most strongly criticized practices of the former Railway Executive. In order to rebut the accusation that the co-ordination of public transport had been jeopardized by the separation of railways from the other nationalized transport undertakings, the Government made token recognition of the principle of co-ordination by creating a National Transport Advisory Council, but no useful results were achieved. Co-ordination had little place in British transport policy until the latter part of the 1960s, and then only in local passenger movements.

John Ratter became the Member of the Board functionally responsible for engineering, architecture, and industrial design. The responsibility for the railway main workshops was removed from Regional control and given to Sir Steuart Mitchell, a Member who had come to the Board with a distinguished record in public service.

At the beginning of 1963 the engineering responsibilities and titles at Board headquarters reflected the current practice on the railways of mainland Europe, although similar groupings of responsibilities had existed in the former Company organizations in Britain. J. F. Harrison was now Chief Engineer (Traction and Rolling Stock) and included electrical engineering in his department. A. N. Butland was Chief Engineer (Way and Works) and took over organizational responsibility for signal engineering, which was then under A. W. Woodbridge. Although mechanical and electrical engineering were to remain under one organizational roof, civil and signal engineering were to be separated again when taken over respectively by A. Paterson and J. F. Tyler.

Beeching's experience as a member of the Stedeford Group had convinced him that some new blood was needed in the changed situation of the railway. The quality of the men taken into the railway team from outside the industry was mixed. Some were to make an outstanding contribution: others made their mark by their very failure to make a contribution, and there were those who drifted in like shadows and so departed.

The Beeching era continued to be less than favourable to engineers. It was a time when dis-investment appeared to take priority over investment. The new marketing aggression, which had grown from regulatory freedom, made it fashionable to assert that a railway needed a market before it needed rails or rolling stock. The early railway builders concentrated on the engineering problems of supply rather than the commercial questions of demand, which never flagged. It was only natural that, as a result of road competition, when supply exceeded demand, the positions should be reversed. There was a general feeling that the railway should be reduced in size before further investment could be contemplated. Indeed, there was the inference that previous managements had required the engineers to introduce a great deal of new equipment into railway activities which had a doubtful long-term future. As a situation this was the case, although the Commission could have retorted that it was the Government of the day which had got its railway priorities wrong in the early 1950s. In its turn, the Commission had to accept some blame. It had tried to burst out of its unhappy financial position by unduly accelerating the flight from steam to diesel when it should have been more active in trimming the scope of railway activities. The engineers had done no more than do the job to which they had been appointed, although there was little doubt that there had been, during the time of the Railway Executive, an ill-judged delay in the development of main-line diesel traction.

The engineers also had to face some deep examination of their practices, particularly from newcomers to the industry who found it difficult to understand the reasons for the long lead times in railway design and development or the apparently obsessional emphasis placed on safety. The two-way argument was useful to all the parties involved, but it was fortunate for the future of the railway that the engineers managed to resist the kind of economies which would have prejudiced safety standards, or severely reduced operating speeds. It is true that the normal maintenance of way and works on many routes suffered from the uncertainty associated with the probability of line closure. In the main, however, the effect of financial restrictions placed on maintenance budgets in the 1960s was compensated by significant improvements in productivity which were appearing at the same time.

The main development associated with the 1962 Act was the famous report *The Reshaping of British Railways*, published in March 1963 within three months of the British Railways Board taking over from the Commission. It was the first major publication appearing on the world transport stage which clearly outlined the place of railways within the national transport system. Much of what the document stated was already well known – and had been advocated by voices within British Railways – but now a comprehensive picture of rail strengths and weaknesses appeared in one report, along with diagnosis and prescription. Beeching himself did not favour the linking of his name with the report, as he placed much emphasis on the corporate effort, but no member of the team involved in its preparation could fail to acknowledge the weight of his personal contribution, which included the careful drafting of many paragraphs in his own handwriting.

The conclusions of the report of principal interest to the engineers were:

The continued replacement of steam by diesel locomotives for main-line traction.

Transfer of the modern multiple unit diesel trains displaced by the withdrawal of passenger services to continuing services still hauled by steam locomotives.

Selective improvement of inter-city passenger services and rationalization of routes.

Increase in block train movement of coal by provision of loading facilities at collieries and the establishment of coal concentration depots.

Study and development of a network of 'Liner Train' services.

The closure of a large number of passenger and freight stations dealing with low volumes of traffic and the rapid withdrawal of freight wagons.

The cost savings due to station closures, the lifting of track, and rolling stock withdrawals have always tended to obscure the positive impetus which the report gave to directing investment towards the railway of the future, particularly the inter-city passenger services, the Liner Train, and the concentration of freight traffic. By way of emphasizing these positive aspects of reshaping, the Board published in February 1965, a further report on *The Development of the Major Trunk Routes*, which set out to show how the through route system could best be developed to match the future pattern of demand for rail services. The Board took the view that the course of reshaping rail activities would be distorted unless rail and road competition was on an equitable basis. The Trunk Routes report was preceded, therefore, by a *Study of the Relative True Costs of Rail and Road Transport over Trunk Routes*, a notable document which began the still continuing debate on the extent to which the lorry should pay for the roads it uses. A fourth great exercise of the Beeching period, which would have raised to the level of debate the problem of the commuter services, and inevitably have pinpointed the question of their social claim on support payments, never appeared before the public.

The years following the 1962 Act were remarkable both for ideas generated and the action taken to implement them. There was no doubt that Beeching represented the views of many railway managers of the day, who believed in directing investment into a thriving railway network rather than spreading it thinly over a bigger, but declining, system. Others initially resisted his approach and then, recognizing its inevitability, became vociferous supporters. It was significant that one of his last remarks before leaving the Board in 1965 was to express his regrets that, in spite of the achievements of his four years in the Chair, he had not solved the problem of relationships between Board Headquarters and the management at Regional level. A combination of the persuasive Beeching personality and the unifying purpose in his plans had brought a unity to British Railways, which began to crumble when a new Government opposed to many of his ideas caused him to seek a change.

It has already been mentioned that one of the functions reserved to the Board in the 1962 legislation was the control of railway main workshops. This was a reversion to the system of control by which the workshops had been administered with outstanding success during the days of the Railway Executive. It was a wise move as there was a need for further investment in the modernization of workshops equipment which would be accompanied by a considerable reduction in workload following the reshaping proposals. Without central control of the thirty-two main works which existed in 1962, rationalization and re-equipment would have made slow progress. Sir Steuart Mitchell became Deputy Chairman in 1963, but had already prepared a Workshops Plan, which will be referred to in a later chapter. At this point it is only necessary to emphasize that this was one further step in adjusting main works capacity in conformity with change in the railway itself, and another stage beyond the rationalization after amalgamation in 1923 and unification in 1947. Following the Modernization Plan the Mechanical Engineering Committee and General Staff of the Commission had initiated workshops plans, but progress was slow until the 1962 Act returned the workshops responsibility to Headquarters.

H. O. Houchen, who had brought his engineering experience from the British Overseas Airways Corporation, was appointed General Manager of British Railways Workshops. R. C. Bond, who had been Technical Adviser during the days of the Commission's General Staff, and Chairman of the Mechanical Engineering Committee, was now back in a Board organization with functional Members where the role of Technical Adviser had no place at Board Headquarters. He became, therefore, Technical Adviser to the newly formed British Railways Workshops Division on 1 January 1965 and, later, General Manager when Houchen became a Member of the British Railways Board. During 1963/4 Bond was President of the Institution of Mechanical Engineers, so achieving the highest position in his profession.

Bond retired in 1968, but had secured the appointment as his Deputy of A. E. Robson, then Chief Mechanical and Electrical Engineer of the London Midland Region. Robson did not immediately succeed him, due to the unexpected retirement of J. F. Harrison, Chief Engineer (Traction and Rolling Stock). Robson succeeded Harrison but, after a short stay at Board Headquarters, took charge of the Workshops Division under its new designation of British Rail Engineering Ltd.

Returning to the Beeching period, it would be wrong to think of it as being associated only with reports and reshaping of the railway. The year 1964, which happened to mark the return of the first Labour Government since the defeat of its predecessor in 1951, included some significant engineering events. The new Engineering Research Laboratories at Derby were opened during the year and the new Liner Train freight system was well on the way to becoming a national network. Some 1520 route miles had by then been equipped with the new British Railways Standard Automatic Warning System, in addition to the 1400 miles already fitted with the former Great Western equipment. The year also marked the appearance of the train known as XP 64, which was the most ambitious attempt made until that time to determine what kind of carriage was really wanted by the passenger. Until that time the British Railways standard Carriage (Mark 1), introduced during the early days of the Railway Executive, had been in production for over a decade and it was appropriate to introduce new features in carriage design with the active co-operation of the users.

Clearly, it was difficult to follow Beeching. S. E. (later Sir Stanley) Raymond was Chairman of British Railways between 1965 and 1968. It was a time when the railway gave the impression of having exhausted itself in the immense activity of the preceding three years. It was symbolic that steam traction was phased out by 1968; it seemed that the railway itself was running out of steam. The initiative in policy making was now increasingly to be taken by the Minister of Transport – Mrs Barbara Castle MP – who did not take long to realize that the 1962 Act had not solved the problems of railway finance.

It will be recalled that the White Paper outlining the drastic proposals for the railways, which were introduced with the 1953 Act, was prepared without any consultation with the British Transport Commission. The approach now taken was very different with a view to a thorough examination of the railway situation by Ministry and Board leading to a more lasting solution than any of the earlier attempts. A Joint Steering Group set up by Minister and Chairman of the Board made a very thorough study of the causes of the financial problems of British Railways and reported in July 1967.

The results of the Steering Group's work proved to be a constructive contribution to the policy decisions which were later to be taken in respect of British Railways. Further, it can be said that this work, along with other contributions made by the Minister's advisers, resulted in what could justifiably claim to be the most far-sighted legislation affecting railways in Britain since the Transport Act of 1947. The outcome was the Transport Act of 1968, which introduced what has become the basis of a bi-partisan attitude to transport policy. This policy is the recognition in statute of the separate social and commercial roles of the railway: a feature which was known to exist but had been ignored when raised by the Parliamentary Select Committee in 1960.

The 1968 Act also emphasized the need for co-ordination between train and bus, although at local rather than national level. In respect of freight traffic, British Railways now took on the aspect of a wholesaler specializing in train loads and private siding traffic. Control of less than car load freight, collection and delivery, and the Liner Train business were transferred to the newly created National Freight Corporation.

The year of 1968 was one of the great turning points in the story of railways in Britain. It can be said to have initiated the most stable period of relationships between Board and Government, and within the inland transport industry itself, since the exceptional circumstances of the Second World War. The railways had started life as specialized carriers, hauling coal from colliery to tidewater. The technological advance of the steam locomotive had then reduced transport by road to a minor role, while rail grew to be the country's universal carrier. Motorized road transport began to reverse the situation in the 1920s and by 1968 legislation had been introduced which again recognized the specialized character of the railway in the British transport scene. Rail had re-found its role.

Deficit financing was now abolished, but the Government was willing to give support to certain services. The rest could be abolished, or kept by British Railways at their own commercial risk. This would result in some reductions in rolling stock and track capacity, with financial cushioning during the cut-back period. The Government also undertook to give financial support to selected areas of engineering research and the Advanced Passenger Train was an early beneficiary.

By 1968, the magnitude of the reconstruction of the railway during the twenty years since nationalization could now be discerned. The route system had been reduced from 20000 miles to under 11000. Staff numbers had dropped from over 640000 to 296000 and 20000 steam locomotives had been replaced by diesel or electric traction. Wagons had been reduced from 1165000 to 430000, the number of terminals more than halved and that of marshalling yards cut from 973 to 184.

The year will also be remembered for its engineering milestones. The opening of the new Euston Station as the gateway to the 100 miles/h electric services on the West Coast Main Line, involving the demolition of the famous Euston Arch and Hardwick's Great Hall, symbolized the spirit of the age. Again, the running of the last scheduled steam-hauled train on 11 August 1968 would by itself have gained the year a place in railway history. Less well known is the significance of 1968 in the development of the Liner Train, then to be known as Freightliner. Mentioned in the *Reshaping of British Railways* report of 1963 as one of the areas for future freight development, Freightliner had not only established itself as a national network by 1968 but had expanded to France and Belgium, including two new container ships on the Harwich–Zeebrugge route. By any standards it was a very remarkable achievement to have proceeded from the drawing board to a national network, followed by international projection, within so short a time.

So 1968 was a year of solid achievement as well as one that involved the changes in direction and organization required by the Transport Act. Not only had the Sundries and Freightliner Divisions to be transferred to the administrative control of the National Freight Corporation. The Act had abolished the statutory Regional Railway Boards, although the British Railways Board continued their existence as non-statutory bodies as part of their management structure. The Act had, at the same time, required the Board to submit for the Minister's approval a scheme of organization and during 1968 the firm of McKinsey & Company, Inc. were asked to examine the organizational structure at Board and top management levels as the first stage in a task which was to continue for over four years. The Board also established in 1968 its own organization for long-term planning. The Corporate Plan was now to be the machinery by which the Board set targets for the railway and its other businesses regarding net revenue required to meet the Board's objectives; also the resources in manpower, materials, and investment required by every department to play its part in the Plan. In theory at least, it would now be possible to anticipate changing situations rather than always being in the unhappy state of reacting to them. Massive 'one off' exercises such as the Modernization Plan or the Reshaping Plan should never again be needed in this rolling programme of long-term planning. On the whole, this new approach to planning was to have a stabilizing effect, although national economic circumstances were to prove a disrupting feature.

H. C. (later Sir Henry) Johnson became Chairman of the Board on 1 January 1968. His period in office was characterized by good relations with Government, a style of leadership more managerial in character than that of any of his predecessors and a deep personal interest in his staff. As a lifelong railwayman, mainly in traffic management, he understood the ways of engineers better than any of his predecessors as Chairman of the Board or the Commission. In some ways this made him far from easy to convince as to the merits of some new development: his traffic department experience caused him to prefer the predictability of well-tried equipment to the unknown performance of some novel proposal. The detailed knowledge which he brought to any discussion made it lively and decisive. His great capacity to motivate people brought the boost to morale at Board Headquarters needed to accelerate the movement generated by the 1968 Act.

In 1968 there were three engineers among the Members of the British Railways Board H. O. Houchen retired in 1969, John Ratter left in 1970 to join the World Bank while Dr Sydney Jones stayed until 1976, latterly as a Part-time Member. In the new Headquarters organization introduced in 1972, the Members of the Board reverted to non-functional responsibilities. One Member also took on the responsibility of being Chief Executive (Railways). In this capacity he was Chairman of the Railway Management Group, which consisted of five Executive Directors in charge of the Headquarters functions, five Regional General Managers (the Eastern and North Eastern Regions had now been amalgamated), and the General Manager of British Railways Workshops, later to become British Rail Engineering Ltd.

As General Manager of the Workshops at that time A. E. Robson was the only engineering voice within the Railway Management Group. The passenger business, the freight business, finance, and personnel were each the responsibility of an Executive Director. All the engineering departments and the operating department reported to the Executive Director, System and Operations. There were now three engineering departments at Headquarters: Chief Mechanical and Electrical Engineer (T. C. B. Miller), Chief Civil Engineer (A. Paterson), and Chief Signals and Telecommunications Engineer (J. F. Tyler). This was less than generous recognition of the engineering responsibilities at Headquarters, although alleviated in some measure when I. M. Campbell, who had been both a Regional Civil Engineer and a Regional General Manager was appointed as Executive Director, System and Operations and brought more engineering experience into the Railway Management Group. In the Regions the position was rather different in that there was at this time one Assistant General Manager who had oversight over the engineering departments.

By the end of the 1960s the British Railways passenger business was confidently shaping its future. The Inter-city expresses covered Britain with a network of fast, interval services which were proving very attractive to the traveller. The results of market research indicated, however,

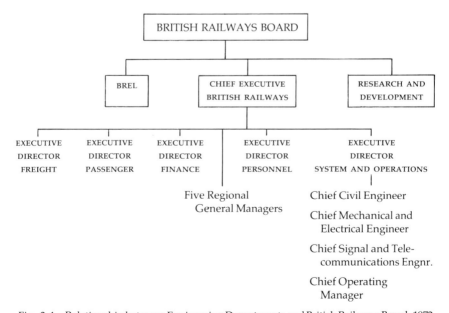

Fig. 3.4 Relationship between Engineering Departments and British Railways Board, 1972

that the revenue-earning potential of Inter-city could be considerably increased by introducing journey times which would require the regular running of trains at speeds exceeding 100 miles/h. In 1968 evidence was produced indicating that, under British conditions with average speeds of the order of 70 miles/h, an increase of one mile an hour can be expected to lead to a minimum increase in traffic of 1 per cent. Although more sophisticated modelling techniques have subsequently been developed, the 1968 formula has stood the test of experience over several years.

The pursuit of higher rail speeds in the later 1960s was by no means limited to Britain. The High Speeds Symposium organized by the International Railway Congress Association in Vienna during June 1968 indicated the depth of interest in high speeds among the world's railways. This conference brought out two features of particular significance to British Railways. One was its belief, not shared with all railways, that there was no purpose in high speed except as a means of achieving a commercial objective, so emphasizing once again the 'value for money' criterion attached to railway engineering development in Britain. The other was the knowledge that, although the Inter-city service provided by British Railways was unequalled in the overall quality available to the passenger (i.e., the package combining comfort, frequency, and speed), other countries, particularly France and Japan, offered a limited number of faster schedules than were to be found at that time in Britain.

British Railways was developing the Advanced Passenger Train (APT), which would reduce journey times in accordance with commercial needs and without requiring new track. Unfortunately, its expected date of introduction was too far ahead to meet the net revenue targets of the 1970s. At the same time, there were limits to the extent to which schedules involving speeds exceeding 100 miles/h could be achieved with existing locomotives and track. It was, therefore, fortunate for the commercial department when the Chief Mechanical and Electrical Engineer (then T. C. B. Miller) proposed that a more conventional engineering solution than APT would allow speeds of 125 miles/h to be run within a comparatively short time scale. The outcome was the High Speed Train (HST), which is described in a later chapter. Here, it is only necessary to say that no time was lost by the Executive Director of the passenger business in providing the financial justification for what was termed 'the intermediate solution' and that HST was, during the 1970s not only to achieve its commercial objectives but also to establish the world's fastest schedules except for certain trains on specially constructed tracks in Japan.

The freight business during the later 1960s was not as well placed as the passenger business. Freight was considered by the Government to be a purely commercial railway activity, which would have to pay its own way in the competitive environment of inland freight transport. Its struggle to achieve financial viability was to achieve success a decade later. The amount of train-load business was steadily increased in relation to the less economic wagon load traffic and more efficient wagons, including many capable of carrying loads of 100 tons, were coming into service. Freightliner, although not to be profitable until later in the 1970s, was steadily increasing its carryings. The real problem was the wagon-load business, which was dragging down the profitability of the freight activity but was too potentially important to jettison, even after transferring every possible load to train-load or Freightliner operation. The problem was tackled from many angles. The sales activity was damped down until service quality, assisted by train planning and advance traffic information, could match the quality of the new wagons becoming available in a saleable package. By 1974 the newly designed Total Operations Processing System (TOPS) came on stream and began its progressive effect on the improvement of productivity and quality of rail freight services in Britain. In 1977, when over 80 per cent of BR freight traffic was passing in train-load quantities, the new 'Speedlink' service was launched, after four years of preparation, carrying siding-to-siding wagon-load traffic on a limited number of routes where high quality service could be assured.

Sir Henry Johnson had retired in 1971 and was succeeded by the Rt Hon Richard (later Sir Richard) Marsh, a former Minister of Transport responsible for the implementation of the 1968 Transport Act. The Marsh period experienced some differences between Ministry and Board in the interpretation of Board objectives, which had come to the surface on earlier occasions when the railway financial situation showed signs of

Fig. 3.5   A Freightliner train carrying a load of containers used in the deep sea shipping trade (BRB)

weakening. At the beginning of 1969, British Railways had been in public ownership for twenty-one years. In that year, as well as in 1970 and 1971, there was a working surplus in BR's operating account but in 1971 the Board warned the Government of a worsening financial situation. It was fortunate for the Board that this situation coincided with a growing national concern regarding environmental issues. Indeed, there was a feeling throughout the developed countries of the world that there was something fundamentally wrong with a transport system which was allowed to invest heavily in over-used sections of the road infrastructure which were paralleled by under-used railway tracks.

It was a time also when the transport policies of the European Communities were beginning to make some impact on attitudes in the United Kingdom. The other member countries of the Communities had always regarded their railway systems as more central to their transport strategies than had been the case in Britain, and the relationships between railways and governments had been codified well before Britain acceded to the Treaty of Rome in 1973. It was, therefore, not surprising that in its Review of Railway Policy in November 1973, the Government took the view that there should be no substantial change in the size of the railway network and expressed support for the idea of a virtually new railway from London to the British end of the Channel Tunnel.

The Railways Act of 1974 included a number of financial provisions which were welcomed by the Board, including Section 8 which made available financial grants to industry to meet the investment costs involved in putting their freight on rail. The whole approach now seemed so much more positive than the solutions of the period between 1951 and 1962. Unfortunately, the Board's confidence in the new attitude was short lived. A further national economic crisis resulted in the investment programme being cut by a third. Over a period of five years in the mid-1970s no single investment programme remained intact for as long as six months. The additional staff of 9000, recruited in the optimistic atmosphere following the Review of Railway Policy in 1973, was reduced by 6000 in the following year.

Although the vulnerability of British Railways' investment plans to external events was to be so evident in the 1970s, there was a steady stream of engineering developments. In 1971, for example, approval was given to the electrification of the suburban services of the former Great Northern line, air-conditioned carriages of both 1st and 2nd class types were introduced as the standard on main-line trains, work was started on the Mark III carriage, a start was made on the Merseyside loop scheme, construction of the first High Speed Train was well advanced and the new Signal Repeating Automatic Warning System was under trial on the Southern Region.

By 1973, the West Coast Main Line electrification had reached Preston, twenty-seven High Speed Train sets had been approved for the London,

Fig. 3.6   In 1971 approval was given to the scheme for the electrification of the Great
Northern suburban services. The scheme was completed in 1977 (BRB)

Bristol, and South Wales routes, the prototype of a new high-density
train was in passenger service on the Southern Region, and authority was
given to proceed with the building of an electric locomotive incorporating
thyristor control. Although economic storm clouds dominated 1974, it
was the year in which a five-hour timing was made possible between
London and Glasgow by the completion of the West Coast electrification,
and the Advanced Passenger Train had been tested at 136 miles/h.

In 1975 the Public Expenditure White Paper (Cmnd 6393) imposed
three constraints on the Board. Investment was pegged in real terms at a
figure of around 30 per cent below the expectations of the Railway Policy
Review of 1973, support for the passenger business was pegged for five
years at the 1975 level, and the freight business was required to be
self-supporting by 1978. The more encouraging news of the year was that
the Advanced Passenger Train had created a British speed record of
nearly 153 miles/h and that 2·5 million tonnes of freight would be carried
under proposals made during the year for private siding grants under
Section 8 of the 1974 Act.

The Government published in April 1976 its consultation document
'Transport Policy', welcoming views from all quarters on the policy review which had been completed. The Board submitted its comments in
the following July and the White Paper 'Transport Policy' of June 1977,
gave the prospect of a new stability within the railway, although at a level
which showed the constraints of the national economic situation on the
revenue support and investment funds which the Government could
make available. Public expenditure cuts would continue to restrict investment in railways, but the basis of a rolling investment programme
had now been established for the first time since the railways were
nationalized. This allowed for a reasonable measure of forward planning,

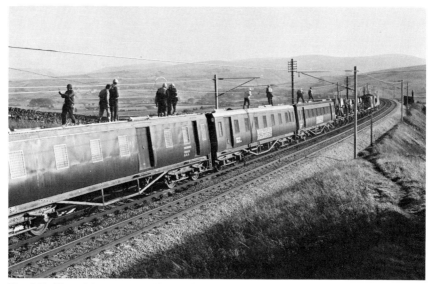

Fig. 3.7   The wiring train on Shap Fell during the electrification of the West Coast Main
Line between Preston and Carlisle (BRB)

so allowing more efficient use to be made of manpower and physical
resources. The result was the Transport Act of 1978.

During the period of consultation which led to the publication of the
White Paper in 1977, there was a change in the Chairmanship of British
Railways. Sir Richard Marsh relinquished his appointment on 11 September 1976 and his place was taken by Peter (later Sir Peter) Parker, who
came from private industry but with experience of public service. One of
the new Chairman's early innovations was an organizational change at
Board Headquarters. The position of Executive Director in charge of each
of the five railway functions, created in January 1970, was abolished.
Members of the Board again took on functional responsibilities, as had
been the case in 1947 and 1962. I. M. Campbell became the Member
responsible for the engineering departments. Engineers reporting
directly to him were M. C. Purbrick (Chief Civil Engineer), G. S. W.
Calder, later K. Taylor (Chief Mechanical & Electrical Engineer), A. A.
Cardani (Chief Signal & Telecommunications Engineer) and Dr K. H.
Spring, later Dr A. H. Wickens (Director of Research). As Campbell was
also Chairman of BREL until early in 1979, the engineering activities were
under a more co-ordinated form of control than had previously existed in
British Railways. Figure 3.8 indicates the nature of the BR Headquarters
organization in 1977.

It is revealing to compare Fig. 3.8 on page 87 with the earlier organizational charts on pages 65 and 81. The 1955 organization was characterized by the complications of the statutory devolution of authority. By
1972 systematic attention was given to the objectives and organization of

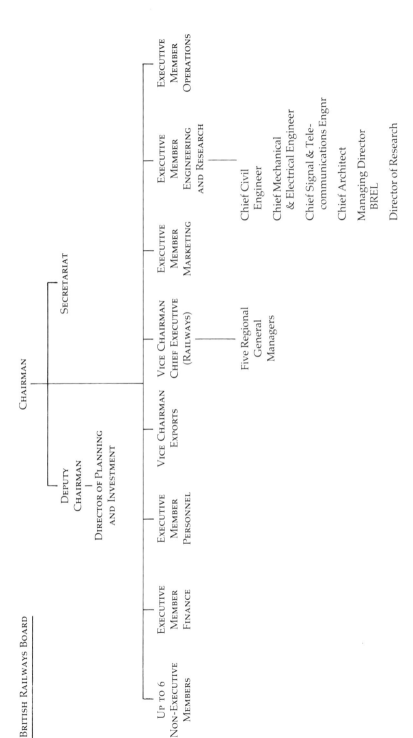

BRITISH RAILWAYS BOARD

CHAIRMAN

DEPUTY CHAIRMAN

DIRECTOR OF PLANNING AND INVESTMENT

SECRETARIAT

UP TO 6 NON-EXECUTIVE MEMBERS

EXECUTIVE MEMBER FINANCE

EXECUTIVE MEMBER PERSONNEL

VICE CHAIRMAN EXPORTS

VICE CHAIRMAN CHIEF EXECUTIVE (RAILWAYS)

EXECUTIVE MEMBER MARKETING

EXECUTIVE MEMBER ENGINEERING AND RESEARCH

EXECUTIVE MEMBER OPERATIONS

Five Regional General Managers

Chief Civil Engineer

Chief Mechanical & Electrical Engineer

Chief Signal & Tele-communications Engnr

Chief Architect

Managing Director BREL

Director of Research

Fig. 3.8   Relationship of Engineering Departments to British Railways Board, 1977

all the Board's activities. The resulting emphasis on the importance of marketing resulted in the engineering departments occupying a secondary role. By 1977, however, the departmental balance was restored and a simpler form of organization at Headquarters was introduced with a return to functional responsibility at Board level. By this time a clearer understanding of Headquarters and Regional roles was also emerging. The translation of business requirements into engineering specifications was also undergoing further development. In this connection, it is of interest to compare the Riddles organization in Fig. 2.2 on page 32 with Fig. 3.9, which outlines the proposed organization at BR Headquarters of the Chief Mechanical and Electrical Engineer's Department, as outlined by K. Taylor in his Presidential Address to the Railway Division of the Institution of Mechanical Engineers on 1 October 1979. In 1948 the emphasis was on standardization, and it was logical to divide the work into locomotive, rolling stock, and electrical groups. In the new organization, it will be noticed that there are three product groups under one Traction and Rolling Stock Engineer. These groups have the responsibility for translating the business specification into engineering terms, so that the lowest total cost-effective solution can be established. This emphasizes the extent to which production, maintenance, operating, and commercial requirements are now brought together in meeting the separate demands of the inter-city, suburban, and freight services.

In the late summer of 1978, the Board set up a small group at Headquarters to deal with strategic issues and the long-term planning of all the Board's activities. The first Director of Strategic Development was Geoffrey Myers, a civil engineer and formerly General Manager of the Eastern Region. He reported to David Bowick, Vice-Chairman (Rail) and formerly Chief Executive of British Railways. Bowick had been succeeded by I. M. Campbell, who thereby became the first engineer to become responsible for managing British Railways. Earlier engineers who had been General Managers of former companies included Aspinall (Lancashire and Yorkshire), Thornton (Great Eastern), and Milne (Great Western).

For the purpose of a narrative on railway engineering it would be felicitous to associate the arrival of the engineer in high places with the progressive improvement for the third year running (1976/7/8) upon the financial objective which British Railways agreed with Government. This would be reading too much into the association, although it would be appropriate to emphasize the sense of balance that pervaded these years. There was a tolerance and understanding between Government and Board. Government recognized, for example, that a rolling investment programme was essential for rail planning purposes. In turn, the Board realized that it had to trim its targets to a worsening economic situation.

There was also better balance within British Railways itself. The inherited values of 1970, which lumped all the engineering departments

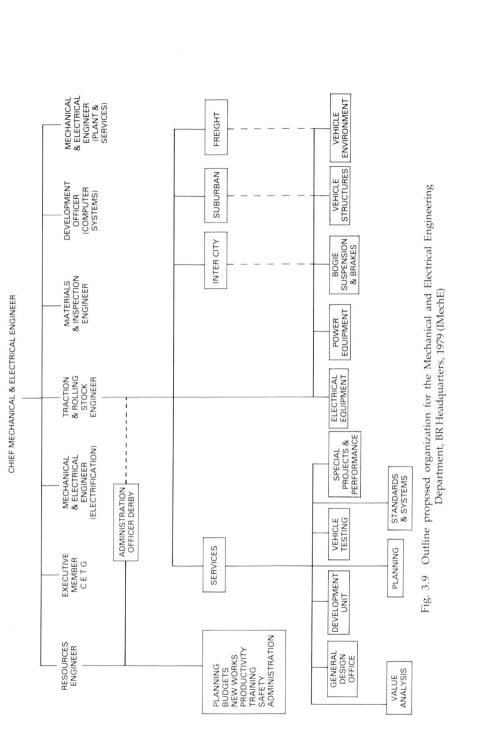

Fig. 3.9 Outline proposed organization for the Mechanical and Electrical Engineering Department, BR Headquarters, 1979 (IMechE)

along with the operators into one of five functional bags, had now been adjusted and a lift given to engineering morale.

These were not the only factors at work. Environmental and resource considerations – particularly energy – the new disciplines of EEC transport policy, the confidence in railways expressed in the Transport Act of 1978, relationships between Secretary of State and Chairman of the Board and the skill with which the Chairman has emphasized the contractual nature of Government support have all made their contribution to the manner in which British Railways looks forward to the 1980s.

It is pertinent to contrast this situation with the half century of turmoil which followed the railway amalgamations of 1923. This was the painful transition from a railway system, which shouldered obligations consistent with its powerful semi-monopoly position, to a railway which was for too long expected to bear these obligations after any pretensions to monopoly power had disappeared. After years of trial and error with conflicting political attitudes, British Railways has reached a situation where there has been a slowing down in the swinging of the pendulum between politically partisan solutions. The 1968 Transport Act, with some changes of emphasis in 1974 and 1978 has so far withstood political change. Although change must always be expected – and welcomed – as part of the transport scene, it is hoped that the engineers in the 1980s will have less of the political and organizational turbulence experienced by their predecessors.

British Railways has entered the 1980s, however, with some harsh realities to face. Over the previous four years, the level of financial support to the passenger service has fallen, in real terms, by 25 per cent and the situation in the country's heavy industries has seriously affected freight revenues. At the same time, the trade unions are unlikely to accept serious erosion in the real incomes of their members, and there are limits to price increases as a means of raising revenue without the substantial improvement in the quality of rail service, which is so closely related to investment in new equipment. All eyes will, therefore, be on urgent measures to reduce costs by improving productivity. Even on optimistic assumptions, the Board's potential cash-flow gap will need short-term assistance not only from increased productivity, but also from financial measures not in the 1979 statute book. As the Minister of Transport (Norman Fowler MP) advised the Chairman of the Board on 9 November 1979 '. . . it is my firm policy that there should be no substantial cuts in the passenger rail network', it appears that the very limited investment resources available will be thinly spread. The challenge to engineering ingenuity has never been greater.

For it is the mounting urgency of the investment demands which particularly concerns the engineers. The Chairman's Commentary in the Annual Report of the British Railways Board for 1979 included the following words of warning:

Fig. 3.10   The equipment required for a modern railway is available in Britain. The problem arises with the availability of investment in resources to produce the equipment in sufficient quantity. APT undergoing commissioning trials on the London–Glasgow main line, where it reached 160 miles/h (BRB)

Unless our investment levels are lifted by some 30 per cent just to replace worn-out assets, the consequences will be lower standards of speed, frequency, comfort, and reliability on rail services. And this is not a progress into decline which can be reversed overnight, or corrected within existing financial constraints.

The 1980s also begin with the need for additional major investment decisions of critical importance to the future of railways in Britain. As well as the urgent need to lift investment levels to avoid deterioration in existing service standards, there is the wider requirement to meet the demand for higher standards in future years, the wisdom of main-line electrification as an oil substituting strategy and the inevitability of a fixed link with the railways of mainland Europe. Later chapters will enlarge on the individual priorities. Meanwhile, Chapter Four considers an earlier situation, when the cumulative effects of years of capital starvation led to the greatest surge of railway investment in Britain since the days of the Railway Mania.

CHAPTER FOUR

The Plan for the Modernization of British Railways

U NTIL 1955 a comprehensive railway modernization programme had never existed in Britain. The nearest the Companies came to such a situation was when the Southern Railway progressively introduced a series of electrification schemes south of London in the 1930s, or with the standardization of locomotive types on the LMS. The Government commissioned the Weir Committee to study the case for main-line electrification but, although the report published in 1931 was favourable, the Companies considered the expenditure to be financially unattractive while the Government was not willing to give financial support. Under the Railways (Agreement) Act of 1935 a few new works schemes were promoted as Government assistance measures during a period of economic depression. These included the Liverpool Street–Shenfield and Manchester–Sheffield–Wath electrification proposals but were not part of a comprehensive plan.

The individual Companies prepared their post-war development programmes. The LNER, for example, explained in 1946 that, over and above the £40 million accumulated during the war for arrears of maintenance, the programme of new works would require about £50 million over a period of five years. As this was more than double the Company's expenditure on capital account during its history, it could rightly be considered optimistic when its booklet entitled *Forward* ended with the words 'the problem of finance must and no doubt will be solved'. The advent of nationalization resulted in a new situation, where the development programmes became a rather nostalgic reminder of Company aspirations until some of the items later appeared as Regional recommendations.

It has already been explained that British Railways began their years of public ownership in a period of severe austerity. The British nation had met the cost of the Second World War to a considerable extent by living on capital. A large part of the country's overseas assets had been sold and by 1948 the credits granted by the United States and Canada were exhausted. An acute dollar shortage developed and the investment proposals for 1948 had to be severely cut. At the end of 1947 the Chancellor of the Exchequer presented his proposals to Parliament in regard to capital investment in 1948. He emphasized that 'These limited and valuable resources must be concentrated as far as possible on those types of investment which will most quickly strengthen our capacity to export. . .' Railways were regarded as making some contribution to exports, with freight traffic justifying greater priority than passengers.

Although one-fifth of the carriages in 1948 were over 35 years of age, the building programme was limited to 1000 vehicles a year. As freight traffic had priority and 29 per cent of the wagon fleet was over 35 years of age, with serious maintenance problems, the wagon building programme survived the axe. So did the programme for building locomotives, where nearly 40 per cent were over-age and causing difficulty owing to the increasing number of breakdowns. The most severely cut part of the programme was that relating to permanent way, where no provision was allowed for overtaking any arrears of wartime maintenance. Parliament was assured that rail travel would not be rendered less safe, although speed restrictions could be expected.

And what fate awaited the major new works projects which had started, or were in view, before the end of 1947? The Manchester–Sheffield–Wath electrification had started before the war and, because of its heavy coal traffic, was allowed to proceed. So was the new Woodhead tunnel, which was an essential component in the electrification scheme. The Liverpool Street–Shenfield electrification project was part of a wider London scheme, which was from half to three-quarters complete and was also allowed to make progress. Prominent among the works which did not go ahead at this time was the rebuilding of Euston Station.

When it could be expected that there would be some easing of the post-war situation, another shadow appeared to darken the prospects for railway investment. In 1951, the Commission referred in its Annual Report to the handicaps imposed by the growing impact of re-armament on the facilities which they wished to offer to passengers and to industry. Owing chiefly to shortages of labour and steel, it had not even been able to carry out the restricted investment programme which it had been allowed. By 1953 it was evident that the railways of Britain had been run down to a level which was causing very grave anxiety. It was estimated by P. Redfern in the *Journal of the Royal Statistical Society* in 1955 (Series A, Volume 118, No. 2) that the net dis-investment in railway assets between 1937 and 1953 amounted to £440 millions at 1948 price levels. The Companies had not had the financial resources to embark either upon main-line electrification or the replacement of an out-dated freight wagon fleet. Their relationship with the State had always been a distant one. When that relationship changed with the advent of public ownership, the State was unable even to make good the arrears of wartime maintenance, let alone authorize part of the modernization which the Companies could not afford in the 1930s.

Elsewhere in Europe, the approach had been very different. In 1918, or five years before the creation of the four main-line Companies in Britain, the Swiss Federal Railways introduced their plans for the electrification of the system. Within twenty years 90 per cent of the country's rail traffic was electrically hauled. By 1944 a second modernization programme provided for new locomotives and rolling stock: also, a plan for major track works to improve the route capacity of the Swiss railway system. On the other side of the Alps, the Italian State Railways began their first major modernization plan in 1922: this involved the modernization of workshops and carriages, along with over 2000 route miles of electrification. The second Italian programme – the post-war reconstruction plan – was virtually completed by 1952. It was followed in 1953 by a five-year plan for more electrification and other improvements. A fourth plan involved, in its first stage, the expenditure of £150 millions on further electrification and the modernization of rolling stock.

Apart from the Swiss plans and the first of the Italian plans, European modernization of railways was closely associated with post-war reconstruction. Soon after the war, a National Committee for the Electrification of the Belgian Railways recommended the electrification of about one-third of the system. Work began in 1947 and by 1957 over half the task had been completed. There was no overall plan for the modernization of the French National Railways, but re-equipment proceeded systematically from the end of the war as part of the national planning process. From 1945 to 1957 the equivalent of £1230 millions was spent, with electrification, signalling, and freight handling as the main beneficiaries.

The German Federal Railway spent £2550 millions on re-equipment between 1945 and 1958 on reconstruction and modernization. Rather less than half this total was accounted for by war damage reconstruction and renewals. It was on the Netherlands Railways, however, that the most complete modernization took place. In 1945 the system hardly existed but by 1958 a combination of re-equipment and re-shaping of the system had produced one of the world's most efficient enterprises. The first plan, costing over £100 millions, included the electrification of all the main lines. The second plan was completed between 1953 and 1958 and concentrated on the provision of diesel traction on the subsidiary lines.

At a time, therefore, when British Railways were unable to find the resources to overtake wartime arrears of maintenance and keep pace with investment schemes authorized in the 1930s, the mainland railways of Europe had either been modernized or were well advanced in that direction. One major reason for this striking difference was the closer identity of interest that had existed over a longer period in mainland Europe between railway and government. Another was the extent of the wartime destruction of railway equipment in many countries and the use of Marshall Aid for railway reconstruction. Again, it could be argued that Britain's diversion of very scarce resources to re-armament in the early

1950s put a brake on the re-equipment of all industries at a critical time. Whatever arguments are put forward, however, to explain why investment in British Railways was so far behind European levels, the plain fact is that railway re-equipment ranked low in the British Government's thinking on capital projects.

It is not generally known that the Railway Executive produced a Development Programme in April 1953: in the following month the Act providing for the abolition of the Executive received the Royal Assent. It was evident that one or two Members of the Commission and the Chairman of the Railway Executive had reached the conclusion that there was more likelihood of a bold modernization plan achieving a reasonable level of investment than could ever result from a number of relatively small submissions. The programme was prepared by a group of senior officers of the Executive under the chairmanship of J. L. Harrington and including John Ratter (Chief Officer Civil Engineering).

There is little evidence of much detailed planning work forming the basis of this development programme. The Executive knew at this time that its days were numbered and wisely drew heavily on the ideas of the Regional Managers who would soon be playing an increasingly important part in the making of major decisions. The programme provided for

Fig. 4.1   Electrification was the major item in the 1953 Development Programme initiated by the Railway Executive, but the Executive itself was abolished before any action could be taken. It was to be 1966 before these electric multiple units would be in regular service on the London Midland Region (BRB)

an estimated expenditure of £500 million spread over a period of ten to twenty years, and was considered to be the minimum required to meet essential needs.

Electrification, with an expenditure of £160 million, was the major item in the programme. The economic realities of the time are brought back to mind when it is read that the case for electrification was partly justified by the release made possible for export of 14 million tons of locomotive coal. The proposed schemes included the main lines between London and Newcastle, London, Birmingham, Manchester, Liverpool, and Glasgow, London and Manchester via the Midland route, and London, Bristol, and South Wales.

The proposals were summarized as follows:

	Estimated Expenditure £m (1953 prices)
Electrification	160
Major improvements to running lines	60
Modernization of signalling and telecommunications	30
Re-siting and modernization of marshalling yards	50
Rationalization and modernization of freight terminals	50
Fitting continuous brake to freight rolling stock	40
Introduction of diesel railcars	17
Reconstruction of passenger stations	40
Helicopter terminals and services	40
Marine services	13
Total	500

The diesel locomotive had no place in the programme and it was said that 'The improved standards of passenger service will be achieved on the principal main lines and suburban routes through electrification.' It was conceded, however, that 'The diesel locomotive may be increasingly introduced in place of steam traction in the course of the normal renewal programme.' The diesel railcar was intended to take over passenger services on other than main-line and suburban routes.

Over a quarter of a century later it appears strange that £40 million should be allocated to terminals for helicopters but in the early 1950s it seemed possible that inter-city helicopter services would become well established within a decade. If so, the railway would wish to become involved by providing the sites for terminals, thereby sharing in the financial success of the new venture and possibly becoming involved in the operation of the helicopter services. Combined rail/helicopter terminals were proposed in London, Birmingham, Bristol, Cardiff, Manchester, Liverpool, Glasgow, Edinburgh, and Newcastle. In the event, the service did not materialize and the railway engineers did not become involved in what could have been some very interesting developments.

There is very little indication of serious consideration being given to these development proposals as a whole by the Railway Executive during the last months of its life, and it is apparent that the whole programme was put aside until the shape of the new organizational changes could emerge.

On its own admission, the year 1953 was one of change and stress for the Commission. Wage demands had increased costs to a degree which resulted in a financial loss on revenue account in the following year. Early in 1954, the Chairman of the Commission (Sir Brian Robertson) alerted the Minister of Transport to the nature of the developing situation. At that time there were three choices open to the Government. First, the whole railway system could have been allowed to decline and become increasingly difficult to work: this course would have been politically unacceptable and socially disastrous. Second, a very large part of the railway system could be closed, so allowing the investment resources which were currently available to provide adequate nourishment for the remaining services. There would have been merit in going some way in this direction but the upheavals already caused by organizational and regulatory change following the 1953 Transport Act were more than could be digested in the short term. Also, the new Government would have been placed in a very vulnerable position if, after claiming to have rescued the railways from the planning excesses of its predecessor, it promptly began to cut the railway system to pieces. It was only to be expected, therefore, that the third course of re-investment would be chosen as the major instrument of railway recovery. At the same time, however, there was an element of compromise in that the investment would be accompanied by some reduction in the scale of railway activities.

It was also reasonable that the Commission would guide the thinking of the Minister of Transport to favour re-investment. It has been seen in Chapter Three how, in one of the most draconian pieces of legislation in transport history, the Government had switched the Commission's objective away from the integration of transport to the opposite pole of competition, introduced a fundamental change in the statutory relationships between the railway and its customers and drastically changed the organizational structure. Within the next decade – and given freedom from interference with the working out of market forces – it would have been possible to detect evidence of the changing shape of the future railway system. By the mid-1960s, therefore, a railway re-equipment plan would probably have concentrated capital investment over a smaller system than that existing in the 1950s. There are sound theoretical reasons put forward in support of delaying investment until the situation is stabilized, but the Commission had good practical reasons for urgent action. It had, from hard experience, little confidence in any government allowing it freedom from interference. There was also a more pressing reason. What kind of railway service could be provided in Britain if modernization did not begin immediately?

In pinning its hopes on investment in a modern railway as an effective way of securing a sound financial future, the Commission recognized the need to restrict the scale of railway activities which would justify re-equipment. Since nationalization in 1948 some 12 per cent of passenger stations and 26 per cent of freight stations had been closed by the end of 1953, and there was every reason to believe that this process would continue – even accelerate – under policies inclined either towards integration or towards competition. Although the physical re-equipment of the railway was to occupy a particularly prominent place in developments during the later 1950s, the modernization of all railway attitudes, with its impact on the rationalization of activities, was an equal partner in the Commission's concept of the reconstruction of British Railways.

The Commission appointed a Planning Committee on 14 April 1954, under the chairmanship of Sir Daril Watson, Chief of General Services at BTC Headquarters. The engineering members of the Committee were:

R. C. Bond, Chief Officer (Mechanical Engineering)
John Ratter, Chief Officer (Civil Engineering)
A. E. Robson, Chief Officer (Carriage & Wagon Engineering)
R. F. Harvey, Chief Officer (Motive Power)
C. C. Inglis, Chief Research Officer
S. B. Warder, Chief Officer (Electrical Engineering)

Reflecting the spirit of devolution in the 1953 Act, a Steering Committee of the Chief Regional Managers was involved throughout the planning task and H. H. Phillips, Assistant Chief Regional Manager of the Western Region chaired the sub-committee concerned with the modernization of traction. John Ratter was chairman of the sub-committees which considered civil/signal engineering and technical staff. Other sub-committees considered traffic forecasts, carriages/wagons, station modernization, marshalling yards, wagon brakes, and the Commission's marine interests.

The Planning Committee reported in October 1954. Its report began with a chapter on traffic forecasts, which had a realistic ring about it although it tended to fall short of the standards of more modern economic survey work. This chapter established the need to distinguish the difference between the estimated demand for coal in Britain and the ability of the coal industry to meet that demand. Besides questioning the official forecasts of coal production, the Committee questioned the ability of the railway to maintain its market share of the traffic volume produced by the heavy industries and did not 'contemplate an increase in the tonnage of general merchandise by rail'. The traffic forecasts also took into account the possibility of concentrating wagon load, as well as less than wagon load, traffic on main centres: also the growth of containerization. They were correct in taking into account changes in traffic patterns, the concentration of future steel production on waterside locations, the strength of increasing road competition, and the extent to which railway modernization would affect the rail share of the transport market, or generate new business.

Bearing in mind the uncertain times and the state of the forecasting art, the traffic estimates were not unrealistic, and have withstood criticism rather better than the official Government figures on which they were partly based. There has been some controversy over the scale of passenger service withdrawals included in the proposals. Regarding short distance passenger travel outside the main industrial areas, the Committee stated 'the railway aim will be directed towards the ultimate withdrawal of the railway from much of this business'. Future argument would concentrate on the meaning of the word 'much' in the context of rail service closures, but the Committee clearly had in mind that over 30 per cent of the passenger travel outside the commuter and long-distance categories would disappear from British Railways.

Most of the proposals of the Planning Committee were to be incorporated in the Commission's official publication, but there were some interesting aspects of the Committee's report produced in October 1954, which were not included in the later document. For example, the Committee explained that the changeover from steam to diesel should be carried out in specified areas through the flexible mechanism of the annual locomotive building programmes. The Committee was also careful to point out that its diesel locomotive proposals assumed that satisfactory designs would be introduced into service within a reasonable period. It made the point that the designs then in service had not achieved that high degree of utilization which would be essential for the economic displacement of steam locomotives. It had the confidence, however, to propose that the building of all new steam locomotives should terminate within a few years and that no express passenger or suburban steam locomotives should be built after the 1956 programme.

The Commission considered the Planning Committee's recommendations and published in December 1954 their proposals, although these were not publicly announced by Sir Brian Robertson until 24 January 1955. The document *Modernisation and Re-equipment of British Railways* was an expanded, and more polished, development of the Planning Committee's report. It appeared that the public relations shadow now loomed larger than the engineering substance in the proposals. There had never been such an opportunity since nationalization to put over a modern image of the railway to the British public. The number of main-line diesels recommended by the Committee was now reduced but the cautionary note was excluded. Also, no reference was now made to diesel loco-motives being introduced through the mechanism of the annual building programmes. The West Coast Main Line of the London Midland Region was included as a main-line electrification scheme alongside that of the Eastern Region from King's Cross to Leeds and Doncaster, which had been accorded the priority ranking by the Planning Committee. The Committee, in its consideration of permanent way, had talked of 'a general maximum speed of 90 m.p.h., wherever possible'. The Com-mission's document referred to 'speeds of at least 100 m.p.h. where conditions will permit'.

Apparently, the West Coast Main Line was included in the electrifica-tion proposals after S. B. Warder (Chief Officer, Electrical Engineering) had assured the Commission that the resources were available for developing the two main-line schemes. Later, it became evident that one scheme had to have priority over the other. By that time the Styal line, in Cheshire, had been electrified on the 25 kV a.c. system. This preliminary work on the West Coast route system, combined with the greater traffic potential of the London–West Midlands–South Lancashire–Glasgow corridor, gave the West Coast considerable leverage over the claim of the East Coast route, where electrification to date has been confined to suburban services.

The 'Modernization Plan', as the Commission's proposals were generally called, certainly received widespread public approval. The leader in the *Manchester Guardian* on 25 January 1955, captured the mood when it said:

> The Transport Commission's plan for the railways is what we have all been waiting for for a long time. At last the Commission seems to have thrown off its defeatism and begun to think in a large way of how it can revivify a transport system that has slipped much behind that of other countries. . . . The Commis-sion's report . . . is an amazing revelation of how a once great service now lags behind the rest of the world. . . . The new programme stands for a new spirit which the public will welcome. . . . Now there is at last the chance of carrying through an expansionist policy; capital is available; public pressure for transport improvement is mounting. . . . All that we have read about or seen of the modernized railway systems of the United States and the Continent is to be transferred to England's green and pleasant land. The prospect is exciting.

The Modernization Plan provided for the spending of £1240 millions over 15 years, but nearly half this sum (about £600 millions) would in any event have had to be spent during the same period merely to maintain the existing equipment. Also, the average spending of £80 millions a year did not seem so great when put alongside the figure of nearly £600 millions being spent on British roads and road vehicles in 1955. Again, the figure was modest when compared with the spending on railways in some other countries. When the Plan was published in Britain, the German Federal Railways, for example, were investing about £200 millions a year in their system. Over twenty years later, the European re-equipment plans were to be dwarfed by the Federal funds made available to railways in the USA under the Railroad Revitalization and Regulatory Reform Act of 1976. Even so, the Modernization Plan of 1955, which the Government supported 'as a courageous and imaginative plan' represented a very substantial commitment to the future of railways in Britain.

It is important to be reminded of the underlying aim of the Plan. This was 'to exploit the great natural advantages of railways as bulk transporters of passengers and goods and to revolutionize the character of the services provided for both – not only by the full utilization of modern equipment but also by a purposeful concentration on those functions which the railways can be made to perform more efficiently than other forms of transport, whether by road, air or water'.

The development of the main components of the expenditure under the Plan will be considered in the appropriate chapters, but the components themselves were summarized in the report as follows:

> First, the track and signalling must be improved to make higher speeds possible over trunk routes, and to provide for better utilization of the physical assets; there will be an extended use of colour-light signalling, track circuits, and automatic train control, the further introduction of power-operated signal boxes, and the installation of centralized traffic control where conditions are suitable; and the extended use of modern telecommunication services   £210m

Fig. 4.2   One of 'the great natural advantages of railways' referred to in the Plan is exemplified by this 3000 ton train carrying iron ore from Port Talbot to Llanwern (BRB)

Secondly, steam must be replaced as a form of motive power, electric or diesel traction being rapidly introduced as may be most suitable in the light of the development of the Plan over the years; this will involve the electrification of large mileages of route, and the introduction of several thousand electric or diesel locomotives £345m

Thirdly, much of the existing steam-drawn passenger rolling stock must be replaced, largely by multiple-unit electric or diesel trains; the remaining passenger rolling stock, which will be drawn by locomotives (whether electric, diesel or steam) must be modernized; the principal passenger stations and parcels depots will also require considerable expenditure £285m

Fourthly, the freight services must be drastically remodelled. Continuous brakes will be fitted to all freight wagons, which will lead to faster and smoother operation of freight traffic; marshalling yards and goods terminal facilities will be re-sited and modernized, and in particular the number of marshalling yards will be greatly reduced. Larger wagons will be introduced, particularly for mineral traffic, and loading and unloading appliances will require extensive modernization in consequence £365m

Fifthly, expenditure will be required on sundry other items, including improvements at the packet ports, staff welfare, office mechanisms, etc; and a sum of at least £10 million for development and research work will be associated with the Plan, making a total of £35m

Total £1240m

Say £1200m

The document then considered the elements of the Plan in some detail and separately for Way and Works, Traction, Passenger Traffic, Freight Traffic, and Sundry Items. A separate section considered the provision of

Fig. 4.3   'Steam must be replaced as a form of motive power'. The BR standard Class 3 tank locomotive came into production in 1951. Building ceased in 1954 (BRB)

staff. The Plan found the Commission with technical staff resources adequate only for the level of past programmes. Competition for trained staff from manufacturing industry had already extended the resources dealing with a modest volume of railway investment. The low level of investment over many years had restricted recruitment: now the Modernization Plan itself became a recruiting booklet. The new staff intake included a number of men with basic technical knowledge, but with no railway experience. At the same time, there had to be rapid promotion of the younger engineers to positions of greater responsibility. These changes required different, and extensive, training programmes. In addition, there had to be extensive use made of consulting engineers, architects, and contractors.

In March, 1955 Sir Allan Quatermaine, formerly Chief Engineer of the Great Western Railway was invited to return to the railway on a part-time basis to advise on the technical training and recruitment of civil and signal/telecommunications engineers. E. J. Larkin, Assistant Mechanical and Electrical Engineer of the London Midland Region undertook similar work regarding mechanical and electrical engineers. The Diesel Training Centre at Derby was one of Larkin's recommendations. Sir Brian Robertson also wrote to contacts in North America and to F. Q. den Hollander, the retiring President of the Netherlands Railways, which was now in the final stages of its own modernization programme. As signalling installations were expected to be bottlenecks in the re-equipment of British Railways, Robertson requested the temporary secondment of signal engineers.

The Chief Signal and Telecommunications Engineer of the New York Central Railroad visited Britain to assess the situation. He recommended the concentration of the resources of all the Regions in turn on priorities drawn up on a system-wide basis. The top priority was the electrification of the West Coast Main Line from London to Liverpool and Manchester. As the London Midland Region was urgently needing more engineers, the recommendation would have concentrated resources on that Region at the expense of schemes in other Regions. These were not, however, times when firm central decisions could be taken by the Railway Executive, which had been abolished in 1953. It was no cause for surprise when the other Regions did not favour the proposal to concentrate signalling resources in this way, and the proposed pooling of resources did not occur.

The decision was now taken to recruit signal engineers from the USA and the Netherlands. London Midland Region officers went to New York to interview engineers who were willing to assist in the laying out of schemes at the drawing board stage. There were many American engineers who were willing to join the British team; some were not suitable or looked for salaries which could not be offered by British Railways. Eventually, six American engineers were chosen and a further eleven volunteers from Netherlands Railways came to the London Midland Region.

There were some sensitive personnel situations, particularly as the Americans were receiving salaries three times those of their British Railways equivalents. The overseas engineers were almost wholly concentrated in the Carlow Street offices in London and their stay was comparatively short, lasting up to two years. As American and Dutch signalling principles and practices differed from those on British Railways, a special training programme had to be arranged. The 'guest' signal engineers, after familiarizing themselves with the new situation, progressively increased the value of their contribution.

The objectives of the Modernization Plan were intended to be achieved by a combination of three elements: physical re-equipment, higher levels of productivity, and the rationalization of the activities of the railway. The Plan was also accompanied by, although not specifically linked with, three statutory changes of a very different kind which resulted from the Transport Act of 1953. The first was the fundamental re-structuring of public transport in Britain; the second was the re-organization of British Railways; the third introduced new methods of charging for railway services. Any one of these statutory changes, as well as the individual elements combined in the Plan, could have had a significant effect on railway finances over differing time scales. Their combined effect was to complicate the assessment and monitoring of railway financial performance. The further factors introduced by large wage awards, delays imposed by the Government on railway price increases and recession in the heavy industries were to make the calculation of the financial benefits of the Plan almost impossible to calculate with reasonable accuracy.

The first adjustment to the Plan came in 1956. In the February of that year the Government blocked proposals made by the Commission to increase charges. The Commission agreed to postpone the increases, but only on the understanding that a fresh assessment of its position and prospects would be undertaken. The result of this re-appraisal appeared in the White Paper 'Proposals for the Railways' (Cmnd 9880), dated October 1956. The document included a memorandum submitted by the Commission to the Minister (Harold (later Lord) Watkinson MP). This memorandum gave particular attention to the physical progress of, and the philosophy underlying, the Modernization Plan. Of special interest was a table showing how the Commission expected to 'cross the line' from annual deficit to annual surplus in 1961 or 1962 and to proceed towards a more substantial surplus in 1970. It is known that, for a number of reasons which were not associated with the physical re-equipment of the railway, the reality differed from the estimate. The aspect of interest to the modernization story is the improvement in net revenue which the Commission estimated would be achieved from the different activities then in hand. The figures in the White Paper were as follows:

Improved contribution from British Railways	1961 or 1962 £m.	1970 £m.
(a) Modernization (Re-equipment)	+35	+85
(b) Pruning services	+ 3	+ 3
(c) Productivity	+ 5	+10
(d) Commercial freedom	+20	+25
	+63	+123
Less: interest on Modernization borrowings	−25	−40
	+38	+83
Annual rate of deficit at starting point (excluding interest on deficits and finance of Modernization Plan)	−40	−40
Total	Say, Balanced	Say, +50

These figures supported the estimated annual financial improvement of £85 millions included in the Modernization Plan and emphasized the great importance of the Plan to the Commission's finances. The Minister accepted that the Commission's arguments presented a convincing case and agreed that the rate of investment for the railways in 1957 should be about £120 millions, although he would not commit himself to a figure for future years. The Modernization Plan was now envisaged by the Government as a more palatable alternative to the price increases required to meet inflating costs. The Plan itself was now expected to cost £1600 millions, much of the increase being caused by extensions to the proposals, with inflation and more precise estimates accounting for the rest. It seemed a far cry from the day in 1935 (referred to in Chapter One), when Lord Stamp told the LMS shareholders that main-line electrification, however desirable, was beyond the reach of their Company. What is more, and as if to wash away the guilt of intervening in the Commission's affairs by blocking price increases, the White Paper commending the proposals was presented to Parliament during the month following that in which the memorandum was received from Sir Brian Robertson. There is no doubt that the Government recognized the difficulties faced by the Commission and did what they could to assist, thereby opening themselves to criticism in later probings into the Commission's affairs.

The administrative arrangements for implementing the Modernization

Fig. 4.4   The completion of the electrification of the London to Manchester and Liverpool services was critical to the Commission's plan to achieve a financial surplus by 1970. The northern approaches to Crewe Station before, and after, electrification (BICC)

Plan reflected the decentralization of railway management which had been statutorily introduced following the Transport Act of 1953. The Regions were required to prepare their schemes, and it was clear that some were better equipped for the task than others. Projects involving an expenditure of over £100000 had to be sent to the Commission for approval. The Regional General Manager was expected to consult the British Railways Central Staff on items of this magnitude (or where a reserved subject was involved) before submitting the proposal to his Area Board. The Area Board, if it approved the item, would then put it to the Commission, where there would be the opportunity for the General Staff to intervene. The Plan was, therefore, built up from Regional schemes prepared in conformity with the objectives in the document *Modernisation and Re-equipment of British Railways*. The Commission's Headquarters had a guiding role along with three main areas for decision critical to the success of the Plan as a whole. These were the system of electrification to adopt, the choice of continuous automatic method of braking and methods of train heating. The decisions taken will be discussed at a later stage.

The engineers on the British Railways Central Staff also put forward their contributions, which had to be approved, along with other proposals, by bodies such as the Works and Equipment Committee, the Railway Sub-Commission, and the Commission itself. Perhaps, however, it is the Technical Development and Research Committee which should be singled out as having filled a very important niche in the modernization story.

The Technical Development and Research (TD and R) Committee first met on 11 January 1954. J. C. L. Train, the one engineer who was a full-time Member of the Commission in 1954, was the Committee's first chairman. The other two members were F. A. Pope, the full-time Member with considerable experience of diesel railcars in Northern Ireland and H. P. Barker, a part-time Member, whose contribution has been referred to in Chapter Three. Another member of the Committee who will be well remembered was F. Q. den Hollander, former President of the Netherlands Railways and, at the time of his TD and R association, Chairman of the Office of Research and Development (ORE), which is the research arm of the International Union of Railways. He had been responsible for the very successful reconstruction and modernization of the Netherlands Railways and his experience of diesel multiple unit working covered a period of twenty years. It was helpful, therefore, to have his early confirmation that he agreed with the lines on which diesel multiple units were being developed on British Railways. There was no need to have his views on shunting locomotives, as he was known to regard the British Railways diesel as the best available at that time. He had strong views on main-line diesel locomotives and was not in favour of hydraulic transmissions. Also, the den Hollander view on 50-cycle a.c. electrification was that more development was needed before it should be adopted as standard practice on the railways of Britain. So there were some lively debates at meetings of the TD and R Committee which, although never having more than five members, was attended by the Chief Engineers on the Central Staff and the Regional General Managers. The Committee dealt with all the technical interests of the Commission, and ranged over road motor, marine, and dock engineering matters as well as the railway engineering disciplines.

The TD and R Committee was closely involved in the different aspects of the Modernization Plan. Realizing the strains which the Plan would impose, the Committee made some perceptive comments on 29 June 1955, in the following notes for guidance:

> 1. Technical and Traffic Officers understandably, but perhaps too greatly, pre-occupied by the transitional technical situations which must arise between the situation of today and the situation of 1970.
>
> 2. Risk of eventual equipment being based upon a series of compromises born out of the transitional difficulties and not reflecting clearly enough the dominant needs of the future which are not simply to improve the operation of British Railways but to effect changes which at the least must be major and in many cases must be transcendental.
>
> 3. The Committee concludes that if our eventual equipment is to be appropriate to the situation of 15 years hence it will be necessary to introduce reforms and new equipment of a type which will *not* be fully appropriate to the transitional period. The Committee urges the Commission and its officers to accept the view that it will be necessary during the transitional period to *live in two worlds at once*: if necessary, to provide two types of service concurrently – the old and the new – and to accept transitional operation inconveniences in order to ensure that when the railways are re-equipped they are modern and not compromised by these passing problems. In particular,
>
>> i. Do not let vacuum vehicles stand in the way of the air brake.
>> ii. If DMU expresses better do not stick to locomotive hauled trains.
>> iii. Do not let steam heating stand in the way of electric heating for all new main line stock.

In making these comments the Committee must have foreseen the temptation to shy away from making the correct long-term decision due to short-term problems. But the Committee did not confine itself to advice on general principles. It encouraged for example the development of disc brakes on railway rolling stock and the testing of high-speed diesel engines. It recognized the need for the widespread development of air conditioning in carriages and saw that the container would revolutionize inter-modal freight movement. The automatic coupling for freight wagons was frequently on its agenda, but it by no means confined its attention to mechanical engineering matters. Problems of soil stabilization and rail-end stresses were examples of its interest in civil engineering. It is also of interest to recall that this Committee's range of modernization items included the need for self-help luggage trolleys and the development of telex seat reservation. It noted with satisfaction that the first digital computer to be installed on any railway system was at Swindon and was always ready to support new ideas in technological areas.

The Research Advisory Council was also concerned with all aspects of the Commission's technological progress, but was a little further removed from the development of the Modernization Plan because it was concerned with longer time scales. Included in the membership of this Council were several of the nation's eminent scientists under the chairmanship, in 1957, of Professor R. V. Jones, author of *Most Secret War*. The Commission's Technical Adviser and Chief Research Officer were also members, and thereby provided a channel for the contribution of the railway engineers and a link with the TD and R Committee. The work of the Research Advisory Council will be covered in Chapter Eleven.

There was, therefore, a great deal of scientific and technological talent available to support the Commission's engineers during the development of the Modernization Plan. The accusation has been made that the Plan produced equipment which was often outdated in relation to technological development in the wider world. The extent to which this accusation can be supported would be due neither to any lack of awareness of the technological opportunity nor to a reluctance to seize it. One reason related to the time available to develop the standards of safety and reliability necessary for adoption on one of the world's busiest railway systems. The Southern Region, in particular, did not welcome any developments in its high density commuter network, which would have reduced the seats available to passengers at peak periods (e.g. sliding carriage doors) or upset the knife-edge situation on which its standard of reliability rested.

A more fundamental reason was that the plan for physical modernization was outstripping the pace at which commercial practices were being modernized. This statement merits elaboration. The 1953 Act had transferred much of the decision making from Commission Headquarters to the Regions although this did not apply in the field of reserved functions, where engineering design was so important to the progressing of the Modernization Plan. It had also given to the railway enough commercial freedom of action to allow it to move towards the reshaping of its activities, although not on a significant scale. Many of the little-used passenger services could be submitted for closure but a consultative process necessary with both users and staff, took time. Also bus companies had to be subsidized by British Railways to provide alternative services. The reshaping of the freight activities took even longer to achieve as it relied upon pricing freedoms which had not yet been granted in full measure. The devolution of authority to the Regions had introduced new forms of commercial enterprise but at the cost of fragmenting the general strategy.

The upshot of this situation was that the main re-shaping of the

Fig. 4.5   The Modernization Plan brought electric services to Glasgow's commuter services. A North Clydeside train stops at Westerton (BRB)

activities of the railway followed much of the physical modernization when it should have preceded it. Consequently, some of the new equipment provided by the engineers was to meet traffic demands which would decline, or vanish, within the next decade. Electrification schemes were sometimes saddled with trackage of doubtful traffic value. A freight traffic distribution system was perpetuated before new commercial forces were unleashed to render parts of it redundant. The timing of events was unfortunate. The regulatory changes affecting pricing freedom and the obligation to carry should have taken place several years in advance of the physical re-equipment, which was itself over a decade later than it should have been to lessen some of the financial difficulties in which the Commission found itself. The eventual compatibility between the commercial and engineering modernizations was to arrive as the 1960s merged into the 1970s.

To return to the Modernization Plan itself, the year of 1956 was to be remembered for the taking by the Commission of three major policy decisions affecting the engineers. It was decided to adopt the 50-cycle a.c. system of electrification, as will be described in Chapter Seven. The three-year moratorium on the ordering of further diesel locomotives was ended and a choice was made between the vacuum and air forms of automatic continuous brake. The decision on the brake question illustrated the effect of allowing short-term considerations to dominate the proper long-term answer and justifies examination.

In 1889 the Regulation of Railways Act gave the Board of Trade power to order a railway company to provide the continuous brake on all passenger trains. Freight trains were not required to comply with the order. Neither was it considered appropriate to require the Companies to standardize on the vacuum or air type of brake. Consequently, some Companies used one system and some the other. The opportunity to standardize came after amalgamation of the Companies into four groups in 1923. As, at that time, vacuum braked vehicles outnumbered their air braked counterparts by three to one – and the operating requirements of the day were met by either system – it was understandable that the decision favoured the lower cost vacuum brake. The necessary conversions were carried out, and a considerable amount of dual fitting was necessary as the air brake continued to be used on many local services.

Very few non-passenger-carrying vehicles were fitted at that time with either the air or the vacuum brake, although the problem had long been on the action list of both railway engineers and operators in Britain. The inheritance of loose coupled freight trains with their braking capacity limited to the locomotive, the brake van, and hand brakes on wagons had always restricted freight train loadings and speeds to nineteenth- rather than twentieth-century standards. The system also required the civil engineer to provide catch points on rising gradients so that wagons breaking away from the rest of the train would be derailed before causing even more serious damage. On approaching falling gradients, it was often necessary to stop the train and pin down sufficient hand brakes on the wagons to prevent the train running away out of control. These were unfortunate legacies of the private ownership of wagons, which had traditionally been regarded as a cheap form of storage, as well as a means of freight movement. In the main, it was the railway owned wagons on the fast goods services that were fitted with the automatic continuous brake.

The Railway Executive attached great importance to the leap forward in freight operating efficiency that would result from the introduction of continuous brakes on all wagons. In 1951, tests were carried out on the former Midland main line which involved 11000 miles of train running trials and exhaustive research. The objective was to make a thorough study of the relative behaviour of the air and vacuum brakes under the freight train operating conditions appropriate to the second half of the twentieth century. Unfortunately, with the limited investment resources available in the early 1950s there was no immediately practical outcome from the work.

Under the Modernization Plan it was possible to reconsider the fitting of continuous brakes to wagons within the £365 millions allocated to the remodelling of the freight services. In October, 1955, a committee which had been appointed to put forward recommendations produced its report. The Chairman was R. F. Harvey, Chief Operating and Motive Power Officer. Two further engineers within the six-man group responsible for the recommendations were R. C. Bond, Chief Mechanical Engineer and A. E. Robson, Chief Officer, Carriage and Wagon Engineering. It was the clear recommendation that the air brake should be adopted as the future standard for all vehicles on British Railways. In addition, it was recommended that the assessment of the case for the automatic coupler should be made available as early as possible. One interesting indication of the practical approach generally associated with the engineering aspects of the Plan emerged during the examination of the brake question. The Committee considered the possibility of introducing some completely new system, which would replace both the air and vacuum brakes. Although its members appreciated the potential advantages of, for example, the oleo-electric brake, this braking system was rejected because there would be delay due to the five years which would be required to develop and prove the method.

At a meeting on 8 December 1955, the Technical Development and Research Committee agreed that the superiority of the air brake over its vacuum rival fully justified the additional expenditure in first cost of £30 millions. Three of the Regions were represented at that meeting and do

Fig. 4.6　A new mineral wagon fitted with the vacuum continuous automatic brake. Terminal restrictions required many new wagons to be built with a capacity of only 16·5 tons (BRB)

not appear to have recorded their objection to the decision. The Regional General Managers then convened a separate meeting, where they discussed their deep concern over the serious disturbance to the operation of the railway which would occur during the period when vacuum and air braked trains would be running over the network at the same time. The Southern Region, with its air braked electric services and limited freight activities, was the one Region prepared to go along with the air brake decision. The majority Regional view was, however, so firmly opposed to the decision of the Headquarters officers, supported by the TD & R Committee that on 16 February 1956, the Commission ruled that the vacuum brake should be adopted as the standard system on British Railways.

Although not conceded at the time in such blunt terms, it was evident that the Commission had, for reasons of short-term operational benefit, made the wrong long-term decision. Events were later to show that the decision was wrong in both engineering and operating terms as some of the operating practices of today would not have been practicable without air braking. It was evident that Sir Brian Robertson himself was disturbed by the turn of events. Knowing how H. P. Barker and F. Q. den Hollander had been closely associated with the TD and R Committee's warning against the right technical choice being sacrificed to expediency, he wrote personally to each of them and explained the reasons for the decision. He also contacted the Chairman of the Westinghouse Brake and Signal Company as the Company had already initiated investment in new facilities which would be available to meet the demand anticipated for the new air brakes. The supporters of the vacuum brake within the Regions claimed that it would have taken an additional two agonizing years of transition to adopt the air brake as standard. Ten years later, the decision taken in 1956 was reversed and vacuum made way for air.

The decision to adopt the vacuum brake as standard was one of the few cases where the engineers on the British Railways Central Staff failed to introduce their choice of standards within the framework of the functions reserved to the Commission following the 1953 Act. Some of the problems which arose in connection with diesel design will be referred to in Chapter Six, but many of the difficulties regarding standards arose in the less centralized areas of signalling and telecommunications. Signalling, particularly when associated with electrification schemes, proved to be the most serious of the bottlenecks in the progress of the Modernization Plan. It was found that decentralization was resulting in a variety of specifications for signalling equipment with resulting delay and escalation of costs. Following a specially convened meeting to discuss the problem, the manufacturers undertook to consider standardizing equipment and the Regions agreed to restrict the number of specifications for similar components.

Reference has already been made to the first re-appraisal of the

Modernization Plan which was carried out in 1956. With some extensions to the Plan estimated at £160 millions, along with more accurate estimates and cost escalation, the total cost of £1240 millions increased to £1660 millions. 1958 was another year when the Commission's financial position began to hold out little prospect of being in balance by 1961 or 1962, as forecast in 'Proposals for the Railways' in 1956. Robertson again proposed to the Minister that the Plan should be re-appraised, and the result was published in July 1959. Again, it was advocated that the progress of the Plan should be accelerated in order to secure the earliest possible return on the investment funds which were being made available. It looked as if only £1420 millions out of the £1660 millions would be spent by 1963.

Much has been written about the economics of the Modernization Plan and more than one chapter could be devoted to the often conflicting evidence which has been put forward in Parliamentary Select Committees and by academic writers. Perhaps the criticism was most appropriately summarized by C. D. Foster in his book *The Transport Problem* (Blackie & Son, 1963) when he said that the profitability of the Plan was established on a basis 'not very different from that which has normally been used to work out priorities for road construction'. The fact remains that there is no generally accepted quantification in financial terms of the results of the Modernization Plan.

It is important, however, to recognize that the nation had expected profitability to emerge almost from the first year of the Plan, although its implementation was intended to begin within five years and to be completed within fifteen years after 1955, with the full financial benefits emerging in the 1970s. There was a feeling that the public's faith in the new railway had been misplaced when railway finances were seen to be worsening so soon after a prospectus of future benefits had been published. Even if the effects of years of capital starvation could have been cured overnight, there were other strong forces working against the financial health of the Commission in the second half of the 1950s. Reference has already been made to the organizational re-structuring of British Railways, the changed competitive situation between road and rail, and the Government's refusal to allow badly needed price increases. Finances were already worsening when the 'Guillebaud' report in 1960 recommended very substantial increases to make railway pay comparable with other industries. It was also a time when industrial recession reduced traffic levels generally and coal carryings, the staple railway traffic, fell to a particularly low level. To quote again from Foster's book, the Commission was certainly 'dogged by bad luck' during the early years of implementing the Plan. It is sufficient, however, to note the impact of these adverse factors, and then proceed to examine how the Commission implemented the Plan and handled the resources which the Government had so unexpectedly made available.

As the Commission had never before had the opportunity to carry out any investment planning on a large scale, it had to contend with a shortage of long-term planning staff and also of engineering capacity. The new statutory organization also complicated procedures, as the six Area Boards now shared in decisions relating to the modernization of a national railway network which, under the 1948 organization, would have been the responsibility of the Railway Executive. The American economist, Professor L. L. Waters, writing in the April 1955 issue of the *British Transport Review* expressed the opinion that 'An inescapable conflict exists between the new Plan and the move to decentralization embodied in the Act of 1953.' The Commission, would, however, have been foolish to forgo the investment opportunity presented to it in 1955, and it had to make the best of the environment in which it was placed at that time. Given a different legislative framework and commercial atmosphere (still several years away), the Commission could more closely have matched its engineering revolution to the modernization of all its railway activities.

There is no doubt, for example, that the engineering resources could have been more effectively used if they had been devoted to a much smaller railway network. If it had been possible to anticipate the freight situation of the 1970s when the Modernization Plan was being designed, there would have been less reason to perpetuate the small freight wagon, build some of the big new automated marshalling yards, or continue to provide for the needs of the fragmented retail coal trade. Although major legislative changes were still to come, these developments were anticipated to some extent in connection with the freight business, and the withdrawal of unremunerative passenger services was clearly provided for in the Plan.

Although the Commission was able to make some progress towards its objective of 'purposeful concentration on those functions which the railways can be made to perform more efficiently than other forms of transport', the engineering contribution increasingly dominated the modernization of commercial practices. There were good reasons for this situation. First, the railway underwent so many changes within a short period of time that it was unable to appraise its activities in detail before committing the urgently needed investment. Second, the Government had willed the means to bring about physical modernization, but had taken only the first steps in allowing the railway to determine its commercial objectives. Until 1962, British Railways was to remain a common carrier and to have its rates and fares controlled by the independent Transport Tribunal, with the inevitable constraints imposed by these two features on market planning. Third, while physical modernization was in full flood it was difficult to convince the public that a service should be withdrawn until the service in question had been modernized, and the economics re-assessed. A more Draconian approach had to await a

Fig. 4.7   The building of big, automated marshalling yards perpetuated the image of the wagon as the rail freight unit when greater emphasis was being attached to the importance of the train load (BR/Oxford Publishing Co)

further deterioration in railway finances, and another Act of Parliament.

In spite of these very real difficulties, one puzzling feature of the development of the Plan is the reluctance of the Commission to equate more closely the wider aspects of the Plan (particularly the withdrawal of local passenger services) with the energy devoted to engineering investment. The Modernization Report of 1955 had stressed the need 'to revolutionize the character of the services'. The 1963 report on 'The Reshaping of British Railways' said, in making reference to the Modernization Plan:

> It was a plan to modernize equipment, but it did not envisage any basic changes in the scope of railway services or in the general mode of operation of the railway system. It was expected that the substitution of electric and diesel haulage for steam, concentration of marshalling yards, reduction in number and increased mechanization of goods depots, re-signalling, and the introduction of other modern equipment, would make the railways pay by reducing costs and attracting more traffic.

In making this statement, the British Railways Board understated the intentions of its predecessor's Plan but interpreted correctly what actually happened. The statement also reflected the Board's opinion that the Commission had allowed the engineers to dominate the development of the Plan. In fact, the engineers had re-equipped the existing railway system and the system itself had not been designed for its future role.

The need 'to revolutionize the character of the services' was never out of the Commission's mind, but discussion did not often result in decision. In the autumn of 1959, the Commission opened the British Transport Staff College in Woking. The first course, including a number of engineers, spent some sixty hours in discussion of the Plan within their own syndicates and with visiting Chief Officers and Members of the Commission. It is of particular interest that the time of the course was divided almost equally between the problems of physical equipment and the wider question of re-shaping the activities of the railway. The reports prepared by this course in 1959 closely accord with the prescription for the railway future as outlined in 'The Reshaping of British Railways' report, published over three years later in 1963. They lacked, however, the carefully quantified diagnosis included in the 1963 document, which underlines the fact that the right data for decision making was not assembled in a usable form until the early 1960s.

Enough information was certainly available, however, for reaching decisions about unremunerative passenger services and the treatment of these services within the Plan was neither persistent nor consistent. Passenger stations and services had been closed at a modest pace since nationalization in 1948. By 1956, when the first reappraisal of the Modernization Plan was made, passenger services had been withdrawn from over a fifth of the route mileage of British Railways. It was estimated in that re-appraisal that by 1961 or 1962 additional net savings of some £3 millions a year would be achieved from these pruning activities. By 1958 withdrawals of passenger services were accelerating but the resulting savings were still less than a third of the 1961/62 expectations.

The Commission had several reasons for slackening the pace of withdrawing passenger services, and reference was made to them in Chapter Three. But it was the result of modernization itself that was beginning to restore faith in the revenue earning, and cost reducing, potential of the passenger services. As far back as 17 August 1955, Sir Reginald Wilson, a Member of the Commission and Chairman of the Eastern Area Board, had said in an article on the Modernization Plan in the *Financial Times*:

> In one of the schemes approved by the Commission for the introduction of multiple unit diesel trains, the net return on the outlay (derived partly from reduced working expenses and partly from additional receipts) was estimated at no less than 44 per cent.

Later schemes showed further dramatic improvements, which encouraged investment in services which were still unprofitable after the elimination of steam traction. Indeed, in 1956, the Commission ordered from no less than five contractors a number of rail buses in order to

Fig. 4.8   The results of modernization were beginning to restore faith in the potential of the passenger services. A diesel multiple unit on an Edinburgh–Dundee service crosses the Forth Bridge (BRB)

improve still further the financial results of their loss-making rail passenger services. Rail investment was no longer confining itself to purposeful concentration on those activities to which rail was particularly suitable.

If the root and branch re-shaping of railway activities which followed the Transport Act of 1962 had preceded the engineering modernization, the enormous value to British Railways of that re-equipment would have been even greater. It would have been more heavily concentrated on a smaller network and range of railway activities. The modern planner would also comment that the Plan would better have served its purpose if it had been part of a longer term rolling investment programme, or dovetailed into a wider planning process. The Commission was never in a position, however, to exercise any of these options.

With the benefit of a quarter of a century's experience, it is all too easy to criticize some aspects of a great re-investment programme which proved to be the springboard of railway technological development in Britain. It must be remembered that the Modernization Plan resulted in the scrapping of nearly 18000 steam locomotives and their replacement by new electric services, along with 4200 diesel locomotives and 4600 diesel railcars. The electrified route mileage was doubled and the 25 kV a.c.

system adopted as the new standard. Six thousand miles of track were relaid with continuously welded rail: better braking systems were introduced and standards of passenger comfort greatly improved. Six thousand miles of track were also re-signalled with power signal boxes and colour-light signalling. The Plan resulted in a partnership between the railway equipment industry and British Railways which has resulted in many technological advances with worldwide significance.

And what of the contributions made to the Plan by the engineers in the different departments of British Railways? Their work is the subject of much of what is said in the following chapters.

CHAPTER FIVE

The Final Years of Steam Traction

T HE Chief Mechanical Engineers of the pre-amalgamation Companies, and, from 1923, of the four group railways, were men of considerable standing within their respective organizations. In general, they ranked as second only in status to their General Managers – and were most frequently far better known to the public, who were fascinated by the romance of the steam locomotive. Their popularity and status stemmed from the fact that it was they who designed, constructed, and kept in operation the locomotives which, in the public eye, were 'the railway'. They ascertained from their operating colleagues the tasks which their locomotives would be called upon to perform, and thereafter prepared designs to meet the requirements which were laid upon them. The criterion by which they were judged was whether the locomotives they produced did, in practice, meet the needs of the operators. That apart, their expertise in designing locomotives of types and characteristics required for specific duties could not generally be challenged.

There was a constant search for new developments and techniques in locomotive design and construction and almost any CME, of any major company, was able, after a few years in office, to produce a locomotive with which his name would thereafter forever be associated. In no other sphere of activity within the railway – civil and signal engineering, operations, commercial work, finance – have the names of Chief Officers been so widely associated with their products and innovations as has been the case in the mechanical engineering field.

It is not suggested that public esteem influenced to the slightest degree the policies for which the CMEs sought approval from their General Managers and Boards of Directors. They – the CMEs – were concerned only to provide and maintain locomotives, rolling stock, and general engineering equipment, which, in their judgement, would meet the needs of their railways in the most economical and efficient way. There were very few cases during the inter-war years of new locomotives requiring more than minor modifications before they were able fully to meet the Operating and Locomotive Running Officers' requirements.

The CMEs were, however, fortunate, over the years, in being associated with the development of equipment which so captured the imagination of the public in general. Not, for example, since the early days of the railways had a railway bridge been directly and publicly associated with its designer and builder. Admittedly, CMEs were concerned with machines which still had scope for further development in design, and in the incorporation of new component parts, to increase their efficiency in the performance of their functions, but of course the same applied to some extent, to other engineering disciplines. There have been at least as great advances in signals and telecommunications engineering, but there is no instance in which the name of a signal or telecommunications engineer on the railways has ever been coupled – publicly – with major developments or innovations.

At the time of the outbreak of war in 1939 the four group railway companies were preparing their plans for locomotive developments over the next few years. Almost exclusively, the developments in mind were in the form of steam, although diesel locomotives for shunting were already in existence.

On the London and North Eastern Railway, H. N. Gresley had in 1925 tried out one of the Great Western Railway's Castle class 4–6–0 express passenger locomotives, *Pendennis Castle*, and had been impressed by its superiority over the LNER Pacifics of that time. A significant difference between the two types lay in the long-travel valve gear incorporated in the Castle class locomotives. As a result, trials with the LNER Pacifics with long-travel valve gear were carried out in 1926 and 1927 and, in the light of the benefits achieved in reduced coal consumption, the whole Pacific fleet was modified. Gresley also instituted a number of other successful developments, notable among them being the streamlined A4 Pacifics. The achievements of the Castle class locomotives undoubtedly influenced developments on other railways. In 1926, for example, tests carried out with a Castle on the London, Midland and Scottish Railway West Coast main line led directly to the design and production of the Royal Scot class 4–6–0 locomotives to work the fast and heavy trains between Euston and Glasgow.

The late twenties and the thirties was a period of innovation in design. Developments included Gresley's experimental four-cylinder compound 4–6–2–2 locomotive, No. 10000, in 1929 fitted with a Yarrow water-tube boiler generating steam at 450 lb/in^2 and his 2–8–2 *Cock o' the North*, No. 2001, in 1934 the first eight-coupled express passenger locomotive to be introduced into Great Britain, designed not basically for high-speed, long-distance running, but specifically to overcome the difficult operating conditions of the Edinburgh–Aberdeen route, and W. A. Stanier's 4–6–2 experimental steam turbine locomotive No. 6202. In the later 1930s, too, the LMS, under the direction of Stanier, produced plans for a large streamlined 4–6–4 locomotive to replace the 'Coronation' (or, as perhaps more frequently known, 'Duchess') class 4–6–2s already working the

Fig. 5.1	GWR Castle class 4–6–0 locomotive No. 7017: the locomotive in the picture has a
large tender, which was not fitted to the original builds (BRB)

express passenger service over the West Coast route, whilst at the same
time, Gresley was considering the development of an even larger locomotive – with a 4–8–2 wheel arrangement – for the Anglo–Scottish East
Coast services. An improved A4 type was also on the drawing board.

On the Southern Railway, some three years before he retired in 1937,
R. E. L. Maunsell proposed developing the Lord Nelson Class 4–6–0 into a
Pacific and the three-cylinder U.1 Class 2–6–0 mixed-traffic locomotive
into a 2–6–2, both with wide-firebox boilers. On account of restrictions in
axle loading and total weight then existing, these proposals were unacceptable to the Civil Engineer. When O. V. S. Bulleid succeeded Maunsell
as CME, it was agreed with the operators that the most pressing need was
for a more powerful mixed-traffic locomotive, rather than a larger type for

Fig. 5.2	Gresley's 2–8–2 locomotive No. 2001 *Cock o' the North* (NRM)

Fig. 5.3   LMS 4–6–2 experimental steam turbine locomotive No. 6202 (NRM)

purely express passenger duties. Bulleid's thoughts turned first to a 4–8–2 but turntable limitations ruled this out. Next, he considered a 2–8–2, but the Civil Engineer objected to the use of pony trucks on locomotives which, though essentially for mixed traffics, would often be travelling at express passenger speeds. The final proposal, which was accepted, was for a 4–6–2 with a 21-ton axle load. Thus were born, in 1941 and 1945 respectively, the celebrated Merchant Navy and West Country classes, which incorporated a number of distinctly novel and unconventional features, about which so much has already been written elsewhere.

Only on the Great Western Railway was there little evidence of new locomotive development. The Castle and King class 4–6–0 locomotives, designed by C. B. Collett as developments of Churchward's Star class, still met their full requirements for express passenger working.

It was indeed during the late 1920s and the 1930s, up to the outbreak of war, that the steam locomotive made perhaps its greatest advance in design and – along with certain named trains – reached its zenith in public popularity and approval. Much has been written about the steam locomotive achievements of those days, but perhaps brief reference to some of the most famous of the services they operated might be appropriate.

Even prior to 1860 there were trains from King's Cross to Edinburgh (Waverley) via the East Coast route, leaving at varying times between 09.00 and 09.30, and it was in June 1862 that a train started to leave at the well publicized 10.00 time. There are differing views as to when this regular service came to be known as the 'Flying Scotsman', but an official publication of the LNER in 1925, *The Flying Scotsman – the world's most famous express*, suggests that this was probably about 1875, although it was not until 1927 that it was officially so named.

On 1 May 1928 the Flying Scotsman added to its lustre by taking the record for the longest regular non-stop run in the world – 393 miles. (Incidentally, the first British non-stop run of over 100 miles was over part of the same route – King's Cross to Grantham – on 1 June 1872.) The corridor tenders which were introduced by Gresley in 1928 on certain Pacific type locomotives, to enable a change of enginemen to be effected *en route*, were the only ones of their kind ever built. For many years, however, because of an agreement with the LMS, it was not possible to reduce the running times between London and Edinburgh or Glasgow below 8¼ hours.

Flying Scotsman still runs regularly between London and Edinburgh. Today the diesel-operated High Speed Trains which provide the service, with one stop in each direction, have reduced the overall timing to 4 h 37 min in the down direction and 4 h 40 min in the up.

On 5 March 1935 the LNER achieved a world speed record for steam, when Class A3 Pacific *Papyrus* reached a speed of 108 miles/h down Stoke Bank, between Grantham and Peterborough, during the return journey of a round trip of 537 miles from King's Cross to Newcastle and back, at an overall average speed of 70 miles/h. The outcome of this test was a new service, the Silver Jubilee – Britain's first streamlined train – introduced on 30 September 1935, and covering the 268½ miles between King's

Fig. 5.4   The Flying Scotsman worked by class A1 Pacific
steam locomotive No. 2575, *Galopin*, entering York *c.* 1934 (NRM)

Cross and Newcastle in four hours each way. On the demonstration run on 27 September 1935, from King's Cross to Grantham, 43 consecutive miles were run at over 100 miles/h, with two maxima of 112½ miles/h, thus breaking the rail speed record set up by *Papyrus* earlier in the year. The Silver Jubilee was initially worked by Britain's first streamlined engine – A4 Class No. 2509, *Silver Link* – which went into regular service on the new train only three weeks after being turned out of Doncaster shops.

The second streamlined express over the East Coast route, indeed the first one into Scotland – the Coronation – was introduced on 5 July 1937. It reduced the overall journey time in each direction to six hours, and covered the 188¾ miles from King's Cross to York, start to stop, in 157 minutes – an average speed of 71·9 miles/h.

On 5 July 1937, also, the LMS introduced the Coronation Scot, covering the 401¼ miles between Euston and Glasgow in 6½ hours each way. On

Fig. 5.5   A4 Pacific locomotive No. 2509 passing Hadley Wood with the up Silver Jubilee (NRM)

Fig. 5.6   Three of the LMS Duchess class 4–6–2 locomotives at Crewe, 18 June 1937. No. 6220, *Coronation* is nearest the camera (NRM)

a demonstration run of this train from Euston to Crewe and back, on 29 June 1937, Stanier's Duchess class 4–6–2 engine No. 6220 *Coronation* wrested the speed record from the LNER in attaining a speed of 114 miles/h. The return journey from Crewe to London was covered in 1 h 59 min – an overall average speed of 79·7 miles/h – as good as most of the electric timings today.

The Cheltenham Flyer was introduced in 1923 by the acceleration of an up afternoon express from Cheltenham to cover the 77¼ miles between Swindon and Paddington in 75 minutes (61·8 miles/h). In 1929, the time was cut to 70 minutes (66·3 miles/h), and in 1932 to 65 minutes, an average start-to-stop speed of 71·3 miles/h. The best recorded run was on 6 June 1932, when an average speed of 81·7 miles/h was reached.

The speed records achieved in their turn by these various services were all beaten when, on 3 July 1938, another of Gresley's A4s – No. 4468 *Mallard* – hauling a test train between Grantham and Peterborough, attained the world record speed for steam traction of 126 miles/h – a record which was never beaten by a steam locomotive in Great Britain.

On the outbreak of war in September 1939 the normal course of loco-motive design and development had of necessity to be put into abeyance. Although all the Main Works were soon heavily engaged on Government contracts for a wide variety of war equipment, it was nevertheless vital that the output of locomotive repairs should be maintained, and indeed increased, to provide motive power for the unprecedented volume of wartime traffic. Because of the priority accorded to Government work, locomotive building programmes tended to fall into arrears. From the beginning of the war to the end of 1942 only 587 new locomotives had been built in railway workshops. By this time, however, the demand for new locomotives had become very urgent and priorities were revised. Construction was virtually confined to LMS Class 8 Standard 2–8–0 locomotives, which it had been decided should be the only type to be built for heavy freight service in the United Kingdom. This class of locomotive had been selected by the Ministry of Supply as the most suitable type for service with the armies overseas and 240 of them had been ordered from contractors at the beginning of the war. Output increased substantially and by the end of the war the railway works had built 1284 new locomotives. In addition, between 1943 and 1945, contractors built 935 and 150 respectively of the well-known Austerity type 2–8–0 and 2–10–0 heavy freight engines designed by R. A. Riddles. Contractors also built 377 0–6–0 shunting tank locomotives which, like the others, made a most valuable contribution to the war effort.

With the war in Europe ended, it was possible to resume something of the normal activities of locomotive design and development. Many valuable lessons had been learned during the war years, which were to find their application in locomotives built to meet the needs of the future, inevitably rather different from those existing five years earlier.

The position in regard to steam traction, and motive power generally, on the four group Companies during the last two years before the Transport Act of 1947 would become effective, is nowhere better summarized than in a lecture delivered by the four Chief Mechanical Engineers at the Centenary celebrations of the Institution of Mechanical Engineers in June 1947. This lecture, extracts from which are quoted in the following paragraphs, sets out, with unassailable authority, the policies and intentions of the Companies in regard to their motive power, and describes the situation as it then existed. A section of the lecture was devoted to each of the four principal British railway systems.

LONDON, MIDLAND AND SCOTTISH RAILWAY

Present Position: Policy has particularly aimed at high locomotive availability, to reduce the capital employed and repair costs. This has been secured by:

(1) Producing standard locomotive classes each capable of a wide range of duties, i.e., by enlarging the field of mixed traffic working.

(2) The steady application of improvements, in design and materials, to existing as well as to new locomotive stock.

(3) The concentration on organization of repairs in shops and sheds, so as to reduce the time out of traffic and thus the number of locomotives required.

Ten steam locomotive types have been standardized to cover all the traffic on the LMSR. New engines are of these types, and all except the shunting locomotives contain the following features:

(1) Self-cleaning smokebox, for ease of servicing at running sheds and for keeping tubes clean in service.

(2) Rocking grates and self-emptying ashpans, for reducing shed disposal-time, and for cleaning fires during run.

(3) Manganese steel liners on horn and axle-box faces, to reduce wear, and to increase mileage between shopping.

(4) Outside cylinders and valve gear, for minimum forces on axle-boxes, and ease of maintenance. More than two cylinders are only employed where the power required exceeds that which could be obtained by two cylinders, the size of which is governed by the limits of the loading gauge.

(5) Long-lap piston valves having six narrow rings per head, in order to maintain thermal efficiency over shopping periods.

The development in shopping organization, equipment, and methods, which has taken place year by year, has affected the whole locomotive stock and resulted in high traffic-availability per unit. Practices which amongst others have particularly contributed to this result are:

(1) Shopping organization, calling in locomotives for overhaul only as their condition warrants, but, as far as possible, before they begin to be laid-off in service.

(2) Undertaking all 'classified' repairs in main workshops, where the latest machine tool equipment is used and the work is performed on the 'progressive' system.

(3) The carrying out at each shopping period of such work, and only such work, as is necessary to ensure a further full period in service without inter-mediate attention.

(4) Provision of an adequate stock of spare boilers and other parts so that each locomotive requiring heavy repairs can be fitted from stock.

(5) A unit costing system and standard limits of wear.

So far as shed organization is concerned, the important factors have been:

(1) Synchronization of washouts, periodical examinations, and repairs in order to deal with as much work as possible each time a locomotive is out of service.

(2) Centralization of running repairs into concentration depots where ade-quate facilities and equipment can be utilized economically.

Developments in the Immediate Future: Immediate developments for steam traction are following the policy outlined in the first part of this paper. Further locomotives of two of the most important classes, the 4–6–2 and the mixed-traffic 4–6–0, are to be built with additional modifications designed still further to enhance their overall efficiency. These are as follows:

(1) Roller Bearings: Two 4–6–2 and twenty 4–6–0 locomotives are to be built in 1947 having roller bearings on coupled, carrying, and tender wheels. Since it is the condition of the axle-boxes which mainly determines when the present locomotives require shop repairs, the roller bearing axle-box with manganese steel rubbing-surfaces offers a considerable extension to existing periods be-tween shopping.

(2) Poppet Valve Gear: Twenty 4–6–0 locomotives (ten from amongst those having roller bearings) are to be fitted in 1947 with Caprotti valve gear having a new design of totally-enclosed shaft drive. The aims are better thermal efficiency, as a result of the valves being more steamtight, and additional availability and reduction in maintenance to be obtained from a totally-enclosed valve gear running in oil.

(3) Steel Fireboxes: Boilers for two further 4–6–2 locomotives and ten 4–6–0 locomotives are to be fitted in 1948 with steel fireboxes. The object is to ascertain whether lower overall boiler costs are obtainable with steel or copper.

It is believed that the conventional reciprocating steam locomotive is still

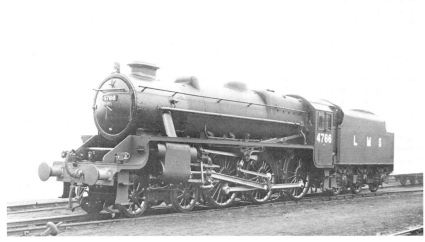

Fig. 5.7   LMS Class 5 locomotive No. 4766 as rebuilt (BRB)

capable of considerable advance and that the ceiling of operating availability and maintenance cost per mile has not yet been reached. If, for the sake of higher thermal efficiency, or still higher availability, any departure from the simple, inexpensive, rugged steam locomotive of normal aspect is envisaged, the LMSR authorities hold that a complete breakaway from steam towards the internal combustion engine is the logical step to take.

LONDON AND NORTH EASTERN RAILWAY

Policy respecting locomotive developments has been largely influenced by the factors governing production in the immediate post-war period, and investigation into advanced designs with a view to production of such units has not formed any part of the LNER's policy. The company's resources of finance, manpower, and facilities, are being concentrated on restoring the basic locomotive stock to its previous level of mechanical reliability, and to the building up of a fleet of modern locomotives of improved performance and greater availability to replace many of the now obsolete classes.

The same broad principles of design, which have proved so successful in the past, are being maintained in the eight new standard designs selected as representative of the traction needs of the company.

Altogether some 150 of these engines are already in traffic, and larger orders are now in hand both in the company's workshops and in the workshops of contractors.

It is not expected that within the limited territorial boundaries of the LNER anything approaching the monthly mileages of 25000, and the mileages between overhaul of some 200000 miles, so common in America today, can hope to be realized. Nevertheless, the fact that steam locomotive mileages of the high order attained in America are possible, undoubtedly points to considerable possibilities in our own case in the future.

Fig. 5.8 Class B1 4–6–0 locomotive No. 8301 *Springbok*: the original locomotive as built by Thompson in 1943. The 'NE' on the tender is short for 'LNER' – an economy measure during the Second World War (BRB)

One of the essential requirements, in order that a wider range of operation such as this may be approached, is a controlled system of boiler-water treatment throughout the whole line.

Research into valve events points to future development in one or two directions. If the piston valve is retained its diameter can with advantage be increased.

On the other hand, poppet valves seem a logical field for study provided that, with the speeds visualized on the large poppet valves, adequate means are provided to close the valves positively and rapidly after emission of steam. From the point of view of simplification of motion details, especially to the middle cylinder of three-cylinder designs, poppet valves have marked advantages.

Much consideration has been given to the question of the steel firebox and its many advantages are not overlooked – in particular the elimination of objectionable overlap of plates at rivet joints which, by welding fireboxes complete, are avoided. Galvanic action is removed by eliminating dissimilar metals, and weight is lessened, enabling higher evaporation per unit of weight to be obtained. Nevertheless, steel fireboxes require the best of waters for their use, and water softening to the pitch required to achieve immunity from scale has not yet been reached in this country.

The LNER has concentrated its design policy on the orthodox steam locomotive rather than on other forms of traction, because of the greater maintenance advantages which accrue from operating a large fleet of straightforward, simple, and similar machines.

For adequate power, three-cylinder propulsion has been favoured in preference to four, and often where the same power could have been produced by two cylinders. Fundamentally, the more nearly the variable crank-effort of a reciprocating engine can be made to approach uniformity, the greater will be the advantage derived from traction from a given adhesive weight.

GREAT WESTERN RAILWAY

The present position of steam locomotives is directly the outcome of a consistent policy initiated by Churchward in the early part of the present century and followed throughout the intervening years in the design of the company's stock. By adopting, as early as 1902, a boiler pressure of 225 lb. per sq. in., superheat, and piston valves with long travel, he set the seal upon locomotive design for the Great Western Railway, and the successful outcome of his pioneer work has been felt on every other railway using steam locomotives.

Two main designs initiated in those early years have persisted, with improvements in detail only, up to the present day. One, a two-cylinder, of which *William Dean* (built in 1902) was the first, has reached its fullest development in the most recent Great Western design, the County class. The two-cylinder type was also applied to freight work, with no alteration to cylinder arrangement and very little modification to valve-gear details.

The success of the early two-cylinder designs prompted Churchward to make the famous comparison with the De Glehn compounds then achieving such remarkable performance in France. The arrival of these four-cylinder compounds on the Great Western Railway proved that Churchward's two-cylinder simple engines were equal in economy to the compounds, but that the four-cylinder arrangement had many advantages for high-speed work. The natural corollary was the design of a four-cylinder simple engine of which the *North Star* was the first, followed successively by similar four-cylinder engines with large cylinders, and by the famous Castle class engines, some of which are still being built. The four-cylinder type reached its maximum size in the King class, which ranks among the most powerful passenger locomotives in the country.

Concurrently with such fundamental changes in basic design, Churchward also introduced the policy of standardization of details, and concentrated particularly on interchangeability of boilers. As a result, the present booked stock of the Great Western Railway consists of 3860 engines – 3575 of Great Western design, of which 3119 are standard locomotives – divided into twenty classes, the whole of these engines being equipped with boilers drawn from a range of seven standard boilers applicable to a number of frames.

The stringent fuel position arising at the end of the war resulted in inability to obtain sufficient coal of the Welsh quality for which the engines were originally designed; this led to experiments in oil firing. In conjunction with the Petroleum Board and the North British Locomotive Company, oil-firing apparatus was designed and applied to ten 2–8–0 '28xx' heavy freight engines carrying one of the standard boilers having a 9 ft. 0 in. firebox. The results were highly successful and the experiment was carried a stage farther by converting one of the 4–6–0 mixed-traffic engines carrying the same boiler, with equally successful results.

The success of these experiments led to the Great Western designs of details being adopted by all companies as standard. They incorporate a weir-type burner situated under the throat plate, similar to the arrangement originally adopted on the first ten engines.

SOUTHERN RAILWAY

A large proportion of the traffic on the Southern Railway is suburban passenger carried in electrically operated, multiple-unit stock; the company operates the largest electrical service in the world.

The density of the traffic around London is such that all freight and non-electrically operated passenger services have to be dovetailed into the electric services, this being the case even with the 'boat trains' to Dover and other ports, and with the South-West and West of England expresses when inside the suburban area.

The past extensions of the electrified areas, and the probable future extensions, delayed the modernization of the steam locomotive stock as each extension made some of the steam locomotives redundant; consequently locomotives of the constituent companies still form a large proportion of the stock.

The inability of the existing steam locomotives to meet the increasing demands of the operating department had become obvious prior to the recent war, and steps were then taken to overcome it by the provision of new and more powerful locomotives.

The old distinction between express passenger engines and others had been removed by developments in design, so that the need for driving wheels of large diameter no longer existed. The term 'mixed traffic', describing an engine able to operate all classes of trains, came into use.

As regards train engines, the traffic requirements could be covered by two classes of tender engines and two classes of tank engines – the former for longer distance services, the latter for all local and short distance workings.

Whilst the benefit of standard parts was not overlooked this was not allowed to override the major need of meeting, in the most efficient manner possible, the operating requirements.

The behaviour of the existing engines in service was investigated with a view to effecting such improvements as would reduce the attention required in the sheds, increase the reliability and extend the availability of any future engines and make them more comfortable and easier to handle.

The first new design was the Merchant Navy class, to operate trains of 600 tons at an average speed of 70 m.p.h., and heavier trains at proportionately lower speeds.

These engines were the first steam locomotives built for use in England that mark a considerable breakaway from long accepted practice.

The main new features incorporated in them are:

(1) Boilers for 280 lb. per sq.in. pressure, with welded outer fireboxes and welded steel inner-fireboxes with two Nicholson syphons.

(2) Totally enclosed valve-gears under continuous lubrication.

(3) Lightened wheels of improved design, giving continuous circumferential support to the tyres.

(4) Clasp brakes on the driving wheels and tender wheels.

(5) Reciprocating weights not balanced, thereby obviating hammer blow.

The use of welded steel fireboxes enabled a very powerful boiler to be provided within the weight available.

These engines with their 21-ton driving-axle loads (a figure only allowed on the permanent way and bridges in consequence of the absence of hammer blow) were used on the main lines, but could not run over the secondary lines such as those west of Exeter.

The second design of tender engines is the West Country class which can operate over 88 per cent of the company's lines.

These engines incorporate the innovations first introduced on the Merchant Navy engines. The reduction in weight has been obtained to some extent by the greater use of welding. The axle-box horns are welded directly into the main frames; the cross stays are fabricated; steel castings have been almost eliminated; and the foundation rings have been formed of plate bent to shape and welded.

The Southern will shortly have in service 120 of these two types of Pacific locomotives of high capacity and advanced design and construction.

Future Tendencies: The requirements to be met by steam tender locomotives having been covered by the two classes referred to above, attention was next given to the types of tank engines needed.

A new type of heavy, mixed-traffic tank engine is under construction and these engines embody further developments of the innovations introduced in the tender engines, all with the object of developing a steam locomotive as easy to maintain and operate as possible. As the locomotive is carried on two six-wheeled bogies, the whole weight is available for adhesion and braking and the engine can run over 97 per cent of the company's system.

Each six-wheeled bogie has a three-cylinder, simple-expansion engine driving the middle axle, which is coupled to the leading and trailing axles. A new design of engine has been adopted, completely eliminating all piston or valve glands subject to steam pressure. Roller-bearing axle-boxes are fitted throughout and the usual horn guides suppressed.

A new design of boiler has been introduced without the usual water legs, so that stay trouble has been eliminated. The engines will carry water treatment equipment, so that there should be no longer any trouble resulting from the failure or absence of water treatment plants.

Automatic lubrication has been carried a stage further so that it is nearly complete.

It is expected that the availability of the locomotives will reach a percentage comparable with that of any other form of traction, i.e., be determined by traffic conditions rather than by locomotive requirements.

The new type of heavy mixed-traffic tank locomotive to which Bulleid referred was the ill-fated Leader class. In his Presidential Address to the Institution of Mechanical Engineers in June 1947, Bulleid specified the conditions which he felt should be met by future steam locomotives, and the means he intended to adopt in achieving the desired results. In his Address, Bulleid said 'What sort of locomotive may we expect to see if it is to meet the majority of our future requirements? It is reasonable to expect it to satisfy the following demands and to include the following new features. The locomotive should be built so as –

1. to be able to run over the majority of the company's lines;
2. to be capable of working all classes of trains up to speeds of 90 m.p.h.;
3. to have its whole weight available for braking and the highest possible percentage thereof for adhesion;
4. to be equally suitable for running in both directions without turning, with unobstructed look-out;
5. to be ready for service at short notice;
6. to be almost continuously available;
7. to be suitable for complete 'common use';
8. to run not less than 100000 miles between general repairs with little or no attention at the running sheds;
9. to cause minimum wear and tear to the track;
10. to use substantially less fuel and water per draw-bar horse-power developed.'

Five of these locomotives were included in the Southern Railway's 1947

building programmes, with a further 31 in 1948. In the event, one locomotive only was completed, at Eastleigh in June 1948. From the beginning
of its trials the *Leader* was beset by serious difficulties and mechanical
failures. It had come out 20 tons above the estimated design weight and
route availability was thus seriously restricted. Because the boiler was
offset from the longitudinal centre line to provide room for the corridor
connecting the cabs at each end, total axle loading on one side was 10 tons
higher than on the other. There was recurring trouble due to breakage of
the gear operating the sleeve valves, and steaming was unreliable. So
persistent were the failures during the first few months of trial running
that Riddles gave instructions for work on the other four locomotives
under construction to be suspended pending the results of further test
running. This included dynamometer car trials between the *Leader* and a
Southern U-class 2–6–0 mixed-traffic locomotive of comparable power.
Coal and water consumption of the *Leader* was 67 per cent and 47 per cent
respectively higher than that of the 2–6–0. This was caused partly by
steam leakage past the sleeve valves and pistons, and partly by excessive
rates of combustion. The firebricks forming the side walls of the firebox
proved to be too thin to withstand the working temperature in the
firebox. They had to be increased in thickness, with the result that the
grate area, originally 43 ft² was reduced to 25 ft². The efficiency of
combustion was thus much reduced.

There were other troubles, too. The crank axle of one of the bogies
broke in half, after only 6000 miles running. Working conditions in the
fireman's cab were quite intolerable. When running chimney first a
stream of hot air down the side corridor often raised the temperature to
above 100°F. The locomotive had to be turned at the end of each trip to
enable it always to run bunker first.

The *Leader* was never able to go into revenue-earning service. Short of
complete redesign and rebuilding it would scarcely have been possible to
modify the locomotive with any hope of success. Riddles had no reasonable alternative but to recommend to the RE that the *Leader*, and the four
other partially completed locomotives should be scrapped. Thus ended in
failure one more among the many attempts to overcome, by extremely
unconventional means, the inherent limitations of the conventional
steam locomotive, without sacrificing its outstanding merits of simplicity
and reliability.

On 1 January 1948, British Railways inherited 20024 steam locomotives
of 448 classes, as shown in Table 5.1.

It is clear from the extracts from the CMEs' lecture, that the companies
had, in their various ways, pursued policies of standardization and reduction of classes. Had the companies remained independent and continued to completion the policies upon which they had been engaged
there would have been only about fifty classes of locomotives running on
our railways. Even supposing this desirable result had been achieved

Table 5.1   Steam locomotives at Nationalization

Railway	Types	No. of locomotives
GWR	95	3856
LMSR	123	7805
LNER	151	6525
SR	79	1838
Total no. of types/ locomotives	448	20024

before nationalization further reductions of classes under one united ownership would have been possible, and indeed essential in the interests of economy of operation and maintenance. As it was, with 448 separate classes of steam locomotive, the scope for further standardization was very large indeed.

Before deciding what should be done in regard to new locomotive building to give effect to the policy of unification and further standardization, so clearly intended by the 1947 Transport Act, after completion of programmes already in progress, details of which are set out in Table 5.2, it was clearly necessary to consider possible alternative courses of action, which could well be influenced by the suitability, or otherwise, of the most modern existing classes as national standards. The essential facts, as then existing, had to be established.

To this end, as recorded in Chapter Two, a Locomotive Testing Committee was set up to organize a series of comparative dynamometer car trials to record the performance and efficiency of the most modern existing locomotives hauling trains of the maximum permitted loads to the best existing timings over selected routes of all Regions.

Secondly, a Locomotive Standards Committee was appointed, with A. W. J. Dymond from Swindon in the chair, and given a two-part remit:
(1) to prepare a list of renewable details which it was desirable to standardize from the point of view of economy in purchase and manufacture, and to recommend the best for future adoption; and
(2) to examine the possibility of selecting for future building one only of existing classes in each traffic category for use on all Regions.

Much valuable information emerged from the first part of the remit. As regards the second part, the Committee did not feel justified in choosing one class only in each traffic category for future building. None of the locomotives selected for consideration could be eliminated because of inferior design or performance. Predictably, the Committee recommended 'that until new standard designs for use throughout British Railways are evolved, each Region should continue to build engines to its existing design.' This recommendation was, however, not accepted.

Table 5.2   Steam locomotives of Company designs built 1948 to 1956

Type	Number built
GWR	
4–6–0 Castle	30
4–6–0 Hall	49
4–6–0 Manor	10
0–6–0 2251	2
2–6–2T 5101	20
0–6–0T 15XX	10
0–6–0T 16XX	70
0–6–0T 57/67XX	41
0–6–0ST 74/94XX	220
Total	452
LMS	
4–6–2 Cl.8	1
4–6–0 Cl.5	100
2–6–0 Cl.4	159
2–6–0 Cl.2	138
2–6–4T Cl.4	147
2–6–2T Cl.2	70
0–4–0 Dock	5
Total	620
LNER	
4–6–2 A1	49
4–6–2 A2	14
4–6–0 B1	136
2–6–0 K1	70
2–6–4T L1	99
0–6–0T J72	28
Total	396
SR	
4–6–2 Merchant Navy	10
4–6–2 West Country	40
Total	50
GRAND TOTAL	1518

Fig. 5.9   LMS Class 2 2–6–0 locomotive No. 6400 as built by H. G. Ivatt just before
nationalization (BRB)

There was at the time a pressing need for new locomotives in the lower
power groups, particularly on the Eastern, North Eastern, and Southern
Regions. During the last two years of its existence the LMS had built three
new classes of small engines, designed by H. G. Ivatt – Class 2, 2–6–0 and
2–6–2 Tank, and a Class 4, 2–6–0. They were entirely modern, very
successful, and had almost universal route availability. Pending completion of new standard designs, 165 of these LMS engines were built for
service on other Regions, 61 going to the Eastern, 49 to the North Eastern,
25 to the Western, and 30 to the Southern, who also built for themselves,
at Brighton, 41 LMS 2–6–4 tank locomotives. These four classes, with
minor modifications, were included in the new BR standard series.

The inter-regional dynamometer car tests took place between April and
September 1948. The fourteen locomotive classes competing and the
routes over which the tests were conducted are set out in Table 5.3

The results of these trials, as they affected locomotive building policy,
have been discussed in Chapter Two. On the more technical aspects of
the performance and efficiency of the locomotives tested, suffice it to say
that the range of efficiency, as measured by coal consumption per unit of
work done, was commendably narrow, as shown in Table 5.4. Compared
with results obtained from similar trials undertaken by the LMS shortly
after the 1923 grouping, coal consumption in the 1948 tests was approximately 25 per cent less – a striking tribute to the improvement in locomotive design over the intervening years.

Fig. 5.10   Locomotive interchange: a Battle of Britain class light Pacific No. 34059
Sir Archibald Sinclair at Norwich Thorpe in 1949

Table 5.3   Inter-Regional Dynamometer Car Trials, 1948:
Locomotives and Routes

Locomotives	Routes
Express passenger LMS Duchess 4–6–2 LMS Re-built Royal Scot 4–6–0 LNE A4 4–6–2 SR Merchant Navy 4–6–2 GWR King 4–6–0	King's Cross–Leeds Euston–Carlisle Paddington–Plymouth Waterloo–Exeter
Mixed Traffic LMS Cl.5 4–6–0 LNE B1 4–6–0 SR West Country 4–6–2 GWR Hall 4–6–0	Marylebone–Manchester St. Pancras–Manchester Bristol–Plymouth
Freight LMS Cl. 8F 2–8–0 LNE O1 2–8–0 GWR Cl. 28XX 2–8–0 WD 8F. 2–8–0 WD 2–10–0	Ferme Park–Peterborough Toton–Brent Acton–Severn Tunnel Jct. Eastleigh–Bristol

Table 5.4 Inter-Regional Dynamometer Car Trials: Coal Consumption

Locomotive Class	Coal Consumption: lb per drawbar horsepower hour
Express Passenger	
LMS Duchess 4–6–2	3·12
LMS Rebuilt Royal Scot 4–6–0	3·38
LNE A4. 4–6–2	3·06
SR Merchant Navy 4–6–2	3·60
GWR King class 4–6–0	3·59
Mixed Traffic	
LMS Class 5 4–6–0	3·54
LNE B1. 4–6–0	3·57
SR West Country 4–6–2	4·11
GWR Hall class 4–6–0	3·94
Freight	
LMS Class 8F 2–8–0	3·52
LNE O1 class 2–8–0	3·37
GWR Class 28XX 2–8–0	3·42
WD 2–8–0	3·77
WD 2–10–0	3·52

It will be seen that the lowest coal consumption was achieved by the LNER 4–6–2, closely followed by the LMS Duchess Pacifics. The best performances in relation to their nominal capacity were put up by the LMS rebuilt Royal Scot and the Southern Pacifics, though the latter were very expensive on coal consumption. The Western Region engines were limited by their overall dimensions to their own routes and those over the ex-LNER. They were thought by some to be handicapped by having to use Yorkshire instead of their usual Welsh coal. Their lower superheat, compared with the other contestants, was reflected in the coal consumption figures.

Nothing which emerged from this historic series of tests made it necessary to modify the preliminary plans, already in hand, for a new range of standard steam locomotives. By the middle of June 1948 E. S. Cox had completed a report on the proposed new locomotives. As originally drafted, the report proposed twelve classes to cover all the principal requirements of British Railways. They were:

(a) *Entirely new designs*

Class 7. 4–6–2 Express Passenger

Class 7. 4–6–2 Mixed Traffic

Class 5. 4–6–2 Mixed Traffic

Class 9. 2–8–2 Freight.

(b) *New designs: developments of existing types*
    Class 8. 4–6–2 Express Passenger
    Class 4. 4–6–0 Mixed Traffic
    Class 3. 2–6–2 Tank, Mixed Traffic.

(c) *Existing Designs, modified in detail*
    Class 4. 2–6–0 Mixed Traffic
    Class 4. 2–6–4 Tank, Mixed Traffic
    Class 2. 2–6–0 Mixed Traffic
    Class 2. 2–6–2 Tank, Mixed Traffic.

In the introduction to his report Cox set out three main considerations which governed his proposals. They were:

(a) that entirely new designs should be put forward wherever a definite step forward in availability and efficiency can be realized;

(b) that new designs should not be undertaken for their own sake, and that where an existing design offers all that is available from the present state of design, it should be continued with only detail modifications; and

(c) that the whole trend should be towards simplification, good accessibility of all parts requiring attention, and reduction in time required for repairs and servicing.

As noted by the Railway Executive Ideal Stocks Committee, of which R. C. Bond, R. F. Harvey, and A. E. Robson were the engineering members, the new standard locomotives were designed

(a) to offer the simplest arrangement, having the least number of moving parts, with maximum accessibility to facilitate examination and repair in Shops and at Motive Power Depots;

(b) to incorporate all the features which experience had shown will promote high availability and high mileage between repairs;

(c) to make first cost and shop repairs cost as economical as is compatible with (a) and (b) above;

(d) to ensure economy in coal consumption by the provision of ample grate areas, high-degree superheat and long-travel valve gears; and

(e) to introduce the maximum number of standard fittings and details so that the stocks of spare parts can be kept to a minimum.

The four entirely new designs were intended to replace the following classes of company locomotives:

LMS	Class 7	Royal Scot	4–6–0
	Class 6	Jubilee	4–6–0
	Class 5	Mixed Traffic	4–6–0
	Class 8	Freight	2–8–0
LNER	B1		4–6–0
	C1		2–8–0

GWR	Castle Class	4–6–0
	County Class	4–6–0
	Hall Class	4–6–0
	28xx Class	2–8–0
SR	West Country Class	4–6–2
	Q1 Class	0–6–0

The proposals in Cox's report took account of the views of the Regional Operating and Motive Power Superintendents, and were subsequently widely discussed with all concerned, particularly those responsible for building and maintenance. As a result the original proposals were modified in a number of important respects. It became clear from the inter-regional dynamometer car tests, which confirmed earlier experience with the A1 and A2 Peppercorn Pacifics, that there could be no justification for two new Class 7 4–6–2s, identical except for a six-inch difference (6 ft 6 in and 6 ft) in coupled wheel diameter. The Class 7 4–6–2 thus became a mixed-traffic locomotive with 6 ft 2 in diameter coupled wheels. Next, it was pointed out that the proposed Class 5 4–6–2 would be more expensive to operate and maintain than existing capable and efficient Class 5 4–6–0s. It would be approximately 11 tons (15 per cent) heavier, and any advantage from the lower average rate of combustion on the larger grate would be nullified by higher capital charges due to the increased first cost of the 4–6–2. Larger stand-by fuel losses and the maintenance costs of the trailing truck would be additional debits. It was proposed therefore, and agreed, that the 4–6–2 should have a rather larger boiler, giving a greater free area through the tubes, and come into power Class 6, and that Class 5 duties would be covered by a 4–6–0 having the same cylinders, motion, and wheels as the Class 6, but with the LMS Class 5 4–6–0 boiler.

There was added to the second group a Class 3 2–6–0 with a 16-ton axle load for the considerable number of routes over which heavier locomotives were prohibited.

Although there was at the time every likelihood that the proposed Class 8 express passenger locomotive, intended to be based on the LMS four-cylinder 4–6–2 Duchess class, and the 2–8–2 freight engine would be required in the future, there was no immediate demand for either of them to be included in a building programme. All the four group companies were well provided with locomotives in the highest power class for the most important express passenger services, and a large number of LMS and WD 2–8–0 freight engines had been turned over to the railways after war service. Nevertheless, much further thought was given to the design of these two proposed classes of locomotive. The drawings for the Britannias had by then been completed, and it was proposed that the 2–8–2 should carry the same boiler. Mindful of the success of his WD 2–10–0,

Riddles had a strong leaning to this wheel arrangement in preference to a 2–8–2. Their relative merits were thoroughly discussed, and when, after further drawing office work, it was found possible to accommodate 5 ft diameter coupled wheels under a wide firebox – though not inter-changeable with the Britannia boiler – the 2–10–0 won the day. Two hundred and fifty-one of these engines were built, 178 at Crewe and 73 at Swindon, between 1954 and 1960. One of them, No. 92220, turned out from Swindon in March 1960, was the last steam locomotive built for British Railways. It was called *Evening Star*, and, determined to the end to maintain their old traditions, Swindon adorned this engine with a copper cap to the chimney.

Replacement of ex-LMS four-cylinder 4–6–2 No. 46202 *Princess Anne* (rebuilt from Sir William Stanier's turbine locomotive), damaged beyond repair in the catastrophic double collision at Harrow in October 1952, provided the opportunity for building one of the proposed new standard Class 8 express passenger locomotives. The original intention that this should have been an improved version of the LMS Duchess class Pacific had, perhaps unfortunately as events turned out, been abandoned. Instead, No. 71000, *Duke of Gloucester* was built with three 18 in × 28 in cylinders, the latest development of Caprotti valve gear, and the Britan-nia boiler with the grate area increased from 42 ft² to 48·6 ft². Compre-hensive tests at Rugby and out on the line demonstrated that the cylinder

Fig. 5.11   BR Standard Class 9F 2–10–0 locomotive No. 92178 on controlled road test with 14-coach train, Hullavington, Western Region, 29 January 1958. Although these loco-motives were primarily intended for freight working, their performance was such that they were on occasions used to work passenger trains (BR/Oxford Publishing Co)

Fig. 5.12   BR Standard Class 7 4–6–2 (*Britannia*) locomotive No. 70000 under construction in the Erecting Shop at Crewe, January 1951 (BRB)

efficiency of this engine was higher than had ever before been achieved by any simple expansion locomotive. The evaporative capacity of the boiler, however, failed to meet expectations and requirements. Coal consumption was very heavy and steaming was by no means wholly reliable. *Duke of Gloucester*, allocated to Crewe North, was unpopular with the footplate staff, and was never able to equal, let alone surpass, the performance of the LMS Pacifics.

The decision on the new standard types having been taken, plans were made to include six of them in the 1951 building programme, to be built at Crewe, Derby, Swindon, and Brighton.

The first BR standard locomotive available for service was a Class 7 4–6–2. This was turned out of Crewe Works on 2 January 1951 – the culmination of a programme formulated some eighteen months earlier. It was named *Britannia* on 30 January 1951, by the Minister of Transport – the Rt. Hon. Alfred Barnes – and sent to work on the Eastern Region. There was a number of teething troubles with these locomotives – broken pistons due to heavy water carry-over, wheels moving on axles, and bent side-rods. When these difficulties, and complaints of uncomfortable and draughty driving cabs, were overcome, little further trouble was experienced. In East Anglia, in particular, they were very popular and did yeoman service. These, and the Class 9 2–10–0 freight engines, made the

Fig. 5.13   BR Standard Class 7 4–6–2 (Britannia) locomotive No. 70030 leaving Ipswich
            Tunnel with the Down Broadsman (BR/Oxford Publishing Co)

greatest impact of the whole range of BR standard types. In general, little
or no difficulty arose in connection with any of the other standard types,
although, as stated previously, there was some evidence of Regional
opposition to the standard locomotives when they were brought into
service. In the main, this was due to preferences for the familiar company
types – a situation which had also existed after the 1923 amalgamation
when, for example, Gateshead drivers accustomed to Raven designs had
found many features to fault in the Gresley Pacifics. Old company loyal-
ties died hard. As a further example, at Peterborough, the L & NW and
Midland Railway footplate staff never saw eye to eye on any issue when
they were concentrated on the Midland shed at Peterborough Spital,
following the amalgamations: they only combined against a new 'common enemy' when former Great Eastern staff joined them in the early
1950s.

   In all, 999 BR standard steam locomotives were built between 1951 and
1960, as shown in Table 5.5.

   At the time the new standard types were developed, and later when,
following the abolition of the Railway Executive and the retirement of
Riddles in 1953, Bond was appointed Chief Officer (Mechanical Engineering) (later redesignated Chief Mechanical Engineer) on the BR Central
Staff, it was taken for granted that steam would continue as the predominant form of motive power on British Railways for many years to

Table 5.5   British Railways: Standard Steam Locomotives Built 1951–1960

	1951	52	53	54	55	56	57	58	59	60	Total
4–6–2 Class 8. 71000 *Duke of Gloucester*	–	–	–	1	–	–	–	–	–	–	1
4–6–2 Class 7. 70000 Britannia class	25	13	7	10	–	–	–	–	–	–	55
4–6–2 Class 6. 72000 Clan class	2	8	–	–	–	–	–	–	–	–	10
4–6–0 Class 5. 73000	29	1	20	25	44	30	23	–	–	–	172
4–6–0 Class 4. 75000	16	4	25	5	13	5	12	–	–	–	80
2–6–0 Class 4. 76000	–	10	25	10	15	19	36	–	–	–	115
2–6–0 Class 3. 77000	–	–	–	20	–	–	–	–	–	–	20
2–6–0 Class 2. 78000	–	4	8	33	10	10	–	–	–	–	65
2–6–4T Class 4. 80000	17	37	18	36	23	20	4	–	–	–	155
2–6–2T Class 3. 82000	–	20	–	12	13	–	–	–	–	–	45
2–6–2T Class 2. 84000	–	–	20	–	–	–	10	–	–	–	30
2–10–0 Class 9. 92000	–	–	–	32	38	45	56	62	15	3	251
Total	89	97	123	184	156	129	141	62	15	3	999

come. The recommendation from the Harrington Committee for a large-scale trial of main-line diesel traction had been rejected by the Railway Executive. The committee of Chief Officers which was in due course to produce the Modernization Plan of 1955 had not then been appointed. There was therefore every reason for the development of steam traction to be sustained. This was by no means confined to the building of the new standard locomotives. The critical examination of every aspect of locomotive design, maintenance, and operation, initiated in 1948, continued with undiminished vigour. For so long as steam traction remained it was clearly to the financial advantage of British Railways that its efficiency should be maintained and indeed enhanced by all available means.

A major contribution to the work of design development was made by the locomotive testing organizations at Rugby, Derby, and Swindon. Gresley, in his Presidential Address to the Institution of Locomotive Engineers in 1927, stressed the need for a locomotive testing plant on which tests, under strictly controlled constant conditions, could be undertaken. Such facilities had been available for many years in the USA and were in use in Germany and France. Churchward had built a stationary test plant in the Works at Swindon as long ago as 1904, but it was of very limited capacity. Gresley was insistent that without a modern plant able to conduct tests on the largest locomotives then in service, or likely to be required in the future, Britain could not maintain its position in the forefront of locomotive engineering. His persistence was rewarded. In 1937, with strong support from Sir Harold Hartley, a vice-president of the LMS Executive, the directors of the LNE and LMS companies authorized the construction of a Locomotive Testing Station at Rugby for their joint use.

R. C. Bond, until then Assistant Works Manager at Crewe, was appointed Superintending Engineer, responsible jointly to Gresley and Stanier, for the design and specification of the plant as a whole and for the various items of equipment. The construction of the Station, already well in hand, with the foundations and structural steelwork nearing completion, was immediately suspended on the outbreak of war. Work was resumed at the end of the war with D. W. Sanford in charge, and the Plant was officially opened on 19 October 1948, with D. R. Carling as Superintending Engineer. Regrettably, Sir Nigel Gresley did not live to see the Testing Station he had so strongly advocated come into operation.

Dynamometer cars for establishing broad relationships between drawbar pull, horsepower, speed, and fuel consumption, and for assessing the loads and timings appropriate to the capacity of locomotives over particular routes, had been in use for many years. Tests on normal service trains, however, were inevitably subject to random variables – wind and weather, signal and permanent way checks, and the human element in driving and firing – and the results had to be interpreted with these random variables in mind.

As the margin for further improvements in the efficiency of steam locomotives narrowed due to constant improvement in design, precise comparisons free from all extraneous variables, obtainable only from testing under strictly controlled constant conditions on a stationary plant, or out on the line, had become essential to further progress.

Fig. 5.14   LMS Class 5 locomotive No. 44765 under test at the Testing
Plant at Rugby (Topical Press Agency)

Such testing falls under two broad heads which can conveniently be defined as

(a) Design Efficiency Testing;

and (b) Performance Efficiency Testing.

The first provides information for those responsible for locomotive design and covers

(i) verification of fundamental data on which design is based;

(ii) the determination of the effects of modifications to design on performance and efficiency; and

(iii) assessment of the effects of special fittings on performance and efficiency.

The second provides data to those responsible for motive power operation and covers

(i) the establishment of loads and timings in relation to engine capacity; and

(ii) the effect of different methods of working and varying states of repair.

The former is most conveniently undertaken on a stationary testing plant, the latter out on the line, either at predetermined constant rates of evaporation by the method brilliantly developed at Swindon by S. O. Ell or over a range of constant speeds controlled within very close limits by a steam locomotive attached in rear of the dynamometer car to provide counter-pressure braking force or by electric braking vehicles.

Shortly before the Second World War the LMS Board authorized the construction of a mobile testing unit comprising a new dynamometer car, three braking vehicles, and a special tender with the coal bunker mounted on weighing scales. Each of the braking vehicles was in effect an electric locomotive designed for braking instead of pulling. Together they could exert a maximum braking effort of 23 tons, each unit being capable of absorbing up to 1500 horsepower. Different gear ratios for the electric generators permitted testing up to maximum speeds of 50, 90, and 120 miles/h. After wartime use as emergency power generators they did valuable work for the purpose for which they were designed.

Though coming into full operation relatively late in the great days of steam, the Testing Station at Rugy, the modernized station at Swindon, and the Mobile Testing units based at Swindon and Derby, between them did most valuable work. At Rugby, for example, from 1948 until the last test was conducted in 1965, thirty locomotives – 25 steam, 2 gas-turbines, 1 electric, and 1 diesel – and one diesel multiple-unit power car, were tested, some of them more than once, involving 2052 separate test runs.[*]

Among the many developments in hand at this time was a renewed interest in the Caprotti valve gear. The first application of this type of

[*]D. R. Carling 'Locomotive Testing Stations,' *Transactions of the Newcomen Society,* 1972–73, Vol. XLV.

poppet valve gear on a British railway was in 1926, when the LMS fitted it to a Claughton class 4–6–0 locomotive (No. 5908). Dynamometer car trials in comparison with a normal piston-valve locomotive showed appreciable savings in coal consumption. In the early 1930s, nine further Claughton class locomotives were fitted and, over a period, a nine per cent saving in coal consumption was recorded. The LNER also fitted Caprotti valve gear to four Great Central B3 Class 4–6–0 express engines. As a class, the B3s were notoriously heavy on coal and the converted engines showed an average saving of 16 per cent in fuel consumption. Shortly before nationalization, Ivatt equipped twenty-two LMS Class 5 standard 4–6–0 locomotives with Caprotti valve gear. Not only was there a saving in coal consumption, but it was possible considerably to extend the time between piston and valve examinations. With this experience in mind, Caprotti valve gear was fitted to the one Class 8 4–6–2 standard locomotive *Duke of Gloucester* and tests with this locomotive confirmed the results obtained by Ivatt with the Class 5s. Bond therefore obtained authority to fit 30 of the Class 5 4–6–0 BR standard to be built in 1955 with this valve gear. If steam traction had continued, poppet valve gears might well have replaced piston valves on the larger locomotives.

Another project which was pursued was the fitting of ten of the Class 9 2–10–0s with Crosti boilers, successfully used in Italian locomotives, in which the hot gases of combustion were turned back through a tubular feed-water heat exchanger and ejected by a multiple blast pipe and chimney just in front of the fireman's side of the cab. Results, however,

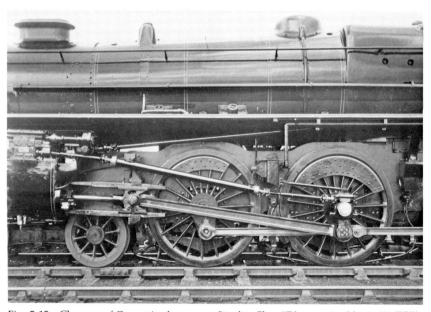

Fig. 5.15   Close-up of Caprotti valve gear as fitted to Class 5F locomotive No. 44686 (BRB)

were disappointing. Savings in fuel consumption were less than predicted by the manufacturers and were more than offset by increased maintenance costs of the heat exchangers. Furthermore, smoke and steam from the chimney just outside the cab made conditions on the footplate almost unbearable. This development was not, therefore, further pursued and the heat exchanger drums were removed.

In 1958, three of the 2–10–0 locomotives were fitted with mechanical stokers. Tests had shown that if heavy power-braked coal trains were to run with one locomotive at speeds up to 60 miles/h, a combustion rate well beyond the capacity of a single fireman would be needed. Previous trials on a Bulleid Merchant Navy Class locomotive in 1949 had indicated that stoker firing was expensive, in terms of fuel consumption. Tests on the 2–10–0 class at the Rugby plant had demonstrated that, when burning coal at the maximum possible rate, stoker firing produced no more steam than was obtained from the maximum short-term hand-firing rate, but a stoker-fired locomotive could maintain this maximum indefinitely and therefore had greater sustained capacity. The equipment could, however, only be fully exploited on services which, in terms of train loading and speed, demanded maximum output. A potentially important development was frustrated by the rising tide of diesel traction on such services.

The testing units at Derby, Swindon, and Rugby were at this time conducting a programme of steaming tests on a number of locomotives of the former Company designs. The Kings, Castles, and Halls of the GWR had their steaming qualities considerably improved by modifications to chimney and blast-pipe proportions. Adjustments to boiler tube and front end dimensions of LMS Class 6 4–6–0s, LNER V2 Class 2–6–2s, and Ivatt Class 4 2–6–0s also led to improved steaming rates.

Individual costing of classified repairs in Main Workshops and Motive Power Depots, introduced first by the LMS Railway in 1927, was extended to all Regions of British Railways in 1949. Approximately 10 per cent of the total locomotive stock was included within the costing arrangements, the classes selected being those of modern design likely to remain in service for a considerable number of years. In addition to providing factual information, in the absence of which one had to rely on general technical experience, the individual costing figures were valuable in providing justification for the premature breaking-up of unsatisfactory locomotives or for their rebuilding.

Bulleid's Merchant Navy and West Country Pacifics proved themselves fully capable of working the fastest and heaviest Southern Region expresses but they were very expensive to operate and maintain. Novel features incorporated in these engines – intended to reduce the extent and cost of maintenance – had the opposite effect. The chain-driven valve gear and inside motion enclosed in an oil bath were main causes of unreliability and loss of availability. Steam distribution was erratic, and the 'air-smoothed' boiler casing was the cause of much trouble and expense in maintenance. Minor modifications led to little improvement in performance. For the three years 1950–52 the repair costs per mile of the Merchant Navy and West Country locomotives, compared with those for other classes of comparable capacity, were as shown on the Table below.

Table 5.6   Repair Costs per mile, Merchant Navy and
West Country Classes, 1950–2

Region	Class of Locomotive	Repair Cost: Pence per mile
Southern	Merchant Navy	13·707
	West Country	11·948
	Lord Nelson	10·707
E & NE	A1	7·007
	A4	9·576
	A2	8·888
LM	Duchess	9·576

On the strength of these figures, and statistics of coal consumption and availability which were equally unfavourable, a case was made, and accepted, for a major rebuilding of the Merchant Navy and West Country classes, which it was estimated would bring substantial savings in operating and maintenance costs over the remaining life of the locomotives. The main features of the rebuilding were the substitution of the chain-driven valve gear by three sets of Walschaerts gear and elimination of the oil bath. A new inside cylinder and saddle to accommodate a normal cylindrical smokebox were provided, and the air-smoothed outer casing removed. Though the extension of electrification and the introduction of diesel traction on the Southern Region cut short the programme, the locomotives of both classes that were rebuilt were entirely successful and met all expectations. Dynamometer car tests of one of the rebuilt Merchant Navy locomotives showed that coal consumption had been reduced by 14 per cent compared with the locomotives as they were before modification.

The long-sustained commitment to locomotive feed-water treatment continued. An important factor determining the cost of boiler repairs is the quality of the feed-water. Impurities present in natural water vary widely. Untreated 'hard' waters deposit layers of hard scale on firebox plates, stays, and boiler tubes, causing overheating, wastage, and leakage. Other waters are corrosive and give rise to pitting and wastage of the internal surfaces of the boiler, and grooving and cracking at the bends of the flanged outer firebox plates.

To a varying extent, all the four group companies installed chemical

Fig. 5.16   Rebuilt Southern Region Merchant Navy Class locomotive
No. 35022 *Holland-America Line* (NRM)

treatment plants for dealing with their worst hard water. Gresley brought
T. Henry Turner, a chemist, into his organization to deal with water
treatment problems, and progress on the LNER was largely due to
Turner's influence. The LMS Railway dealt with the matter equally
thoroughly, bringing into operation, between 1936 and 1943, 158 softening and treatment plants in England. A consequence of this treatment
was to raise the concentration of dissolved salts in the boiler water, which
above a certain level causes priming, to avoid which approximately seven
per cent of the water fed to the boilers had to be discharged to the track
through a continuous blowdown valve. The object of this ambitious
scheme was to bring all feed waters up to the quality of the soft waters of
Scotland, which, if achieved, would result in very substantial savings in
boiler costs.

Although there was a significant increase in the mileage between heavy
boiler repairs, this was due more to improved boiler design and maintenance procedures than to water treatment as such. The anticipated
overall savings were not being achieved. Information obtained during a
visit to the United States of America by a party of senior LMS and LNE
officers in 1945 proved beyond doubt that water treatment, properly
applied, could, and did, ensure completely clean boilers free from scale
and corrosion, but only if the whole operation was controlled far more
closely than had hitherto been the case. It was essential to ensure that
virtually 100 per cent of the feed water was in fact treated as intended; that
accumulations of sludge were removed each day by intermittent blowing
down through a large valve fitted at the firebox foundation ring; and that
the water actually in the boilers should be checked by chemical analysis
every day.

Armed with this knowledge, a rigidly supervised trial was put in hand

Fig. 5.17   Water softening plant, Frodingham, LNER 1934 (NRM)

with fifty standard Class 8 2–8–0 freight locomotives between Toton and Brent, the results of which were encouraging. There still remained the problem of hard adherent scale which blowdown could not remove. It was not until after nationalization that further knowledge provided a solution to this problem. By this time, however, the current state of water treatment on all Regions was being reviewed by a committee under the chairmanship of T. F. B. Simpson.

In their report, in May 1952, the Simpson Committee noted that, if a feed water could be used which would not give rise to scale and corrosion and would not cause priming, the annual costs in relation to boiler repairs, boilerwashing, and coal consumption could be reduced by around 8·67 per cent, quite apart from which there would be improved availability of locomotives, a reduction in dirty and unpopular manual tasks and the possibility of employing steel instead of copper in the manufacture of locomotive fireboxes.

After considering the various systems which were in use, and in particular the French TIA (Traitement Integral Armand) System, introduced on a small scale on the Southern Region, the Committee recommended that a complete and comprehensive system of internal treatment of water on the tender, based on the principles of the TIA System, and using in addition anti-priming compounds, should be adopted by BR, for application to all locomotive boilers in England and Wales. This in turn would necessitate all locomotives being provided with intermittent blow-down valves to remove the resulting sludge from the boilers, at Motive Power Depots. The report also recommended the types of chemical reagents to be used and the organization to be set up for ensuring that the application of the treatment was properly controlled.

It was suggested that the work involved should be programmed over a period of approximately ten years, but, like so many other plans for the further development of the steam locomotive, the proposals for the extension of feed-water treatment were overtaken by the decision to switch to diesel and electric traction.

Nevertheless it must be said that, in its final years, steam traction was more efficient than it had ever been before. The good work of Churchward, Gresley, Stanier, and others a generation or more earlier had been built upon by their successors to the stage when steam locomotives, in the last few years of their life, were vastly improved machines.

When the last time-tabled steam train on the BR ran on 4 August 1968, with a 'Farewell to Steam' tour from Liverpool to Carlisle and back a few days later, it was assumed that the days of steam traction were over. There were, however, even at that time, a small number of the more well known locomotives in private ownership and these occasionally ran on special excursion trains operated on behalf of the owners. Now, there are around 300 standard-gauge locomotives in the ownership of private individuals and Preservation Societies. Because of the problems which were created by private owners and societies making their own contacts at various levels of the railway organization, a temporary ban was placed on the movement of privately owned locomotives in steam, around the end of 1967, but the way was again opened, in the following year, for such locomotives to operate, subject to rigidly applied rules as to the channels through which the appropriate arrangements should be made, for journeys over selected routes and using nominated locomotives. Now, there is a clearly defined annual programme of steam operation – either as special trains or on regular services on some lines in mainly holiday areas – using not only locomotives owned by members of the Steam Locomotive Operators' Association (SLOA) but also locomotives from the National Railway Museum in York. In 1980, 18 routes, totalling over 1000 miles, have been approved for steam-hauled excursions and 36 steam locomotives listed which might be considered for running over BR lines, subject to condition, detailed examination and approval by the Regional CM & EE and route clearance by the Chief Civil Engineer (see Tables 5.7 and 5.8).

Additionally, other locomotives, including replicas of the three loco-

Table 5.7   Approved routes for steam-hauled excursions on BR lines, 1980

Route	Mileage
York–Harrogate–Leeds	39
York-Church Fenton–Leeds	25
York–Sheffield (via Pontefract)	46
Hull–York (via Goole)	50
Newcastle–Carlisle	60
Middlesbrough–Sunderland–Newcastle	48
Guide Bridge–Sheffield	40
Carnforth–Barrow–Sellafield (including Dalton Curve)	64
Carnforth–Leeds	64
Chester–Newport	136
Settle Junction–Carlisle	73½
Birmingham (Moor Street)/Saltley–Didcot	77
Tyseley–Stratford on Avon	22
Hatton/Lapworth–Stratford on Avon	9
Dundee–Ladybank–Thornton–Dunfermline–Cowdenbeath–Thornton–Dundee (circular)	91
Edinburgh–Aberdeen	130
Dundee–Stirling–Edinburgh	90
Dalmeny–Winchburgh Junction	4½

Table 5.8   Steam locomotives for consideration for running over BR lines, 1980

Locomotive		Name	Depot
No	Class		
Former GWR design			
4930	Hall	*Hagley Hall*	Bewdley
5051	Castle	*Earl Bathurst*	Didcot
5900	Hall	*Hinderton Hall*	Didcot
6000	King	*King George V*	Hereford
6960	Hall	*Raveningham Hall*	Bewdley
6998	Hall	*Burton Agnes Hall*	Didcot
7029	Castle	*Clun Castle*	Tyseley
7808	Manor	*Cookham Manor*	Didcot
Former LMS design			
4767	5	*George Stephenson*	Grosmont
4871	5	—	Carnforth
4932	5	—	Carnforth
5000	5	—	Bewdley
5025	5	—	Strathspey
5305	5	—	Hull
5407	5	—	Carnforth

Locomotive		Name	Depot
No	Class		
5593	6	*Kolhapur*	Tyseley
5596	6	*Bahamas*	Dinting
5690	6	*Leander*	Carnforth
6115	7: Royal Scot	*Scots Guardsman*	Dinting
6201	8: Princess	*Princess Elizabeth*	Hereford
6229	8: Coronation	*Duchess of Hamilton*	York NRM
43106	4MT	—	Bewdley
Former LNER design			
246	D49	*Morayshire*	Falkirk
2005	K1	—	Grosmont
3442	K4	*The Great Marquess*	Bewdley
4472	A3	*Flying Scotsman*	Carnforth
4498	A4	*Sir Nigel Gresley*	Carnforth
4771	V2	*Green Arrow*	York NRM
60009	A4	*Union of South Africa*	Markinch
Former SR design			
30850	Nelson	*Lord Nelson*	Carnforth
30925	Schools	*Cheltenham*	York NRM
35028	Merchant Navy	*Clan Line*	Hereford
BR design			
70000	7MT	*Britannia*	Bewdley
92220	9F	*Evening Star*	York NRM
Historic Lomomotives			
790	LNWR: Precedent	*Hardwicke*	York NRM
1000	Midland Compound 4P	—	York NRM

NRM: National Railway Museum

motives taking part in the Rainhill Trials in October 1829 (*Rocket, Novelty,* and *Sans Pareil*) and one diesel hydraulic locomotive (No. 1062 *Western Courier*) were listed for inclusion in the cavalcade at Rainhill in May 1980 in connection with the 150th anniversary of the Trials and the opening of the Liverpool & Manchester Railway.

What is in no doubt is that the steam trains have proved an enormous success. In recent years, most tours have achieved a very high percentage loading and some trains have had to be run in two parts.

So that, after all, the steam locomotive did not die. How long it can continue to live on must depend very largely upon two main factors – the length of time the boilers can be maintained in a condition of safety which will satisfy the boiler inspector, and to what extent it will be possible to find staff capable of driving steam locomotives, or perhaps more likely, of firing on large engines, running at express speeds over fairly long dis-

Fig. 5.18   Each summer there is an extensive programme of steam-hauled trains. One of the locomotives used is the former LNER Pacific No. 4472 *Flying Scotsman*, here seen with the Cumbrian Coast Express.

tances. Even now the latter factor is becoming something of a problem. As the matter stands the agreement with the SLOA is due to run until 1985. Whether, then, steam will die yet another death is a matter for conjecture.

CHAPTER SIX

Diesel Traction

Prior to the Second World War, the railways of Britain, although fully aware of the trend of events in other countries, were by no means convinced of the alleged advantages of diesel traction, except for shunting, for which it was well established on the LMS and under trial on other railways. By the late 1930s the LMS had proved, beyond any doubt, that diesel locomotives were technically suitable and operationally and economically superior to steam for shunting purposes. They developed a standard 350 h.p. locomotive, with English Electric engine and electric transmission, capable of handling trains of up to 1000 tons in weight. Operating costs were estimated at around 50 per cent of steam costs, given one-man operation and at least two-, preferably three-shift working. The other main-line companies also placed in service a number of basically similar units. Following nationalization, the proven 350 h.p. diesel-electric locomotive became the principal standard machine for British Railways, although there still remained some requirement for locomotives of lower power, with mechanical or hydraulic transmission, for work in smaller yards throughout the country.

Both before and after the formation of the four group companies, there were numerous attempts to develop railcars and rail motors, self-contained units powered by steam or internal combustion engines, for use on secondary services or branch lines. Among the most interesting of these were petrol-engined cars used by the Great Northern Railway between Hatfield and Hertford in the early part of the century; by the LMS – with pneumatic tyres – between Oxford and Bletchley in 1932; a special vehicle, for use either on rail or road, which the LMS tried, again in 1932, for a short time between Blisworth and Stratford on Avon; and the Armstrong-Whitworth diesel-electric cars brought into service on the Tyneside lines by the LNER in 1934. Little headway was made, however, largely because operators rather expected the railcar to do all that a steam train could do, and cope with goods wagons as well as a varying passenger load. With the growth of road passenger services, too, the demand for secondary and branch line services diminished and there was a sufficiency of suitable steam locomotives and passenger stock remaining available to cover the connecting services which were still left, which further slowed down the development of alternative means of providing for the more lightly loaded and slower services.

It was the LNER which first showed interest in diesel units for main-line service operation. In 1933, the German State Railways introduced the Flying Hamburger, a two-car streamlined articulated train which operated between Berlin and Hamburg at an average speed of 77·4 miles/h over the 178 miles, with a maximum speed of 100 miles/h. In 1934, Gresley visited Germany and travelled with the train. He was considerably impressed by its performance and arranged for a team of German engineers to come to Britain to assess the possibility of such a service on the East Coast route. A train consisting of three articulated coaches, weighing 115 tons, giving a 4¼ hour service between King's Cross and Newcastle, was proposed. Accommodation on the train would have been inferior to that in an ordinary third-class coach and it was therefore considered unlikely that the novelty of the higher speed of the proposed service would prove sufficiently attractive to justify its introduction. Instead, trials were carried out with a standard Pacific locomotive, which proved that faster over-all times could be maintained, with a train of much greater weight, comfort, and capacity, and the 'Flying Hamburger' concept was therefore dropped. From the investigation, however, emerged the streamlined A4 Class Pacific and the Silver Jubilee train.

The LMS, too, in 1935, developed an articulated three-car set for main-line service, powered by Leyland diesel engines and with hydro-mechanical transmission. With a high power/weight ratio, it had advantages in its rapid acceleration and ability to maintain high speeds on rising gradients, but it could not haul additional traffic, and there were complaints of excessive vibration, the infiltration of diesel fumes, and inadequate heating facilities. The unit was tried out on the Oxford–Bletchley–Cambridge line and subsequently replaced steam on some services between St Pancras and Nottingham, but was finally withdrawn from public service at the end of 1939.

It was, however, the Great Western Railway, when C. B. Collett was Chief Mechanical Engineer, which did most towards the introduction of diesel railcars. From 1934 onwards, the GWR introduced a fleet of 38 vehicles, of which 37 remained in service at the time of nationalization. The units were used mainly on local services but covered also a number of fast business services, principally between Cardiff and Birmingham. The more powerful cars were capable of hauling an additional coach.

The slow development of diesel traction on Britain's railways was in sharp contrast to the progress in this field in the United States, where dieselization was swift. The first diesel locomotives, used for shunting, were put into service in the period 1925–30 and a number of high-speed diesel-electric trains followed the introduction of the Burlington Zephyr, by the Chicago, Burlington and Quincy Railroad, in 1934. The pheno-

Fig. 6.1   Diesel rail-car built for use on the GWR late 1930s (R. M. Tufnell)

menal growth period in diesel traction dated from about 1940, and by 1949 nearly half the passenger and shunting work and one-third of the freight traffic were covered by diesel-electric traction. This trend continued over the next ten years, by which time the majority of the railroads in the country were dieselized. One of the main factors contributing to this rapid progress was the ample indigenous availability of oil, at reasonable prices, which ensured that the railroads would meet no problems in this respect.

Somewhat similar considerations applied in Canada where, after a period of some doubt on the score of availability of oil fuel, there was also a relatively speedy conversion from steam to diesel traction. On the other hand, on the Continent of Europe, where traffic densities and operating conditions were very different from those in North America, financial appraisals of the alternatives to steam indicated that, except for shunting and secondary and branch-line services, electrification was the preferable choice, especially as all oil supplies had to be imported.

The situation in these countries was well known to the British loco-motive engineers. There were frequent contacts with Continental col-leagues and, after the war, British railway teams paid a number of visits to the USA. The joint LMS/LNER visit in 1945 has been referred to in a previous chapter. Southern Railway officers also visited America around that time. Furthermore, there had been a number of papers read at meetings of the Engineering Institutions, which recorded the progress being made towards dieselization on the North American Continent and the improved operating and financial results which were being achieved.

With the ending of the war in 1945, the railways were free to resume a full programme of motive power development. With personal knowledge of diesel traction in the USA acquired by British railway officers during their visits to North America now available, the time had clearly come to gain practical experience of internal combustion engined locomotives in main-line services.

First in the field was the LMS, whose Chief Mechanical and Electrical Engineer, C. E. Fairburn, in 1945 initiated discussions with The British Thompson-Houston Co on the production of a prototype 1500 h.p. locomotive, with a Paxman engine and electric transmission. These negotiations were not completed by the time Fairburn died at the end of 1945 and his successor, H. G. Ivatt, widened the scope of inquiry by bringing Crompton Parkinson and English Electric into the discussions. By May 1946, arrangements had been made with English Electric for the construction of two 1600 h.p. locomotives, the mechanical parts to be built at Derby and the diesel engines and electrical power equipment by the English Electric Company. Special efforts were made to complete at least one of these locomotives before the demise of the LMS on nationalization, and the first (No. 10000) was turned out of Derby Works in December 1947. The second (No. 10001) was placed in service in July 1948. To Ivatt, therefore, and his team, must go the credit for putting into traffic the first diesel main-line locomotive to be designed and built by British Railways.

Ivatt also initiated, in 1946, the design of an 827 h.p. diesel electric locomotive for secondary and branch line services, or for hump shunting work. This (No. 10800) was built by the North British Locomotive Co, with Paxman engine and BTH electrical equipment. It entered service in 1950 and was for some time used for passenger work on the LM Region.

In 1947, Bulleid, of the Southern Railway, was negotiating for the construction of two prototype diesel locomotives, similar to 10000 and 10001, but with the diesel engines up-rated to 1750 h.p. for use on

Fig. 6.2   1600 h.p. CC diesel-electric locomotive No. 10000: the first post-war diesel main-line locomotive to be built for use in Britain: built by the LMS and put into traffic shortly before nationalization (NRM)

subsidiary lines in electrified areas. These locomotives, Nos. 10201 and 10202, authorized by the Southern Railway and built in Southern Region workshops at Brighton, were brought into service in 1950–1. A third SR locomotive (No. 10203), of advanced design and rated at 2000 h.p., should not strictly speaking be included amongst those authorized at the time of nationalization, being designed in conjunction with the English Electric Co in 1951, and put into service in 1954. It was, however, developed as a direct consequence of experience with the two 1750 h.p. locomotives, and therefore formed part of this group of experimental locomotives.

In 1953, the five prototype English Electric locomotives were all allocated to the Southern Region, to secure the benefits which could accrue from concentrated operation and maintenance. Concentration on the LM Region was impracticable, because the two SR locomotives could not accommodate train heating boilers of sufficient capacity to operate the heavy Anglo-Scottish services in winter.

All the locomotives achieved satisfactory – indeed, at times, excellent – performances. Numbers 10000 and 10001, working as a twin-unit on the Anglo-Scottish services, had run 50000 miles in three months; 10201 and 10202 each ran 130000 miles in their first year, mainly on Southern Region services to the west of England; 10800 ran 40000 miles in passenger and freight services in its first year. All of these locomotives were prototypes and inevitably there were technical problems. Nevertheless experience with them provided most valuable information and a sound basis for the preparation of specifications for the initial batch of diesel locomotives ordered under the Modernization Plan.

In 1947, the LNER prepared a scheme for converting the East Coast Anglo-Scottish services to diesel traction, with twenty-five 1600 h.p. diesel-electric locomotives, to be used in pairs, replacing thirty-two Pacific steam locomotives. This project did not, however, materialize. The Great Western Railway acquired two gas-turbine locomotives for trial, to which further reference is made later in this chapter.

Reference has already been made in Chapter Two to the concern which the BTC felt at the lack of progress by the Railway Executive in the preparation of plans for a change from steam to alternative forms of traction, to the setting up of the Harrington Committee in 1948 to investigate the future balance of advantage between the various types of traction for service on BR, and to the recommendation made by that Committee in their report dated October 1951.

The report was forwarded to the BTC in February 1952, after consideration by Riddles and his senior officers. It is of interest to recall the comments which Riddles made in his report to the Railway Executive on 23 January 1952:

(a) Excluding particular cases, where there were overwhelming economic advantages, it seemed clear that the Executive's motive power policy must be founded on coal, which was available within the United Kingdom, rather than on oil, which had to be imported. If this view was accepted, then the clear alternatives for BR were steam traction and electrification.

(b) Electrification would gradually replace steam as justification could be demonstrated, route by route, and as capital became available. This assumed the co-existence of the two forms of motive power for many years ahead. If an orderly and well justified programme of electrification was prepared, then modifications to the annual provision of steam and electric rolling stock would follow naturally, but this required to be done in a manner which would produce the lowest operating costs in steam working during the years in which it still remained. He agreed that further electrification schemes should be planned and costed, although it was a matter for discussion whether King's Cross to Grantham should be the first priority. More immediate and greater financial returns might be gained from concentrating on the electrification of the London, Tilbury, and Southend line, and extension of the Southern Region electrified system east of Portsmouth, and/or other suburban electrifications.

(c) He did not support the recommendation that a comprehensive scheme should be drawn up for a large-scale trial of diesel traction on main-line services, because

(i) of his view that, as part of the national fuel policy, motive power policy should lean towards the use of home-produced coal, rather than imported oil;

(ii) the hope of a large reduction in the first costs of diesel locomotives was illusory. Development costs of the existing prototypes were largely borne by the manufacturers of the diesel engines and electrical equipment and first costs of production models were likely to be three or four times the cost of steam locomotives of comparable power;

(iii) the high annual mileages necessary to bring down operating costs would be difficult to achieve;

(iv) it was unnecessary to build a large fleet of diesel locomotives in order to form a sound opinion of their performance. Sufficient data would be forthcoming from the operation of the five existing prototypes and the sixth which was yet to come;

(v) from the environmental point of view, the smoke or smell from a diesel engine, without good maintenance and handling, could be as objectionable as from a steam locomotive;

(vi) the problem of train heating with diesel locomotives had yet to be overcome; and

(vii) estimates included in the report suggested that, based on the working of Euston–Glasgow express passenger trains, diesel operation would be more costly, per train mile, than steam operation.

(d) He accepted that the diesel shunter was a special case, working as it did in conditions very different from those which obtained on the main line. Even in this case, economical substitution of steam by diesel was only justified in circumstances which permitted two- or three-shift working, with one man on the footplate, and it was on this basis that the Railway Executive had decided on a five-year programme for this form of motive power. The economics of single shift working had not yet been clarified, and if two men were required on the footplate, for trip working, the economics of even two- or three-shift working might be in some doubt.

(e) He noted the recommendations which had been made in regard to the detailed investigation of schemes for the introduction of diesel railcars, and this matter was already under examination by a separate working party.

In April, 1952, a report was submitted to the BTC, by their own staff, dealing with the recommendations of the Harrington Committee and taking into account Riddles' views. Implicit in the report was the conclusion that no more steam locomotives should be built – a conclusion with which the Railway Executive did not agree. They still maintained their opinion that the modern steam locomotive, with its improved availability and utilization, had enabled a significant cut to be made in the fleet and that further steam locomotives should be built to ensure that, over the years during which steam would still be a major factor, full advantage could be taken of the reduced maintenance and operating costs made possible by modern design. The BTC report also disagreed with the Railway Executive in relation to the introduction of diesel main-line locomotives. Whereas the Executive regarded electrification as the most sensible alternative to steam, the BTC supported the concept of a large-scale experiment with diesel main-line locomotives.

As Riddles mentioned in his comments on the BTC report, one of the recommendations of the Harrington Committee was already in process of implementation. The Railway Executive had agreed upon a programme for the construction of a further 162 diesel shunters – mostly 350 h.p. diesel-electric – in the 1952 annual renewal programme. Further programmes followed, bringing the total number of diesel shunting locomotives built up to the end of the Modernization Plan to around 2000, well over half of these being BR/English Electric type 350 h.p. Six of these locomotives were converted in 1965 into three permanently coupled 'master and slave' units, rated at a total of 700 h.p., for hump shunting at Tinsley Yard, Sheffield. The remainder of the comprehensive programme were locomotives of lower power, built in roughly equal proportions by BR and private manufacturers. In the main, the smaller locomotives had mechanical transmission but there were a few, built by NBL, with Voith hydraulic transmissions.

In so far as diesel railcars were concerned, the Railway Executive had acted with commendable promptitude. Already, by the time the Harrington report was passed on to the BTC, a working party of senior officers had been set up to assess the scope for the employment of light-weight trains. This working party recommended, in March 1952, that rail-car operation should be introduced in certain lightly trafficked areas of the country, with priority being given to the Bradford–Leeds–Harrogate–Halifax services in the West Riding of Yorkshire and on lines in West Cumberland. The combination of one-man operation, light-weight stock, and the superior thermal efficiency of the diesel engine were expected to produce very significant savings in operating costs – 26d (about 11p) per mile, all-in, including interest on capital, for a diesel unit, compared with 87d (36·25p) per mile for steam.

By the end of 1952 plans were well advanced for Derby Works to build light-weight vehicles with under-floor engines of the type – Leyland 125 h.p. – used in public service road vehicles. The decision to build stock of this kind had also involved considerable work in the design and provision of new facilities at workshops and also at motive power depots for their maintenance. After the trial runs with the first two-car unit in April 1954 the difficulties experienced with under-floor engines and mechanical transmission, and the modifications which were necessary to achieve anything resembling a reasonable standard of reliability, emphasized to

Fig. 6.3   A Class 08 350 h.p. diesel shunting locomotive: the standard design
in general use on BR (BRB)

Fig. 6.4 One of the earlier diesel multiple unit two-car trains (BRB)

the suppliers of equipment, and to the BR engineers, the extent of the problem to be solved in adapting to rail use, involving steel wheels moving over steel rails, mechanical equipment specifically designed for road use, where cushioned tyres were in contact with tarmac surfaces.

Chapter Four has referred to the content and development of the Modernization Plan. In the traction context, the Plan specified the reasons for the intention to eliminate steam traction. They were

    (a) the growing shortage of large coal suitable for locomotives;

    (b) the insistent demand for a reduction in air pollution by locomotives and for greater cleanliness in trains and at stations;

    (c) the need for better acceleration; and

    (d) the wasteful use of labour on unattractive tasks for which it would be increasingly difficult to find staff.

The relative advantages of electrification and dieselization, in their respective fields, were considered and particular proposals in the latter context were set out.

Reference was made to the then current programme for the construction of diesel shunting locomotives, which would be completed in 1957, and the further programme in preparation. The Plan provided for the elimination of shunting and trip working by steam locomotives and for about 1200 diesel locomotives, additional to those already authorized, to replace approximately 1500 steam locomotives.

The Plan accepted that, where traffic was within their capacity, a considerable improvement in net revenue could be secured from the replacement of steam services by diesel multiple-unit trains, ranging from single units to six-coach trains. It noted that a start had already been made on the introduction of this type of train in various parts of the country. A wide extension of diesel multiple unit working was envisaged, to include three principal types of service: inter-city express services, secondary and cross-country services, and branch-line services. The total number of diesel multiple unit vehicles which could be so employed was estimated at about 4600, including those (300) at that time in use or on order. Subsequent orders were to introduce varying designs of units and manufacturers, and reference to these will be made later in this chapter.

So far as main-line services were concerned, the Plan regarded the introduction of diesel traction as a half-way house to electrification. The point was made that diesel traction yielded many of the advantages of electricity and in addition could be introduced more quickly. It was essentially a flexible form of traction, with a wide range of utility. A very substantial investment was accordingly proposed in diesel main-line locomotives, with the object of achieving, as soon as possible, a complete change-over from steam to diesel traction in specified areas. By this means, the maximum economies would be obtained through the closing of steam motive power depots, and it would also be possible to obtain experience of the operating costs of diesel traction, without mixed working involving the two forms of traction. The intention was to standardize designs of locomotives as much as possible.

By the end of the 15-year period covered by the Plan, it was envisaged that about 2500 main-line diesel locomotives would be in use. For example, in the Western Region it was intended to eliminate all steam working beyond Newton Abbot and also to employ diesel locomotives based in that area for hauling a large proportion of the passenger and freight trains to London and Bristol and back. On the Southern Region, the greatest early advantage would be secured by employing diesel locomotives to replace steam services between Waterloo and Exeter, and between Waterloo, Southampton, Bournemouth, and Weymouth. In these two schemes alone, around 200 main-line diesels would replace over 300 steam locomotives. Changes to diesel traction would also be progressively implemented in other areas.

The extension of the use of diesel shunting locomotives, and the introduction of diesel multiple units on branch line and secondary services, were completely logical decisions, which the Railway Executive, had it still been in existence, would have whole-heartedly supported. Indeed, it had been responsible for initiating and pressing on with these changes.

The choice of diesel main-line locomotives presented a much greater problem than the selection of multiple units or diesel shunting locomotives. Only seven such locomotives were in existence in the United Kingdom at the time of the Modernization Plan – the five English Electric locomotives, the North British 827 h.p. locomotive, previously referred to, and the Fell locomotive, which will be mentioned later. To Bond, who had been appointed Chief Officer (Mechanical Engineering) – later, Chief Mechanical Engineer – in 1953, fell the responsibility, in consultation with Warder on the electrical side, for the preparation of specifications for the locomotives to be ordered, the securing of tenders, and the submission of proposals to the British Transport Commission.

It was an essential feature of the comprehensive trials which were to be carried out that the locomotives to be ordered initially should be capable of covering the whole range of traffic operations on the railways. In the first instance, it was the intention that this range of work should be covered by three groups of locomotives – 800/1000 h.p., 1100/1250 h.p., 2000 h.p. Later, this grouping was extended to five in number, to cater for two classes of locomotive with hydraulic transmission – 1000 h.p. and 2000/2200 h.p. – and the 2000 h.p. group with electrical transmission was extended to include locomotives operating at 2300 h.p.

The specifications which were prepared allowed contractors considerable freedom in regard to detail design, except in regard to certain features, which were closely defined:

(a) axle loads were to be within the range 16–20 tons;
(b) the total weight, wheel spacing, and overall dimensions were specified, to comply with permissible loading on bridges and to ensure as wide a route availability as possible;
(c) maximum speed, over the range of types, was to be 75–90 miles/h;
(d) the design of the bogies to be adopted was laid down.

Experience with the riding of the Manchester–Sheffield–Wath electric locomotives showed that for speeds up to 75 miles/h the design of heavily loaded four-wheeled bogies called for a great deal of further development. It was in this context, however, that experience with the LMS and SR prototype locomotives was particularly useful, especially in relation to the bogies for the Type 4 English Electric and BR/Sulzer locomotives. In these cases the choice lay between the LMS double bolster bogie and pony truck and a straightforward adaptation of the eight-wheeled SR bogie. This later design was chosen for the new builds of the types in question. The Swindon-built diesel-hydraulic locomotives were fitted with a German design of bogie, which, however, was not as successful on BR lines as it was in Germany.

Invitations to tender were sent to all British locomotive building firms, to three in the USA, one in Canada, and one in Australia. More than 200 separate proposals were received, with wide variations in performance characteristics, axle loadings, and total weights. The wide range of possibilities which came forward reinforced the view, already taken, based on advice from America and confirmed by British experience with diesel shunting locomotives, that the greatest benefit would accrue from maximum standardization in design and power ranges. At the same time, the designs selected had to provide sufficient breadth of experience to enable decisions to be taken on the designs and power ranges on which to standardize.

Whilst consideration was being given to the specifications for the initial build, thoughts were directed to the possible adoption of alternative forms of transmission. There was evidence that the hydraulic and hydro-mechanical transmissions adopted as standard by the German Federal Railways might prove to be an acceptable alternative to electric trans-mission, particularly in view of the claims made for them, namely lighter construction and lower first and maintenance costs. The diesel-hydraulic shunting locomotives already in service, built by North British Loco-motive Co, had given promising results; trials had been carried out in Scotland with a locomotive built by the firm for use in Mauritius; and, at their own expense, they had prepared preliminary designs for 1000 and 2000 h.p. locomotives suitable for British requirements. Senior Officers of the Western Region had also shown an interest in this form of trans-mission and Bond, Cox, and two Regional Officers – R. A. Smeddle, the Chief Mechanical Engineer, and H. H. Phillips, Assistant General Manager – visited Germany and confirmed the view that this form of equipment could present an acceptable alternative form of transmission.

Having considered all the tenders which had been submitted, and the range of designs necessary to provide performance data for later stan-dardization, Bond recommended the construction of 174 locomotives, incorporating engines from seven manufacturers, transmissions from eight, and mechanical parts from seven. Details are given in Table 6.1

No locomotives were ordered from General Motors. The firm offered to adapt two locomotives for use on BR and send them, free, to the United Kingdom, for trial purposes, but the Commission found themselves unable to accept this offer, because of Government restrictions on dollar spending. On the other hand, General Motors were not prepared at that time to grant a licence to any manufacturers in the United Kingdom to build to their designs.

The first of the 174 locomotives – a type 1 English Electric 1000 h.p. was delivered in June 1957 and was allocated to the London Midland Region. The remaining locomotives were delivered during the next two years, with the last one, a 2300 h.p. type 4 built at Derby coming into traffic in 1960, by which time a considerable number of additional locomotives from subsequent programmes – a total of 421 by the end of 1959 – had been delivered.

At the time the orders were placed for the first batch of diesel main-line locomotives it was recommended by the BTC Officers concerned – and accepted by the Commission – that no further orders should be placed for three years. Delivery periods quoted for the new locomotives varied from 15 to 24 months, and if these dates were met there would be from 1 to 1¾ years available for trial running, assessment of operating performance,

Table 6.1   The Initial Build of Diesel Main Line Locomotives

Type	Subsequent classification	h.p.	Wheel arrangement	Mechanical parts	Engine	Transmission	No. to be built
Diesel-electric							
1	15	800	BB	Clayton	Paxman	BTH	10
	16	800	BB	NBL	Paxman	GEC	10
	20	1000	BB	Eng. Elec.	EE	EE	20
2	21	1000	BB	NBL	MAN	GEC	10
	23	1100	BB	EE	EE	EE	10
	24	1160	BB	BR	Sulzer	BTH	20
	26	1160	BB	Birmingham Rly C&W	Sulzer	Crompton Parkinson	20
	28	1200	CB	Met. Vickers	Crossley	MV	20
	30	1250	A1A A1A	Brush	Mirrlees	Brush	20
4	40	2000	1CC1	EE	EE	EE	10
	44	2300	1CC1	BR	Sulzer	Crompton P.	10
Diesel-hydraulic							
2	22	1000	BB	NBL	MAN	Voith	6
4	41	2200	A1A A1A	NBL	MAN	Voith	5
	42	2200	BB	BR	Maybach	Mekydro	3
Total							174

and evaluation of financial aspects – by no means too long a period. During the same period, also, an assessment had to be made of the longer term requirements to meet the operating needs of the Regions. Experience in fact showed that, from the technical and cost points of view,

Fig. 6.5   One of the initial builds of diesel-electric locomotives: the English Electric 2000 h.p., Type 4 (BR/Oxford Publishing Co)

three years would have been too short a period for a number of inherent weaknesses in design to come to light.

In the event, the Commission retracted on their undertaking to allow three years for consideration of the standardized designs which were to follow. In July 1956, the Members discussed a report on Passenger Traffic Policy and agreed to consider requests for additional diesel main-line locomotives, provided that there was sufficient technical evidence to show that the types of locomotive requested were fully able to meet the requirements of the services for which they were intended, and that substitution of steam by diesel locomotives was economically justified by the manner in which they would be operated. At this stage, therefore, the need to prove the locomotives in the first batch was still recognized. In May 1957, however, the Commission became concerned at the deteriorating financial situation and decided – even before any of the initial batch had been delivered – that accelerated provision of diesel locomotives and the quicker withdrawal of steam was the high road to financial stability. In reaching this decision, the Commission stated that they would be prepared to go further than they had already gone in regard to ordering diesel main-line locomotives, in spite of the risk of unsatisfactory performance in the early stages. This would be on the basis of plans presented by the Regions, which should provide for the absolute minimum of types and makes of locomotives and for a concentration of diesel traction in specified areas so as to eliminate steam locomotive working and maintenance. The decision, which was strongly resisted by the Chief Mechanical and Electrical Engineers, frustrated the purpose of the three-year trial period, which was intended to provide a basis upon which the number of locomotive types could be reduced to a minimum and to ensure that they were completely capable of meeting the requirements

Fig. 6.6   Two Brush type 2 locomotives at work in Temple Mills Yard (BRB)

which the operators placed upon them. Instead, to meet the new situation, a good deal of personal judgement had to come into the decision as to what further types should be built.

The failure to adhere to a reasonably long trial period before further orders were placed resulted in unnecessary additional expense, at a later date, when the need for modifications became apparent. Furthermore, the subsequent deliveries of diesel locomotives were made at such a rate that the Regions' ability to maintain them properly was overwhelmed. In consequence, performance was unreliable and the early stages of diesel operation were inevitably attended by dissatisfaction and disappointment within the railways, complaints from the public and arguments with the contractors.

The decision by the Commission to abandon the three-year trial period and insist on a considerable speed-up in the rate of dieselization inevitably created problems for engineering and operating officers, both at HQ and in the Regions. The Commission demanded that Regional requirements should be related to particular traffic schemes. In order that such schemes should be comparable one with another, the engineering officers at BTC HQ issued a code of practice to be followed by all Regions in submitting their proposals. This called for main-line locomotive schemes to be compiled separately from those for multiple units and laid down the financial, operating, and maintenance data to be used in assessing the overall results under existing and prospective conditions.

A Main Line Diesel Locomotive Panel was set up under Bond in April 1955, to obtain from General Managers their long-term requirements for diesel locomotives, and to consider these in relation to potential supply. The Panel found that Regional plans contemplated numbers of locomotives quite beyond the capacity of both the railway workshops and the private contractors, particularly in so far as power equipments were concerned. They recommended, therefore, that, in the submission of schemes, the principles to be followed should be that

(a) plans prepared by the Regions should provide for the progressive elimination of steam from complete areas or services;

(b) for the first three years' programme (1958–60), authorization should not exceed the number of diesel locomotives required to replace steam locomotives which were in the normal course due for withdrawal, except that additional locomotives should be authorized if they were an essential part of an electrification scheme due for completion by the end of 1960, or if spare capacity still remained in any of the railway workshops;

(c) in subsequent years, the number of diesel locomotives to be built should be those required for planned schemes for progressive introduction, area by area, subject to economic justification;

(d) an interim stage of dieselization should not be proposed on routes planned for electrification before 1970, unless such an interim stage could be financially justified in itself and would not prejudice completion of the later electrification; and

(e) priorities should be established as between different types of loco-motives – electric, diesel, steam – in the event of the numbers of diesel locomotives scheduled for authorization exceeding building capacity or the permissible level of expenditure. In this context, steam locomotives for freight and mixed traffic services would not be authorized at all, unless diesel-electric power equipments were not available in sufficient numbers to utilize capacity in railway shops and there was a proven need for such locomotives to maintain or improve services pending ultimate electrification or conversion to diesel traction.

A further primary requirement was a clear statement of the factors upon which the future selection of diesel locomotives should be based. A report, 'Selection of Diesel Locomotive Types', was therefore prepared in mid-1956 by Cox, Bond's Principal Assistant, on technical aspects of the choice of types, comparing the traction characteristics of steam and diesel locomotives – five diesel power ranges replacing nine steam motive power classes – and setting out the relative merits of single and multiple locomotive operation. That guidance was very necessary in this latter area was evident from the fact that there existed a clear difference of view as to whether locomotives should be matched, in terms of power, to the different categories of work to be carried out or whether there should be a greater degree of concentration on locomotive types of lower and medium power, to be used in multiple on classes of work beyond their individual capacities. Whilst the latter course was beneficial, from the point of view of maximum standardization of types and from the high degree of utilization which would be achievable, experience with the two LMS 1600 h.p. diesel locomotives, and the quotations received from manufacturers for the first build of locomotives under the Modernization Plan, showed that the overall cost of two or more locomotives would be substantially greater than that of one locomotive designed to produce the same output. Moreover, overall weight and length would be greater. Table 6.2 demonstrates the comparison between single loco-motive working and double-heading, based on information received from contractors in quotations submitted for the first batch of diesel locomotives.

It was obviously right that, in the long term, if properly based economic cases were to be presented for expansion of dieselization, the number of types ordered for use should be reduced to a minimum. The difficulty, at that stage, was deciding of what that minimum should consist, bearing in mind the limited information on performance which could be accumulated in the short time available.

The matter was, however, dealt with by Bond and Warder in a report, in July 1957, entitled 'Limitations of Variety'. In this report, they set out

Table 6.2   Comparison between Single Locomotive
Working and Double-heading

Total power requirement: h.p.	Locomotive units available: h.p.	Weight: tons	Length: feet	Cost: £000
1000–1200	1000	72	50	68
1500–1700	1500	114	60	80
2000–2400	2000	134	64	100
	1000 + 1000	144	100	136
2500–2800	1000 + 1500	186	110	148
3000–3600	3000	110	70	140
	1500 + 1500	228	120	160
	1000 + 1000 + 1000	216	150	204

the principles on which they had based their recommendations, namely
that
 (a) the primary objective was reliability and all questions of relative
     efficiency, weights, and types of equipment must be subservient to
     this over-riding need;
 (b) given reliable power equipment and mechanical parts, availability
     would be best promoted by the highest degree of standardization.
     Ideally, this would be achieved by
      (i) a single series of mechanical parts, highly standardized as to
          detail;
     (ii) one basic engine design, using standard components, the
          power of the engine being determined by the number of
          cylinders of common size;
    (iii) transmission and control gear, electric or hydraulic, being con-
          fined to the least possible variety of components;
     (iv) all locomotives (subject to whether electric or hydraulic trans-
          mission) being capable of multiple running without restriction;
          and
      (v) driving controls being so standardized as to simplify the train-
          ing of footplate staff;
 (c) since under British conditions it was manifestly impossible to
     obtain sufficient productive capacity from one firm only, and con-
     siderable time must elapse before other firms could undertake
     construction of a selected firm's equipment under licence (even if
     they were willing to do so) it would be necessary in the first instance
     to specify more than one make of power equipment, but the
     number so specified must be kept to the minimum;
 (d) the choice of power equipments should be made in accordance
     with certain priorities, namely

(i) those designed and manufactured in the United Kingdom;

(ii) those of foreign origin but manufactured in this country; and

(iii) those of foreign design and manufacture already on order, in respect of which it might be possible to arrange manufacture in this country;

(e) the high-speed light-weight diesel engine of German origin should be confined to equipments on the Western Region, pending further experience; and

(f) the standardization of renewable parts should be pursued to the utmost, within the selected locomotive types.

It was in mind that about 500 diesel main-line locomotives would be needed in the second batch, in the 1959 building programme, and no one contractor could provide engines on that scale. It was, however, possible to limit recommendations to two types of engine (English Electric and Sulzer) and three types of electric transmissions (English Electric, British Thomson-Houston, and Crompton Parkinson), for all Regions other than the Western.

Also contained in the 'Limitation of Variety' report were strong re-commendations in regard to means of standardization on chassis con-struction and mechanical parts. The recommendations in regard to mechanical parts, however, were not accepted, mainly because of pres-sure from manufacturers that they should be permitted to produce their own designs of equipment, as selected BR standards, to provide them with a 'shop window' for export purposes.

The exception to the standardization rule was the Western Region, who were allowed to continue their interest in diesel-hydraulic locomotives. The General Manager of the Region (K. W. C. Grand) put forward a strong case for further diesel-hydraulic locomotives to be built. Less cost, less weight, and less training necessary to convert from steam to diesel-hydraulic than from steam to diesel-electric operation were the main supporting arguments. A further build of diesel-hydraulic locomotives was therefore authorized, with some misgivings, in February 1957. Later in the same year, the Region asked for further locomotives with hydraulic transmissions. New types – Class 35, 1700 h.p. Beyer Peacock/Maybach/ Mekydro BB and Class 52, 2700 h.p. BR/Maybach/Voith CC – in due course emerged and were built in appreciable numbers. Before long, the instinctive misgivings which had been felt earlier were confirmed. Prices rose vis-à-vis diesel-electrics; the weight advantage was dissipated; and there were maintenance difficulties. In 1959, despite pressure from Paddington, a stop was put on further diesel-hydraulic development when the question of inter-Regional running with diesel-electric loco-motives on the LM Region, over the Birmingham–Bristol route, became an issue.

To the last, the Western Region engineers maintained their preference for the diesel hydraulics. They contested the view expressed in a report

Fig. 6.7   A Type 4, Class 42 (Warship class) diesel-hydraulic locomotive as running on the Western Region until 1972 (BR/Oxford Publishing Co)

dated May 1966, by J. F. Harrison, then Chief Engineer (Traction and Rolling Stock), that persistent and expensive troubles with the diesel-hydraulics were primarily due to lack of adequate design of equipment purchased direct from Germany or from licencees in the United Kingdom. Nevertheless no-one can doubt the wisdom of ceasing production of a different type of locomotive, restricted to service on one only of the (then) six Regions. The last of the diesel hydraulics No. 1023 *Western Fusilier*, was withdrawn in April 1977, and is preserved in the National Railway Museum at York.

The plan which the LNER developed in 1947 for the introduction of diesel locomotives on the GN main line, though not acceptable at that time, was revived some fourteen years later. In 1934, the firm of D. Napier and Son acquired the development rights of an aircraft engine produced in Germany and first used in a Junkers aircraft in 1929. After the Second World War, English Electric, who had in the meantime absorbed Napiers within their organization, were asked by the Admiralty to develop an engine suitable to power fast patrol boats. Based on the original German design, they developed an eighteen-cylinder engine, rated at 2500 h.p., the eighteen cylinders being arranged in three banks of six, at 60° to each other, with a crankshaft at each corner of the resulting triangular structure. Development of this engine, to be known as the 'Deltic', began in 1947, the first engine ran in 1950, and sea trials took place in 1952.

Sir George Nelson, Chairman of the English Electric Company, foreseeing the need for express passenger locomotives of greater power than those of 2300 h.p. included in the Modernization Plan, in 1955 authorized, as a private venture, the design and construction of a CC type locomotive, weighing 106 tons (compared with 130 tons for the 2300 h.p. locomotive), powered by two 'Deltic' engines providing up to 3300 h.p. At that time, it was the most powerful diesel locomotive in the United Kingdom and remained so for a further decade, until the 4000 h.p. prototype Kestrel locomotive was built by Brush/Sulzer, in the mid-1960s.

The prototype Deltic went into service on the LM Region in November 1955, mainly on fast freight trains between London and Liverpool. It was withdrawn from service for minor modifications, before resuming further trials in the autumn of 1956, on passenger services between London and Liverpool and on the West Coast route to Carlisle. The LM Region showed no great enthusiasm for the Deltic. Harrison, who was then CM & EE of the LM Region, took the view that high speed engines – the Deltic operated at 1500 rev/min – were unsuitable for traction purposes, in which field the norm was for engines operating at around 850 rev/min.

It so happened that around this time (1957) the Eastern and North Eastern Regions had submitted proposals for the electrification of the East Coast route, proposals which, in the event, were not agreed by the Commission. G. F. Fiennes, the then Line Traffic Manager, Great Northern, who had been brought up to believe in the LNER's big-engine policy, had found that the English Electric Type 4 2000 h.p. locomotives introduced on to the East Coast route were insufficiently powerful to meet his proposed requirements and he turned to the possibility of using Deltic locomotives instead, in his efforts to stem the loss in revenue which was taking place on these services. He produced a scheme under which twenty-three Deltics would give a much improved service and at the same time displace fifty-five steam locomotives. At first, these proposals met with some opposition, due to the fact that the maximum speed of the locomotives (105 miles/h) could not be used owing to line speed restrictions; and the need which would arise for some structural alterations to the platforms at King's Cross. So far as the maximum speed was concerned, stretches of the East Coast route within the Eastern Region were then in the process of being upgraded to permit of speeds of up to 100 miles/h, in anticipation of electrification, and this objection was therefore not sustainable. The Eastern Region management was also reluctant to adopt the proposals, because they felt that the introduction of Deltic working would inevitably delay electrification. In time, however, and following an approach by Sir George Nelson to the Chairman, the Commission gave authority in May 1959 for the construction of twenty-two locomotives, to be delivered during 1960/61.

Trial running with the prototype on the Eastern Region started early in 1959, between King's Cross and Doncaster, and both running and braking tests were generally satisfactory, although the need emerged for some modifications – particularly to the bogies and the steam heating boilers. The production units were seven tons lighter and had a wider route availability than the prototype. Twenty locomotives were delivered between March 1961 and the end of the year, and the remaining two by April 1962. The accelerated services which Fiennes was so eagerly seeking were introduced from September onwards. An availability of 88·5 per cent was achieved in the second year and since then these locomotives have given outstanding service and have proved to be one of the major successes of the changeover to diesel traction.

Because the Deltic was a highly rated engine it required specialized maintenance and more frequent overhaul than the conventional slower speed engines. For the first time, therefore, the contract for the construction of the locomotives provided for a maintenance period of five years from the delivery of the first locomotive, during which the English Electric Company would supervise the depot maintenance of the engines and electrical equipment and would themselves undertake the periodical overhaul of the engines. It was impracticable for these to be overhauled in situ and the work was therefore carried out on a unit replacement basis, the engines for overhaul being returned to the firm's works for attention. The overhaul programme and the provision of spare engines was arranged to secure that no more than one locomotive was out of service waiting engines at any one time. Work to be undertaken under the contract was confined to major overhaul or repair arising from normal wear and tear, design modifications, defective workmanship or defective material. The Company undertook, unless prevented by factors outside its control or by any failure on the part of the Commission, to ensure that

Fig. 6.8 A 3300 h.p. Deltic locomotive – the most powerful diesel-electric locomotive in service on BR at that time – working The Flying Scotsman on 13 April 1962, in the train's centenary year. The train is seen crossing Welwyn Viaduct on its northward run to Edinburgh (BRB)

the 22 locomotives were available to operate an aggregate diagrammed mileage of 4·5 million per annum during the maintenance period, provided that no single locomotive was rostered to work more than 220 000 miles per annum. The overhaul contract continued in being for some ten years, after which the work was undertaken in the railway workshops at Doncaster.

The introduction of diesel locomotives and multiple unit trains inevitably involved radical changes in the equipment at main works, as well as in day-to-day servicing and maintenance facilities at motive power depots. Even with the promise of a three-year standstill period for trials with main-line locomotives, the task of ensuring that the requisite maintenance facilities would be available by the time they were required would have been a difficult one. The fact that the three-year trial period was abandoned made the task even more difficult within the time available. So far as new motive power depots were concerned, a Committee was established to specify standard layouts, to which all proposals put forward by the Regions should conform.

The widespread introduction of diesel traction posed many problems. There was the question of organization. Steam locomotives were maintained by the Motive Power Department. Responsibility for the main-

Fig. 6.9   An interior view of the Diesel Maintenance Depot at Stratford, Eastern Region, showing two of the three working levels. The locomotives in the picture are an English Electric Type 4 and a Brush Type 2 (BR/Oxford Publishing Co)

Fig. 6.10   The new Laira diesel depot Plymouth (BRB)

tenance of the relatively few diesel locomotives and diesel multiple units then in service rested jointly upon the Motive Power Department and CM & EE Department, the electrical work involved being covered by electricians from the Outdoor Machinery Section of the Regional CM & EE's organization. In some areas, the maintenance of electric multiple unit stock was also involved. Some changes in organization were clearly necessary. Bond and his officers took the view that all day-to-day maintenance should be the responsibility of one Department, and that the Motive Power Department should retain its separate identity and be responsible for all running maintenance work – steam, while it still existed, diesel, and electric. The Commission, however, decided that the Motive Power Department should be absorbed into the Operating Department, as the new forms of traction were introduced, area by area, but that the Depot Managers should be responsible for maintenance to standards laid down by the CM & EEs. From the technical maintenance point of view this was a satisfactory solution to the problem, but the divided responsibility of the Depot Managers to the Operating and CM & EE Departments not unnaturally caused difficulties.

It was of course necessary to compile comprehensive schedules laying down periodical and mileage examinations and day-to-day maintenance at Motive Power Depots. In this important work, the CM & EE Department received much valuable advice from the manufacturers in respect of their engines and power equipment.

The switch to diesel traction entailed a considerable amount of training, of both drivers and maintenance staff. Maintenance staff attended courses arranged by the manufacturers at their Works and each Region established its own training schools for both categories of staff. At Derby, a Diesel Training School was set up at the Railway Training Centre in September 1956, with courses for groups of officers and supervisors from the Motive Power and the CM & EE Departments, and supervisors from the Main Works.

There were those, both in the United Kingdon and abroad, who, prior to the introduction of diesel traction, took the view that men brought up with steam locomotives would be quite incapable of conversion to the operation and maintenance of this new form of traction. Events proved them to be quite wrong. On the contrary, the aptitude displayed by footplate and maintenance staff was one of the most remarkable features of the change from steam to diesel traction.

Continuous scrutiny of the performance of the locomotives was maintained by the Diesel Development Unit, established at Derby in June 1956 to provide a focal point for recording and analysing statistics and information on general mechanical performance, from which to draw conclusions as to what was needed to be done to improve reliability and reduce maintenance costs. Based on the information thus available, decisions could be taken with confidence regarding the classes of locomotives to be included in future building programmes and those for which no further orders would be placed. In the latter category, the decision taken was that the North British/Paxman Type 1 (Class 16), the English Electric Type 2 (Class 23), the Metropolitan–Vickers/Crossley Type 2 (Class 28), and the North British/MAN Type 4 (Class 41) should not be repeated.

From 1961 onwards, until the Modernization Plan period ended in 1970, the old types which were repeated, and the new types which were introduced, were as set out in Table 6.3:

Table 6.3   Diesel Main Line Locomotives: Existing Types repeated and New Types introduced during Currency of Modernization Plan

Type	Class	h.p.	Wheel arrange- ment	Mechanical parts	Engine	Transmission	No. built	Year new types intro- duced
1	14	650	0–6–0	BR	Paxman	Hyd. (Voith)	56	1964
	15 (i)	800	BB	Clayton	Paxman	Elec. (BTH)	34	—
	17	900	BB	Clayton/ Beyer P.	Paxman	Elec. (GEC/CP)	117	1962
	20 (i)	1000	BB	EE	EE	Elec. (EE)	208	—
2	21 (i) (ii)	1000	BB	NBL	MAN	Elec. (GEC)	48	—
	22 (i)	1000	BB	NBL	MAN	Hyd. (Voith)	52	—

Type	Class	h.p.	Wheel arrange-ment	Mechanical parts	Engine	Transmission	No. built	Year new types intro-duced
	24 (i)	1160	BB	BR	Sulzer	Elec. (BTH)	} 458	—
	25	1250	BB	BR/Beyer Peacock	Sulzer	Elec. (AEI)		1961
	26 (i)	1160	BB			Elec. (CP)	} 96	—
				BRCW	Sulzer			—
	27	1250	BB			Elec. (GEC)		1961
	30 (i) (iii)	1250 1365	A1A A1A	Brush	Mirrlees	Elec. (Brush)	243	—
3	33	1550	BB	BRCW	Sulzer	Elec. (CP)	98	1960
	35	1700	BB	Beyer Peacock	Maybach	Hyd. (Mekydro)	101	1961
	37	1750	CC	EE	EE	Elec. (EE)	309	1960
4	40 (i)	2000	1CC1	EE	EE	Elec. (EE)	190	—
	42 (i)	2200	BB	BR	Maybach	Hyd. (Mekydro)	35	—
	43	2200	BB	NBL	MAN	Hyd. (Voith)	33	1960
	44 (i)	2300	1CC1	BR	Sulzer	Elec. (CP)	127	—
	45	2500						1960
	46	2500	1CC1	BR	Sulzer	Elec. (Brush)	56	1961
	47 (iv)	2750	CC	Brush/BR	Sulzer	Elec. (Brush)	512	1962
	50	2700	CC	EE	EE	Elec. (EE)	50	1967
	52	2700	CC	BR	Maybach	Hyd. (Voith)	74	1961
5	55	3300	CC	EE	EE	Elec. (EE)	22	1961
Total							2919	

Notes:
(i) Existing types: number built includes those in initial build of 174.
(ii) Some of this class were later re-engined with Paxman 'Valenta' 1350 h.p. engines, and became Class 29.
(iii) Class 31 when re-engined with 1470 h.p. English Electric engines, in 1965/69.
(iv) Subsequently derated to 2580 h.p. (1966/72).

A team of BR senior officers went to the United States in 1957 and were able to see at first hand the massive increase in diesel operation which had taken place since the previous visit ten years earlier. In 1947, some 27 per cent of passenger workings had been covered by diesel locomotives; by 1957, this figure had risen to 91 per cent. Similarly, on freight and shunting work the use of diesel locomotives had risen from 12 per cent to 88 per cent, and from 32 per cent to 93 per cent respectively. It was evident that the principles on which British Railways were working for the operation and maintenance of diesel locomotives were broadly in line with the practices followed in the USA, although the Americans had reached the stage of development and experience where they were finding it possible to increase the periods between routine examinations and Main Works repairs. A particular advantage which applied in the USA, but not in the UK, was that a large majority of the diesel locomotives were obtained from one manufacturer – General Motors.

With regard to diesel multiple units, reference has already been made to the plans for their introduction in place of steam-hauled trains, on selected secondary services, and to the design and construction of the vehicles required. Thereafter, a massive programme of construction was begun.

During 1954 a full scale review of requirements for diesel railcars was undertaken. This indicated a demand for a great multiplicity of types and some rationalization of stated requirements was necessary before specifications could be prepared for issue to manufacturers. Prior to this, 150 h.p. British United Traction and 180 h.p. Rolls Royce engines had become available, and their higher power enabled steel to be used in body construction, thus avoiding the use of expensive light alloys. Following the review, tenders were sought for open type motor and trailer vehicles, in both 57 ft and 63 ft 6 in lengths, with five different seating layouts in each size. The vehicles were to conform to the normal loading gauge and to sustain an evenly distributed vertical loading equivalent to three times the normal load of seated passengers and luggage. Bogies of 8 ft 6 in wheelbase with 3 ft diameter wheels and roller bearing axleboxes were specified. Under-floor engines giving a power-weight ratio for motor car and trailer of 6 : 1 and for motor car alone of 10 : 1 were to be installed, with fuel capacity for at least 500 miles. Maximum speed was to be 65 miles/h; and a one-man control system permitting up to eight vehicles to run in multiple was to be provided.

So far as heating was concerned considerations of weight and space precluded the inclusion of a steam heating boiler and water supply, whilst electric heating would have required a generator on each car, which would have absorbed something of the order of 70 h.p. An automatic oil-fired heating system, not requiring the attention of the guard, was therefore specified. This was, however, a constant source of complaint, arising from indifferent motor performance, ignition difficulties and a smell of burning oil due to the proximity of the heater and ventilation air intakes. Improved equipment was installed in later builds and some of the earlier vehicles were modified.

Tenders were submitted by a number of private builders and British Railways Workshops. A series of orders was placed in 1954–5 for services in rural areas, including East Anglia, Northumberland, and Lincolnshire, and to avoid delays due to waiting power equipments, arrangements were made to control the allocation of engines and transmissions between the approved vehicle suppliers and the railway workshops, so making the best use of the available capacity. So far as British Railways were concerned, the construction of diesel multiple units was concentrated on Derby and Swindon, except those for the Southern Region, which were built at Eastleigh.

By the end of 1970, at the termination of the Modernization Plan period, there were 3621 diesel multiple unit vehicles in service, including diesel-electric units on the Southern Region, against the 4600 called for by the plan. In the meantime there had been a large measure of standardization of power equipments, namely

BUT (Leyland	: 125 h.p.
BUT (Leyland)	: 150 h.p.
BUT (Leyland/Albion)	: 230 h.p.
BUT (AEC)	: 150 h.p.
Rolls Royce	: 180 h.p.
Rolls Royce	: 238 h.p.

Most of the units were fitted with Leyland 150 h.p. equipment. Transmission was by mechanical gear box in conjunction with a fluid flywheel, except for the vehicles with Rolls Royce 238 h.p. engines which had Rolls Royce 'Twin disc' torque converter transmission, and the initial light-weight cars which had a Lysholm-Smith type of torque converter transmission. The exception to this range of power equipments was the Eastleigh-built stock for use on the Hastings and Hampshire services, which were fitted with 600 h.p. English Electric above-floor engines and electric transmission.

Standard types of units were evolved, as set out in Table 6.4

Additionally, 22 two-axled railbuses were purchased in the mid-1950s, for use on lines of very light traffic. These included vehicles built by Wickhams, AC Cars, Park Royal Vehicles, and Bristol Commercial Vehicles, and by a German firm. None of these proved to be satisfactory and they were all withdrawn from public service by the end of 1961. There were also eleven other two-axled vehicles built by Park Royal which normally operated in sets of three, all of which were withdrawn in the 1960s.

A further development in diesel operation was the introduction of the 'Blue Pullmans' on the LM and Western Regions in 1960/61. These were 'de luxe' trains and are referred to more fully in Chapter Eight.

Undoubtedly, the rapid introduction of diesel traction and, consequently, the rate at which maintenance procedures and facilities had to be planned and provided, imposed a very heavy burden upon the mechanical and electrical engineering staffs, both at HQ and in the Regions. This was intensified by the many technical problems which arose during the early (and indeed the not-so-early) days of diesel operation. There were transmission failures and problems with engine frame, cylinder liner, and piston head fractures, largely arising from metal fatigue. This is not, however, a book which attempts to list all the

Table 6.4   Standard Types of Diesel Multiple Units

Type of service	Length	Accommodation	No. of body-shell types	No. of internal arrangements
Low density (branch line, feeder and cross-country services)	57 ft	Two or three passenger doors each side; gangwayed; open seating (5 across, second; 4 across, first).	3	6
Low density (branch line, feeder and cross-country services)	63 ft 6 in	Two or three passenger doors each side; gangwayed; open seating (4 across, second; 3 across, first); miniature buffet, if required	4	4
High density (mainly suburban)	63 ft 6 in	Passenger doors between each pair of seats; open or compartment seating (5 across, second; 4 across, first); not gangwayed	7	6
Inter-City	63 ft 6 in	Two or three passenger doors each side; gangwayed; open or compartment seating (4 or 5 across, second; 3 or 4 across, first); miniature buffet, buffet or kitchen restaurant	12	21

technical difficulties which arose, or to explain what action was taken to put them right. Suffice it to call brief attention to some of the factors which contributed to the difficulties which the engineers faced at that time. The unreliability of steam heating boilers and the difficulties experienced with some designs of engines may be quoted as examples. It was found necessary for certain types of locomotives to be completely re-engined. Reviews carried out in 1961 showed that none of the diesel locomotives in use at that time were anywhere near achieving the miles per casualty obtained with equivalent classes of steam locomotives. On the other hand, the daily mileage of diesel locomotives in stock was appreciably higher.

At the time the diesel main-line locomotives were introduced, BR coaching stock was equipped with steam heating only. Short, therefore, of the conversion of all hauled stock to electric heating, there was no option but to put steam heating boilers on the locomotives. Unfortunately there was no really reliable heating equipment of this type available, at that time, either in the United Kingdom or overseas, and the boilers were a constant source of trouble, quite apart from the fact that, during the heating season, many workings which might otherwise have been single-manned had to have two men on the footplate one of whom had to give constant attention to the steam heating boiler.

A number of investigations were carried out, jointly with the suppliers of the equipment, to find a means of improving the heating arrangements. The situation was, however, never completely resolved until, with the electrification of the West Coast main line, a start was made on fitting coaching stock with electric heating facilities. A formal decision was then taken by the BRB to standardize on electric heating on all loco-motive-hauled coaching stock.

Serious problems arose with Mirrlees, MAN, Maybach, and some Sulzer engines. Mirrlees engines of 1250 h.p., with which the Brush Type 2 (Class 30) locomotives were equipped when built, developed fractures in the cylinder block and crankcase structure. The locomotives were re-engined with English Electric 1470 h.p. engines between 1965 and 1969, the Mirrlees engines being sold back to the firm. The difficulties with the MAN engine were largely due to two factors: excessive oil consumption created fires in the exhaust manifold and thermal cracking of piston crowns and high exhaust temperatures gave insufficient margin for reliability. The cylinder heads of the Maybach engines developed thermal cracks, resulting in coolant leaks and subsequent damage. The Sulzer engines performed well as originally designed for 2300 h.p. and gave reasonable service when they were uprated to 2500 h.p., but when they were further uprated to 2750 h.p. they gave serious and continual trouble, due to fatigue fractures in the engine structure. The whole fleet was subsequently de-rated to 2580 h.p.

The exceptionally cold winter of 1962–3 brought particular problems, due to freezing of the coolant water and continuing difficulties with the steam heating boilers. During the spring and summer of 1963 a series of investigations took place into the means of avoiding such troubles in the future and there was a considerable programme of 'winterization' modifi-cations, no less than 2000 locomotives being modified to give extra pro-tection against damage by frost.

Over the years, since the Second World War, both before and after the BTC decision to move away from steam traction, a number of specialized diesel and gas turbine locomotives were built and tried out, either in static tests or in running. The British locomotive building industry, jointly with the diesel engine makers, were in the forefront of this initiative. They were concerned to demonstrate their ability to provide the more powerful locomotives which BR were clearly going to need. Some of the most important of these developments, additional to the Deltic locomotive

Fig. 6.11   A Sulzer 2750 h.p. power unit from a Class 47 locomotive, later derated
to 2580 h.p. (BRB)

developed by the English Electric Co, described earlier in this chapter, are
mentioned in the following paragraphs.

Of the seven main-line diesel locomotives in use, or on order at the time
of nationalization, six were equipped with electric transmission. The
power equipment and mechanical transmission system for the seventh
were designed by Lt-Col L. E. R. Fell, a senior Rolls Royce engineer.
Authority was given by the LMS Railway Board in October 1947, for the
construction of one 1600 h.p., 4–8–4 Fell diesel-mechanical locomotive,
incorporating several novel features. Two pairs of Paxman engines, each
pair coupled to a supercharger driven by a third diesel engine, transmitted their power through torque converters and a complex gearbox to
the coupled wheels. The locomotive (No. 10100) was built at Derby and
put into service early in 1952. Fell maintained that mechanical transmission would provide an improved power/weight ratio and would be
more reliable in operation than an electrical system. This, however, was
not borne out in practice. The prototype locomotive ran for some months
on main-line services on the LM Region but due to the complicated design
it spent a great deal of time out of service under repairs and the design
was eventually dropped.

Soon after the end of the Second World War, the Great Western
Railway became interested in the possibilities of gas turbine propulsion
for rail traction. In the early 1940s, the Swiss Federal Railways put into

Fig. 6.12   The 'Fell' 4–8–4 experimental diesel-mechanical locomotive No. 10100 (NRM)

service a 2200 h.p. gas turbine locomotive with electric transmission. The advantages claimed for gas turbine operation were improved power/ weight ratio; a thermal efficiency nearly 2·5 times that of steam traction (although not, at that stage, as good as that of the diesel locomotive); the ability to burn residual, and therefore cheaper, fuel; reduced servicing needs between trips and therefore higher utilization; and decreased maintenance compared with diesel locomotives. On the other hand, there were disadvantages, including the fact that maximum thermal efficiency can only be achieved under continuous full load conditions – a situation which is rarely reached in normal railway operation. In these circumstances, efficiency, in terms of fuel consumption, was not very different from that of a good steam locomotive. Other adverse factors were the noise created by the operation of the compressor, the smell of exhaust fumes and their effects on the brick lining of tunnels.

F. W. Hawksworth, CME of the Great Western Railway, visited Switzerland to see the locomotive in operation. In 1946 the GWR Board agreed to the construction of two gas turbine locomotives for experimental purposes. One of these (No. 18000) was built by Brown-Boveri Ltd, and the other (No. 18100) by the Metropolitan-Vickers Electrical Co Ltd. The Brown-Boveri locomotive, which was to be rather larger than the original Swiss locomotive, was designed to run on two three-axle bogies, the outer axles on each being driven, giving a net output of 2500 h.p. Maximum speed was to be 90 miles/h. The Metropolitan-Vickers locomotive also ran on three-axle bogies, but in this case all the axles were motored and the maximum net output was 3000 h.p. In the process of design of the latter locomotive, alterations were made which permitted a higher ratio of compression than was at first contemplated, thus raising

Fig. 6.13   Metropolitan-Vickers 3000 h.p. gas turbine locomotive No. 18100, ordered by the GWR before nationalization, after conversion to electric operation in 1958, for driver training on the Styal line (A. H. Emerson)

the thermal efficiency to a level at which the original proposal to incorporate a heat exchanger could be dropped.

The Brown-Boveri locomotive was delivered in 1949, and, after static and running trials, worked its first passenger train in May 1950. A number of problems arose – compressor failures, traction motor failures, train heating boiler difficulties, cracking of turbine blades, heat exchanger fires, and combustion chamber failures – but, nevertheless, the locomotive worked a total of over 122000 miles up to September 1952. The expected fuel economies and improved acceleration and gradient climbing were realized.

The Metropolitan-Vickers locomotive was delivered in December 1951, and in this case, too, the initial trials and operation in service were reasonably satisfactory, but with somewhat similar difficulties, particularly in relation to turbine blades. As experience progressed, however, it was evident that neither locomotive would achieve sufficient benefits to justify any further similar construction, or indeed to warrant their maintenance in service, in the light of the specialized attention which they required. The Metropolitan-Vickers locomotive was converted to electric operation in 1958 and was the first locomotive to be brought into use for driver training on the Styal line section of the Crewe–Manchester route. It has since been broken up. The Brown-Boveri locomotive was returned to the Continent some years ago for use by UIC (ORE) for equipment testing.

In the early 1950s the Government saw the railways as a potential market for further developments in gas turbine propulsion. The initiative taken by the GWR was something of which the Ministry of Fuel and Power warmly approved, and was now used to stimulate the BTC into further experiment in the same direction. The Ministry set up a committee, with BTC representation, to pursue the possibilities of using gas turbine locomotives and a number of projects were considered. Most of these were abandoned but two were further developed before dying in their infancy.

The first of these was a 1750 h.p. locomotive, with a gas turbine designed to operate on pulverized coal. It was to be built under Ministry sponsorship by the North British Locomotive Co, with a gas turbine power unit by C. A. Parsons & Co. Construction of the locomotive was started and progressed a fairly considerable way, but, in the event, so many problems arose with some of the principal components whilst under static tests that the project was abandoned.

Whilst the construction of the NBL locomotive was in progress, the National Gas Turbine Establishment published, in July 1954, the results of studies which demonstrated that, by an increase in gas temperatures and speed of rotation, oil-fired gas turbines could be made more competitive with diesel engines for rail traction purposes. Consulting engineers, Messrs Rendel, Palmer and Tritton, were therefore commissioned to undertake a design study of possible 1500 and 3000 h.p. locomotives. Their report, published in August 1956, did not, however, encourage further prototype development.

On its own initiative, the English Electric Co was at the same time considering the application of its industrial gas turbine design to a locomotive and in 1954 one of the company's engineers (J. O. P. Hughes) made contact with the Commission in regard to the possibility of designing and building a gas turbine locomotive for trial on British Railways. Following discussions with Bond, it was agreed that the locomotive, to be built as a private venture by English Electric, should have a final drive

Fig. 6.14   English Electric experimental gas turbine locomotive GT3 on test between Carlisle and Preston, 6 October 1962 (Derek Cross)

connected through a train of gears to the leading axle of a 4–6–0 wheel arrangement – broadly in line with the design adopted by Sir William Stanier for his steam turbine locomotive No. 6202 twenty years earlier – rather than a duplex drive to separate bogies, in line with contemporary diesel locomotive design. By thus avoiding unnecessary complexity in transmission design, it was thought that it would be easier to assess the practical advantages of gas turbines compared with diesel engines for rail traction. The locomotive, of 2700 h.p., built by The Vulcan Foundry, and known as GT3, was subjected to comprehensive tests at the Rugby Locomotive Testing Plant and in special train running, at express timings, on LM Region main lines. It ran very well, but was not sufficiently reliable to employ on revenue-earning services. Unfortunately, finance was not available to carry out the further developments which were necessary to determine whether or not the locomotive could have fulfilled its objective as an economic alternative to diesel traction.

In 1961, the Brush Company built, as a speculative venture, a CC diesel-electric locomotive powered by two Maybach 1400 h.p. engines. This locomotive, named *Falcon*, worked first on the Western Region and later on the Eastern Region, and was engaged on both passenger and freight workings. It was purchased by BR in 1970, but after a number of engine failures, involving long periods under repair, it was withdrawn from service in 1975. Based on experience with this locomotive, the Brush Company were asked by BR to modify the design to accommodate one Sulzer engine of 2750 h.p. This was the origin of the standard Class 47 locomotives, of which over 500 are in service.

A prototype locomotive in the high power range, sponsored as a combined private venture by Birmingham Railway Carriage and Wagon

Fig. 6.15   Class 47 locomotive No. D1500: the first of the Class (NRM)

Co, Associated Electrical Industries, and Sulzer was put into service in 1962. Built by BRCW, named *Lion*, and painted white, it was a CC weighing 114 tons. The Sulzer 2750 h.p. engine was coupled to a generator providing power for electric train heating as well as traction. A boiler for steam heating was also installed. This locomotive ran on the Western Region for a short time.

The English Electric Company's contribution to the contractors' competitive efforts to secure adoption of their own design as the future standard high-power diesel-electric locomotive for BR was DP.2 (Diesel Project 2: Diesel Project 1 being their original Deltic locomotive). This was a CC locomotive, weighing 105 tons, equipped with an English Electric engine of 2700 h.p. The design of the mechanical parts was based on that of their Deltics. DP.2 went into service between Euston and Liverpool in May 1962, and later on the East Coast route, and it performed so well that an order for 50 locomotives, based on this design, was placed in 1964. These are the Class 50 locomotives, in which were incorporated a number of modifications to the DP.2 design – not all of which were immediately successful. The original prototype was, unfortunately, damaged beyond repair when, working an East Coast main-line express, it collided, near Thirsk, with some derailed wagons of a freight train on an adjacent track.

In January 1968, the Brush Company, then part of the Hawker Siddeley Group, handed over for service on BR a further locomotive which they had built as a private venture. This was *Kestrel* – a CC locomotive with a 4000 h.p. Sulzer engine. Its designed speed was 125 miles/h, but because of its axle load of 21 tons was limited to 90 miles/h. *Kestrel* was later fitted with a pair of Class 47 bogies to reduce its weight and was then permitted to run at up to 100 miles/h. It was, however, mainly used on freight services, in which its potential output of 4000 h.p. could seldom be exploited. *Kestrel* was sold to the USSR in 1971.

It is now some 25 years since diesel main-line and shunting locomotives and diesel multiple units began to appear on the railways of Britain, in any significant numbers. In that time, there has been little or no change in the design of the diesel shunting locomotives, which have continued to meet requirements with complete satisfaction. At the end of 1979 there were 972 diesel shunting locomotives on the books, of seven different types, as shown in Table 6.5.

So far as diesel multiple unit stock is concerned, by 1968 it had become apparent that a major part of the fleet of some 4000 vehicles, which by that time were twelve to fourteen years old, would soon have to be replaced. In passenger comfort, particularly in respect of the quality of ride and of heating and ventilation, as well as in reliability these vehicles had fallen far short of the standards which were expected.

On the initiative of T. C. B. Miller, the then Chief Engineer (Traction and Rolling Stock), a study was therefore undertaken to determine how best the requirements of the immediate future could be met and what

Fig. 6.16 The prototype English Electric diesel electric locomotive DP2 (R. M. Tufnell)

Fig. 6.17 'Kestrel', industry's design for a locomotive of higher power than any other then in use on BR (T. C. B. Miller)

Table 6.5   Diesel Shunting Locomotives at end 1979

Class	h.p.	Wheel arrange-ment	Mechanical parts	Engine	Transmission	No. in service at end 1979
01	153	0–4–0	Barclay	Gardner	Mechanical	1
03	204	0–6–0	BR	Gardner	Mechanical	58
05	204	0–6–0	Hunslet	Gardner	Mechanical	1
06	204	0–4–0	Barclay	Gardner	Mechanical	5
08	350	0–6–0	BR	EE	Electric	878
09	350	0–6–0	BR	EE	Electric	26
13	700	0–6–0 + 0–6–0	BR	EE	Electric	3
			(Permanently coupled twin units)			
Total						972

standards of comfort and performance should be set to meet the demands of the various categories of passenger travel in trains of multiple unit formation. It was recognized that the requirements fell into two basic types, namely high density suburban commuter trains, capable of a maximum speed of 75 miles/h but with a high initial rate of acceleration on account of frequent stops, and Inter-City trains, to meet an emerging demand for prestige services with infrequent stops, providing a high standard of passenger comfort and a maximum speed of 125 miles/h.

At the time these requirements were being considered, the use of gas turbine engines as prime movers for rail traction was again being explored. In the autumn of 1968, during a meeting of the Traction and Rolling Stock Committee of the UIC in Paris, the representatives of almost all the European Railways were given a demonstration run in a two-car turbo-train from Paris to Vierzon, during which a speed of 143 miles/h was reached. The turbine employed was a helicopter engine adapted for the purpose. At that time, it was the intention that the Advanced Passenger Train (APT) then being developed in the Research Laboratories at Derby should be fitted with gas turbines.

Notwithstanding the impressive performance of gas turbines in other applications, it was decided that these engines had not reached a stage of development at which they could be recommended for rail traction purposes, a decision which was independently reached in other parts of the world around the same time. The alternative was to rely on diesel engines with electric transmission.

These basic principles having been established, work went ahead on preparing outline designs for the high density units and for the High Speed Train (HST). Whereas the former would be three-car units capable of running in multiple by coupling two, three, or four units together, the

Fig. 6.18   Two pictures of the Inter-City 125 High Speed Trains in operation on
East Coast services (BRB)

High Speed Train was to be a self-contained unit consisting of seven passenger vehicles with a power-car at each end – a fixed formation train, not a multiple unit train.

Up to this point, the ideas incorporated in the designs had been exclusively those of the engineers engaged on the project but before the end of 1968 the proposals concerning the High Speed Inter-City train, were presented to the Commercial and Operating Departments and were well received, the time being ripe for some major advance in passenger train performances and amenities. An advance from 100 miles/h to 125 miles/h, accompanied by a new design of main-line passenger vehicles (Mark III) – referred to in more detail in Chapter Eight – was exactly what was needed to fill the gap pending the arrival of the APT in revenue-earning service. Authority for the detailed design of a prototype train was given by the BR Board on 24 February 1969.

It was calculated that a train consisting of seven Mark III coaches, with a power car at each end, would require diesel engines giving a total power output of 4500 h.p. This meant an engine of 2250 h.p. was required in each power car but at that time there was no diesel engine of British design and manufacture on the market to produce this power at an acceptable weight. However, work had been going on for some time, sponsored by British Railways and the Admiralty, by Davy Paxman and Co of Colchester, on the development of their 'Ventura' engine, which had been employed in diesel-hydraulic locomotives on the Western Region with some success and which had been fitted to a number of NBL Class 29 diesel-electric locomotives operating in the Scottish Region. An improved twelve-cylinder version of the Ventura engine (named the 'Valenta') was selected as having the necessary characteristics for the new project.

Experience with the 100 miles/h service on the LM Region, where four-axled electric locomotives of six different types provided the motive power, had shown that heavy unsprung weight on the locomotive wheels had an excessively damaging effect on the track and that low total axle loads were necessary at very high speeds. This led, at an early stage in the development of the design of the 125 miles/h train, to a new investigation of the dynamic effects on the permanent way of vehicles with various axle loads and with differing proportions of those total loads spring-mounted on the bogie frames or partly carried on the axles. These tests, many of which were carried out at Cheddington, on the LM Region main line from Euston to Crewe, confirmed that the proportion of unsprung weight was the critical factor and it was clear that for speeds up to 125 miles/h the unsprung weight of any pair of wheels must not exceed 2½ tons.

Thus equipped to run at 125 miles/h and to do so without incurring excessive maintenance costs the third and most important requirement was to be able to stop within the braking distances provided by the existing signalling. It was, indeed, this requirement which limited their maximum speed to 125 miles/h.

The brake system adopted is the BR standard two-pipe automatic air brake, which provides the HST with a stopping distance from 125 miles/h somewhat less than that of existing locomotive-hauled trains from 100 miles/h. Girling disc brake units are fitted to all wheels and additionally a cast iron tread brake acts on each wheel of the power cars during a brake application to maintain wheel/rail adhesion. All axles, both on the power cars and on the coaches, are provided with wheel slide protection. At the first sign of a wheel tending to slip, the brakes are immediately released, and restored when the condition has been remedied.

The bogies under the power cars are of light-weight box type all-welded construction, with a minimum of wearing parts to reduce maintenance, and incorporating Alsthom links type primary and flexicoil type secondary suspensions.

Construction of the prototype train began in mid-1970 – the power cars at Crewe and the coaches at Derby – and it went into service in 1972 to undergo a long and comprehensive testing programme, during which, on 12 June 1973, it attained a speed of 143 miles/h between Thirsk and Tollerton on the East Coast main line – a record for a diesel-hauled train.

Prototype testing indicated that only minor modifications were necessary in the production design, and relatively little difficulty has been experienced since. The trains have been very well received by the public. On 10 April 1979, a normal time-tabled train on the Paddington–Bristol run covered the 94 miles to Chippenham in 50 min 31 s, an average of 111·7 miles/h.

A total of 91 High Speed Trains have so far been authorized – some nine-car, including two power cars, some ten-car. The services in which they are being, or will be used, are summarized in Table 6.6.

Plans are under consideration for the construction of fourteen further sets – seven to augment the King's Cross–Edinburgh services, and provide connecting services between the East Coast route and Hull, Sheffield, and Teeside, and seven for a second stage of NE/NW-SW/SE/S. Coast Services.

New maintenance depots for the High Speed Trains, of sufficient length to accommodate a complete train of nine or ten vehicles on one road, have been provided at Old Oak Common and Bristol (St Philips Marsh) on the Western Region, Bounds Green, Newcastle (Heaton), and Leeds (Neville Hill) on the Eastern Region, and Edinburgh (Craigentinny) on the Scottish Region. The diesel maintenance depot at Plymouth (Laira) is being altered to cater for trains working the West of England services.

The High Speed Train won two awards – the Viva Shield in 1977 and the Design Council Award in 1978. The Viva Shield is presented annually by the Worshipful Company of Carmen, a London Guild. It is awarded for the invention, development or idea which contributes most notably to

Table 6.6 Employment of High Speed Trains

Class	No. of sets.	Coaches per set: (incl. 2 power cars).	Service	Introduced/ to be introduced commencing
253	27 (+ 2 spare power cars)	9	Paddington–Bristol/ South Wales	Oct. 1976
254	32 (+ 2 spare power cars)	10	King's Cross–Edinburgh/ Aberdeen King's Cross–West Riding	May 1978 May 1979
253	14 (+ 1 spare power car)	9	Paddington–West of England	Nov. 1979
253	18 (+ 2 spare power cars)	9	NE/SW services: Edinburgh–Newcastle– Birmingham–South Wales	1981

the advancement of transport as a whole. This was the first time the Award had been presented for an achievement in rail transport. In making the Design Council Award, the judges commended the train for the high quality of its passenger comfort, ventilation, insulation, and suspension.

For the high density commuter services, diesel multiple units (Class 210) with 1100 h.p. above-floor engines, have been designed. Two prototype units – three-car and four-car sets – are in the course of manufacture. The first prototype will have a Paxman 'Ventura' engine and Brush electrical equipment. The second train will have a German design MTU engine, with GEC equipment. Each set will be basically three-car, but an extra vehicle can strengthen either to four-car. The first should be completed in mid-1980 and will undergo trials in West and South Yorkshire. The second unit is due later in the year and both units will then undergo trials in the Birmingham area. The units will be fitted with a new power bogie (BP 20), with welded box section frames, rubber spring and hydraulic damper primary suspension, and air spring secondary suspension. They will have BSC 'Tightlock' couplings which will couple the vehicles and the electrical connections, eliminating the need for jumpers. The body-shell will be suitable for both electric and diesel multiple unit stock.

It is hoped that these units, which will have a maximum speed of 90 miles/h, will eradicate many of the deficiencies which have engendered the public view that travel by diesel multiple unit train is uncomfortable and generally to be avoided, if possible.

For lightly loaded secondary routes or country services, it is felt that the new Class 210 unit will be too expensive to be justified. In such cases, simpler vehicles, usually operating as two-car sets, would be more suitable. A study was therefore undertaken to evaluate vehicle body designs and manufacturing methods and, as part of this, two shortened Leyland National bus bodies were joined together, to produce a vehicle 50 ft long, mounted on a two-axle underframe. This vehicle has already undergone trials hauled by a locomotive at speeds up to 90 miles/h. As a result, a decision has now been taken to build a prototype two-car railbus, which, whilst retaining the concept of a Leyland National Bus body on a two-axle underframe, will incorporate a number of modifications. The front-end developed for the Class 313 electric multiple-unit will be used and the body will be integrated structurally with the underframe to carry some of the load. The railbus will be powered by a 200 h.p. turbo-charged underfloor engine, with mechanical gearbox in each car. Delivery of the prototype, which will have a maximum speed of 75 miles/h, is expected towards the end of 1980.

Pending the provision of new trains, an extensive programme of improvements in respect of lighting, interior accommodation, and noise reduction by improved engine mountings, is being undertaken, covering some 2200 vehicles – approximately two-thirds of the existing fleet.

At the end of 1979 there were 3005 diesel multiple unit vehicles in

Fig. 6.19   Experimental version of the new type light-weight railbus being developed by BR for rural services. The use of a standard Leyland bus body on a modified underframe reduces the overall cost of the rail vehicle (BRB)

service, of which 991 had been reconditioned. There were also 290 diesel-electric multiple units on the Southern Region.

At the same time as the new designs of diesel multiple units were under consideration, attention was also being directed towards the future requirements for diesel locomotives, particularly bearing in mind the changing character of, in particular, freight traffic, with its emphasis on block train movement at higher speeds. After taking into account all the factors involved, the choice lay between a 3000 h.p. BB locomotive and a 4500 h.p. CC locomotive. The former would be capable of 80 miles/h maximum, and of multiple operation, and be able to replace all existing locomotives in Types 1 to 4 for freight use. The 4500 h.p. locomotive would have a gross weight of 120 tons and be suitable for heavy freight operation at up to 80 miles/h, or alternatively, possibly for mixed traffic working at up to 100 miles/h.

During 1974, it was decided that the most urgent need was for a high-powered locomotive for heavy freight working. The need for rapid delivery precluded the preferred strategy of designing a locomotive specifically for freight purposes. Instead, an existing locomotive design (Class 47) was altered to achieve the best compromise. Thirty of these locomotives (Class 56) were ordered from the Brush Company in September 1974, to be erected in Rumania, the first of these being delivered in 1976.

These locomotives are powered by a 3250 h.p. Ruston engine and fitted with Brush electrical equipment. They have a maximum speed of 80 miles/h. The bogie design is based on the Schlieren type used extensively

Fig. 6.20   Class 56 diesel main-line locomotive: the most modern type in operation

in Europe, with modified coil spring primary and flexicoil secondary suspension. Minor problems were experienced with the traction motor suspension bearings due to ingress of water during transit. These were replaced and thereafter performed satisfactorily. Some difficulty was also experienced with the primary suspension and the cab air conditioning but these too have been put right.

Orders have been placed with BR Engineering Ltd for the construction of 105 further locomotives of this type. The first of these was delivered in 1977, and in all 69 had been delivered by the end of 1979. The remainder of the order is scheduled for completion by 1983.

In the meantime the diesel fleet continues to contract and withdrawal of the Deltics is likely to start in the early 1980s.

At the end of 1979, 2289 diesel main-line locomotives of sixteen different types were in service, as shown in Table 6.7

Table 6.7   Diesel Main Line Locomotives in Service, end 1979

Type	Class	h.p.	Mechanical parts/engine/transmission	No. in service at end 1979
1	20	1000	EE/EE/EE	217
2	24	1160	BR/Sulzer/BTH	1
	25	1250	(BR/Sulzer/AEI)	
			(Beyer Peacock/Sulzer/AEI)	301
	26	1160	BRCW/Sulzer/Crompton Parkinson	42
	27	1250	BRCW/Sulzer/GEC	61
	31	1470	Brush/EE/Brush	251
3	33	1550	BRCW/Sulzer/Crompton Parkinson	94
	37	1700	EE/EE/EE	308
4	40	2000	EE/EE/EE	183
	44	2300	BR/Sulzer/Crompton Parkinson	3
	45	2500	BR/Sulzer/Crompton Parkinson	126
	46	2500	BR/Sulzer/Brush	53
	47	2580	BR and Brush/Sulzer/Brush	508
	50	2700	EE/EE/EE	50
5	55	3300	EE/EE/EE	22
	56	3250	Brush and BR/Ruston/Brush	69
Total				2289

At the time of writing, only one further development in diesel traction is in mind – a class 58 3250 h.p. diesel locomotive, to which further reference will be made in Chapter Fifteen.

CHAPTER SEVEN

The Impact of Electrification

THE possibilities of using electricity for traction purposes were recognized by engineers as soon as the practicability of transmitting electrical energy was demonstrated. The earliest known applications of electricity to traction were in the 1830s. An electric car was produced in 1835 by Thomas Davenport in America, running on a circular track and in 1839 a small electric locomotive, constructed by Robert Davidson, was tried out on a line in the Edinburgh area, achieving a speed of four miles/h. In the first instance, the car was operated by a battery external to the car and in the second case by a battery carried on the locomotive. Furthermore, a booklet issued in the mid-1930s by the British Electrical Development Association records a comment by the first of a long line of railway engineers – George Stephenson – to a young engineer in 1847:

> I have the credit of being the inventor of the locomotive and it is true I have done something to improve the action of steam for that purpose. But I tell you, young man, that the day will come when electricity will be the great motive power of the world.

Thus, the possibility of electrified railways was foreseen – and indeed developments in that direction were taking place – not long after the birth of steam railways and certainly before Dr Rudolf Diesel invented his internal combustion engine.

It was in 1840 that the idea of using the rails for the conveyance of electric current was conceived and patented, but until the late 1850s only batteries are mentioned as the source of current supply. By then, however, the dynamo was in the course of development and this form of supply, carried through a third rail between the tracks, was used in Werner von Siemens' electric train, which ran successfully at the Berlin Trade Exhibition in 1879. This three-car train, hauled by a two-axle electric locomotive, carried about twenty passengers at a speed of around four miles/h.

The first public electric railway in the world was brought into service in 1881, again in Germany, between Berlin Anhaltt station and the suburb of

Lichterfelde Ost, (1½ miles) achieving a maximum speed of 30 miles/h. Two years later, the first public electric railways were introduced in the United Kingdom.

In August 1883, Magnus Volk, Electrical Engineer to the Brighton Corporation, built the first quarter-mile section of an electric railway along the sea front, extended during the following year to about 1½ miles in length, a third rail being added to convey current to the motors. The original four-wheeled car was propelled by current generated at 50 V by a 2 h.p. gas engine, speeds up to 6 miles/h being achieved. This railway, modernized over the years, continues to operate, carrying up to one million passengers a year.

In September 1883 an electric railway, seven miles long, constructed to a 3 ft gauge, was brought into use between Portrush and Giant's Causeway in Northern Ireland. Direct current at 550 V d.c. was fed to a third rail but in 1899 overhead wire collection was adopted. This line was the first example in which hydro-electric power was used for railway traction. The service was withdrawn in 1950.

Another electric railway, about one mile in length, was built on a private estate at Carstairs, Scotland, in 1888–9 and in 1890 the opening of the City and South London tube railway, using electric locomotives, demonstrated the possibilities of electric traction in respect of both cleanliness of operation and rapid acceleration from frequent stopping points. It foreshadowed the London Underground system as we know it today. In the next decade, the Isle of Man Electric Railway, the Liverpool Overhead Railway, and the Waterloo and City Railway were brought into use but it was not until early in the 1900s that really significant developments began to take place. The subsequent introduction of electric railway traction, up to the time of nationalization, is summarized at Table 7.1. Additionally, two electrification projects were in progress at nationalization – one suburban and one main line.

Development of railway electrification in Britain had, up to 1914, been based almost entirely on direct current supply, using a conductor-rail contact and making use of the valuable characteristics of the d.c. traction motor, which had already proved its reliability. The practicability of the third-rail system, using the running rails for the return of current to sub-stations, had been effectively established.

Generating stations in the earlier years supplied direct current but at the turn of the century the country's electricity supply was beginning to assume its present form as turbo-alternators were brought into use for the generation of alternating current. For some years frequency was not standardized and it was not until 1926 that Parliament took the decision which eventually led to the adoption of a 50-cycle standard frequency throughout the country. Early rotary convertors, necessary to convert a.c. to d.c. for traction purposes, required a lower-frequency a.c. current for satisfactory performance. Consequently, railways, unless they had their

Table 7.1   Electrification on the Main Line Railways at Nationalization

Year introduced	Route	Main line rly co	Route miles	System
1898	Waterloo & City Rly: Waterloo–Bank	SR	1½	600 V d.c. centre 3rd rail: converted 1940 to 660 V d.c. standard 3rd rail.
1903	Mersey Railway: Liverpool–Birkenhead Park/Rock Ferry	LMSR	5	650 V d.c. 3rd and 4th rail: converted 1956 to 3rd rail
1904	Newcastle–Monkseaton–Whitley Bay–Newcastle	LNER	42	630 V d.c. 3rd rail
1938	Newcastle–South Shields			De-electrified by stages
1905	Tyne Commission Quay	LNER	1	600 V d.c. overhead
1904/13	Liverpool–Southport/Crossens/Ormskirk	LMSR	37	630 V d.c. 3rd rail (initially 4th rail): Crossens service withdrawn 1964: Marsh Lane–Aintree electrified 1963
1908	Lancaster–Morecambe–Heysham	LMSR	10	6·6 kV a.c. 25-cycles overhead: converted to 50-cycles 1952: service withdrawn 1967
1909/25	LB & SCR London suburban lines	SR	43	6·6 kV a.c. 25-cycles overhead: converted 1928/29 to 660 V d.c. 3rd rail
1912	Grimsby–Immingham Tramway	LNER	4½	500 V d.c. overhead: closed 1961
1913/18	Manchester–Bury–Holcombe Brook	LMSR	14	1200 V d.c. 3rd rail: (Bury–Holcombe Brook originally electrified at 3·5 kV d.c. overhead in 1913 and converted in 1918: Bury–Holcombe Brook de-electrified 1951)
1914/27	LNWR London Suburban lines: Euston/Broad Street–Watford/Richmond and branches	LMSR	38	630 V d.c. 4th rail: Willesden–Earl's Court, South Acton–Kew Bridge withdrawn 1940: Watford–Rickmansworth withdrawn 1952: converted to 3rd rail 1970
1915	Newport–Shildon*	LNER	19	1500 V d.c. overhead: de-electrified 1935
1915/39	LSWR London suburban lines/SR London suburban lines and main lines to Brighton, Hastings, and Portsmouth	SR	721	660 V d.c. 3rd rail
1931	MSJ & A line: Manchester–Altrincham	LMS/LNER Joint	9	1500 V d.c. overhead: converted to 25 kV a.c. 50-cycles in 1971
1938	Wirral lines: Birkenhead–New Brighton/West Kirby	LMSR	11	650 V d.c. 3rd rail

*Not strictly valid to the situation at nationalization, but included for its relevance to the historical development of electrification.

own power stations, had to use frequency-changers to provide a frequency lower than the standard of 50 cycles per second.

On nationalization, then, the electrified railway system in Britain was very largely as it had been at the time of the railway amalgamations in 1923, with only the Southern Railway making much progress. It was mainly a low-voltage d.c. rail-collection system, limited almost entirely to suburban services in the vicinity of London, Liverpool, Manchester, and Newcastle. Only three suburban routes had deviated from the third-rail pattern. One of these – the South London line – was originally electrified on the 6·6 kV a.c. overhead system but was later converted to d.c. third rail; the Lancaster–Morecambe–Heysham electrification, introduced in 1908, had also adopted the 6·6 kV a.c. overhead system – presumably as a result of information obtained by Midland Railway officers during a visit to America in 1901; and the joint LMSR/LNER electrification of the Manchester South Junction–Altrincham line in 1931 had used the 1500 V d.c. overhead system, the decision no doubt being influenced by the proceedings of the Weir Committee (referred to later) which was sitting at that time. Certain Southern Railway services apart, only one railway – the North Eastern – had ventured into the main-line electrification field by converting the heavy mineral line between Newport and Shildon to a 1500 V d.c. overhead system in 1915, using ten 0–4–4–0 1100 h.p. locomotives, built at Darlington, with Siemens electrical equipment, to cover the service.

From 1923, up to the time of the Second World War, progress to completion was mainly restricted to relatively few suburban electrifications in the London and Liverpool areas and on South Tyneside, and no further advance was made in the extension of electrification to main lines. Indeed, the only real main-line electrification – and that only for the

Fig. 7.1 Newport-Shildon 1500 V d.c. locomotive No. 8 built by the former North Eastern Railway: shown here with LNER lettering after the amalgamations (NRM)

working of coal traffic – between Newport and Shildon, was abandoned in 1935: an operating success, but, because of the decline in the coal trade, a financial failure. Had Sir Vincent Raven been appointed Chief Mechanical Engineer of the LNER, instead of Gresley, there might have been a different story to tell of electrification on the East Coast route. A North Eastern Railway proposal, approved in 1919, for electrifying the main line from York to Newcastle, was in fact abandoned after the amalgamations, work in the meantime having been held up at Government request, awaiting the report of the Kennedy Committee (referred to later) on the choice of systems for main-line electrification. A prototype 1800 h.p. 4–6–4 electric locomotive, with Metropolitan-Vickers equipment, was built at Darlington for service trials over the route but was not available for testing on the Newport–Shildon line until May 1922, by which time the NER had tended to lose interest in the project and the LNER had neither the money nor presumably the will to continue the scheme. The locomotive was run in dynamometer car tests on the Shildon line and, after renovation, on the MSJ & A line, but after a long period in storage, was broken up in 1950.

Similarly, H. E. O'Brien, Electrical Engineer of the London and North Western Railway, who had been concerned in previous Lancashire and Yorkshire Railway electrification projects in the Liverpool area, had plans for electrification between Crewe and Carlisle. These plans, too, were abandoned by the LMS on amalgamation, when a management with different views and priorities took charge.

During the period between 1923 and the Second World War a number of other main-line electrification schemes were examined. In 1927, the Great Western Railway commissioned Sir Philip Dawson, who had earlier been much involved in the planning of electrification schemes on the Southern Railway, to prepare a scheme for the electrification of the main line from Taunton to Penzance, and of branches west of Taunton. The figures produced purported to show a return of 7·3 per cent of the net capital expenditure, but the basis of the estimates was considered to be unsound and the project was not developed.

In November 1929 Gresley and his Chief Electrical Engineer, H. W. H. Richards, who had moved from the Southern Railway in 1928, produced a scheme for the electrification of the GN suburban lines – a project first seriously considered as far back as 1903. Gresley's proposals included the main and local lines from King's Cross to Welwyn Garden City, the Edgware, High Barnet, and Alexandra Palace Branch and the Hertford Loop Line as far as Hertford, a total of 53 route miles (178 single track miles) comprising some 85 per cent of the GN suburban area. It was also proposed, under the scheme, to run LNER services in place of the LMS North London trains then operating over GN suburban lines and from Canonbury Junction to Broad Street; over the Metropolitan Company's 'Widened Lines' from King's Cross to Moorgate Street; and on the GN and City (later the Northern City) tube section from Finsbury Park to Moorgate – an additional 8 route miles (17 single track miles). To permit of operation over the LMS and Metropolitan Company's lines, operating on 650 V d.c. and 600 V d.c. fourth-rail systems respectively, it was at that stage proposed that a 750 V d.c. third-rail system should be adopted. The replacement of steam by electric traction was estimated to reduce the costs of operation by 33 per cent, with a return on capital of nearly 12 per cent.

In January 1931 Gresley submitted an addendum to the proposal, reporting the outcome of investigations into the adoption of a higher voltage d.c. system with overhead current collection. This had indicated that there were unlikely to be any insuperable objections to superimposing an overhead system on LMS and Metropolitan lines already equipped for fourth-rail current collection. Revised recommendations were therefore put forward, that the electrification should be on the 1500 V d.c. overhead system, the main reason advanced for this change being the reduced capital outlay which would be required if, as was hoped, it was later decided to electrify the main-line services out of King's Cross. The revised proposals would involve some increase in capital costs, but annual maintenance costs would be less and the overall return on capital would be little affected. It seems reasonable to suppose that in amending his proposals on power supply Gresley was influenced by the investigations then being carried out by the Weir Committee, of which his Chief General Manager, Sir Ralph Wedgwood, was a member.

The LMS, in 1936, examined the possibilities of electrification from Euston to Rugby, including the Northampton Loop, a total of 114 route miles, on the 1500 V d.c. overhead system. The proposals excluded yards and sidings, which were to be operated by diesel locomotives. The gross outlay, as estimated, could not, however, be justified by the savings which were likely to be obtained. The route was too short to permit of a sufficient revision of rolling stock and train crew rosters to produce the requisite level of savings.

The Southern Railway, too, in 1936 proposed to complete the electrification of their Eastern and Central Sections, on the d.c. third-rail system. The proposals estimated a return of ten per cent on the net capital outlay, without allowance for traffic stimulation. The full scheme covered the electrification of 623 route miles, additional to over 700 route miles already electrified. Later proposals, in 1947, limited the proposed increase in route miles to 284, on principal routes only, leaving secondary and branch lines to be worked by diesel or other forms of traction.

None of these schemes came to fruition at that time. The main-line companies found it impracticable to raise capital for the electrification of further lines, even in those cases in which the projects stood in good prospects of paying off, financially, in the longer term.

As early as March 1920 the Minister of Transport set up the Electrification of Railways Advisory Committee, under the chairmanship of Sir Alexander Kennedy, to consider and advise on, inter alia,

I. whether any regulations should be made for the purpose of ensuring that the future electrification of railways in this country is carried out to the best advantage in regard to interchange of electric locomotives and rolling stock, uniformity of equipment and/or other matters;
II. if any such regulations are desirable, what matters should be dealt with, and what regulations should be made; how far it is desirable, if at all, that railways or sections of railways already electrified should be altered so that they may form parts of a unified system.

In their report, in 1921, this Committee expressed the view that it was desirable that certain general regulations should be made for observance by the Railway Companies when electrifying their lines, to ensure standardization of those methods and appliances which were likely to prove the most satisfactory under British conditions. The regulations to be introduced should put no avoidable difficulties in the way of adoption in the future of any improvements in methods or appliances which might from time to time become available. The Committee also recommended that a d.c. system, preferably at 1500 V with overhead collection, should be adopted, with 750 V d.c. third or fourth rail as an alternative when this was advantageous. Higher voltages should also be permitted, if desired, provided they were in multiples of 1500 V d.c.

This was followed, in 1927, by a further Committee – the Railway Electrification Committee – under the chairmanship of Col. Sir John Pringle, Chief Inspecting Officer of Railways at the Ministry of Transport, with a remit

To review the recommendations made by the Electrification of Railways Advisory Committee, 1921, and to report what modifications, if any, should be made in these recommendations, having regard to the developments which have taken place since that date.

This Committee, of which Gresley was a member, along with H. Jones and Lt-Col F. A. Cortez-Leigh, Electrical Engineers respectively of the Southern and LMS Railways, confirmed, in their report dated July 1928, the earlier recommendations that there should be two standard voltages – 1500 V d.c. overhead and 750 V d.c. third rail. The report also made recommendations in regard to methods of collection and the form of contacts for the high- and low-voltage systems; the structural standardizations required for the inter-running as between different railways of electric locomotives; and the standards to be observed in relation to both third-rail and overhead equipment. Jones, representing the Southern Railway, declined to sign the report, disagreeing with the recommendations in regard to methods of collection and forms of contact for use in connection with the higher voltage system.

At that time, electric power was taken from locally owned power stations, or from power stations owned by the railways themselves. This was a satisfactory solution in so far as suburban electrifications were concerned but the absence of any general system of cheap power supply militated against electrifications of any significant length. This situation was remedied by the creation of the Central Electricity Board and the national grid, as a result of the Electricity (Supply) Act, 1926, which enabled the railways to obtain bulk supplies of electric power at any point on their systems, so avoiding the cost of erecting power stations and at the same time removing the uncertainty about the cost of current. The situation was further improved in 1934 by an Act which permitted the Board to supply electricity direct to railway companies instead of through the intermediary of distributing authorities, a development initiated by the railways themselves.

A third Committee, under the chairmanship of Lord Weir, was set up in 1929, with a remit as follows:

> In view of the progress which is being made towards widespread availability of high tension electrical energy, to examine into the economic and other aspects of the electrification of the railway systems in Great Britain, with particular reference to main line working, and to report their conclusions.

By its term of reference, the Committee was obliged to consider the economic and other results of electrifying the entire railway system of the country in one operation – clearly a very different matter from dealing with particular routes and services. Quite obviously, the case for electrification, on a complete network basis, would be adversely affected by the enforced inclusion of those routes and services which would not in themselves justify conversion to this form of traction.

It was decided quite early that it would be impracticable, because of the amount of work involved, to make a detailed examination of the electrification of the complete system and arrangements were therefore made for consultants – Messrs Merz and McLellan – to conduct investigations into two sections of the railway system, as under:

(a) The LNER main line from King's Cross to Doncaster and Leeds, with branches from Grantham to Nottingham, Boston and Lincoln; the line from Doncaster to March, via Lincoln, Sleaford, and Spalding; the line from Peterborough to Grimsby and Cleethorpes via Boston; the lines from Louth and from Willoughby to Mablethorpe; the Skegness branch; and the connecting line from Coningsby Junction to Bellwater Junction.

(b) The LMS main line from Crewe to Carlisle; including the Winwick –Golborne and Whelley loops; the line from Weaver Junction (north of Crewe) to Liverpool Lime Street; the branch lines to

Windermere, Over and Wharton, Garston and Morecambe; and the Lancaster–Morecambe–Heysham line.

The main features of the reports submitted are extracted in Table 7.2.

Table 7.2   Summary of Reports on Projects investigated by Merz and McLellan

	LNER Scheme	LMSR Scheme
Total route mileage	492	193
Total track mileage	1944	843
Trailing ton-miles per annum, electric	6 000 000 000	2 225 000 000
Trailing ton-miles per annum, steam hauled	—	395 000 000
Engine miles (electric)	21 000 000	7 950 000
Engine miles (steam)	—	1 590 000
Traffic density: trailing ton-miles per running track mile per annum (Estimated comparable average density for the whole country: 3 000 000).	4 300 000	4 050 000
Net capital outlay	£8 646 000	£5 123 000
Savings in working expenses	£ 624 600	£ 127 800
Percentage return on net capital	7·22	2·5

The reasons for the comparatively poor return on the LMS scheme were the relatively limited size of the project, due in part to connecting lines not being included, and the resultant low utilization of the electric locomotives when only part of a through route is electrified.

The Weir Committee took the view that limited schemes, involving dual steam and electric working, were generally unlikely to prove worthwhile, and that the only way to secure the full benefits of electrification would be by the complete substitution of steam haulage by electricity. Application of the results of the two pilot schemes to general estimates prepared for the electrification of the whole railway system in Britain suggested that, if the work was carried out over a period of 15 to 20 years, a slightly higher return than the 7·22 per cent calculated for the LNER scheme might be expected.

In summarizing their report, issued in 1931, the Committee found no reason to question the recommendations of the Pringle Committee that two alternative standard systems should be adopted – 750 V d.c. third-rail collection and 1500 V d.c. overhead collection. In the investigation into the two specific projects, and the application of the results to the network as a whole, the 1500 V d.c. overhead system had been assumed.

The Weir Committee came to the conclusion that if the traffic density on any route exceeded 2·3 million trailing ton-miles per single track mile per annum, electrification of that route should be profitable. At that time, the average traffic density of the railways in Britain was estimated at 3 million trailing ton-miles per single track mile per annum. In the area of the LNER considered by Merz and McLellan, the comparative average figure was 4·3 million. In so far as individual routes were concerned, some 4500 route miles – 29·8 per cent of the lines not thus far electrified – carried traffic above this level. The upward trend of capital costs, amongst other factors, has led over the years to a change in the traffic density at which electrification can be expected to pay and by 1950 the figure was set at around three to four million trailing ton-miles per single track mile per annum, covering some 4000 route miles, of which 3000 had a traffic density in excess of five million trailing ton-miles.

The report concluded that a comprehensive programme of electrification was the only method of achieving complete success, if the decision was taken to alter the haulage system. The Committee suggested that the mere magnitude of the sum involved in the complete electrification of the railways should not in itself be a deterrent.

The case for railway electrification was strongly supported by a Royal Commission on Transport, sitting at the same time as the Weir Committee. In their report, published in 1930, the Royal Commission stated:

> It would be greatly to the interests of the Railway Companies, and at the same time tend to the great convenience of the public, if all suburban lines were electrified, not merely in London but in all districts where there is intense passenger traffic.

In fact, a wider interpretation of the Commission's report suggests that they felt there could be advantage in not restricting electrification to suburban services, commenting that capital expenditure by the railway companies on road transport would be better spent on electrification, since increased railway facilities attracted more traffic, whilst participation in road traffic merely increased the competition from which the railways were suffering so severely.

Apart from the fact that the Weir Report may have influenced the choice of system in some of the abortive proposals which were prepared by the railway companies in the early 1930s, there was no immediate change in the position in regard to electrification.

Successive Governments had been unwilling to provide financial assistance for a change from steam to electric traction, until worsening economic conditions in Britain in the mid-1930s enforced some change in this attitude. The railways were particularly hard hit, due to the deteriorating industrial situation and the increasing competition from road transport. In 1935, as a contribution to stimulating the national economy and providing much-needed employment, the Government agreed, by the Railways Agreement Act, to give financial support to two electrification schemes.

Both electrification schemes were on the LNER – the intensive commuter service between Liverpool Street and Shenfield and the heavy trans-Pennine freight and mineral service between Manchester, Sheffield, and Wath. Only the latter scheme could be regarded as a main-line electrification. In agreeing to give financial support to these projects the Government would undoubtedly have been influenced by the findings of the Weir Committee. The Second World War, however, brought an end to work on these two schemes and they were not completed until after nationalization. Nevertheless, they are the first schemes with which we are particularly concerned in reviewing the activities of railway engineers since 1948 and certainly they were the beginning of the change in attitudes towards electrification – except, of course, on the Southern Railway and Region – and the growing eagerness amongst railwaymen to electrify as and when the necessary finance could be made available.

The history of the Great Eastern suburban services has been one of continuous growth, from the time a steam service was introduced on the first section, between Mile End and Romford, in June 1839. By the time of the 1923 amalgamations, the Great Eastern was carrying the most intensive suburban steam service anywhere in the world. By the early 1930s, it had become apparent that increasing traffic demands could no longer be met by quadrupling track, opening new stations, and modernizing signalling methods, but that electrification – which had been considered on several occasions since the early 1900s but always hitherto deferred, mainly for financial reasons – was essential to provide relief to the seriously overloaded peak services.

In July 1935 and March 1936, therefore, the LNER produced proposals for the electrification of the local lines between Liverpool Street and Shenfield, the main lines from Liverpool Street to Gidea Park, and the line from Fenchurch Street to Stratford. The total route mileage involved was 20; single track mileage 100. The congested suburban traffic in the area was to be further relieved by extending the Central London tube eastwards from Liverpool Street to Stratford and Leyton, to join up with the LNER lines to Loughton, Ongar, and Newbury Park. A new tube was also to be constructed between Newbury Park and Leytonstone. These two schemes were approved by the Standing Joint Committee established under the London Passenger Transport Act of 1933, to co-ordinate requirements in the London suburban area, and therefore qualified for financial assistance by the Government.

The 1500 V d.c. system was adopted for the lines to Shenfield in anticipation of the electrification being extended at some future date to Southend and Colchester. The scheme, as originally authorized, covered

(a) the provision of rolling stock – 92 three-car units to provide nine-car services on the Liverpool Street–Shenfield line and six-car services on the Fenchurch Street–Stratford shuttle;

(b) a flyover at Ilford to transpose the local and through lines and thereby relieve conflicting movements immediately outside Liverpool Street station; the rearrangement of track work in the Liverpool Street station area; the provision of additional headroom at a number of bridges; and the remodelling of Stratford station to provide the necessary interchange with the extended Central Line;

(c) the erection of overhead line and supporting structures; the provision of power supplies; and the construction and equipment of sub-stations and track-sectioning cabins;

(d) the construction of cleaning, servicing, and maintenance facilities at Ilford.

A much improved service was planned, with an increase of around 50 per cent in trains into and out of Liverpool Street during the peak hours and running times reduced by 20/30 per cent. The reduction in cost per loaded train mile under electrification was estimated at 28 per cent.

Work on the electrification started in 1937 and by the outbreak of war about six miles of overhead structures had been erected, the Ilford flyover had been completed and the reconstruction of several bridges had been carried out. Early in 1940, however, work was suspended and was not resumed until 1946 under the direction of H. H. Swift. Electric services operated in part from 26 September 1949 and in full from 7 November 1949.

The second electrification approved for financial aid by the Government – the Manchester–Sheffield–Wath project – was of quite a different kind. Whereas the Liverpool Street–Shenfield line was electrified to provide relief for a congested suburban commuter traffic, the MSW route was electrified primarily to expedite the movement of coal traffic. The MSW

Fig. 7.2   Departure of the inaugural train from Liverpool Street on the opening of the electric services to Shenfield on 26 September 1949 (BRB)

provides the first example of a British main line with both freight and passenger traffic operated by electric traction, the electrification of the Newport–Shildon line having been for freight movement only.

The lines to be electrified were amongst the most important east/west freight routes in the country, connecting the East Midlands and South Yorkshire coalfields and industrial areas with those of Manchester and Merseyside. The line from Sheffield to Manchester ran through the Pennines via two single-line tunnels, three miles long, with long steep gradients on both sides, the ruling gradient being 1 in 100. The line from Wath to Barnsley Junction, the connection with the Sheffield–Manchester route, is even more steeply graded and sharply curved. The heaviest grade is the 1 in 40 Wentworth Bank, just over two miles in length, on which four steam engines were needed, two hauling and two banking, to handle a 1000 ton train. When the Garratt locomotive built for banking purposes over this route was available, it replaced the two 2–8–0 banking engines otherwise employed. The difficulties of working heavy freight trains over this route, due to the long and steep grades, and the limitations imposed on line capacity by the Woodhead tunnels, which were badly ventilated, to the extreme discomfort of train crews, were the principal grounds for the conversion of the route to electric traction.

The first proposals were prepared by the LNER in 1926. Significant operating and maintenance savings and a 50 per cent increase in line capacity were forecast but, presumably for capital finance reasons, the proposals were not developed. When in 1936 the LNER revived the scheme, it was the intention to retain the old Woodhead Tunnels, open wire telephone circuits, semaphore signalling, and steam shunting locomotives. Seventy-eight new electric locomotives were to be built, the ten used on the withdrawn Newport–Shildon electrification being transferred to the MSW for banking purposes. Forty-one 40-ton vacuum-fitted goods brake vans were included in the proposals to assist braking on the trains. Eight three-car electric multiple unit trains were to be introduced for the passenger services between Manchester and Glossop and Hadfield. Eleven sub-stations were to be provided, controlled from a control room at Penistone.

Work on the scheme, estimated to give a return on capital of 6·64 per cent, started in 1938 but, like the Liverpool Street–Shenfield project, was suspended in 1940.

In December 1944, a LNER Committee reviewed the scheme and modified it to secure further benefits from the increased expenditure which would be involved in post-war conditions, and to take cognisance of changed traffic requirements. The modifications agreed included revised engine-changing facilities for both passenger and freight trains; the introduction of lighter, faster trains requiring one banker only on the Wath route and none on the direct route, and dispensing with the need for the 40-ton brake vans; a requirement for a new tunnel to be driven at

Fig. 7.3   The first of the BB locomotives for the MSW line. This locomotive (No. 6701)
built at Doncaster in 1946, was the one which was loaned to the Netherlands Railways
after the war (BRB)

Thurgoland; and replacement of all semaphore distant signals by colour-lights. The locomotives from the Newport–Shildon electrification were no longer needed, only one being retained for use as a shunting loco-motive at the Ilford depot until the Liverpool Street–Shenfield lines were converted to the a.c. system. Work was resumed in 1946 but the Liverpool Street–Shenfield electrification was given priority and for the next two or three years progress on the MSW route was slow.

In the meantime, attempts to repair the old Woodhead Tunnels had failed and in 1947 it was decided to construct a new double-line tunnel, a decision which had a major influence on the overall time-table for the electrification. Work on the tunnel, which is referred to again in Chapter Nine, started in February 1949 and was completed by October 1953.

The final scheme, as approved by the Railway Executive after a review of the project in 1950, provided for 58 BB 1868 h.p. and seven CC 2700 h.p. locomotives. One of the BB locomotives had been completed before the project was stopped on the outbreak of war. It was tried out on the Manchester South Junction–Altrincham line and, after the war, was sent to the Netherlands Railways for extended tests. BR engineers spent some time in Holland to assess the capabilities of the locomotive, which was affectionately named 'Tommy' by the Dutch. On the return of the loco-motive to Britain, the Netherlands Railways presented the General Manager of the Eastern Region (C. K. Bird) with a Delft plate commem-orating the loan of the locomotive and the co-operation between the two railway administrations. The seven Co-Co locomotives were withdrawn from service and sold to the Netherlands Railways in 1968–9.

The future of the MSW line is now in some doubt. A number of factors contribute to this. Of the four routes across the Pennines, the one via the Woodhead Tunnel – with no through passenger services – has the greatest surplus capacity and the least potential for traffic increase in the future. The volume of coal traffic passing over the route has declined

Fig. 7.4   Work in progress on the erection of three d.c. electric locomotives at Dukinfield in 1950. Mechanical parts, bogies, and bodies for the MSW locomotives were constructed at Gorton Works and traction motors and electrical equipment by Metropolitan-Vickers at Trafford Park. Erection of the locomotives was undertaken at Dukinfield (BRB)

considerably owing to pit closures in the Wath area and the development of the Selby coalfield will further influence the pattern of coal distribution, with a reduced demand for cross-Pennine movement. On balance, it seems likely that it may be found to be more economical to close the MSW line as a through route.

The Plan for the Modernization and Re-equipment of British Railways, announced by the BTC in January 1955, has been fully covered in Chapter Four. As noted therein, it provided for a major change in traction policy, with a widespread move from steam to diesel and electric power. It accepted that there was a wide field for the electrification of suburban services and indicated a number of routes which were then under consideration for conversion, namely

Shenfield to Chelmsford and Southend Victoria (approximately 30 route miles: already authorized and in process of implementation);

London, Tilbury, and Southend Central line (approximately 85 route miles);

Liverpool Street to Enfield, Chingford, Hertford East, and Bishop's Stortford (approximately 55 route miles);

King's Cross and Moorgate to Hitchin and Letchworth, including the Hertford Loop (approximately 60 route miles);

Glasgow Suburban lines (approximately 190 route miles).

Fig. 7.5 Class 76 1500 V d.c. BB locomotive No. 26020 in Reddish Depot, prior to working
the first train through the new Woodhead Tunnel (A. H. Emerson)

It was proposed, under the Plan, that all these schemes should be completed.

It was also the intention to extend the Southern Region electrification to all main routes east of a line drawn from Reading to Portsmouth. This would extend the electrified zone to Ramsgate, Dover, Folkestone, and (via Ashford) Hastings, and, in conjunction with diesel services, would eliminate steam from all the lines in the area mentioned. This programme would entail electrifying about 250 route miles.

The Plan also stated that there was a wide range of main-line services on which the traffic levels might provide a good economic case for electrification, subject to the amount of civil and signal engineering works which might be involved. The BTC recognized that there was a physical limit to the amount of main-line electrification which could be carried out within the period of the Plan (up to 1970) and signified their intention to

Fig. 7.6 Class 77 1500 V d.c. CC locomotive No. 27000 built for the MSW line. These
locomotives were eventually sold to the Netherlands Railways and are still in use, with some
modification to cab layout and braking system (BRB)

concentrate on two major trunk routes and one of lesser density. The trunk routes chosen were the main line of the Eastern and North Eastern Regions from King's Cross to Doncaster, Leeds, and (possibly) York, and the London Midland Region main line from Euston to Birmingham, Crewe, Liverpool, and Manchester. The subsidiary main-line route would be the extension of the existing electrification from Liverpool Street (which would soon reach Chelmsford) to Ipswich, including the Clacton, Harwich, and Felixstowe branches.

In proposing the East Coast main line for electrification, the Plan had followed the recommendations of the Harrington Committee in 1951. Ultimately, however, the BTC decided to postpone the East Coast scheme and instead to give priority to the LM Region route. Electrification of the West Coast main line would serve a greater number of large cities, whereas the East Coast route was largely concerned with mineral traffic and covered a much more sparsely populated area with relatively small towns. Other projects which in the event were not pursued under the Plan were electrifications beyond Colchester to Ipswich, Harwich, and Felixstowe.

An Electrification Committee was set up, comprising:

S. B. Warder (Chief Officer, Electrical Engineering, BTC: Chairman).

R. C. Bond (Chief Officer, Mechanical Engineering, BTC).

J. H. Fraser (Chief Signal and Telecommunications Engineer, BTC).

R. F. Harvey (Chief Officer, Operating and Motive Power, BTC).

C. W. King (Chief Civil Engineer, BTC).

J. R. Pike (Chief Commercial Officer, BTC).

A. E. Robson (Chief Officer, Carriage and Wagon Engineering, BTC), to recommend priorities for electrification schemes included in the Plan. It published its first report in March 1957. Summarizing the authorizations already given, it set out proposed priorities for further electrification work and emphasized the need for a continuous flow of plans for further schemes early enough to ensure that work could proceed without interruption and that associated non-electrification works could also be programmed to suit.

The Committee's proposals for electrification were set out in three groups, as under:

Group	Period covered	Route miles	Single track miles
A	Up to 1970: in Modernization Plan and additional thereto	3145	8151
B	1970–1980	1645	4083
C	After 1980	683	2144
	Total	5473	14378

This was truly an ambitious programme, covering about one-third of the entire rail network of the country. It was a programme based mainly on engineering capability to electrify and took relatively little account of the commercial potentialities.

Following the issue of the report, the BTC agreed the basis for future planning of progressive electrifications during the period 1963 to 1990, additional to what was in the Modernization Plan. The lines they listed were

  (a) the East Coast route: Leeds and York to Newcastle, Edinburgh, Dundee, and Aberdeen;

  (b) the West Coast route: Weaver Junction to Carlisle, Glasgow, Perth, and Kinnaber Junction (for Aberdeen);

  (c) Glasgow to Edinburgh;

  (d) East Anglia: principal lines beyond Ipswich and Bishop's Stortford;

  (e) principal lines in Lincolnshire, South Yorkshire, and Nottinghamshire;

  (f) principal routes in the North-East coast area and the West Riding of Yorkshire;

  (g) the former Midland main line from St Pancras to Leeds and Manchester;

  (h) Southern Region lines from Waterloo to Southampton, Bournemouth, Weymouth, and Exeter.

In July 1959 a White Paper (Cmd. 893) 'Reappraisal of the Plan for the Modernization and Re-equipment of British Railways' set out the achievements under the Plan to the end of 1958 and re-examined in detail the future course of the Plan, with particular reference to the five years to the end of 1963. The White Paper noted that the Liverpool Street–Shenfield electrification had been extended to Chelmsford and Southend Victoria in 1956 and confirmed the decision to switch resources from the Great Northern main line in order to complete the whole of the electrification of the LM Region route from Euston to Birmingham, Crewe, Manchester, and Liverpool. It deferred electrification from Colchester to Ipswich and Harwich and on the Great Northern main line until after 1964 but inserted electrification beyond Bishop's Stortford to Cambridge within the latter time-scale. The electrifications beyond Colchester and Bishop's Stortford and on the GN main line still rank, twenty years later, as future possibilities, although the former may well soon be coming forward for approval.

For thirty years prior to nationalization there had been intermittent reassessments of the systems of power supply which should be adopted for electric railway traction in Britain. In 1948, the BTC thought it desirable to review the situation once again, in the light of developments in electrical technology since the early 1930s. A Committee of Railway Executive and London Transport technical and operating officers, with a representative from Merz and McLellan, was therefore set up for this purpose, under the chairmanship of C. M. Cock, Chief Officer, Electrical Engineering.

This Committee reported in 1950 and endorsed the recommendations of its predecessors that the 1500 V d.c. overhead system should be the standard for future electrifications, except for certain reservations in regard to the Southern Region. It did not, however, rule out the possibility of using direct current at 3000 V or high-voltage single-phase alternating current at 50 cycles per second. In considering the a.c. system, the Committee recognized the advantages it possessed in minimizing the cost of fixed installations, but on information then available considered that this would be counter-balanced by the greater cost of locomotives and motor coaches and by other drawbacks of a technical nature. The Committee estimated that some 6500 route miles (43·4 per cent of the rail network) had a traffic density which would justify electrification on economic grounds. At that time, less than 1000 route miles were electrified or in course of conversion, about 720 miles on the Southern Region and 240 miles on other Regions.

The Committee's recommendations were accepted by the BTC, who decided that, whilst extensions to the Southern Region electrification should continue on the low-voltage d.c. third-rail system, the standard for main-line and suburban electrifications elsewhere in the country should be on the 1500 V d.c. overhead principle.

They did, however, authorize the restoration of electric services on the Lancaster–Morecambe–Heysham line of the LM Region, to gain first-hand experience of the 50-cycle a.c. system under British conditions. The existing overhead line was reconditioned to take 6·6 kV at industrial frequency. Stock originally built for the Willesden–Earls Court electrification in 1914 was fitted with new equipment by the English Electric Co and transferred to the Lancaster–Morecambe–Heysham line for the trial running.

To adopt the 1500 V d.c. system was the logical decision at that time, if there was to be rapid progress in the conversion of routes to electric traction. The technical problems had been solved and the system gave good results. Certainly, the engineers were not unaware of the possibilities of a high-voltage a.c. system. Indeed, there had been a.c. systems, albeit at a lower voltage and a lower frequency, installed on the Lancaster–Morecambe–Heysham and the LB & SCR lines some 40 years earlier. Apart from isolated experiments overseas, however, the 25 kV 50-cycle a.c. system was to a large extent an unknown quantity. Whilst it opened up the possibilities of considerable economies, and could produce clear advantages in operating efficiency, there were at that time a number of unsolved problems.

Overseas, electric traction was being introduced, at varying rates of progress and, as in Britain, a variety of supply systems had been adopted. Before the Second World War, the tendency had been to favour the a.c.

overhead system, with the higher voltage d.c. overhead system as second choice. After the war, there was an expansion of railway electrification but, because until the mid-1950s the problems associated with a.c. traction at industrial frequency and the benefits to be gained therefrom had not been clarified to an acceptable degree, the trend was to adopt the d.c. overhead system. By then, roughly two-thirds of the world's electric railways' route mileage was d.c. operated and one-third a.c. operated, on a varied assortment of voltages and frequencies.

It was in Hungary that the first trials were undertaken with a 50-cycles a.c. system, on the lines from Budapest to Komarom (56 route miles), operating at 16 kV, opened in 1932 and extended to Hegyeshalom (61 route miles) in 1934. The German State Railways, too had been experimenting with 50-cycle electrification, at 20 kV, between Freiburg and Neustadt (35 route miles) since 1936. In order to consolidate and extend this experience, the French Railways opened a short experimental 50-cycle section in Savoy in 1950, operating at 25 kV, between Aix-les-Bains and La Roche-sur-Foron (48 route miles). The system was demonstrated at an international conference organized by SNCF, which was attended by R. A. Riddles and S. B. Warder. The tests were so successful that the French Railways decided to adopt the 25 kV single-phase 50-cycle a.c. system for the electrification which they proposed to undertake in northeastern France on a route which carried the heaviest industrial traffics in the country. This decision was made notwithstanding the fact that in the French central and south-western provinces some 2000 single track miles had already been electrified on the 1500 V d.c. overhead system.

Operation of the section between Valenciennes and Thionville (173 route miles) on the 25 kV a.c. 50-cycle system began in July 1954 and in May 1955 the French Railways invited the international group of railway engineers to a conference at Lille, at which they presented the complete results of their experience after nine months operation. They demonstrated that considerable economies had been achieved in the cost of fixed equipment, after taking into account the cost of additional insulation and the alterations to structures required to provide the greater electrical clearances for the overhead wire, necessitated by the higher voltage. Further, the claim was made that, contrary to earlier expectations, the a.c. locomotives were cheaper and lighter than their d.c. counterparts for equivalent duties.

Experience was in the meantime accruing of the trial running on the Lancaster–Morecambe–Heysham line, which was also proving beyond question that standard d.c. motors used in association with mercury arc rectifiers were entirely satisfactory and reliable in operation. Trials were also being carried out with germanium rectifiers, which at that stage showed great promise – the first time such rectifiers had been used for traction purposes anywhere in the world.

Following the Lille conference, a committee was set up under the chairmanship of E. Claxton, Assistant Electrical Engineer (Development), BR Central Staff, to consider requirements for the electrification of the LM Region main line from Euston to Manchester, Liverpool, and Birmingham, and the advantages and disadvantages of the two systems – 50-cycle a.c. and 1500 V d.c. The results of the Lancaster–Morecambe–Heysham trials, the Aix-les-Bains–La-Roche-sur-Foron developments and the Valenciennes–Thionville project were taken into account by the committee in preparing their report. On the basis of the information provided by this committee, Warder prepared a report in September 1955 comparing the two systems, in relation to estimates of the costs of construction and operation over the LM Region routes in question.

The report covered a wide range of relevant issues:

(a) *Power Supply*

With 1500 V d.c. electrification a large number of sub-stations is required. Generally, individual supplies to them from the national grid were not practicable and a railway-owned distribution system was therefore necessary. With the a.c. system, supply would be simpler and more reliable, with less equipment needed and reduced building costs. The fewer sub-stations required would be owned by the Central Electricity Authority and minimal cabling would be necessary. Power consumption would also be less with a.c. The balance of advantage in this context lay with the 25 kV a.c. system from every point of view. Little difference as between the two systems was expected in so far as the provision of supervisory control installations was concerned, although the scale of facilities was greater for a d.c. system because of the larger number of lineside switching stations.

(b) *Overhead line equipment*

The 1500 V d.c. overhead system, with a contact wire cross-section of 0.6 to 0.75 in^2, involves the use of a compound catenary to support a heavy weight of copper above each electrified track. Because of the higher voltage, the 50-cycle a.c. system permits the use of a much lighter contact wire, of 0.23 in^2 cross-section, requiring only a single catenary. The weight of copper required under the a.c. system is about one-third of that needed under the d.c. system. This reduction in weight of copper permits lighter supporting structures to be provided. The a.c. overhead system therefore economizes materials and is easier and cheaper to maintain.

(c) *Electrical clearances*

Different electrical clearance standards apply in different countries. In Britain the clearances required in connection with the 1500 V d.c. overhead system were as then laid down in Statutory Rules and Orders 1932 No. 827, 'The Railway (Standardization of Electrification) Order 1932.' This specified that

The standard clearances, after allowance has been made for curvature and superelevation, including any movements of the live wires or conductors, and lateral movements of the collectors under any circumstances likely to arise, shall be

(a) through tunnels, under bridges, or other structures between the maximum load gauge likely to be used on the line and the underside of any overhead live wire or conductor . . . normally 10 inches

(b) between any part of any structures and the nearest point of any overhead live wire or conductor . . . 6 inches

Provided that in cases of exceptional difficulty the above clearances (a) and (b) may be reduced to 4 inches as a minimum.

For 25 kV a.c. operation, it was proposed, after studying the clearances adopted in other countries, to adopt a minimum clearance of 11 in static and 8 in passing. The demand for this increased clearance at bridges and tunnels would involve high civil engineering costs in raising bridges or lowering tracks, which would not be incurred with 1500 V d.c. Where civil engineering works could not be carried out at reasonable cost, the line voltage would need to be reduced to 6·25 kV. Automatic switching from one voltage to the other would be initiated by means of track magnets at the changeover points, operating on the locomotive circuits. Locomotives and motor coaches would have to be able to operate over their full speed/power range at either voltage.

(d) *Signalling and telecommunications*

As a general rule, electrification would be accompanied by cabling of open line telecommunications circuits and the replacement of semaphore signals by colour-light signals, combined with a big increase in the amount of track circuiting. Some additional expense would be incurred in cabling Post Office circuits close to the railway and in immunizing certain circuits with earth connections.

(e) *Rolling Stock*

Experience on the French Railways and elsewhere indicated that the a.c. rectifier locomotive had definite advantages over the d.c. resistance-controlled locomotive of similar power: better adhesion permitted lighter locomotives to be used and afforded easier control. Although, type for type, locomotives might be more costly in the earlier stages, eventually, with bulk production, this disadvantage should disappear. Similarly, there was no reason to fear that the a.c. system would in any way prejudice the full development of multiple-unit trains for any service for which they would be economically appropriate: there should indeed be prospects for the expansion of multiple-unit working. Maintenance costs for a.c. units should be no higher than for d.c. units.

   The estimated cost of electrification of the Euston–Manchester–Liverpool scheme by the 25 kV a.c. and 1500 V d.c. systems indicated that the total cost involved in adopting the former system would be appreciably less than the cost of the latter. Cost advantages obtained in power supply and overhead equipment, after taking account of the cost of providing increased clearances, and of train heating and lighting, would be partly off-set by increased outlay on motive power and signalling equipment. Recommendations accordingly were submitted to the BTC who, subject to the approval of the Minister of Transport, decided on 17 November 1955 to depart from the electrification systems hitherto used and to adopt as a standard for future electrifications an overhead supply of alternating current at industrial frequency (50-cycle), generally at a rating of 25 kV. The only exception to this ruling would be those parts of the Southern Region where a change in the existing third-rail system was not practicable. These proposals were approved by the Minister and made public on 6 March 1956.

The decision was not popular in all quarters. The 1500 V d.c. system was by this time well established and successful and there were those within the railways who felt that a change, not exactly in mid-stream but when a significant mileage of line had been electrified on this system, would lead to difficulties. This was not only because, to the railways of Britain, it was a new system which would present teething troubles of unknown proportions, but also because, as lines already equipped came to be extended, there would be complications in regard to change-overs in system, or in carrying out conversions from the old to the new. Delays to the programme of electrification were also considered inevitable whilst new designs were developed and tested.

One who was opposed to the change was Mr den Hollander, General Manager of the Netherlands Railways, who was a member of the BTC's Technical Development and Research Committee. Electrifications which had been carried out in the Netherlands were on the 1500 V d.c. overhead system, and den Hollander was a dedicated d.c. man. Also, the British electrical industry had mixed feelings on the subject. Whilst they recognized that the change would give them a better entree to overseas markets for a.c. equipment, they were concerned not only that they would lose their 'shop window' for d.c. electrifications but also regarding the design and development problems which would arise and the delays which would perforce occur.

The die having been finally cast, there followed a period of intense activity, over some ten/eleven years, when the railway operators and engineers, and the manufacturers and contractors, were heavily occupied in planning, replanning, and implementing a succession of electrification projects, some of which had already been authorized for the 1500 V d.c. system.

The BTC decided, in October 1955, that a pilot main-line scheme would be introduced as soon as possible on the LM Region, to gain experience with the high-voltage system under British conditions. Later in the same month they approved the electrification of the Crewe–Manchester line as the proving ground for the new equipment.

In March 1956 it was decided that priority attention should be given to the Styal line, from Wilmslow to the junction with the main line at

Longsight, a diversionary route of low traffic density from the main Crewe–Manchester line, for use for the testing of electrical equipment and rolling stock and for driver training. The Metropolitan-Vickers gas turbine locomotive No. 18100, built for the Western Region, was converted to straight electric operation, renumbered E.1000, and used for driver training. Some units built for the Glasgow suburban and LT & S lines were also tested there. The Styal line was energized in May 1958.

Another trial line, from Colchester to Clacton, was used for a variety of equipment tests – power supply arrangements, the type of catenary to be used, the effect upon signalling and telecommunications installations, overhead line equipment, locomotive and multiple-unit performance. This line provided the first 25 kV public service in the country.

Experiments to test the proposed clearances were carried out at a number of locations – on the Fenchurch Street to Bow Junction line to test the effect on the clearances of uplift of the wire when a train passed underneath; in Liverpool Street station to establish whether it would be necessary, in particularly tight conditions, to restrict uplift; and at Crewe, to test the clearances necessary in tunnels. In all these cases, the tests were carried out whilst steam trains were still passing beneath the wires.

The most interesting of the tests took place at Colchester St Botolphs soon after the introduction of electric services in April 1959. The test was arranged after a locomotive fireman was electrocuted, as a result, it was alleged, of the high-voltage current arcing a distance of nine feet between the wires and the locomotive. At a meeting with Ministry Inspecting Officers, after the accident, British Railways electrical engineers strongly refuted any suggestion that the current could, in fact, arc to that extent. Brigadier C. A. Langley, Chief Inspecting Officer of Railways, then asked for a practical test, which he would attend, to be carried out to establish just how far an arc could jump. This took place at St Botolphs under a length of wire energized at 25 kV, with representatives of the engineering and operating departments and the trades unions present. A J20 class steam locomotive, making plenty of smoke, with a dummy man, graphited to make it as near as possible to the human body in its ability to attract the current, placed astride the boiler, was positioned beneath the wires. The wire was then gradually lowered and only when it was within 1¾ in of the chimney top and the dummy man did a flash-over occur. The adequacy of the proposed 11 in clearance was thus convincingly proved.

The suburban a.c. electrification schemes were planned for 6·25 kV operation in congested areas where the costs of providing the full clearances required for 25 kV working would have been prohibitive. This was still the situation when the West Coast main-line electrification was initially planned but developments in overhead line equipment design, combined with a reduction in the loading gauge from 13 ft 6 in to 13 ft 1 in, enabled the whole of the scheme to be designed for 25 kV operation.

Reductions in the electrical clearances have been agreed on two occasions, in the light of operating experience. There are now three standards, 'Normal', 'Reduced', and 'Special Reduced', each having static and passing values. The present values for 25 kV a.c. are:

	Normal	*Reduced*	*Special Reduced*
Static clearance	270 mm (10·6 in).	200 mm (7·9 in).	150 mm (5·9 in).
Passing clearance	200 mm (7.9 in).	150 mm (5·9 in).	125 mm (4·9 in).

In the case of the Reduced and Special Reduced values, the passing clearance between a pantograph and a brick or masonry bridge or tunnel may be further reduced to 80 mm (3·2 in), subject to the prior approval of the Railway Inspectorate. The choice between the three ranges of Normal and Reduced conditions depends on circumstances, with the object of employing that which is greatest without incurring significant extra expense. The Special Reduced Clearance requires a bridge headroom of only 4390 mm (14 ft 5 in) at supports and 4350 mm (14 ft 3½ in) between supports. This is only adopted where there is exceptional difficulty or expense in obtaining reduced clearances or better, and the prior approval of the Railway Inspectorate must be obtained.

As a result of the reduced clearance requirements, and during the relatively slack period in new electrification works in recent years, the opportunity has been taken to concentrate on eliminating 6·25 kV areas installed in previous electrification projects. The need to do this was highlighted by the fact that as traffic increased on the Great Eastern suburban lines it became apparent that the limits of the existing 6·25 kV power supply system were rapidly being reached. The introduction of 19 new four-car electric multiple units (Class 312/1) in 1974–5 to augment the existing fleet precipitated an investigation into the best manner of strengthening the system for both immediate and long-term developments.

The immediate conversion of the line from Gidea Park to Shenfield to 25 kV was recommended, with subsequent conversion of the remaining GE/LTS 6·25 kV lines in stages as circumstances required. By the end of 1978, approximately 60 per cent of the GE 6·25 kV lines had been converted or were in the process of conversion and the intention is to complete the elimination of 6·25 kV operation during 1984. Conversion of the 6·25 kV lines in the Glasgow area, connected with the electrification of the Argyle line – a project sponsored by the Greater Glasgow PTE involving re-opening the Glasgow Low Level Line between Partick and Cambuslang and providing a new junction with the existing North Side electric line at Kelvinhaugh – was completed in November 1979.

The principal advantage derived from the elimination of 6·25 kV is the facility to simplify new locomotive and multiple unit designs by avoiding the need for dual voltage selection and traction equipment. It has also enabled thyristor-controlled equipment (referred to later) to be specified for all a.c. traction, which, because of unacceptable levels of inductive interference, might not have been possible for 6·25 kV operation.

The need for a reasonably firm forward programme of electrification cannot be over-emphasized. The preparation of plans for an electrification project of any significant size is an arduous and lengthy task. Lack of continuity, with inevitable gaps in work-load, compels the railways and contractors alike to disperse their electrification teams and it takes time to build them up again. Enthusiasm and impetus is lost, costs are higher, and the time when financial benefits can be reaped is deferred.

The planning of an electrification project involves many railway departments and there must be a continual interchange of information between them. Planning methods as between Regions have varied to some extent but, in all essentials, a similar sequence has been followed. First, there must be a review of traffic levels under steam or diesel operation, and an assessment made of the potential increases which might be secured under electrification. Then, notional timetables must be produced by the operators to provide the pattern and intensity of train service to meet that potential and an estimate made of the locomotive, rolling stock, and other facilities which would be required. Thereafter, an overall survey of the route is required, assisted where necessary by aerial photography to formulate a broad idea of the physical facilities which would be needed, which lines and/or sidings could be dispensed with, what diversionary lines or sidings should be covered by the project, or in what other ways the route might need to be rationalized. Decisions are then required on the level of power supply and whether the proposed service would call for re-organization or renewal of the signalling system.

At that stage there have to be detailed inspections of the route, either departmentally, for later co-ordination, or by a joint 'walk-out' by railway departments and contractors concerned, to decide precisely

(a) what track alterations are necessary;
(b) which bridges or tunnels will need to be modified or rebuilt to provide the necessary clearances;
(c) what station platforms and buildings and other lineside structures require to be modified or reconstructed;
(d) where feeder stations, track sectioning cabins, switching facilities, and neutral sections are necessary;
(e) where overhead line support structures will be sited;
(f) where new signalboxes, relay rooms, and signal posts will be located, bearing in mind the need for clear signal sighting;
(g) where depots for the three engineering departments, with sidings and loading facilities for works trains, and adequate storage space for steelwork, cable and conductor wire drums, signalling, and civil engineering materials should be sited;
(h) where maintenance depots should be located;

(i) in which areas special arrangements need to be made, for example at level crossings or where power lines cross the track; and

(j) what wayleaves and easements will be necessary.

Next, the route needs to be split into suitably sized sections for the allocation of work and sequence priorities, and detailed data sheets prepared of the items to be dealt with in each section.

The time has then arrived when all the planning has to be brought together in a submission document for authority. The necessary financial data include the capital outlay involved, the estimated annual operating and maintenance costs compared with present methods of operation, the likely financial effects of alternative proposals (for example, dieselization instead of electrification), the renewal costs which would be avoided, and the estimated financial effect of the project, in terms of return on capital outlay. A target date for completion of the project, by stages if appropriate, and the spread of expenditure over the period are also required.

Submission made and authority given, a further period of intense activity follows, before work on the ground can actually start. This includes seeking tenders and letting contracts, ordering materials, agreeing power supply arrangements with the Central Electricity Generating Board, and working out line possession and works train programmes. Line possessions always constitute a very acute problem. Traffic must operate as normally as possible during construction work, unless acceptable diversionary routes are available.

Table 7.3 lists the electrification projects which have been undertaken since nationalization.

The map on the next page illustrates the extent of electrification at the end of 1979, amounting to approximately 21 per cent of total route miles.

When the BTC decided to abandon their earlier adoption of 1500 V d.c. in favour of high-voltage single-phase 50-cycle a.c. as the standard for main-line and suburban electrification, work was already well advanced on the Chelmsford and Southend Victoria extensions at 1500 V d.c. It would inevitably have caused considerable delay to the modernization of the services in question if a decision had been taken to convert work already completed to the a.c. system before further progress was made. The electrification was therefore completed on the 1500 V d.c. system.

In July 1958, however, it was decided that in the interests of ultimate economy and operating efficiency in the area concerned, and over the further routes destined for electrification, it was preferable to adopt alternating current throughout and face up to the technical problems and temporary operating inconvenience during conversion of the existing electrified lines to the new system. Electrification of the North-east London lines (Liverpool Street to Enfield, Chingford, Hertford East, and Bishop's Stortford) and the Fenchurch Street to Tilbury, Southend Central, and Shoeburyness lines was due for completion in 1960 and 1962 respectively and a study of the situation indicated that it would be

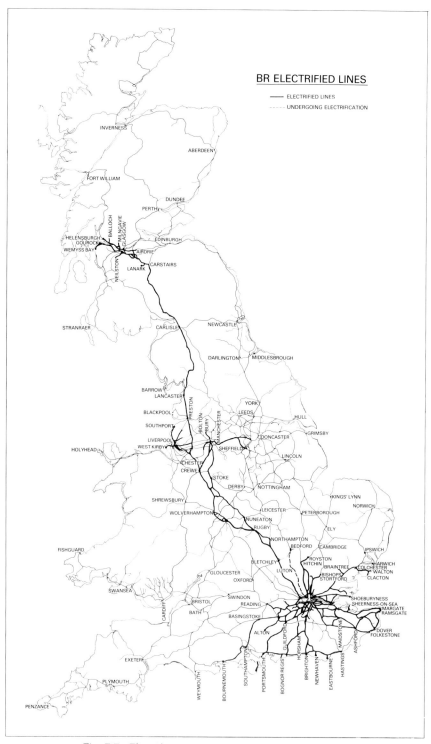

Fig. 7.7   Electrification progress on BR by end 1979

Table 7.3   British Railways: Electrification Schemes after nationalization.
(Electrification on 6·25 kV or 25 kV a.c. 50-cycle overhead system,
unless otherwise stated)

Date service introduced	Route	Route miles
EASTERN REGION		
Sept. 1949	Liverpool Street–Shenfield (1500 V d.c. overhead).	20
Sept. 1954	Manchester–Sheffield–Wath (1500 V d.c. overhead).	73
Jun. 1956	Shenfield–Chelmsford (1500 V d.c. overhead)	10
Dec. 1956	Shenfield–Southend Victoria (1500 V d.c. overhead)	21
Apr. 1959	Colchester–Clacton–Walton	24
Nov. 1960	Liverpool Street–Shenfield (Conversion to a.c.)	20
Nov. 1960	Shenfield–Southend Victoria (Conversion to a.c.)	21
Nov. 1960	Liverpool Street–Enfield/Chingford/Hertford East/Bishop's Stortford	46
Mar. 1961	Shenfield–Chelmsford (Conversion to a.c.)	10
Jun. 1962	Chelmsford–Colchester	23
Jun. 1962	London–Tilbury–Southend Central	74
May 1969	Lea Valley (Clapton–Cheshunt)	9
Oct. 1977	Braintree–Witham	6
Nov. 1976	GN Suburban: Stage I: Inner Suburban: (750 V d.c. 3rd rail through Northern City Line Tunnels)	70
Feb. 1978	GN Suburban: Stage II: Outer Suburban	
LONDON MIDLAND REGION		
	Euston–Manchester/Liverpool/Birmingham:	
Sept. 1960	Stage I: Crewe–Manchester: Styal Line	495
Jan. 1962	II: Crewe–Liverpool	
Euston–Manchester/Liverpool, Apr. 1966:	III: Crewe–Birmingham	
	IV: Rugby–Birmingham–Lichfield	
	V: Rugby–Euston	
	VI: Rugby–Stafford	
Euston–Birmingham, Mar. 1967	VII: North Staffordshire Line (Cheadle Hulme-Colwich)	
May 1971	Manchester South Junction–Altrincham (Converted to 25 kV a.c.)	9
	BR and Mersyside PTE projects:	
May 1977	Merseyside Loop, below Liverpool:	2
	Link Line, Sandhills–Moorfields.	2
Oct. 1977	Liverpool Central–Garston	5
Target 1982	St Pancras/Moorgate–Bedford	53

Table 7.3   Electrification Schemes continued

Date service introduced	Route	Route miles
LONDON MIDLAND AND SCOTTISH REGIONS		
May 1974	{ Weaver Junction–Gretna Junction	132
	{ Gretna Junction–Glasgow Central	103
SCOTTISH REGION		
	Glasgow Suburban:	
Nov. 1960	Stage I, Phase 1: North of Clyde:	52
	Glasgow Queen St–Helensburgh–Balloch–Milngavie–	
	Bridgeton–Springburn–Airdrie	
May 1962	Stage I, Phase 2: South of Clyde:	29
	Glasgow Central–Neilston–Motherwell via King's	
	Park–Cathcart Circle	
Jun. 1967	Stage II: Glasgow Central to Gourock and Wemyss Bay	35
	Lanark Branch and Hamilton Circle	10
Nov. 1979	Argyle Line (Partick–Cambuslang) Greater	4¾
	Glasgow PTE: 'Trans-Clyde')	
SOUTHERN REGION		
	Kent Coast (750 V d.c. 3rd rail)	
Jun. 1959	Stage I: Gillingham–Ramsgate; Sittingbourne–	78
	Sheerness; Faversham Junction–Dover Marine	
Jun. 1962	Stage II: Sevenoaks–Dover; Folkestone Harbour	132
	Branch; Buckland and Deal Junction to Minster	
	Junction; Ashford–Ramsgate via Canterbury West;	
	Maidstone East–Ashford; Paddock Wood–Maidstone	
	West	
Mar. 1967	Isle of Wight (Ryde Pier–Shanklin): (630 V d.c. 3rd rail)	9
Jul. 1967	Bournemouth Line (Sturt Lane, near Brookwood–	90
	Branksome, and including Lymington Branch) (750 V	
	d.c. 3rd rail)	

impracticable to achieve these targets without first converting the existing 1500 V d.c. lines, to permit co-ordination of working and flexibility in the use of rolling stock over all the electrified routes in the area.

A target date of late September 1960 was set for the conversion. The major problems arose in connection with the modification of the overhead line equipment. To have adopted 25 kV a.c. entirely would have involved insulator changing throughout and led to considerable disturbance of services, due to the amount of bridge raising which would have been involved. These difficulties were avoided by adopting between Liverpool Street and Southend Victoria the 6·25 kV a.c. system, for which existing clearances were adequate. On the Shenfield–Chelmsford section the electric services were replaced for a period of some months by diesel traction, to permit of the conversion of equipment for 25 kV. Whilst it was possible to retain, with some modifications, the 33 kV three-phase switchgear at supply points, it was necessary to replace d.c. equipment at sub-stations and track sectioning cabins with new 25 kV/6·25 kV a.c. equipment, generally in new buildings, the need to maintain d.c. traction supplies right up to the change-over precluding the possibility of utilizing existing sub-station buildings.

So far as rolling stock was concerned, fitting the units with a.c. equipment was rejected, in favour of the addition of transformers and rectifiers to give a constant voltage of 1500 V, with the retention of the existing d.c. traction motors and resistance controls. This was a less expensive solution, was more easily carried out, and made it possible to continue to operate the stock on direct current, after conversion, pending the change-over. Some structural re-design was necessary as the transformer and rectifier had, by reason of weight and space, to be accommodated in, and the pantograph on, the coach adjacent to the motor coach, instead of the motor coach itself. At the change-over, 70 units built for the LT & S line were put into use on the converted lines, pending the conversion of the remainder of the allocated stock. The final changeover between Liverpool Street, Shenfield, and Southend Victoria was carried out in the course of one weekend, 4–6 November 1960, without significant interruption of electric train services and on the Shenfield–Chelmsford line in March 1961.

The meticulous manner in which the conversion was planned and implemented reflects very considerable credit on all concerned. Technically, it was probably a more demanding task than the planning and implementation of a new electrification project, because of the very short time which was available for the conversion.

In October 1960, British Railways, in co-operation with industry, held a four-day international conference at the Institution of Civil Engineers, to demonstrate the progress which had been made with electrification in Britain. Some forty papers were presented, covering all aspects of electrification. Included in the Conference programme were visits to the LM Region Crewe–Manchester electrification and Eastern Region schemes – the Colchester–Clacton–Walton electrification, which was by then in operation; the conversion projects out of Liverpool Street, which were approaching completion; the North-east London lines, and the London–Tilbury–Southend Central project, on which work was in progress. An embarrassing incident occurred on the visit to the North-east London lines electrification. A large party had visited the signalbox at Hackney Downs and was afterwards embarked in an electric multiple unit train for a journey over the Bishop's Stortford line to Broxbourne, to see the new station and signal box there. They were the first passengers to travel in an electric train over this route. Unfortunately, the signalman at Hackney

Downs turned the train on to the Chingford line, which had not yet been energized, instead of on to the Bishop's Stortford line. The result – a vivid flash, a sudden halt, an ignominious haul back into Hackney Downs station by a steam locomotive commandeered from a train passing in the up direction, a new start, and an apologetic explanation to the visitors, broadcast down the train in three languages! One of the authors was O/C Train for this visit and the incident is stamped indelibly upon his memory.

The stock which was to be used on the Enfield–Chingford–Hertford East–Bishop's Stortford services ran for over a year on the Colchester–Clacton branch, with generally satisfactory results. When the full electric services were inaugurated on the North-east London lines, however, considerable trouble was soon experienced with the traction motors, transformers, and rectifiers. Failures were so frequent that it was eventually necessary to withdraw trains for modification. This led to an enforced reduction in peak-hour services from 18 to 15 trains per hour into and out of Liverpool Street. In order to establish the cause of the failures, an inquiry was undertaken by the Chief Inspecting Officer of Railways. A train was specially equipped as a mobile laboratory to record and analyse the behaviour of the power equipment under all conditions of service. The failures were found to be mainly due to excessive voltage surges in the equipment. A number of modifications were subsequently made, including the replacement of the mercury arc by silicon rectifiers and the fitting of surge suppression components in the secondary winding circuits of the transformers.

Electrification from Liverpool Street to Chelmsford and of the Colchester–Clacton–Walton branch left a gap of some 23 route miles between Chelmsford and Colchester and it was logical to electrify this section, to cater for the expanding population beyond Chelmsford and to provide passengers from the Clacton, Frinton, and Walton areas with through services into and out of Liverpool Street. This work was completed during 1961–2 and through services brought into operation in 1962.

In the meantime, electrification of the Fenchurch Street–Tilbury–Southend Central–Shoeburyness route was approaching completion. This project was initially planned for 1500 V d.c. but was changed to high-voltage a.c. operation before work actually started. Some rationalization of facilities with London Transport lines, which ran alongside from Bromley to Barking and Upminster, was undertaken. Considerable trouble was experienced on this route due to the effect of sea spray upon the overhead line equipment and pollution by dust from the cement works at West Thurrock Junction caused damage to insulators.

With the completion of this electrification in 1962, the Great Eastern suburban services were virtually complete. There remained only the Lea Valley line, between Clapton and Cheshunt, and the Witham–Braintree branch. The former route, used for freight and locomotive-hauled passenger trains to and from Cambridge and East Anglia, was electrified in 1969 and so permitted an expansion of electrified services from the areas of continuing population growth around Hertford, Harlow, and Bishop's Stortford. This electrification was also a pre-requisite of any future main-line electrification beyond Bishop's Stortford. It was over this route that the new Mark III overhead equipment, referred to later, was first used.

The Witham–Braintree branch was the last line in the Great Eastern suburban area which would justify electrification. The overhead systems design and implementation of the project were carried out in 1976–7 by the Eastern Region's own staff – a practice which is now advocated for all small schemes – the only work contracted out being the digging of the mast foundations.

The electrification of the Great Northern suburban services, included in the Modernization Plan, was finally approved in August 1971. The scheme covered the inner suburban services between Moorgate, Welwyn Garden City, and Hertford North as a first stage, and the outer suburban services between King's Cross, Hitchin, and Royston, on the Cambridge branch, as a second stage. A diesel service from Cambridge connects with the electric service at Royston. In order to bring the inner suburban services into Moorgate, arrangements were made to take over the London Transport Northern City line from Drayton Park to Moorgate, with connection to the GN lines at Finsbury Park.

The plan involved:

(a) major alterations at King's Cross station;
(b) modernization of 34 other stations;
(c) renewal, reconstruction or track lowering at 51 bridges;
(d) track lowering in 14 separate tunnel bores;
(e) extensive remodelling of the tracks between King's Cross and Wood Green;
(f) the erection of a new flyover at Welwyn Garden City to take inner suburban trains over the main line, to avoid conflicting with Inter-City trains;
(g) the provision of a new maintenance depot at Hornsey and carriage sidings at Welwyn Garden City, Hertford North, and Letchworth;
(h) the renewal of signalling and telecommunications equipment, with a new signal box at King's Cross replacing 57 smaller boxes;
(i) the provision of power supplies, with sub-stations, track sectioning cabins, and an electrical control room:
(j) the erection of overhead equipment over 67·3 route miles of track; and
(k) the relaying and reballasting of track and the installation of third-rail equipment on 2·7 miles through the Northern City Line tunnels.

The GN inner suburban motor coaches incorporate special equipment to enable them to operate on both the 25 kV a.c. overhead contact and 750

V d.c. third-rail contact system, with current collection through panto-graphs and conventional shoegear respectively. Specially designed change-over equipment has been installed on the trains, for activation at Drayton Park, which is electrified on both systems, with a time delay on the signalling.

In carrying out this work the engineers were faced with particularly onerous problems. A heavy service of Inter-City trains already passed over the King's Cross–Hitchin route and it was decreed by management that no more than six minutes delay should be imposed on any train. The restrictions which this decision placed upon line possessions led to a number of innovations in construction methods, including the winching in of conductor wires

A suggestion that the main line between Wood Green and Langley Junction, near Stevenage, should be closed for a time, with all trains being diverted via the Hertford Loop, was discarded, not only because the Inter-City services would have suffered unacceptable delays but also because it would have involved the contractors in considerable staffing difficulties. Despite all these problems, both inner and outer suburban services were introduced in reasonable conformity with the target dates originally set.

An unusual feature of the GN suburban electrification was the need to make provision for the haulage of construction and materials vehicles into the Northern City Line tunnels. For health reasons, the use of diesel locomotives was not permissible. The situation was met by the con-version, at Doncaster Works, of four redundant Class 501 d.c. motor cars into BB battery-driven locomotives, the traction battery being installed in the passenger compartment. The locomotives usually operated in permanently coupled pairs, with a capability of hauling a trailing load of 270 tons at speeds up to 25 miles/h. Similar units have been used in Glasgow and on Merseyside and will be used in later construction work on the Midland (St Pancras) suburban scheme.

In regard to the LM Region main-line scheme, work on the direct Crewe–Manchester line was completed to schedule in September 1960. In the meantime, planning continued on the electrification of the other lines involved, the complete project being divided into stages, as indicated in Table 7.3 above. In October 1958 the BTC had recorded that the planned timing for the completion of electrification on the LM Region was no longer acceptable and would have to be speeded up a great deal. Later in the year, it was ordained by the BTC that the LM Region scheme must be given top priority. Electrification schemes actually in progress on other Regions were not to be interfered with, but it might be necessary to postpone any which had not yet started. During the construction period, traffic had wherever possible to be diverted to East Coast or Western Region routes, to provide the maximum working time practicable on the LM Region routes. A report prepared in 1959 set out plans for completing

Fig. 7.8 Battery-driven locomotive first used to haul works trains during electrification works in Northern City Line tunnels. Each locomotive consists of two redundant motor cars, suitably modified to accommodate the batteries (BRB)

the project by 1964, instead of Euston to Manchester and Liverpool in mid-1968 and to Birmingham by the end of 1970, as originally envisaged in 1956, when the initial plans were drawn up.

In the event, that degree of acceleration was not to be realized. In the later 1950s/early 1960s British Railways were beset by financial difficulties. Earlier chapters have indicated that ever since nationalization it had become the practice of Government to attempt to overcome such difficulties, whether financial or otherwise, by re-organization, sometimes preceded by an independent, or partially independent, committee of investigation. The solution sought by the Government in the early 1960s was no different. In addition to an investigation by the Parliamentary Select Committee on Nationalized Industries, requested by Sir Brian Robertson, the Government set up a committee under the chairmanship of Sir Ivan Stedeford, to which reference has already been made in Chapter Three. In the course of its investigations, the Stedeford Committee examined the case for the LM Region electrification and took the view that its justification would be difficult to prove.

Despite the Committee's doubts, the project continued but, following the appointment of H. C. (later Sir Henry) Johnson as General Manager of the LM Region in 1962, work was suspended for a time whilst a review of the project was undertaken to establish whether all its elements could be fully justified. Subject to the elimination of certain lightly trafficked routes from the project, it was allowed to proceed. In all, about a year was lost in the completion of the project as a result of these doubts and reviews.

Thereafter, introduction of electric services was by stages, until the full service operated from Euston to Manchester and Liverpool in April 1966 and to Birmingham in March 1967. Thus a project spread over ten years or so, involving not only the electrification works themselves but also a vast associated programme of bridge raising and reconstruction, station re-building or renovation, track works, and signalling, was brought to a close. The electrification proved to be a complete success, from every point of view. In a paper to the Chartered Institute of Transport in January 1968*, 'Main Line Electrification – a First Appraisal', H. C. Johnson commented on the increase in passenger traffic as a result of the electrification. In the first four weeks, journeys were up by 59 per cent on the London–Manchester services and 60 per cent on the London–Liverpool route: receipts were up by 53 per cent and 46 per cent respectively. In the first year after through electric services were introduced between London and Manchester/Liverpool, the increase in journeys and receipts, compared with the previous year, is shown in Table 7.4 below:

Table 7.4 Increase in Passenger Journeys and Receipts after first year of through electric services, Euston to Manchester and Liverpool

	Per cent increase in	
Service	Journeys	Receipts
London–Manchester	54	40
London–Liverpool	55	38
London–Northampton	30	34
London–Rugby	41	34
London–Bletchley	65	41
London–Watford	105	84
Total outer suburban services	68	43

The London–Birmingham electrification had only been in operation a short time when H. C. Johnson's paper was published. Even so, in 24 weeks, the number of journeys between London and Birmingham had increased by some 25 per cent and the receipts by just over ten per cent. Even greater increases were being obtained from inter-provincial journeys such as Birmingham–Manchester and Liverpool–Coventry.

Chartered Institute of Transport Journal Vol. 32 No. 8 January 1968.

Fixed equipment and rolling stock presented little difficulty in operation. There were inevitably some failures but these had little or no adverse effect upon the services. Indeed, passenger train punctuality reached a new all-time high, with 93 per cent of trains on time.

A number of important lessons were learnt from this, the first significant main-line project using the a.c. system. In the first place, there was an over-provision of fixed equipment on running lines and in sidings: alleged needs were more closely questioned in later projects. Secondly, planning should take more positively into account the extent of route rationalization which would be possible or desirable in connection with a project. Thirdly, the importance of speed, as represented by journey time, must be borne in mind in defining commercial and operating needs, and physical provision for such speed must be made accordingly.

The last years of the 1960s saw something of a hiatus in electrification. Apart from the work which was in progress on the Lea Valley line, only one other small project was in hand. The Manchester South Junction–Altrincham line had been electrified on the 1500 V d.c. overhead system in 1931. By 1969 power supplies and cables needed renewal and the existing three-car electric multiple unit sets were life-expired and in poor condition. It was therefore decided to convert the line to the 25 kV a.c. system, so allowing integration with the Euston–Manchester/Liverpool services. No additional rolling stock was needed. Work on the electrification and on the associated extension of the Manchester (Piccadilly) power signalling scheme was started early in 1970 and brought into operation in May 1971. In order to minimize interference with passenger services, the whole of the works involved were carried out on week-day nights and on Sundays.

Concurrently with the installation of 50-cycle a.c. electrification on the Eastern and LM Regions, suburban electrification on the same system was in progress in the Scottish Region, in the Glasgow area. First proposals in regard to suburban electrification were outlined to the LNE and LMS Companies in 1946 by Sir Robert Inglis, LNER Divisional General Manager in Scotland. These proposals were re-examined in 1953 and in 1954 the first of two schemes, for the electrification of suburban lines to the north of the Clyde, between Glasgow Queen Street and Helensburgh, Balloch, Milngavie, Bridgeton, Springburn, and Airdrie, was submitted. This was followed in 1955 by a second scheme, covering the lines to the south of the Clyde, from Glasgow Central to Neilston and Motherwell via King's Park, and including the Cathcart Circle. These two schemes were originally submitted on the 1500 V d.c. system, but were changed, in 1956, to the high-voltage a.c. system and were brought into operation in 1960 and 1962 respectively. The Milngavie branch was used for testing purposes.

The first electric services north of the Clyde came into operation on 5 November 1960 but had to be withdrawn on 18 December 1960 because of a series of transformer failures on the multiple-unit stock. Fortunately, the steam locomotives and coaches in use prior to 5 November had not been dispersed and it was possible to reinstate steam working at very short notice. The reintroduction of steam working, virtually overnight, represented a highly efficient performance on the part of all departments involved.

Five major incidents had led to the decision to withdraw the electric units from service. One of these took place during a rehearsal run on 3 October 1960, but the others occurred in service. In two cases there were serious explosions and in one of these people were injured. Investigation revealed that the transformer secondary windings had overheated, the heat generated turning cooling oil into gas which in turn damaged the transformer tank and cover, by pressure or explosion. In the last of the five cases, on 17 December 1960, the transformer tank cover had burst open and had come down perilously near the track. It was at that stage that the decision was taken to suspend the service.

No similar trouble had been experienced with the first of the units concerned during the time it ran 6700 miles on test on the Styal line, and only minor difficulties had been met with in the course of test running on the Glasgow lines. By the time the public service was introduced, 183000 miles had been run in the course of trials and commissioning, without major problems arising.

The incidents which had occurred were closely investigated by Brigadier C. A. Langley, Chief Inspecting Officer of Railways. He presented an interim report on 13 January 1961 and a final report on 17 March 1962. Static and running tests were conducted of transformer and associated equipment, under varying conditions. A series of modifications was carried out. The main transformer windings were redesigned, so that their strength to withstand electromagnetic forces was very much increased. The transformer's oil cooling system, the air-blast circuit breaker, automatic power control, and rectifiers were also modified. Renewed tests showed that these modifications eliminated voltage surges and, following further running trials, the service was reopened on 1 October 1961.

Even after these modifications, however, and the reintroduction of public services, backfiring of the mercury arc rectifiers continued at an alarming rate, which could have led within a very short space of time to another spate of transformer failures. The official report attributed the failures to the inability of the transformer windings to withstand the effect of frequent short circuits, caused almost certainly by the backfiring of the mercury arc rectifiers. The troubles which were experienced undoubtedly hastened the development of the germanium and silicon rectifiers.

Stage II of the Glasgow suburban electrification covered Glasgow Central to Gourock and Wemyss Bay. Work began in 1965 and the service came into operation in September 1967. It was not until the Argyle line was electrified in 1979 that there was a physical electrified link between the north and south sections of the electrification, in the immediate vicinity of Glasgow.

The 6·25 kV areas south of the Clyde, apart from the east side of the Cathcart Circle, were converted to 25 kV in conjunction with West Coast main-line electrification following the reduction which was found to be possible in the electrical clearance required.

The decision to adopt the high-voltage a.c. system as the standard for future electrifications did not apply to the Southern Region, where the low-voltage d.c. third-rail system, already extensively installed, was to be retained.

The Modernization Plan included the electrification of the Kent Coast services, covering Gillingham–Margate–Ramsgate, Faversham–Dover and the Sheerness Branch in Stage I and Sevenoaks–Ashford–Dover–Ramsgate, Maidstone East–Ashford–Canterbury West–Minster, and Maidstone West–Paddock Wood in Stage II. The Kent project involved a heavy programme of civil engineering works, including the quadrupling of the track in certain areas; the rebuilding of Folkestone Central and Ashford stations; construction of substations, maintenance depots, and carriage cleaning facilities; and laying-in conductor rail and cable routes, as well as resignalling. Stage I services were introduced in June 1959 and Stage II in June 1962.

When the time came to plan for the Waterloo–Bournemouth electrification, however, the economic advantages of adopting the 25 kV a.c. or the 1500 V d.c. overhead system, from the end of the existing electrified system at Sturt Lane Junction (between Brookwood and Farnborough) were assessed before a final decision was taken to retain the low-voltage d.c. system over this route. The study indicated that the cost of a dual d.c./a.c. system, with increased clearances and signalling modifications, would have been nearly 20 per cent more than continuing the low-voltage d.c. system throughout. Similarly, conversion of the existing system to a.c. from Waterloo to Sturt Lane was investigated, but this, too, was shown to be prohibitively expensive.

The Bournemouth electrification was continued through to Branksome, to gain access to the maintenance depot and berthing sidings constructed near the former Bournemouth West station, closed in 1965. Electrification through to Weymouth would have been logical but this extension could not be financially justified. To overcome this problem, four-car units, with two motor coaches giving 3200 h.p., are coupled to non-motored units leading from Waterloo, which on arrival at Bournemouth are detached and worked by a type 3 diesel locomotive under push-pull arrangements to and from Weymouth. This was the first time this operating technique was adopted in Britain and it was only put into operation after comprehensive tests, the outcome of which was approved by the Ministry Inspecting Officers.

Whilst most of the passenger services are covered by multiple-unit sets, certain traffics, including boat trains, still need to be locomotive-hauled, to enable them to be operated over dockside lines. To meet this requirement, ten electric booster locomotives, originally built for the Kent coast electrification, were converted in 1967 to electro-diesels and provided with multiple-unit control so that they could also be used on the push-pull services.

The Bournemouth electrification was the Southern Region's first venture into high-speed electric traction. Commercially and technically it was a success.

The Isle of Wight services between Ryde Pier and Shanklin were electrified at the same time as the Waterloo–Bournemouth line. Former London Transport rolling stock was used for the passenger services, being transferred from the mainland by car ferry.

The 1970s saw some continuing change-over to electric traction – Weaver Junction to Glasgow on the LM and Scottish Regions; the important GN suburban and the minor Witham–Braintree branch schemes on the Eastern Region; the Argyle line scheme in the Scottish Region; and now the LM Region St Pancras–Bedford project.

The Weaver Junction–Glasgow electrification was the second true main-line scheme to be authorized on the high-voltage a.c. system in Britain and was an extension of the Euston main-line project. Indeed, the section from Weaver Junction, through Carlisle, to Gretna Junction was included as Stage III of the initial LM Region proposals.

It was in May 1957 that the BTC originally accepted that plans should be prepared for the continuation of electrification from Weaver Junction to Gretna to link up with a proposed Scottish Region electrification to Glasgow, as one comprehensive scheme. The justification for the electrification was stated to be the large number of through trains which would operate from other electrified lines south of Weaver Junction; the high traffic density between Weaver Junction and Preston; the reduced time required for electric locomotives to haul trains over Shap summit; and the financial benefit which might be derived from the possible closure of the Settle–Carlisle route.

When the total project was originally prepared it included also, as a secondary objective, an extension from Carstairs to Edinburgh (29 route miles) and certain linked lines, namely

Liverpool to Manchester (31 route miles);
Preston to Blackpool (17 route miles);
Lancaster to Morecambe (4 route miles);
Carnforth to Barrow (29 route miles);
suburban lines south of Glasgow, serving the Hamilton, Motherwell and Lanark areas (11 route miles).

In March 1966 the Minister of Transport was informed that a re-examination of the proposals confirmed that the balance of advantage was in favour of electrification, as compared with diesel traction, and he then approved the development of a firm project.

Plans were developed over the next three years and the comprehensive Weaver Junction–Glasgow scheme was authorized in February 1970. Particular attention was directed towards route rationalization. Proposals on this aspect were embodied in a separate submission, providing for track simplification by the removal of redundant points, crossings, and sidings and the remodelling of existing layouts; the installation of continuous welded rail; the renewal of the signalling system and the replacement of existing manual signal boxes by power boxes.

Work on the ground started early in 1971. It was carried out under conditions of great difficulty, particularly on the LM Region section. In Scotland, the availability of alternative routes made it possible to divert main-line trains for a period each day but comparable facilities were not available south of the border. The only available alternatives, for example the Settle–Carlisle line, were too long to use without importing considerable delay into the Anglo-Scottish services. To some extent, the problem was overcome by laying in a large number of facing points for single-line working of normal service trains and to enable works trains to cross over to the opposite line when required. Full electric operation commenced in May 1974, and in all the circumstances, it was a satisfactory achievement that the works were completed virtually on time and at a cost within ten per cent of the estimates.

Authority was given in November 1976 for the electrification of the Midland line from St Pancras to Bedford. Completion is planned for 1982.

Fig. 7.9   A wiring train at work on the Weaver Junction–Glasgow
electrification in 1971 (BRB)

Marketing studies demonstrated that the principal London terminal for this service should be Moorgate and the decision was taken to utilize the Metropolitan 'Widened Lines' between King's Cross and Moorgate (little used since the electrification of the GN suburban services via the Northern City route) for St Albans–London services during the peak periods and also for three trains per hour from Luton and Bedford, off-peak. Interchange between this line, to be known as the Midland City Line, and London Transport will be on the site of the former King's Cross (City Widened Lines) station, where a new station, to be known as 'King's Cross Midland', is being provided.

The project involves the installation of the high-voltage a.c. overhead system throughout, necessitating the rebuilding or lifting of 34 over-bridges and the lowering of the track through some tunnels, to provide the necessary clearances. Rationalization and modernization of the track is being undertaken to increase the maximum speed to 100/110 miles/h, on fast lines and 75 miles/h on slow lines. Due to tight clearances and curvature, the speed through the Midland City Line tunnels will be restricted to 30 miles/h. New maintenance, servicing, and cleaning facilities are being built. Existing signalling will be replaced by multiple-aspect colour-light signalling, controlled from a new box at West Hampstead, the area of control of which will at some future stage be extended to cover lines of the Eastern and Southern Regions, in the London area. The

Fig. 7.10   The Electrical Control Room at Penistone, MSW. This controls the incoming high-tension supply and the outgoing 1500 V d.c. supply to the sub-stations on the electrified route (GEC)

Fig. 7.11   Hornsey Electrical Control room, controlling power supplies for the GN Suburban electrification. It will also control supplies for the St Pancras–Bedford route and has spare capacity to meet further needs in the future (BRB)

control room at Hornsey, provided in connection with the GN suburban electrification, will control the power supply.

It is of interest to note that, initially, control rooms were sited near CM & EE maintenance centres and covered areas corresponding as closely as possible to that of one or more operating controls. The modern concept, however, is for electrical control rooms to supervise as large an area as practicable. One control room will therefore encompass a number of maintenance and operating areas. To assist in the control function, a mimic diagram is provided in the control room, showing the whole of the remotely controlled electrified route. A factor in increasing the range of control rooms has been the introduction of the micro-processor. By using these techniques in the control room at Hornsey, provided for the GN suburban electrification, its range will extend to the St Pancras–Bedford route and later, if required, along the Midland line to Leicester, as well as as far north as Doncaster on the East Coast main line. Another such room at York could cover requirement into the east side of Scotland.

From the time of the adoption of the 25 kV a.c. system as the British standard, research and engineering effort has been continuously directed towards reducing the costs of electrification, not only in regard to the amount of equipment required but also in its design, development, and production. Design was one of the functions reserved to the BTC but Warder, recognizing the contribution which the electrical industry could make in the various electrification fields, set up Development Committees to process developments in all aspects of equipment design. The Regional Electrical Engineers were members of these committees and in this way the Regions too were involved in the decisions which were made. The Research and Development Division was also increasingly brought into the electrification picture. Their part in this will be dealt with rather more fully in Chapter Eleven. Sufficient to say at this stage that they contributed to a number of important developments, particularly in the design of overhead equipment.

The time which elapsed between the initial LM Region main-line electrification and the authorization of the Weaver Junction–Glasgow project provided the opportunity for railway engineers and manufacturers to make a thorough re-appraisal of both equipment design and power supply requirements, with a view to reducing the cost of electrification per single track mile to a level at which further schemes would

Fig. 7.12   1500 V d.c. overhead equipment, supported on heavy steel portal type structures, spanning several MSW tracks approaching Manchester London Road (later re-named Piccadilly) Station (A. H. Emerson)

Fig. 7.13   An electric locomotive hauling an express train under standard Mark I overhead equipment as installed during the 25 kV a.c. electrification of the lines out of Euston. The overhead lines and the steel supporting structures are much lighter than those necessary for 1500 V d.c. installations. The return wires are seen on the left-hand side of the picture (BRB)

Fig. 7.14 Mark IIIA multi-track overhead equipment, as provided for the GN Suburban electrification, showing the further reduction in weight in the overhead equipment and the headspan type of supporting structure (BRB)

become viable. Improvements covered all aspects of power supply and distribution. New designs of overhead line equipment and new types of catenary support structures were evolved. Transformers were improved in design, so that at alternate feeder points only one transformer was required instead of two. New types of sub-stations were designed and vacuum interrupter switchgear, brought into this country from America and virtually maintenance free, was introduced in place of oil circuit breakers.

So far as the overhead line was concerned, a wide range of trials was undertaken, using the test units referred to later in this chapter to

Fig. 7.15 The 1500 V d.c. sub-station at Shenfield. The high-tension supply at 33 kV three-phase a.c., carried along cables parallel to the track, is terminated at outside switchgear on the sub-station raft. Rectifiers and circuit breakers are in the brick building (BRB)

Fig. 7.16   A brick building of the type installed on the electrification out of Euston, to house the a.c. switchgear supplying 25 kV single-phase current to the overhead equipment. There is a considerable reduction in the size and cost of the sub-station, and in the number required, compared with 1500 V d.c. system (BRB)

Fig. 7.17   The type of sub-station introduced with the Weaver Junction–Glasgow electrification. The building and switchgear are prefabricated and assembled on site. All electrical connections to and from the building are by overhead cables. This design has made a significant contribution to the reduction in costs of a.c. electrification. (BRB)

measure train speeds, current levels, pantograph movements, and other relevant data. Other research efforts led to the introduction of galvanized malleable cast-iron fittings on support and register assemblies; ceramic bead insulators, enabling the effective length of neutral sections to be considerably reduced; and other developments in contact wire design to give satisfactory service at high speeds.

The development of overhead line equipment on British Railways since the introduction of high-voltage a.c. electrification by J. E. Broughall, E. Claxton, and, more recently, N. Howard is traced in Table 7.5.

Fig. 7.18 A neutral section of the type initially installed on the electrification from Euston to the north-west. The neutral section separates the supplies from adjacent feeder stations and allows a train to pass without short circuiting the electrical system through the pantograph. A neutral section at this stage of development was a very complex installation (A. H. Emerson)

Fig. 7.19 An electric locomotive passing through a modern neutral section at Tamworth. The simple section insulators – four in all in series in each wire over each track – replace the complex system shown in Fig. 7.18. The development of fibre-glass rod, covered with PTFE or ceramic beads, made possible the design of these section insulators, resulting in a substantial saving in costs (BICCC)

Table 7.5   Development of Overhead Line Equipment

Mark	Date introduced	Main routes on which used	Principal developments compared with previous Mark
I	1957	Colchester–Clacton–Walton Bethnal Green–Enfield/Chingford Lower Edmonton–Hertford East/Bishop's Stortford Chelmsford–Colchester Euston–Manchester/Liverpool Fenchurch Street–Shoeburyness Glasgow Suburban Stage I	—
II	1966	Glasgow Suburban Stage II	Galvanized malleable cast iron components and galvanized steel tubes used extensively on the live side of insulators, replacing copper alloy materials and copper clad steel tubes. 'Sagged simple' catenary construction: i.e., eliminating the auxiliary catenary by allowing some pre-sag in the contact wire
III	1968	Lea Valley (Clapton–Cheshunt)	Distance between catenary and contact wire reduced: insulator creepage distance reduced. Portal type structures replaced by headspans for multi-track locations, except for very poor ground ˉ Use of metric units
IIIA	1972	Weaver Junction–Glasgow GN Suburban Witham–Braintree	Aluminium/steel catenary introduced in place of copper. Standard catenary–contact wire distance further reduced on cantilever construction
IIIB	1978	St Pancras–Bedford	Structure and foundation loadings and allocation undertaken by computer
IIIC	1980		Version of Mark IIIB incorporating 'Imperial' dimensioned fastenings and copper catenary, for use on small schemes adjacent to Mark I and III areas

(See Fig. 7.20 illustrating types of overhead line equipment)

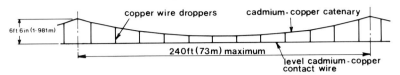

Simple catenary equipment, Mk. I

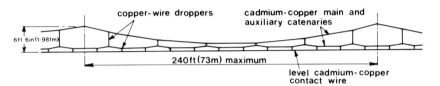

Compound-catenary equipment, Mk. I

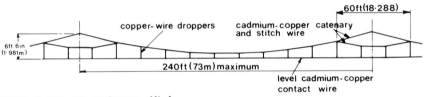

Stitched-catenary equipment, Mk. I

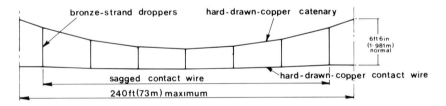

Sagged simple-catenary equipment. Mk. II

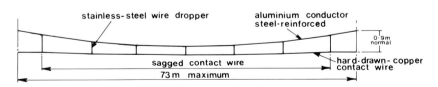

Sagged simple-catenary equipment, Mk. III A

Fig. 7.20 Comparison of overhead equipment longitudinal cross sections. Types of overhead line equipment developed on BR, to meet various speed requirements – simple for slow lines and sidings; stitched for speeds up to 75 miles/h; and compound for 100 miles/h. Sagged simple was developed later, during the search for cost reductions, and Mark IIIA equipment is suitable for 125 miles/h and over

Satisfactory current collection demands that the tension in the contact wire remains constant as the wire expands or contracts with changes in ambient temperature. The equipment originally designed for the West Coast main line was suitable for speeds only up to 100 miles/h and the decision to operate the first electric Advanced Passenger Trains over the route, at speeds up to 125 miles/h, made some redesign of the overhead equipment necessary. Experiment showed that one factor which could assist towards achieving this objective was an improvement in the tensioning arrangements.

At the same time, serious trouble was experienced with the overhead wire already installed on the route. Sagged simple equipment was erected, to standards appropriate to moderate British conditions, with spans up to 240 ft in most cases, although restricted to 215 ft in known exposed areas. Very high winds which were experienced during the first two winters of operation caused the contact wire to be blown off the pantograph on a number of occasions, resulting in serious damage to the overhead wires and disruption of the service. These blow-offs were attributed to the fact that higher wind velocities were met with than had been predicted by meteorological experts. The higher wind speeds were found to have been caused by reduced ground surface roughness on the approach side (for example, in an open sea situation), funnelling from valleys at right angles to the line, the acceleration of air flowing up and over an embankment, or a combination of these factors. These not only caused the sagged contact wire to move away from its normal position, but also the locomotive and pantograph to rock. When these two movements occurred in opposing directions the contact wire came off the side of the pantograph head, causing the latter to rise and strike the catenary equipment. Experiment showed that this trouble could be overcome by modification of the tensioning arrangements, together with the erection of additional structures in especially troublesome areas. The introduction of tapered roller bearings into the tension weight pulleys effected a significant improvement in tensioning. The increased wire tension has greatly improved current collection, allowing 125 miles/h operation by the prototype APTs.

In total, electrical fixed equipment costs have been reduced, in real terms, by some 30 per cent but the situation has now been reached when further economies will be largely dependent on improvements in installation techniques.

One development which can contribute to a further reduction in overhead line equipment costs is the introduction of computerized methods in overhead system design (OSD). A working party of CM & EE and Research and Development staff has established that computerized OSD is a feasible and economic proposition, with significant savings in manpower, in speeding up the production of documents, including drawings and materials bills of quantity, and in expediting the introduction of inevitable design changes during the process of installation. After initial tests on a number of small schemes, the system was first used to produce the final drawings for open route sections of the St Pancras–Bedford project. Cross-section drawings of standard cases, which include arrangements of some complexity, are produced by computer, and in other cases the computer carries out the design calculations and selects the appropriate masts and foundations for inclusion on manually produced drawings.

By the commencement of the a.c. electrification programme, several specialized construction trains had been developed for overhead line equipment. These included excavating trains for digging foundations, concreting trains with on-board concrete mixers, wiring trains with special conductor-drum wagons, and flat-topped coaches to provide working platforms at conductor height. Steel erection is undertaken by conventional cranes working with bogie bolster wagons. The Regions originally provided their own construction trains, in conjunction with overhead line equipment contractors, but since 1970 a common pool has been held by the CM & EE, BR Board, for use on any Region as required. The trains are constantly up-dated with new equipment.

Maintenance trains are similar to the wiring trains, with messing, stores, and workshop accommodation. In addition to routine maintenance, they are also used during the repair of equipment after incidents causing damage to the overhead line.

The constructional methods adopted inevitably involve continuing demands for maximum possible line possessions. There has therefore to be a complicated programme of works train operations in order to make the best use of possessions which the operators can provide. In order to reduce the demand for possessions to a minimum, continuing efforts are made to evolve different methods of installation, including off-track means of providing foundations and the winching in of conductor wires.

It was appreciated from the start that, in order to ensure optimum performance from the overhead contact wire, it would be necessary to examine its behaviour and that of the pantograph under actual running conditions. It was to meet this requirement that a two-coach unit was developed, in 1959, by British Insulated Callender's Cables and the LM Region, to provide recordings of various parameters to enable areas of poor current collection to be pin-pointed and attended to. The Eastern Region had a similar test coach. With the rapid development of new techniques and equipment, however, the original recording facility became largely obsolete and the increasing age of the two vehicles prevented their use at higher line speeds. It was therefore decided to obtain a replacement vehicle. The new test coach, converted from a Mark I passenger coach and equipped with a fully-instrumented pantograph, was built in 1972 and is designed to be hauled by a diesel locomotive on all electrified lines. The signals from the pantograph are transmitted to the recording equipment by a radio telemetry link when running under 'live' overhead equipment and by a direct wire system when the overhead equipment is 'dead'. This method of using a pantograph mounted on a test vehicle ensures that all electrified lines are being checked to the same basic standard, irrespective of the differing behaviour of individual locomotive-mounted pantographs. It also enables newly erected lines to be similarly checked before energization. A prominent feature of the test coach, which is known as MENTOR (Mobile Electrical Network Testing Observation and Recording), is the centre dome provided to allow visual inspection of the performance of the pantograph in relation to the over-head equipment. MENTOR is under the control of the CM & EE, BR Board, for use by all Regions, associated with a regular maintenance programme.

Where the third-rail contact system is in use, current collection has been relatively free from trouble, except during very cold weather, when ice is liable to form on the conductor rails, thereby insulating the train from the power. This is still a major source of trouble, although it has been overcome to some extent by the development of de-icing trains, which, in severe weather conditions, spread a special non-conducting oil on the conductor rail, to prevent ice adhering to the rail, and remove any thin layers of ice that may already have formed.

The overhead system has, however, presented a number of problems because of atmospheric pollution and difficulties during severe weather.

Fig. 7.21   Test coach MENTOR records the behaviour of overhead equipment and panto-graph and enables areas of poor current collection to be identified (BRB)

With a d.c. overhead system it is necessary to guard against corrosion of fittings due to electrolysis, because of the unidirectional nature of the current and the difficulty in keeping insulators perfectly clean. Special arrangements need to be made for the periodic cleaning of insulators which are not rain-washed to remove atmospheric pollution or pollution by other forms of traction. The electrolysis problem does not arise with a.c. traction but other difficulties have occurred. These have been in two main areas – flashovers leading to insulation failures and inductive inter-ference with signal and telecommunications circuits.

Insulator failures have mainly arisen from three causes:

    (a) Heavy pollution, attributable to steam locomotive smoke and steam and exhaust fumes from diesel locomotives. These difficulties have arisen mainly at locomotive standing points or shunting locations and have been largely eliminated by the repositioning of insulators or by fitting deflector plates. Insulators have also been coated with protective silicone-based grease.

    (b) General pollution, attributable to atmospheric deposits – dew, fog, frost, ice; relatively light pollution from passing diesel trains; but in the main industrial pollution, for example cement dust, the severity of which is measured by deposit gauges placed on the track. In such cases, insulators are again coated with protective grease.

    (c) Birds, particularly rooks and owls in country areas, short circuiting insulators. Owls have presented especial problems in tunnels: in one instance, at Shugborough on the West Coast route, owls caused insulator failures on seven occasions in one day. Modified designs have largely overcome this problem.

The other main area of difficulty – and one that has been appreciated ever since the high-voltage system was first considered – is that the disposition of overhead wire and running rail creates for the a.c. system an unbalanced circuit. This results in magnetic induction caused by traction current inducing voltages in neighbouring parallel conductors, such as Post Office and railway telecommunications cables. This issue is considered in Chapter Ten.

The BTC Annual Report for 1948 records that at the date of nationaliz-ation there were sixteen electric locomotives owned by British Railways. These were

    (a) the ten 0–4–4–0 locomotives previously used on the Newport–Shildon line;

    (b) the 4–6–6–4 prototype built for the proposed York–Newcastle service;

    (c) the two 0–4–4–0 type employed on the Tyne Commission Quay;

    (d) two 750 V 0–6–6–0 1470 h.p. locomotives built by the Southern Railway in 1941; and

    (e) the first of the 0–4–4–0 1868 h.p. locomotives built for the MSW electrification in 1946

In 1948 a third CC 1470 h.p. locomotive was built at Ashford for use on the Southern Region.

Since nationalization, the further electric locomotives which have been introduced are as set out in Table 7.6

Table 7.6   Electric Locomotives introduced after Nationalization

Class	Wheel arrangement	h.p.	Max. speed: miles/hour	No. of locos	Builder/electrical equipment	System/Region/	Year introduced
71	BB	2550	90	24	BR/EE	750 V d.c. 3rd rail/overhead: S. Region	1958
73/0 electro-diesel	BB	1600 elec/ 600 diesel	80	6	BR/EE EE. diesel engine		1962
73/1 electro-diesel	BB	1600 elec/ 600 diesel	90	42	BR/EE EE. diesel engine	750 V d.c. 3rd rail or diesel: S. Region	1965
74 electro-diesel	BB	2500 elec/ 650 diesel	90	10	BR/EE Paxman diesel engine		1967
76	BB	1868	65	58	BR/Met. Vick.	1500 V d.c. overhead: E. & LM Regions (MSW)	1950
77	CC	2700	90	7	BR/Met. Vick.		1953
81	BB	3200	100	23 Type A 2 Type B	BRCW/ AEI (BTH)		1959
82	BB	3300	100	10(A)	Beyer Peacock/ AEI (MV)	25 kV a.c. overhead: LM. Region	1960
83	BB	2950	100	12(A) 3(B)	Vulcan/EE		1960
84	BB	3000	100	10(A)	NBL/GEC		1960
85	BB	3200	100	40(A)	BR/AEI (MV)		1960
86/0	BB	3600	100	39	BR/Vulcan/ AEI/EE		
86/1	BB	4600	100	3			1965
86/2	BB	4040	100	58			
87/0	BB	4600	100	35	BR/GEC	25 kV a.c. overhead: LM. & Scot. Regions	1973
87/1	BB	4600	100	1	BR/GEC (Thyristor)		1974

Notes:
(a) 10 Class 74 rebuilt from Class 71.
(b) Classes 81 to 85: now no distinction between Type A and Type B.
(c) Classes 86/1 and 86/2: as rebuilt 1972.
(d) Classes 71, 74, and 77 now withdrawn: Class 84 in process of withdrawal.

When the specifications for the initial fleet of 100 a.c. locomotives – namely 25 AL1 (now Class 81), 10 AL2 (Class 82), 15 AL3 (Class 83), 10 AL4 (Class 84), and 40 AL5 (Class 85) – were drawn up and the orders placed, the Modernization Plan was in its early stages and it was expected that locomotives might be required for service both on the LM Region main line from Euston to Manchester and Liverpool and on the Eastern Region main line from King's Cross to Leeds or York. For the former, it was decided that a mixed-traffic locomotive would be the most suitable, as maximum utilization could be obtained by using the same locomotive on both passenger and freight services. On the Eastern Region main line, however, it was thought that much of the main-line passenger working would be covered by multiple-unit trains and that locomotives would be required mainly for freight working. The fleet as built therefore comprised 95 mixed-traffic locomotives, referred to as Type A, the remaining five (Type B) being built with a different gear ratio, in order to obtain early experience of a locomotive with a bigger drawbar pull, such as might ultimately be required for working high-speed fully braked freight and mineral trains. As the electrification of the Eastern Region main line did not take place, the special freight working requirement did not arise. In these circumstances the Type B locomotives were converted to Type A at a very early stage.

The specifications listed the types of duty which the locomotives would be required to cover. The Type A locomotive was to be capable of hauling

(a) a 475-ton express passenger train from Manchester (London Road)

Fig. 7.22   Class 73/1 electro-diesel locomotive No. 73105: a type in use on the Southern Region for working trains on to and off electrified routes (BRB)

to Euston at an average speed of 67 miles/h with a maximum running speed of 100 miles/h;
(b) a 950-ton freight train between Manchester (Longsight) and Willesden at an average speed of 42 miles/h, with a maximum speed of 55 miles/h; and
(c) a 500-ton express fully-fitted freight train between the same points at a maximum speed of 60 miles/h.

The locomotive had also to be capable of working the 950-ton train for ten miles at 10 miles/h, a requirement which might arise during conditions of thick fog. The Type B locomotive was to be capable of hauling a 1250 ton mineral or freight train between Longsight and Willesden at an average speed of 42 miles/h, with a maximum speed of 55 miles/h, under the same conditions as specified for Type A. The duties specified reflected the intention of the Modernization Plan to achieve a marked increase in the speed of both passenger and freight trains.

At the time the orders were placed, the civil engineers attached great importance not only to the maximum axle load but also to the wheel diameter in relation to that load – known as the P/D ratio. The maximum axle load permitted was 20 tons and the minimum wheel diameter 48 in. In these circumstances it was decided to use a flexible drive on the first 100 locomotives, to reduce the unsprung weight on the axles to a minimum. The problem for the manufacturer was made more difficult by the requirement for rigid compliance with the loading gauge, which is particularly restrictive when associated with the wheel diameter stipulated. Calculations of probable weights disclosed that there was a likelihood of contravening the permissible axle load and a considerable measure of redesign was therefore necessary.

Also, at that time, there was no experience in Britain of building a.c. locomotive equipments and the BTC decided to adopt d.c. motors fed through rectifiers. Time has shown that this decision was correct. Although the semiconductor rectifier was making rapid progress at this time, it was felt that there had not been sufficient experience to warrant its use for locomotives, where operating conditions might frequently depart quite appreciably from those stipulated. The initial Class 81 and 84 designs were therefore provided with various types of mercury arc rectifiers, but thirty Class 85 were built with germanium and ten with silicon rectifiers.

The single-anode water-cooled mercury arc rectifiers fitted to the Class 83 and 84 locomotives proved generally unrealiable: the multi-anode air-cooled rectifiers fitted to the Class 81 and 82 locomotives were somewhat less troublesome but still did not give the standard of reliability required. These were all replaced by silicon diode rectifiers. The germanium rectifiers fitted to thirty Class 85 locomotives also proved unsatisfactory and were similarly replaced.

The Class 85 locomotives were fitted with rheostatic braking of 1000 kW rating to reduce brake block and tyre wear, especially when controlling unfitted trains on falling gradients. However, control of this brake, involving the use of a separate power/brake change-over switch and the master controller as well as the brake valve when hauling fitted trains, proved to be inconvenient in practice. The brake was subsequently modified, with control combined with the driver's brake valve, and its use was extended to later classes of locomotive.

The specifications for the roof-mounted high-tension equipment stipulated the use of Stone–Faively pantographs and indicated the types of circuit breakers, earthing switches, and voltage change-over equipment to be used. The electrical equipments were designed by the individual contractors to give a wide range of variations to enable a comparison to be made of their respective merits.

So far as mechanical parts were concerned, wide freedom was given to the manufacturers to draw upon their particular skills and experience, subject to certain essential provisions, for example, conformity with the British loading gauge; ability to traverse a minimum curve of 4·5 chains; and the incorporation of standard items such as tyres, buffers and drawgear, hose and cable connections, and brake blocks. To meet these requirements and the stringent axle load and P/D ratio, there were four new

Fig. 7.23 Class 81 BB 3200 h.p. electric locomotive No. 3004. The body is being lifted off the bogies by four Matterson jacks, controlled from the trolley seen to the left of the picture. All a.c. electric locomotives and multiple unit trains were designed to accept these jacks, thus minimizing the need for cranes in depots (A. H. Emerson)

bogie designs and five different designs of underframe and body, with which comparative trials could be made.

At the time of ordering the locomotives, British Railways had gained satisfactory experience of bogies with three axles at speeds up to 90 miles/h but no two-axled bogies of proved suitability existed for 90/100 miles/h running. The opportunity was therefore taken to ask manufacturers to submit their designs. The final choice for a future standard would depend upon minimum ride deterioration over large mileages and minimum maintenance costs. Subject to these considerations, lowest weight, greatest simplicity, and least first cost would influence the choice.

Each manufacturer, as well as British Railways' own design staff at Doncaster, was allowed to develop his own body layout, and to propose any combination of design and material for body and under-frame, subject to a standard cab, to be fitted to all classes, and provision for a standard roof arrangement for pantograph and circuit breaker. The underframe/body structure was specified to be capable of withstanding end loading of not less than 200 tons without permanent deflection.

The somewhat generous cab space provided was based upon the need under British operating conditions for ready egress from either side of the cab at any time by the second man, who has certain traffic duties to perform. This affected the available space in the body, which was also reduced by the combination of large wheels and a low roof necessary to accommodate the pantograph equipment within the required structure gauge.

There was obviously a limit to what could be achieved by way of attractive styling in what was in effect a rectangular box but, in consultation with the BTC Design Panel and by adopting a uniform frontal design, along with meticulous attention to all external features, it was possible to produce a generally acceptable appearance.

As the vacuum brake was at that time standard for all British locomotive-hauled rolling stock and because it was desired to obtain the advantages of the air brake on the locomotive itself, the normal British Railways dual brake system was fitted, under which the driver operates a vacuum brake valve acting direct upon the train and controlling the air brake on the locomotive through proportional valves. A straight air brake with separate control was also provided for light locomotive working or for use when working unbraked freight trains.

The locomotives thus incorporated a variety of both electrical and mechanical designs and a series of tests was carried out with a view to comparing the performance of each item of equipment. The tests on the riding of the locomotives recorded accelerations, frequencies, and displacements. They also allowed for adjustments to damping and other characteristics to obtain optimum riding performance for each bogie design. The tests indicated that the bogie fitted to the Class 81 locomotives gave more satisfactory results than those provided on the Classes

82, 83, and 84 locomotives and it was therefore adopted, with some modification, for the Class 85 build. A completely new design of bogie was produced for the Class 86 locomotives.

The Class 81 to 85 locomotives, whilst not giving rise to any major mechanical or electrical difficulties, never really reached the standard of reliability expected, and achieved by the later types. In the Classes 81 and 85 locomotives in particular, failures in service were mainly due to faults in the control equipment, which required redesign.

In 1968–9 the Class 83 and 84 locomotives (totalling 25) were temporarily withdrawn from service, awaiting a review of their future, which depended primarily on whether the project to complete the electrification to Glasgow was authorized. When the decision to proceed with this electrification was taken the locomotives were rehabilitated for further service. It was found possible to withdraw 25 locomotives out of a total of 200 because in the early stages of main-line electrification planning there is a tendency to over-estimate rolling stock requirements. In this instance, the over-estimation was due to three main causes. First, the operators made allowance for lower levels of availability and utilization than were in the event achieved. Second, as experience in operation and maintenance accumulated, availability and utilization standards improved still further. Third, traffic forecasts were based on expected levels six years after the start of the full commercial service, that is, in 1973. As it happened, whilst passenger traffic growth was more than achieved, freight traffic was already being adversely affected by the recession in the national economy. The reasons for selecting Class 83 and 84 locomotives for temporary withdrawal were not solely based on levels of maintenance costs and reliability, although due regard was paid to these factors. Each of these classes formed an individual batch of locomotives, whereas Classes 81, 82, and 85 locomotives had a number of common components, and it was this factor which proved decisive in making the final choice of types for withdrawal.

The later Class 86 and 87 designs, for use following the opening of through services from Euston to Glasgow, incorporated most of the best features of the original designs. After careful consideration it was decided to incorporate axle-hung traction motors on the Class 86 locomotives. Service experience, however, proved that this arrangement generated excessive dynamic loading on the track of up to 56 tons, thus increasing track maintenance costs. The Class 86 fleet was consequently divided into freight locomotives, with a limited maximum speed, thus reducing track damage, and passenger locomotives (Class 86/2) which were fitted with flexicoil secondary suspension, and some also with SAAB resilient wheels, to reduce dynamic track loading.

The 100 Class 86 locomotives proved consistently more reliable in service than the initial batch. Basic design requirements, including the HT tap changing, individual motor circuits, fuseless silicon rectifiers, and

Fig. 7.24   The London–Inverness Clansman worked by a Class 86 locomotive over
Beattock Summit, 29 June 1974 (Derek Cross)

2000 kW rheostatic braking, with the intention of restricting the number
of components and reducing maintenance, were fully justified. They
were fitted with one pantograph instead of two. Fault diagnosis and
remedial action by drivers were made easier and the miles per casualty
increased appreciably.

The Class 87 locomotives, with a new design of bogie and motors
continuously rated at 4600 h.p. were designed for high-speed operation
at up to 100 miles/h. The motors are frame-mounted, with a flexible
drive – very similar to the Class 81 locomotives. The bogies are fitted with
flexicoil suspension. Disc brakes are provided, with a friction brake to
operate at low speeds. Apart from the bogies and traction motors, the
remainder of the design was very similar to the Class 86 locomotive.
Multiple working control was also provided.

At the time the specification for these locomotives was being prepared,

Fig. 7.25   Class 87 BB 4600 h.p. electric locomotive No. 87001 (now named *Stevenson*),
built for the extension of the electrification of the West Coast main line from Weaver
Junction to Glasgow (BRB)

a study was made of the cost of operating high-voltage tap changers compared with thyristor control equipment. Although it was decided that, in view of the additional costs involved and the lack of service experience, the adoption of thyristor control on a fleet basis could not, at that stage, be justified, one locomotive (Class 87/1) was fitted for trial purposes, to ascertain the problems involved and to assess the extent of inductive interference with track circuits and telecommunications. Whilst the amount of interference was found to be somewhat greater than with conventional locomotives, protection of circuits was possible by alterations to signalling equipment and to the circuitry to the thyristors in the locomotives. This form of control increases tractive effort by minimizing wheelslip, and is referred to again later.

At the end of 1979, the electric locomotive stock numbered 310, as set out in Table 7.7:

Table 7.7   Electric Locomotives in stock at end 1979

Class	h.p.	Region	No. of locomotives
d.c. locomotives			
73/0 ⎫	Diesel-electric		6
	1600 electric,	SR	
73/1 ⎬	600 diesel		42
76	1868	E & LM	40
		Regions	
a.c. locomotives			
81	3200 ⎫		22
82	3300		8
83	2950		13
84	3000 ⎬	LMR	3
85	3200		40
86/0	3600		39
86/1	4600 ⎭		3
86/2	4040		58
87/0	4600 ⎫	LM &	35
87/1	4600 ⎬	Sc. Regions	1
Total			310

Until the mid-1950s, the emphasis had been on the development of multiple-unit stock mainly for use on d.c. third-rail suburban electrifications. As soon as the decision to adopt the 25 kV a.c. system had been taken, however, it was necessary to place on order a very large number of multiple-unit trains for the suburban electrifications included in the Modernization Plan. Experience already obtained with three types of equipment by the conversion of the Lancaster–Morecambe–Heysham line to the 50-cycle a.c. system was of considerable value, confirming as it did the wisdom of the decision to adopt d.c. motors for the suburban trains, in line with the decision to use them for locomotives. This experience was limited to three of the four contractors with whom bulk orders were placed and very strenuous efforts had to be made to ensure that over 400 motor coaches were available by 1960, bearing in mind the need to make provision for the conversion work in progress at the same time.

The suburban electrifications themselves differed considerably in character, both as regards station spacing and speed restrictions, and the schedule speed considered to be commercially desirable and economical. The specification for the equipments, whilst bearing this aspect in mind, set out a single set of parameters on which the offers received from the manufacturers could be judged. The performance requirements covered maximum service speed, starting acceleration, and timings for specified routes, with numbers and durations of intermediate stops. The tare weight of a four-car unit on which performance was to be based was originally quoted as 144 tons but this weight was later increased to 153 tons when a decision was taken to use double bolster bogies to give improved riding and fit sound insulation in the vehicle bodies. The specification for the electrical equipment laid down certain common features: all power equipment to be underframe mounted, except high tension roof equipment; forced circulation oil-cooled main transformers; rectifiers to be used in conjunction with d.c. traction motors; and details of control and auxiliary equipment already used in existing d.c. electric stock. All stock was to have a standard control system, enabling all units to couple one with another. Within the framework of the specification, contractors were given freedom to develop suitable circuits and components, under the overall supervision of the BTC engineers.

Contracts initially sought covered equipments for 361 suburban multiple-unit trains, totalling 1301 vehicles, and also equipments for the conversion of 124 existing d.c. suburban multiple-unit trains (404 vehicles) to a.c. working. Table 7.8 lists the orders which were placed, including stock for the Colchester–Clacton–Walton line.

Throughout the design of the trains the advantages of standardization were sought. Many of the standards were also applicable to locomotive-hauled stock and to a.c. locomotives, this extending in the latter case to pantographs, circuit breakers, power control, and certain driving controls and procedures. The Glasgow suburban units incorporate certain special design features, including air-operated sliding doors recessed within the maximum body width permitted by the loading gauge and the streamlined form of cab end.

As with locomotives, mercury arc, germanium, and silicon rectifiers were included in the various designs. The greater size and weight of the

Table 7.8 Initial Orders for Electric Multiple Units and Equipment, following
decision to adopt 25 kV a.c. 50-cycle System

Class	No. of units	Service	Builder/ electrical equipment	Year intro- duced
302	112 × 4-car	LT & S: Fenchurch St– Tilbury/Shoeburyness	BR/EE	1959
303	91 × 3-car	Glasgow Suburban (North of Clyde)	Pressed Steel/ AEI	1960
304	45 × 4-car	Crewe–Manchester/ Liverpool	BR/AEI	1960
305/1	52 × 3-car	Liverpool Street– Enfield/Chingford	BR/GEC	1960
305/2	19 × 4-car	Liverpool Street– Hertford East/ Bishop's Stortford	BR/GEC	1960
306	92 × 3-car	Liverpool St– Shenfield (conversion)	Converted by BR/AEI(MV)	Built 1949, converted 1960
307	32 × 4-car	Liverpool St– Southend Victoria (conversion)	Converted by BR/AEI(MV)	Built 1956, converted 1960
308	42 × 4-car*	Liverpool Street– Chelmsford/Southend (Augmentation stock)	BR/EE	1961
309/1 309/2–3	8 × 2-car 15 × 4-car	Colchester–Clacton/ Walton	BR/GEC	1962

*Including 9 units each with a luggage vehicle, 4 of which were converted into
passenger-carrying vehicles in 1971.

mercury arc rectifiers, and the maintenance problems which arose, led to
this type being dispensed with in later designs, as, eventually, were the
germanium rectifiers, all new and replacement stock being fitted with
silicon rectifiers. All traction motors were axle-hung with rubber resilient
nose suspension.

Other new building included third-rail d.c. stock for the Kent Coast
and Bournemouth electrifications, new a.c. stock for the LM Region
main-line electrification, and replacement d.c. units for the London
Midland and Southern Regions. Table 7.9 sets out the construction which
was undertaken, up to the time new standards were introduced in the
later 1970s.

Table 7.9   Additional and Replacement Electric Multiple Unit Stock built prior to introduction of New Standard Designs

Class	No. of units	Service	System	Builder/ electrical equipment	Year intro- duced
308/3	3 × 3-car	Liverpool Street– Enfield/Chingford		BR/EE	1961
309/4	4 × 4-car (conver- ted 2-car sets)	Colchester– Clacton/Walton		BR/GEC	1973
310	50 × 4-car	LM Region main line	25 kV a.c. overhead	BR/EE	1965
311	19 × 3-car	Glasgow Suburban (South of Clyde)		Craven/GEC	1967
312/0	26 × 4-car	GN Outer suburban		BR/GEC	1975
312/1	19 × 4-car	GE Outer suburban		BR/GEC	1974/5
312/2	4 × 4-car	LMR West Midlands PTE: Birmingham International		BR/GEC	1976
405/2	225 × 4-car	SR London Subur- ban		BR/EE	1948/50
410/1	2 × 4-car	SR Kent Coast		BR/EE	1956
410/2 (i)	20 × 4-car	SR Kent Coast		BR/EE	1959
411/1	4 × 4-car	SR Kent Coast		BR/EE	1956/8
411/2 (i)	107 × 4-car	SR Kent Coast			
414/2	2 × 2-car	SR Kent Coast		BR/EE	1957/8
414/3	121 × 2-car	SR Kent Coast			
415/1	213 × 4-car			BR/EE	1951
415/2 (i)	70 × 4-car			BR/EE	1958
416/1	34 × 2-car			BR/EE	1953
416/2 (i) (ii)	95 × 2-car	SR London Suburban	750 V d.c. 3rd rail		
418/0	36 × 2-car			BR/EE	1959
418/1	40 × 2-car				1957/8
418/2 (iii)	10 × 2-car				
419	10 motor luggage vans	Victoria–Dover boat trains		BR/EE	1959
420/1	18 × 4-car			BR/EE	1965/70
420/2	10 × 4-car				
421/1	36 × 4-car			BR/EE	1963/70
421/2	102 × 4-car	SR main line			
423 (iv)	194 × 4-car			BR/EE	1967
427	12 × 4-car			BR/EE	1978

Class	No. of units	Service	System	Builder/ electrical equipment	Year intro- duced
430	11 × 4-car 4 × 4-car	} Waterloo– } Bournemouth	} 750 V d.c. 3rd rail	BR/EE	1967 1974
445 (v)	2 × 4-car 1 × 2-car	} SR London } Suburban		BR/EE	1971
485	6 × 4-car	} Isle of Wight	630 V d.c. 3rd rail	Former London Transport stock	1967
486 (vi)	5 × 3-car				
491	34 × 4-car	SR Waterloo– Weymouth	750 V d.c. 3rd rail	BR/EE	1967 & 1974
501	57 × 3-car	Euston–Watford	630 V d.c. 3rd rail	BR/GEC	1957
503	26 × 3-car	Wirral and Mersey	600/750 V d.c. 3rd rail	Met. Cammell & BRCW/BTH	1956
504	25 × 2-car	Manchester– Bury	1200 V d.c. 3rd rail	BR/EE	1959
506	8 × 3-car	Manchester– Glossop–Hadfield	1500 V d.c. overhead	Met. Cammell/GEC	1954

Notes:
  (i) Classes 410, 411, 415, and 416 being reconditioned, 1978/82.
 (ii) 13 sets in service in South Tyneside in 1955 later modified for service on SR.
(iii) Previously Classes 414/1–2–3 respectively.
 (iv) 12 sets converted to Class 427 in 1978.
  (v) Prototype high density sets.
 (vi) Ex-London Transport 1927 stock.

For the Bournemouth line eleven 4-car units were provided, each including two 1600 h.p. motor coaches and buffet car, and four further units of the same type were added in 1974. Twenty-eight 4-car and three 3-car units were also provided in 1967, the latter being converted to 4-car units, plus three additional, in 1974, making thirty-four (Class 491) units in total. It was the intention to supplement the service as necessary at peak hours with electro-diesel and diesel locomotives operating push-pull services. For this purpose, nineteen 1550 h.p. diesel-electric loco-motives were converted to push-pull operation and ten of the twenty-four 2500 h.p. (Class 71) electric locomotives built for the Kent Coast service were equipped as electro-diesels, also with push-pull controls. Additionally, twenty-four 4-car units (Class 423) similar to the Class 421 units built for the Brighton line in 1963, were built for the semi-fast services.

Despite efforts to attain the maximum degree of standardization, in the early days of 50-cycle electrification Regions had some latitude in regard to the types and layout of stock they required for use on their own lines. The result was a greater multiplicity of types than was justifiable. As from 1970, BR introduced a stricter control of the supply of multiple-unit trains. A standard design of vehicle comprising a steel underframe and body, with aluminium cladding, was developed for high-density inner suburban traffic or as a low-density unit, for outer suburban and cross-country purposes. The same basic design can be used to form 2-, 3-, or 4-car units, capable of being multipled to suit any needs. The variations of electric supply voltages are catered for and the basic design can be adapted to third-rail 750 V d.c., 6·25 kV or 25 kV, a.c. overhead line equipment.

Ten prototype d.c. vehicles were put in service in 1972, to be used over a two-year period in 250000 miles of intensive trial running on the Southern Region, thus permitting a thorough technical and commercial appreciation to be made before the construction of operational d.c. stock needed to commence. The vehicles incorporated many new features, including waste heat recovery (the use of heat generated in rheostatic braking for train heating) and bogies of an advanced design. This prototype design, which incorporated eight traction motors for three- or four-car units, proved to be extremely attractive but it was later decided that worthwhile cost reductions could be made by some modification. A revised standard will therefore be introduced with the St Pancras–Bedford Class 317 stock. This will replace the riveted aluminium body with an all steel welded structure and will use Mark III main-line coach design principles (referred to in Chapter 8) and, where possible the same jigs and tools. It will be equipped with four larger traction motors to give the same overall performance as the previous eight-motor arrangement. This is intended to be the standard unit for both electric and diesel multiple units on BR and will achieve significant reductions in first and maintenance costs. Longer term developments in multiple-unit design under consideration include welded aluminium extrusion body structure (because of its lighter weight rather than reduced cost) and articulation.

A five-year rolling programme for the construction of electric multiple unit vehicles, for review on an annual basis, has been agreed between the Department of Transport and BR. Under this, fifty-five 4-car sets are proposed to be built each year. Up to 1992 it is intended to build over 3000 of these vehicles, of various types, for use on BR services. Further vehicles will be required for other suburban services, operated by BR but specified and financially supported by Passenger Transport Executives in provincial conurbations. Vehicles for inner suburban services will be one class only, with a maximum speed of 75 miles/h, whereas those for outer suburban services will provide both first- and second-class accommodation, and have a maximum speed of 100 miles/h.

Table 7.10 gives details of stock so far built or under construction to standard body designs developed in the 1970s.

At the end of 1979, a total of 7493 electric multiple unit vehicles were in service on BR (2486 a.c., 5007 d.c.)

The Class 314 stock for the Greater Glasgow PTE and the Class 315 stock for the Liverpool Street–Shenfield line are fitted with thyristor controls: the Class 317 stock for the St Pancras–Bedford services will be

Table 7.10   Electric Multiple Unit Stock built to New Standard Designs

Class	No. of units	Service	System	Builder/ electrical equipment	Year (to be) intro- duced
313	64 × 3-car	GN Inner suburban	25 kV a.c. overhead/ 750 V d.c. 3rd rail	BR/GEC	1976
314	16 × 3-car	Glasgow Trans-Clyde	25 kV a.c. overhead	BR/6 Brush 10 GEC	1979
315	61 × 4-car	Liverpool St– Shenfield	25 kV a.c. overhead	BR/41 Brush 20 GEC	1980
317 (i)	48 × 4-car	St Pancras– Bedford	25 kV a.c. overhead	BR/GEC	1982
507	33 × 3-car	Liverpool– Southport (Merseyrail)	600/750 V. d.c. 3rd rail	BR/GEC	1979
508	43 × 4-car	SR London Suburban	750 V d.c. 3rd rail	BR/GEC	1979
920 (ii)	1 × 3-car	Prototype	25 kV a.c. overhead	BR/GEC	1975

Notes:
(i) The first of a revised new standard, which will form the basis for the design of all subsequent electric and diesel multiple units.
(ii) Prototype inner suburban set for Class 313 and, later, Class 314.

similarly equipped. Thyristor control brings a number of benefits in intensive suburban operation. Load-breaking switches are eliminated, improving reliability and reducing maintenance. Transformer tappings are reduced to a minimum, resulting in a simple and robust unit, requiring less maintenance. Stepless control of tractive effort gives smooth acceleration and the passengers a better ride. A three-car prototype train equipped with thyristors has run extensive trials on the Eastern and Scottish Regions. All electric multiple units built to the new designs are fitted with air-operated disc brakes.

Trials are about to commence of thyristor-controlled units on d.c. lines. A test train is being fitted up and will be run extensively on the Southern Region to prove the traction performance of the equipment and to assess its effect on signalling and telecommunications and on the power supply system. Energy savings are expected to result from the system, estimates varying from 8 to 25 per cent and it is hoped that the tests will clarify this situation.

The prototype Class 314 Glasgow Trans-Clyde set will be used for a

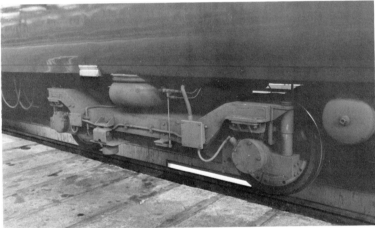

Fig. 7.26 Two views of the BT13 (formerly BX1) bogie fitted in the first instance to the Class 313 GN inner suburban electric multiple unit stock. It will be used for future diesel and electric multiple unit vehicles. The upper photograph gives a general view of the power bogie, before the traction motors and air suspension bottles are fitted. The brake disc is seen on the inside face of the wheel. The other photograph is a side view of the trailer bogie, showing the air suspension bottles and dampers (BRB)

comprehensive test of conventional and tubular axle induction motors (TAIM). This type of motor fits into a hollow axle and eliminates much of the gearing and electrical equipment associated with conventional motors. TAIM can also provide a very efficient braking action and, with the development of modified solid-state control equipment, has potential as an effective rheostatic or regenerative brake. One of the motor cars is fitted with four conventional nose-suspended induction motors and another with two pre-production versions of the tubular axle induction motor developed by the BR Research and Development Division in conjunction with GEC. A third car will remain equipped with d.c. motors of the type currently used on the Class 313 and 314 stock.

Fig. 7.27 A Scottish Region Class 314 electric multiple unit train, built in 1979, showing the main equipment case on the thyristor converter side of the vehicle (BRB)

Fig. 7.28 A Southern Region Class 508 electric multiple unit train, built in 1979, with thyristor control and auto-couplings (BRB)

The increase in speeds on the Southern Region has necessitated changes in the design of the shoegear for current collection. The bonded fibreglass shoe at present in use on express stock is designed for speeds up to 90 miles/h. Should there be any intention of running HST trains at 125 miles/h on this Region, not only would it be necessary to design a new type of shoegear but standards of maintenance of the conductor rails and the ramp angles would need reconsideration. The slightest obstruction or discrepancy in rail level can result in the breakage of the shoegear.

A BR version of the Stone–Faiveley pantograph, with two metallic carbon strips, strengthened in some cases by the addition of a third strip, has generally been used on BR electric locomotives and multiple units. Trials have also been carried out with other types of pantograph. A new type 'High Speed' pantograph, developed jointly by the BR Research and Development Division and Brecknell, Willis and Co has been undergoing laboratory and running tests. It will be subjected to further tests in revenue-earning service on the Advanced Passenger Trains.

In an endeavour to minimize damage to the overhead equipment as a result of a pantograph being damaged or a pantograph carbon being displaced from the head, a skid bar of the same profile as the head was fitted to all pantographs, to provide a smooth and even surface over which the contact wire could pass. These skid bars are insulated and an indication to the driver of loss of power as a result of damage to the pantograph enables the train to be brought to a stand near to the cause of

Fig. 7.29   A Southern Region motor coach, showing shoegear mounted on a hard timber
shoe beam between the two axles of the bogie (BRB)

Fig. 7.30   The High Speed pantograph developed for the APT. The picture shows how the pantograph is mounted, to cater for the tilting of the vehicle on curves (BRB)

the incident. A further development in the early 1970s has been an automatic device for lowering the pantograph, in the event of its being damaged. Besides minimizing damage, this device also assists in locating the cause of an incident, confining the search area to a short length of route on the approach side of where the locomotive or multiple unit comes to a stand. As automatic lowering devices are fitted to pantographs, the provision of skid bars will be discontinued.

The Advanced Passenger Train is a major step forward in railway technology and stems from studies by the Research and Development Division into rail vehicle dynamics. It was in 1964 that the outcome of these studies began to lead to the concept of a high performance train, capable of running at up to 155 miles/h on existing tracks. An experimental train (APT-E) was built in 1972 and tested on a 14-mile stretch of line between Melton Mowbray and Nottingham, which had been adapted for use as a high-speed test track. As a result of these trials, during which a British Rail speed record of 153 miles/h was reached, the construction of three pre-production 14-car trains (APT-P: two power cars and twelve trailer cars) was authorized in October 1974, for testing on the West Coast main line, prior to the construction of trains to go into regular public service on that route. These trains will be scheduled to cut the journey time from Euston to Glasgow from 5 hours to 4 hours 10 minutes with one intermediate stop.

The trains incorporate a number of special features, including a tilting suspension which enables them to negotiate curves, in complete safety, at a speed up to 40 per cent faster than is now permissible with a conventional train, without discomfort to passengers. Light-weight, articulated construction in aluminium has been adopted, to assist acceleration and braking and to minimize track wear. Hydro-kinetic brakes, which can bring the train to a stand within the normal 100 miles/h braking distance, have been adopted and a form of air-conditioning which saves energy by recirculating a high proportion of the fouled air through carbon filters has been installed.

It was originally intended that these trains should be powered by gas turbines, with electric transmission – as indeed the APT-E version initially was – but as no suitable gas turbine equipment was available at an acceptable price for the production models it was decided that the service trains should be powered by electric motors, developing 4000 h.p. per power car. The 25 kV a.c. 50-cycle supply, collected from the over-head line through one pantograph per power car, is stepped down and converted to a controlled d.c. output through transformer/thyristor power equipment mounted within the body of the power car. The hydro-kinetic brake is mounted on each axle, together with auxiliary tread brakes which progressively take over the braking as speed reduces. The braking system includes a towing unit which enables the APT braking system to operate in multiple with a locomotive air brake when being hauled dead. The unit converts the air pressure in the locomotive brake pipe to the electrical signal required to operate the train's braking system.

In the APT-P trains, the power cars are marshalled in the centre of the train – one power car for eleven trailer vehicles for speeds up to 125 miles/h, two power cars for twelve trailer vehicles for speeds up to 150 miles/h. The positioning of the power cars in the centre of the train is principally dictated by the fact that, to achieve satisfactory current collec-tion, power should ideally be taken from the overhead wire at one point only, and, if two power cars are in use, they, with their pantographs, should be adjacent.

Tests with an APT-P train have already taken place on the West Coast

Fig. 7.31 Two APT-P apparently racing neck-and-neck on Beattock Summit. In fact, the one on the right is stationary in the up loop during commissioning trials, whilst the other speeds past on a driver-training run to Carnforth (BRB)

main line and on 20 December 1979 a record speed of 160 miles/h was reached between Quintinshill and Beattock. It is planned that the three APT-P trains will enter revenue-earning service, in accelerated 125 miles/h timings, in the autumn of 1980.

As previously mentioned, the fundamental development of the APT was carried out by the Research and Development Division, with Dr S. Jones. Board Member, and A. H. Wickens, Director of Laboratories, in the lead but when the time came for the production of APT-P trains responsibility was passed to the Chief Mechanical and Electrical Engineer, BR Board – successively G. S. W. Calder and K. Taylor. Senior Research and Development personnel who had been specifically concerned in the original concept were transferred to the CM & EE Department with the project.

The extension of electrification presented the Mechanical and Electrical Engineering Departments with much additional work but no insuperable problems. The Regional Electrical Engineers were all appointed in the early fifties to be responsible to the Regional CM & EEs for the a.c. electrification projects (A. H. Emerson, LMR; J. W. Grieve, ER; and A. Watt, ScR). All had had many years of experience in operating and maintaining electric traction. Thus, there existed in the Department experienced men and established organizations to deal with the work involved and to ensure constant co-ordination with other departments concerned in the overall plans.

As a general rule, it was the practice to set up Electric Traction Engineers' establishments at suitable locations on the route to be electrified, with responsibility for overseeing the progress of work during construction and, subsequently, to take over the maintenance of both fixed equipment and rolling stock in operation. However, on the Liverpool Street–Shenfield electrification construction work was progressed by the Electric Traction Engineer at Stonebridge Park on the LM Region, where staff experienced with electric traction were based, but subsequently maintenance was controlled by the Electric Traction Engineer at Ilford, where the main repair shops for electric trains were built. For the a.c. programme, Eastern and Scottish Regions managed the electrification work from their Regional offices, transferring staff and responsibility to the Electric Traction Engineers when lines were commissioned. On the LM Region electrification six District Electric Traction Engineers were set up at Crewe, Manchester, Liverpool, Birmingham, Rugby, and London but later, following the introduction of a Divisional organization, the Electric Traction Engineers' posts were absorbed therein.

Over the years organizations have changed, each Region adopting a form of organization best suited to its particular needs, with fixed equipment and rolling stock depots sited at points strategically convenient to its electric services, the latter providing facilities for examination, maintenance, cleaning, and servicing. The Eastern, London

Fig. 7.32   The Ilford Electric Depot at night, before conversion of the line to the 50-cycle a.c. system (J. Maltby)

Midland, and Western Regions are divided into Divisions, with Divisional Maintenance Engineers controlling the Maintenance Areas and Depots. However, for electric traction matters on the Eastern Region, Area Maintenance Engineers report directly to Regional HQ. In the Scottish and Southern Regions, Area and Depot Engineers also report to Regional HQ.

From 1970, the CM & EE organization at BRB HQ has been progressively expanded to take over more responsibility in connection with electrification work. Whereas in the past construction work has been dealt with by site teams reporting to Regional HQs, from the start of the Midland suburban scheme in 1978 such teams now report direct to BR HQ, where contract administration, management of the works train fleet, and responsibility for materials supply had already been centred. Certain small schemes and conversion work remain under Regional control, subject to overall responsibility being taken by BR HQ.

The training of drivers for electric operation was a considerable task. Operating instructions and safety booklets were prepared and classrooms were established in all districts to give theoretical and practical instruction. A simulator similar in principle to those used for the training of air crews was set up at Willesden for driver training purposes but, whilst this proved useful in a number of respects, it could not take the place of drivers actually handling trains on the line and its use was, after a time, discontinued.

Generally, each group of electrified services is affiliated to a Main Works, from which spares are obtained and to which locomotives and multiple units are sent for bogie overhaul approximately every two or three years, and a general overhaul every eight to ten years.

As in other spheres of railway engineering, private industry has, over many years, made a striking contribution to progress in electrification. Sometimes on its own initiative and sometimes in collaboration with British Railways, industry has ensured that every aspect of technological progress has been incorporated in the design and manufacture of equipment for each successive electrification project. Consulting engineers, too, have played an important role in the development of electrification on the railways, both before and after nationalization. When the decision was taken to adopt the 25 kV a.c. system, the BTC set up an Advisory Panel, with Warder as chairman, through which the consultants' contributions could be channelled. The services of the panel were directed towards assisting the Chief Electrical Engineer to solve problems of special difficulty arising from the decision to adopt the standard frequency for railway electrification at a nominal line voltage of 25 kV. These formed the subject of specific remits, including investigations into inductive interference with communications circuits; the fitting of lightning arrestors to locomotives; research into the insulation of bridges; the overhead layout at voltage changeover points; and the relative economics of electric and diesel traction over specific routes – London–Bristol–Cardiff on the Western Region and Weaver Junction–Glasgow on the LM/Scottish Regions. The progress which was made could not have been secured without whole-hearted co-operation between the three groups – railway electrical engineers, contractors, and consultants.

Tribute must also be paid to the helpful attitude of the Railway Inspectorate at the Ministry of Transport, under the guidance of Brigadier C. A. Langley, who was the Chief Inspecting Officer for much of the period during which the 25 kV a.c. system was being developed. The advice which he and his officers gave on the numerous issues on which their help was required, including the approval of equipment, safety regulations, driver training, and the investigation of major failures, made the task of implementation so much easier.

It is a matter of great disappointment that it has not been possible in the past to provide the means whereby a rolling programme of electrification can be planned and implemented. The sometimes lengthy gaps between the approval of individual schemes has inevitably led to the dispersal of expertise by the railways and the contractors and, as inevitably, increased costs and implementation times when new projects have, in time, been authorized. At the moment, the only scheme of any magnitude which is in progress is the St Pancras–Bedford electrification. British Railways' longer term plans include further main-line electrification schemes, to which reference will be made in Chapter Fifteen. Whether or not they will be authorized in time to avoid again breaking up the experienced teams will depend on political and economic factors not wholly within the control of the British Railways Board.

CHAPTER EIGHT

Passenger and Freight Services

A PART from the development of the locomotive, the evolution of rolling stock – particularly the passenger carriage – has created more interest than any other aspect of railway engineering. In Britain, the design and construction of rolling stock has been severely constrained by attitudes and factors arising from the framework within which the railway system evolved.

First, there is the continuing physical limitation of the British loading gauge, which has always been small by world standards. It has excluded compatibility with rolling stock on the European mainland. It has also restricted the opportunity to design, for example, double-deck carriages suitable for commuters, on one of the world's densest suburban systems. It precludes the carriage by rail of many containers now moving around the country on road vehicles and has resulted in problems with the carriage of standard ISO (International Standards Organization) containers. In some cases it has been necessary to design and construct carriages for one specific route or group of routes where the loading gauge is more restrictive than in the rest of Britain and it has prevented the use of the straight-sided carriages which have allowed passengers on the mainland of Europe to enjoy over many years the large drop window.

Second, the railways of Britain were in the unique situation of being developed piecemeal by private capital, without Government finance or even, in at least the early stages, guidance. From the earliest days of railways, many of the freight-carrying wagons were in the ownership of their customers, which left a legacy of inefficient freight wagons and working methods to several generations of engineers.

Third, and partly due to the nature of their development and over-investment in the nineteenth century, the railways of Britain between the wars were never in a position either to modernize the whole of their carriage fleets or to invest in an efficient system of freight working. Until 1923 there were over 120 separate railways in the country, with their own investment priorit.es, and the four groups which were then created never generated the required rate of return to encourage adequate investment. With the coming of nationalization in 1948 it was possible to take complete control of the fleets of privately owned wagons, already operating in a common pool since the war. Not that this was in itself an unqualified benefit, but national priorities during the next six years were not favourable to the building of rolling stock or other railway investment.

It is important to appreciate the framework within which the mechanical and electrical engineers have had to approach the task of designing rolling stock. On the one hand, severe constraints on investment resources have made it essential to provide maximum value for money and, on the other, there has been strong commercial pressure to produce standards of comfort in passenger stock which will attract traffic to the railway. Both types of pressure have led to engineering ingenuity of a very high order.

Within the limitations thus imposed upon them, the mechanical and electrical engineers have four principal factors to bear in mind in their approach to the design and construction of passenger rolling stock, namely:

(a) the need to provide stock of adequate structural strength to withstand the traction and buffing loads imposed, with the maximum degree of safety;

(b) the need to provide stock suited, in regard to size, seating capacity, and internal layout, to the commercial and operating requirements of the services to which it will be allocated;

(c) the need to produce standards of passenger comfort and amenity – for example, smoothness of ride, and temperature and ventilation appropriate to the time of the year – compatible with the length and speed of the particular journeys for which the vehicles will be used; and

(d) subject to the demands set out above, the need to achieve the maximum degree of route availability and standardization in design, thereby securing economies in construction.

During recent years, there has been a policy directed towards a general raising in service quality standards, with the consequent phasing out of special facilities, such as Pullman cars.

The advantages of standardization have always been realized and every major change in railway organization has been followed by action to reduce the number of vehicle designs in use. The amalgamations in 1923 permitted the four main-line companies to standardize their coaching stock vehicles, selecting from the designs of the constituent companies those best suited to the needs of the particular group. The result was an initial reduction to a reasonable minimum in the number of vehicle designs and components, varied to some extent – mostly towards, but sometimes away from, further standardization – by subsequent redesigns to meet service needs.

Generally speaking, however, the designs setted upon by the four group companies were in outline broadly similar, although there were variations – for example, in loading gauge, vehicle lengths, type of bogie, drawgear, weight, construction materials – which tended to limit the extent to which interchange working of vehicles between companies was acceptable. Another factor which complicated interchange working was the higher vacuum used by the GWR.

Some designs were also produced with particular objectives in mind. As an example, following trials with the articulation, in pairs, of six-wheeled coaches on three bogies, new eight-coach trains were built by Gresley in 1924–5 for the inner suburban services based on King's Cross. They consisted of two articulated quadruple units, thereby saving three bogies per four-coach unit, and reducing weight and cost. The under-frames at the outer ends of each articulated unit were so designed that motor bogies could be accommodated at a later date, if and when an electrification project which had been under consideration was eventually authorized. Articulation was a design feature which was not widely adopted, although quintuple units were in use on Great Eastern suburban lines for a time, in five- or ten-coach trains, and, later a small number of articulated sets were built for use on both the LMS and LNER.

A unique LNER design was the main-line corridor coach, evolved in 1945 and built after the war, which had two transverse passages dividing the coach into three sections. The intention of this design was to reduce the distance from any compartment to an external door and to minimize congestion in the corridor and at the ends of coaches on the platform. The design did not lose seating space, as there were no doors at the coach ends. These vehicles were not particularly popular amongst the travelling public and the design was not generally repeated after nationalization.

Immediately after the Second World War the Railway Companies' Association set the Chief Mechanical Engineers and Chief Civil Engineers to work to assess the extent to which further standardization was practic-

Fig. 8.1   Five-car articulated set, King's Cross–Leeds (NRM)

able. As a result, a coach of standard external dimensions was tentatively proposed, capable of satisfying the loading gauge in most areas. Widely differing views were, however, held by the separate companies in respect of other constructional features to be standardized and no recommendations were made on such aspects as the use of steel or timber for body framing, the types or dimensions of bogie, or the type of gangway. Additionally, views were varied on interior layouts and the number and positioning of outside doors. Had it not been for nationalization, it seems likely that, apart from the important issue of overall dimensions, the degree of standardization achieved between the four group companies would have been very limited.

After nationalization R. A. Riddles was faced with the same problem as that which had arisen in regard to locomotives – the designs to which new coaching stock vehicles should be built. Again, as in the case of locomotives, the urgent need to overtake arrears of new construction made it impossible, even had it been desirable, to indulge in fundamental changes in design. Riddles therefore appointed a Carriage Standards Committee to review existing practices and recommend standards for new coaches, to incorporate the best features of the former companies designs. In doing so, the Committee took into account the earlier proposals of the Railway Companies' Association for further standardization.

In producing the new designs, four basic decisions were taken:

(a) that, to give greater strength, future coaches should be constructed with all-steel underframes, body framing, and side and roof panels, with extensive use of welding;

(b) that buckeye couplings and Pullman gangways, which had proved to be the most satisfactory in preventing the telescoping of trains in case of accident, should be generally adopted;

(c) that the end loading resistance to traction and buffing stresses should be doubled without, if possible, significant increase in overall weight. Traction stresses are at their highest on the first vehicle of a train, next to the locomotive, with the whole weight of the train behind it, and buffing stresses can be particularly high on a vehicle involved in a collision. The former company designs provided for end loading appreciably less (for example, LNER 120 tons, SR 80 tons) than overseas designs (140 to 360 tons) and to give a proper margin of safety a figure of 200 tons was adopted for the new designs; and

(d) that riding qualities of the new standard stock should be improved. Later reference is made to the tests which were conducted in this respect.

The design of coach ultimately evolved had the following main characteristics:

(a) all-steel construction;

(b) overall length of body, 64 ft 6 in (as on the former SR, and somewhat longer than on the other companies);

(c) maximum width 9 ft at waist level (9 ft 3 in over door handles);

(d) tare weight, 32 tons (rather lighter than former LNER and SR standards and heavier than former LMSR and GWR standards);

(e) wheel diameter, 3 ft 6 in (again, as on the former SR, and rather smaller than on the other lines);

(f) double bolster bogies (following former LNER and GWR practice);

(g) automatic coupler (buckeye) drawgear and Pullman type gangways (former LNER and SR practice).

A helpful factor was that, soon after nationalization, the Chief Civil Engineer produced a rolling stock gauge for passenger coaches which, whilst retaining the 9 ft maximum width at waist level, permitted an increase from 8 ft 2½ in to 8 ft 8 in in width at cant rail height. This was a significant improvement on the standard recommended by the Committee set up by the Railway Companies' Association prior to nationalization and allowed of a very wide route availability. This profile could be associated with two vehicle lengths – 64 ft 6 in for all corridor passenger-carrying vehicles and 57 ft for other passenger and non-passenger coaching stock requiring somewhat more extensive freedom of operation.

So emerged the British Railways Mark I coaching stock, the first of them being completed in time for the Festival of Britain in 1951. Twelve types of stock to these basic standards, with various internal layouts, were included in the 1951 building programme. In all, twenty-one types were designed and developed to meet all traffic demands – main-line, suburban, sleeping, catering – the remaining nine types being included in the 1952–3 programmes.

The Mark I designs had paid some regard to passenger comfort, as influenced by riding qualities and seating arrangements, and the 1955 Modernization Plan envisaged that in building new coaches the demand for higher standards of amenity would be taken fully into account.

In the mid-1950s, A. E. Robson, who had succeeded E. Pugson as Carriage and Wagon Engineer at the BTC in 1954, invited a number of

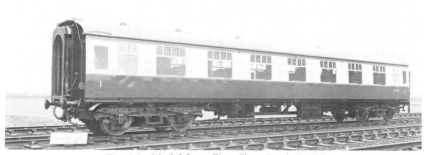

Fig. 8.2   Mark I Open First-Class Coach (NRM)

private builders to produce vehicles demonstrating their ideas on designs of modern passenger coaches suitable for future use on British Railways. Prototypes were submitted by a number of firms and were on public display at an exhibition at Battersea Wharf in June 1957.

Arising from the Modernization Plan, and the recognized need to present the public with a new rail image, the BTC had also arranged for the construction of some diesel-electric Pullman type trains – the 'Blue Pullmans'. In making this decision, the BTC had been influenced by the introduction of the Trans-European Express (TEE) trains in Europe. Two six-car trains were supplied to the LM Region and three eight-car trains to the Western Region. The 36 vehicles were built by Metropolitan-Cammell and each train was powered by two 1000 h.p. NBL/MAN diesel engines, with electric transmission, and with two Rolls Royce 238 h.p. diesel engines to provide for ancillary requirements.

The Midland Pullman was inaugurated between Manchester and St Pancras in July 1960, and provided a fast link between these cities whilst electrification works were in progress on the Euston route. It operated from Manchester to St Pancras in the morning, made a round trip between St Pancras and Leicester at mid-day, and returned to Manchester in the evening, providing a first-class, supplement payment service. The second six-car train on the LM Region was intended to provide a similar high-class business service between Liverpool and Euston, but operating experience with the Manchester train was such that Regional management was reluctant to introduce both services. In effect, therefore, one full train was generally standing spare to cover the one train in service. On the Western Region, the trains, introduced in 1961, operated between Paddington and South Wales, with an intermediate trip from Cardiff to Bristol and back at mid-day, and catered for both first- and second-class passengers. Again, one complete train was normally held in reserve. In 1966, all the trains were concentrated on the Western Region.

Fig. 8.3   The Midland Pullman (BRB)

The interior layout, amenity, and decor – including pressure ventilation for the first time on British Railways – left little to be criticized. Because they were quiet, and modern in appearance, they were popular with the travelling public, but unfortunately the riding of the vehicles was poor. On the basis of the high reputation they had gained on the Continent, Swiss-designed 'Schlieren' bogies had been installed, but proved to be unsuitable for use under British conditions. Furthermore, the trains were not particularly reliable in service and in due course it was decided that there was unlikely to be a viable commercial future for them. They were withdrawn from service in 1974. The design was not repeated; the trains were in effect overtaken by the much improved BR Mark II hauled stock.

Following the Battersea Exhibition, BTC design staff produced their own version of the vehicles considered to be necessary to provide a substantial improvement in the standards of amenity and comfort of rail

Fig. 8.4 A full-scale 'mock-up' of the lounge car projected in connection with the XP.64 train, and said to have been inspired by an Italian model. The design was tried in service but proved to have little potential under British conditions

travel. The Mark I standard coach had been in service for close on ten years and the need was being felt for a new range of vehicles with, above all, greatly improved riding qualities at all speeds up to the then existing maximum of 90 miles/h. A prototype train – XP.64 – was built and went into public service in June 1964, to start a 12-month test period. It consisted of eight vehicles, incorporating a number of new features, including improved bogies, wide entrance doors and vestibules, wider double-glazed windows, better sound-proofing, improved heating and ventilation, improved lighting, adjustable semi-reclining first-class seats, and re-designed second-class seating.

Designs were also produced for new type lounge cars, incorporating lounge sections with seats for three passengers at each end and four individual armchairs in the centre. Concealed lighting, spot-lights for reading, and a curtained, glass partition on the corridor side were provided. The rest of the coach was to be taken up by compartments, ladies' powder room, baggage accommodation, food preparation rooms, or bar facilities. Service trials on Eastern, London Midland, and Western Region main lines suggested that a vehicle of this nature had no real potential in Britian and only three vehicles were in fact converted into lounge cars, the design not thereafter being repeated.

The XP.64 project, intended to test public opinion as to what was needed in future standard coaches, had a powerful influence on coaching stock development. The experimental nature of the design necessitated a reasonable lapse of time to assess public reaction to the various innovations which had been incorporated in the vehicles, although individual elements of the design – integral body construction, improved bogies, pressure ventilation – were built into some vehicles constructed in the meantime.

The first of the new Mark II standard coaches, design of which was

Fig. 8.5   Mark II First-Class Coach (BRB)

based on the XP.64 prototype, was built in 1963. Compared with the Mark I design, the Mark II is slightly longer overall (65 ft 4¼ in) and incorporates a number of design improvements, including

(a) improved bogies;

(b) a new design of floor, with insulation between top and bottom floor panels to reduce noise;

(c) the insertion of insulating materials in body-side and roof cavities;

(d) double-glazed windows;

(e) a system of pressure ventilation and heating, either by steam or electricity;

(f) fluorescent lighting in second-class saloons;

(g) improved designs of luggage rack, incorporating spot-lights for reading; and

(h) a modern design of light-weight seating in open second-class vehicles, based on ergonomic principles.

All second-class stock is of the open type. All except twenty of the initial build of Mark II vehicles retained the vacuum brake, and in the first twenty-one steam heating was provided. The remainder of the 322 Mark II vehicles, built between 1964 and 1966, were fitted with dual steam/electric heating.

Over the next few years, six further versions of the Mark II coach were built and Table 8.1 sets out relevant details, including the main design differences from previous Marks.

In 1968, whilst the building of the Mark IIB stock was in progress, designs for the Mark IIC series were being prepared, to avoid any gap in production in railway workshops. Considerable difficulty was, however, experienced in persuading the Government to authorize the necessary finance. A request for authority to build 600 further vehicles was held up for several months, whilst the Ministry insisted that, instead of building new stock, 600 Mark I vehicles should be modernized. A costing exercise carried out on the instructions of T. C. B. Miller, who had succeeded Robson as Chief Engineer (Traction and Rolling stock) in 1968 (re-designated Chief Mechanical and Electrical Engineer in 1970), showed that to modify and modernize Mark I stock, including the installation of air-conditioning, would in fact be more expensive than to build new vehicles. Even then, authority was not forthcoming, despite continued pressure by the BR Board, until, in February 1969, arrangements were made for the then Minister of Transport, the Rt Hon. Richard Marsh, to visit the Research Laboratories at Derby. When the Staff Representatives at the Carriage and Wagon Workshops at Derby heard of this intended visit they asked that the Minister should meet them to hear their complaints regarding the threatened shortage of new construction work. At that meeting, the Minister told the staff that he would authorize the 600 vehicles. He acknowledged that management had been pressing for authority for the building of the new stock to be put in hand, but stated that it had not been possible until then for the Government to allocate the necessary finance. How much longer the authority would have been deferred, had it not been for the staff's intervention, is a matter for conjecture!

With the introduction of full air-conditioning, the view was taken that it would be illogical to continue with the provision of quarter-lights in the bodyside windows and of drop-lights, which passengers could open –

Table 8.1   Mark II Locomotive-hauled Coaching Stock

Mark	Type	No. of vehicles	Year built	Bogie	Heating	Brakes	Principal differences from previous Mark.
II	FK BFK SO BSO	71 28 187 36	1,1963; Remain- der 1964/66	B4	21 steam 301 dual steam/ electric	302 vacuum; 20 air	—
	Total	322					
IIA	FK BFK SO BSO	42 48 177 22	1967/ 68	B4	Dual steam/ electric	Air	New type gangway with folding doors; improved toilets; corridor partitions, decor and seating layout improved in first class; fluorescent lighting; air brakes
	Total	289					
IIB	FK BFK SO	38 9 64	1968/ 69	B4	Dual steam/ electric	Air	Wide wrap-round end doors; alterations to SO layout, with toilet each end and no centre cross vestibule
	Total	111					
IIC	FK FO BFK SO BSO	48 18 26 118 40	1969/ 70	B4	Dual steam/ electric	Air	New louvred ceiling profile to accommodate ducting for future installation of air-conditioning; introduction of FO; lighting levels improved
	Total	250					

Mark	Type	No. of vehicles	Year built	Bogie	Heating	Brakes	Principal differences from previous Mark.
IID	FK FO BFK SO BSO	49 47 34 128 17	1970/ 72	B4	Electric	Air	Full air-conditioning and electric heating introduced; no sliding ventilator windows; doors fitted with inside actuating locks later replaced by conventional outside actuating locks and droplights
	Total	275					
IIE	FO SO BSO	55 160 14	1971/ 73	B4	Electric	Air	Improved vestibule layout; increased luggage space; smaller toilet; new style seating
	Total	229					
IIF	FO SO BSO	164 277 30	1973/ 74	B4	Electric	Air	Air-conditioning without heating and pressure ventilation unit, and using bodyside heaters. 40 with Pullman type seating: remainder new type seating, with loose covers
	Total	471					
Grand Total		1947					

Notes:
  FK – first class corridor coach.
  FO – first class open coach.
BFK – first class corridor coach with brake section.
  SO – second class open coach.
BSO – second class open coach with brake section.

and leave open – at will, in the end doors. These were therefore fixed, necessitating the provision of inside-opening door locks. A simple handle, recessed to prevent accidental opening, was accordingly developed and fitted. Regrettably, however, a number of accidents did occur with the inside door handles on the Mark II stock and – perhaps rather over-hastily – arrangements were made for conventional outside-opening door locks, in association with drop-lights, to be restored.

Such was the rate of development that from 1964 until the end of the programme for Mark IIF's in 1974 – just ten years of continuous design progress – over 1900 coaches were built, all in BR workshops. Some very fundamental design strides were taken in this period – conversion from steam to electric heating and from vacuum to air brake, and the introduction of full air-conditioning, as well as quite major improvements in other passenger amenities.

The decade 1964–74 undoubtedly saw a greater range of developments in passenger stock design than any other decade in the history of railways. Full credit for this must go to the coaching stock design staff of the CM & EE, and also to the Design Panel staff, for the part they each played in the very significant advances which were made during this period. In this connection, the Rolling Stock Design and Development Panel (Passenger), set up by J. F. Harrison, played a significant role, bringing together all the parties interested in new rolling stock design. A similar Panel was concerned with freight rolling stock design and development, and through these Panels all commercial and operating specifications for rolling stock were agreed.

The British Railways Design Panel was established in 1956 to concern itself with 'the aesthetic and amenity design, both internal and external, of such fixed and movable equipment as is widely used by the Board's passengers, customers and staff, or is prominently visible to them or the general public'. It was involved in the development of passenger rolling stock from the XP.64 project onwards, being particularly concerned in the design of the seating, and in the development of certain glass-reinforced plastic components forming such fittings as interior partitions; the rationalization of furnishing fabrics and internal finishes, in the interests of economy in supply and maintenance; and lighting and other internal fittings.

This was a period indeed when, throughout Europe – and elsewhere in the world also – there was a keen interest in the welfare and comfort of the railway passenger. A group set up by the UIC, and chaired by one of the authors as representing British Railways, was engaged at this time in a comprehensive examination of various aspects of the matter. The group's two reports, entitled 'Optimum Passenger Comfort', issued in March 1969 and June 1972, dealt in some detail with all aspects of the environment in which the passenger finds himself in the course of his journey and the action which should be taken to make the journey as pleasant as possible. In making their contribution to these reports, BR representatives made a particular study of seating requirements – a study which involved the CM & EE's design staff, the Research and Development organization, and specialists in ergonomic factors.

During the construction of the Mark II range, designs for three catering vehicles – full restaurant car, buffet car, and kitchen car – were developed, but subsequent changes in Regional assessments of customer needs prompted the train catering staff at BT Hotels HQ to amend their requirements to provide for buffet cars only. In the event, however, no Mark II series catering vehicles were built, apart from 29 Pullman vehicles built at Derby in 1966 for use on LM Region electric services from Euston to Manchester and Liverpool. These were of three types – parlour car, parlour kitchen, and parlour brake – built to the standard Mark II underframe and body-shell profile. The absence of other new builds led to serious problems in meeting train catering requirements in the 1970s and in 1978 a priority programme for the reconditioning of Mark I catering vehicles had to be put into effect.

By the late 1960s it was becoming evident that a new and more advanced design of coach was necessary to cater for passenger needs in the longer term future. Commercial research had established that higher speeds, up to 125 miles/h, were likely to become increasingly important to the attraction of passengers from intensifying road and air competition and that reliability of service and comfort of travel were considered equally essential. There was, furthermore, a need to develop a suitable design of stock for use on the then proposed Channel Tunnel services and on Trans-European Expresses.

It was apparent, however, that the Mark II design had been developed to the limit and further improvements could not be incorporated. It was desirable, for commercial reasons, that further new vehicles should provide increased seating capacity. The long-distance road coach operators had kept their prices fairly stable by virtually doubling the number of seats per vehicle and whilst the railways could not – and would not wish to – reduce the space per passenger to the same extent, nevertheless some increase in capacity was essential.

A new design of carriage, of increased overall length, was therefore produced, which would, if acceptable, show worthwhile economies in several directions – reduced first cost per seat; a smaller number of vehicles required and therefore reduced maintenance costs; and reduced tare weight in relation to passenger capacity, with consequent savings in haulage power. The first proposal was for a vehicle 80 ft instead of 65 ft long, but a wide survey by the Chief Civil Engineer of the restrictions which would be imposed on a vehicle of such a length revealed that very heavy expenditure on track and structures would be involved, unless the overall body width was reduced by three inches or so. In the light of the demand for improved standards of comfort and increased seating capacity, this limitation in body width was not acceptable. It was, however, established that a 75 ft long vehicle, having a maximum body width of 9 ft, with no protruding door handles and with slightly tapered ends, could be granted route availability similar to that of the Mark II designs.

In the development of the Mark III vehicle – visualized as a locomotive-hauled coach but also suitable for inclusion in High Speed Train formations – the objective was to achieve maximum seating capacity at minimum first cost, a top speed capability of 125 miles/h, and optimum passenger amenities. The design adopted is of integral all-steel construction with one body structure, to which alternative internal layouts are applied, for both first- and second-class seating. The same body-shell has been used for catering vehicles and will be used for sleeping cars. The windows, of maximum width, are spaced in the usual way for first-class compartment or saloon seating layout, but in second-class coaches seat positions are arranged irrespective of window positions. The advantages and disadvantages of uni-directional seating were also explored. Such an arrangement did in fact permit an increase in second-class seats from 72 to 80 but after trials in the prototype the idea was abandoned because of train catering requirements and the strong public preference for conventional type seating.

Interior fittings are designed to permit easy removal and replacement, thus facilitating normal periodic maintenance and, when required, complete modernization in new materials developed during the lifetime of the coach. Automatic treadmat-operated sliding doors were installed at the saloon ends and litter bins were placed in saloons and at the ends of the vehicles. In designing the internal layout, special regard was also paid to the need for ease of cleaning of the vehicles when in service.

Prototypes were built and subjected to technical and service testing early in 1972. They were generally well received and only relatively minor modifications, in the main to air-conditioning equipment, were required

Fig. 8.6   Mark III Second-Class Coach (BRB)

before production orders were put in hand. Very few design changes have been necessary since production started. The only difference between the Mark III vehicles to be used in HST formations and those for inclusion in locomotive-hauled trains is that in the former case (Mark IIIa) they are fitted with control lines and draw power for their ancillary services from the power cars, whereas in the latter case the coaches are individually equipped with motor alternators.

The Mark IIIs have now been in service for the best part of ten years. By the end of 1979, 671 of these coaches (including 446 for use in High Speed Trains) had been put into stock, plus 109 catering vehicles (including 92 for HSTs). There are plans to build 236 sleeping cars, for delivery in 1980/83. The next range of passenger vehicles will be for the Advanced Passenger Trains, stock thereby relieved being allocated to replace some of the Mark I and Mark II vehicles still in service on less important routes.

The BR standard Mark I vehicles were equipped with steam heating by radiant tubular heaters, thermostatically controlled and with passenger manipulation. Ventilation was by roof extractor vents and sliding ventilators in body-side windows. Following experience with the XP.64 prototype and the Blue Pullmans, the initial builds of Mark II stock were equipped with a pressure ventilation system, associated with either steam or electric heating supply. Under this system, in order to secure a better distribution of warm air than was achievable with radiant steam heaters, the heated air, at thermostat controlled temperatures, was fed, under pressure, into the coach at seat level: there was no separate distribution of cool air.

In the meantime, the marketing staff's concern for passenger comfort, heightened by the increasing use of air-conditioning generally, had led them to the view that full air-conditioning should be installed in future main-line stock. Initial reactions of the BR Board to this suggestion were not encouraging but, after market research had confirmed it to be a desirable development, full air-conditioning in future main-line stock was agreed. Pending the availability of equipment and the preparation of design alterations, Mark IIC coaches were fitted with concealed overhead ducting for the distribution of cooled air, thus making provision for later fitting of the full air-conditioning equipment. The Mark IID design was the first to incorporate, in 1970, the full equipment; and BR was the first railway in Europe to provide this facility in all new stock for general main-line service.

At first, some problems were expected to arise in maintaining sufficient power from the locomotive for both traction and air-conditioning needs – a recurrence of a doubt which arose earlier, when electric heating was first installed. To meet this situation, a three-phase supply, generated by the main engine, is fed down the train, converted to d.c. on each vehicle, to drive a motor alternator set, which provides the power for air-conditioning and other ancillary needs on the vehicle. In the case of the

Class 27/2 (Birmingham Railway C&W 1250 h.p.) locomotives, specially adapted to work the Edinburgh Waverley–Glasgow Queen Street push-pull service, however, it was necessary to instal auxiliary engines, Deutz 172 h.p., to drive an alternator to supply train requirements.

Because of the frequency with which doors are opened on suburban services it has not generally been considered an economic proposition to install air-conditioning in high density electric multiple unit trains, particularly where sliding door stock is in use. With such stock, heating is provided by means of pressure ventilation with electrically warmed air.

The riding of coaching stock has been a matter of constant concern to successive generations of railway rolling stock engineers. This is a field in which, until a few years ago, progressive development was by experiment with new ideas, analysis of results, and the introduction of new designs and standards, followed by similar and successive rounds of experiment, analysis, and standardization at intervals thereafter. Recently, however, with a more scientific approach, and better means of measuring and analysing the interaction of track and vehicles, the likely dynamic behaviour of new designs can be more accurately established.

The four main-line companies chose their new standard bogies from amongst the designs of their constituent railways. Similarly, the Railway Executive studied the designs of the group railways before deciding on the bogie to be adopted as a basis for a new British standard, in order to take advantage of the best features of all the existing designs. Test runs took place over the Great Central main line between Marylebone and Nottingham with the latest designs of the companies' coaches, first with wheels having tyres to the designed profile and second with worn tyres. Each coach was tested under 75 per cent load and care was taken to ensure that conditions were similar for each run. Track conditions and the riding qualities of the bogies were recorded for analysis and comparison. Double-bolster bogies of the type used on the LNER and GWR were found to provide the best ride, particularly with tyres in worn condition. Of the two, the GWR bogie did marginally better and was adopted as the new standard, with some modification to the secondary suspension.

The bogies were submitted to exhaustive tests before being adopted as the new standard. They also acquitted themselves very well in a competition, held under the auspices of the Office of Research and Experiment of the UIC, in which they were matched against the best European designs in riding trials in France and Germany. It was found, however, that after about 40000 miles in normal service, there was a rapid deterioration in the wearing parts of the bogie and in the quality of the ride. It was essential, therefore, to find a replacement bogie as quickly as possible and following visits to the Continent – where riding was said to be much better than in Britain, although the permanent way was no better than the British – the decision was taken to adopt the Commonwealth bogie. Ten of these bogies – a United States design, heavy in construction and expensive in first cost – were authorized for trial under locomotive-hauled stock in 1955 and were in service a year later. By the end of 1958, the vehicles had run over 150000 miles, with a complete absence of deterioration in riding qualities. The Commission therefore decided that the Commonwealth bogie should be adopted as standard for all new main-line carriages, pending the development of an improved British type. A large number of existing vehicles was also equipped with these bogies, through special modification programmes. During the same period, consideration was given to various other proprietary bogie and suspension designs, both British and Continental. Some of these underwent trials on a limited scale, but none of them proved to be sufficiently satisfactory in service.

As previously stated, in the early 1950s developments in bogie design could not always be supported by adequate theoretical knowledge of all the factors involved in riding performance. Research into the problems relating to wheel/rail interaction, which had begun when T. M. Herbert was Director of Research, was pressed ahead with added urgency by the Research and Development Division and the mechanical engineers. A notable contribution to this work was made by J. L. Koffman, an engineer of Russian extraction who had specialized in the problems of riding on Continental railways, with which he had many close contacts. He was brought into the Research and Development organization by Herbert, later transferring to the Traction and Rolling Stock Department at BR HQ.

By their membership of UIC, British Railways was involved in all that ORE was doing in this field. An investigation into the practices of sixteen UIC member railways in regard to passenger carriage suspension characteristics identified the design features essential to ensure good riding without deterioration at high mileages. It was decided to apply the results of this investigation to British conditions and the Swindon drawing office, in collaboration with Headquarters, was given the task of

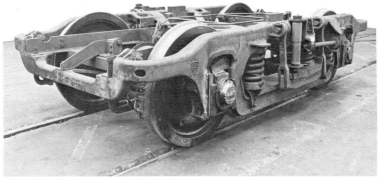

Fig. 8.7 The Commonwealth bogie: an American design used on BR coaching stock pending the development of an improved British bogie (BRB)

Fig. 8.8   The B4 bogie developed at Swindon

designing a new bogie incorporating the recommendations of the ORE report.

A pair of bogies was built at Swindon in 1956, followed two years later by 50 more, improved in certain details. The prototype bogies were found capable of giving very good riding, without deterioration, for up to 150 000 miles between repairs. These B4 bogies, which are 2·5 tons lighter than the previous standard, were fitted to the XP.64 train and in due course to the Mark II stock. Since then, there have been progressive developments in bogie design, which are summarized in Table 8.2.

Table 8.2   Principal Developments in Passenger Vehicle Bogies

Name/code	Year first fitted	Stock to which fitted	Principal features of design/comments
Locomotive-hauled stock			
BR Standard	1951	Mark I	Double bolster; laminated primary springs, coil secondary springs; adapted from best features of group railway designs; subject to rapid deterioration in wearing parts after about 40 000 miles.
BR Modified	1953	Mark I	As above, but with longer swing links and vertical, lateral, and rotational damping

Name/code	Year first fitted	Stock to which fitted	Principal features of design/ comments
Common-wealth	1956	Mark I, by modification	American origin; adopted pending availability of improved British design; coil springing; vertical and rotational damping
B4	1956	XP.64; Mark II; some Mark I rebogied; LMR Pullman parlours and parlour brakes	Based on ORE design; coil spring primary and secondary suspensions; long swing links; vertical, lateral, and rotational damping
B5	1965	LMR Pullman parlour kitchens	Strengthened version of B4
BT10	1976	Mark III, including HST	Fabricated H frame; primary suspension, radius arms and coil spring, hydraulic damping; secondary air springs; lateral freedom provided by swing links; control of body roll by torsion bars
Diesel multiple units			
Original	1955	Early post-nationalization builds	Laminated primary springs; coil secondary springs; as on 1934 Liverpool–Southport electric multiple-unit stock; riding indifferent.
Schlieren	1959	Blue Pullman trains	Swiss type bogies, previously tested on three hauled vehicles; rode badly under BR stock, particularly when new; longer swing link and knife edge anchorage introduced and effected some improvement
B4	1956	Later builds of diesel multiple-unit inter-city stock	See under B4/B5 above
B5	1965		
BT13	—	Future designs of diesel multiple unit stock	See under BT13 below
Electric multiple unit stock			
Original SR	Pre-nation-alization	SR stock	Laminated primary springs, coil secondary springs; riding acceptable on services involved

Table. 8.2   Principal Developments in Passenger Vehicle Bogies (continued)

Name/code	Year first fitted	Stock to which fitted	Principal features of design/comments
BR Mk I		SR stock	As above, but with longer and less inclined swing links; riding deteriorated
BR Mk II	By stages, post-nation-alization	SR stock	As above, but with less inclined swing links; riding still poor
BR Mk III		SR stock	As above, but with lower stressed secondary springs, lateral coupling of bolster and spring plants, metal to metal bearing surfaces at top of swing links; riding improved
BR Mk IV		SR stock	As above, but with vertical swing links
Common-wealth	1958	Kent Coast services, phase II: Liverpool St–Clacton–Walton stock	See under 'Commonwealth' above
BP6 BP7	1971	Prototype four-car high density stock	Fabricated H-type frame and bolster with cast steel spring plants; primary suspension, radius arms and coil springs; secondary suspension, air springs
BP8	1971	Prototype two-car high density stock	Air spring suspension, mounted directly between vehicle body and bogie frame, allowing lateral, vertical, and rotational movement relative to the bogie
BT13	1976	High density four-car units for GN Inner Suburban (Class 313) and subsequent builds	Primary suspension, radial arm axle-boxes attached to frame by rubber bushed pivot pin; springing provided by rubber chevron unit arranged directly over axlebox; secondary suspension by diaphragm type air springs; air orifice damping, eliminating the need for hydraulic dampers in the vertical plane; welded steel bogie frame.

The Table also includes information on bogies fitted to diesel and electric multiple units. The bogies fitted to the early diesel multiple units, based on one designed for the Liverpool–Southport electric multiple unit stock in 1934, provided an indifferent riding performance and some of the units were later fitted with modified bogies. Following the development of the B4 bogie, this, or variants of it, were fitted to some Inter-City type diesel multiple unit stock towards the end of the Modernization Plan programme.

The Modernization Plan foreshadowed an ultimate requirement of 23 000 locomotive-hauled passenger vehicles, the vast majority of which it was expected would be constructed during the period of the Plan. The decision of the BTC in 1956 to retain the vacuum brake as the standard system, notwithstanding a recommendation from its Power Brakes Committee, endorsed by the Board's own Technical Development and Research Committee, that the air brake should be adopted, is referred to later in this chapter. Until the British Railways Board accepted in 1963 that a change to the air brake had become essential to meet future operating conditions, all new locomotive-hauled passenger coaches continued to be fitted with the vacuum brake. Thereafter, in order to overcome the problems arising during the change-over period, due to incompatibility of the two brake systems, a considerable number of vehicles were dual-fitted. The first new coaches to be fitted with air brakes only were twenty Mark II vehicles built in 1966.

As train speeds increase, so does the need for improved braking capacity, if trains are to be stopped within existing signal spacings and very heavy expenditure on signalling work is to be avoided. Up to 100 miles/h, the classic clasp brake, with cast-iron brake blocks, is adequate for passenger trains. Above that speed, up to 125 miles/h, it is possible to stop within the present 100 miles/h braking distances by the use of disc brakes and this type of brake is fitted to Mark III stock. The first passenger vehicles to be fitted with the disc brake, following extensive trials on the Southern Region, were the Class 310 electric multiple units, working out of Euston, in 1966. Trials were also carried out on stock working between King's Cross and Newcastle before the decision was taken to fit this type of brake to the Mark III stock.

The maximum available braking force is limited by wheel to rail adhesion and to counter the adverse conditions which can arise at high speeds with damp, greasy rails, wheel slide protection (WSP) devices, which detect the slightest sign of wheel-slip and instantaneously reduce the brake force on the axles concerned until the wheels regain their proper speed, are essential.

For speeds over 125 miles/h the disc brake is approaching its practical thermal limit. Other forms of braking have therefore been developed – notably, the hydro-kinetic brake with which the Advanced Passenger Trains are being equipped. This brake consists of two sets of rotor and stator vanes, attached respectively to the inside of a tubular axle and to the axle-boxes, the retardation being controlled by the rate of flow of fluid between the rotor and stator vanes. A single rotor and stator pair is effective in one direction of rotation only, a second pair being required for the opposite direction. An auxiliary friction brake is needed to supplement the hydro-kinetic brake's performance below 50 miles/h.

Until the mid-1960s, the heating of locomotive-hauled coaching stock was by steam, of diesel multiple unit vehicles by oil-fired air heaters and of electric multiple unit stock by electric heaters. The difficulties experienced with steam heating and the failure rate of oil-fired boilers on diesel locomotives emphasized the need for a change in the system of heating, whilst the introduction of electric locomotives on the LM Region and of diesel-electric locomotives on all Regions made it sensible to replace steam by electric heating on hauled stock. For an interim period, however, there would be a need to cater for haulage by steam, diesel or electric locomotives and many coaches would therefore require to be equipped for dual steam/electric heating. The first new vehicles to be dual fitted were the Mark II designs in 1964 and this continued until the Mark IID coaches, with electric heating only, appeared in 1970. A programme of conversion of existing coaches to dual heating was also put in hand. In all, around 3000 Mark I and Mark II coaches were fitted with dual heating, either by conversion or during construction. With the change-over from steam to electric heating, the reliability of the heating equipment has improved considerably in recent years. This change, combined with the introduction of full air-conditioning, has considerably enhanced passenger comfort.

The matters to which reference has so far been made in this chapter have related principally to engineering advances in the design and construction of passenger vehicles for main-line services of which perhaps the most outstanding contribution has been made by the High Speed Trains, to which reference has been made in Chapter Six.

In the freight field there has been a much greater revolution in operating methods than with passenger traffic, much of the change having occurred since the 1960s. The Railway Executive inherited around 1·25 million wagons of some 480 different types, including coal wagons which had previously been in private ownership and which were mostly already beyond the normal age for withdrawal from service. They were mainly of small capacity, fitted with grease axle-boxes and braked only by hand. Freight train loading was determined not so much by the haulage capacity of the locomotive as by the ability of the locomotive and brake van to stop the train. Sometimes, before descending steep gradients, it was necessary to stop trains to pin down the brakes on a number of the wagons, and catch points had to be provided for safety reasons on rising gradients steeper than 1 in 260, to derail wagons running away in the wrong direction due to a broken coupling.

The privately owned wagons had been designed to suit the owners' terminal arrangements at collieries, retail coal yards or coal shipping points. The dimensions of these terminal facilities, often small sites with difficult approach curves, tended, for many years, to determine the size and capacity of railway-owned wagons. As the whole of the country's freight terminal facilities could not be modernized overnight, short wheelbase wagons of low capacity and restricted running speed had still to be built, although already obsolete in both commercial and technical terms. In this respect, British Railways lagged well behind most other countries where, because of more generous loading gauges, less restrictive layouts, and different commercial situations, larger capacity wagons were in use. On the credit side, permitted axle loads in Britain were generally higher than, for example, in mainland Europe. There existed a minority of vacuum-braked wagons which were used on the relatively few express freight trains between main centres of industry and population. Some wagons used in international traffic via the train ferries had been dual vacuum/air braked since the 1930s, but, in general, freight trains progressed slowly from origin to destination, with long delays in intermediate marshalling yards.

Further progress towards more efficient operation of freight traffic required very heavy capital expenditure by the railways and their customers on replacing obsolete restrictive depots and wagon loading and unloading plant and equipment, inevitably a lengthy process of development and evolution. This evolutionary policy, which had perforce been followed by the railway companies for many years, and by the Railway Executive, was substantially changed by three separate, though related, events of outstanding importance. The first was the Modernization Plan, an important component of which was the drastic remodelling of freight services, including the fitting of power brakes to all wagons. The second was a new freight charging scheme, which took effect at about the same time and gave firm financial incentives to the customer to use wagons effectively. The third was the Reshaping Plan of 1963, which recognized that the wagon-load business was becoming increasingly uneconomic to the railway and unattractive to the customer. This was to lead to the development of the train rather than the wagon as the basic unit of freight movement. The 'liner-train' system was introduced and customer trains developed, using private sidings at one or both ends of the journey. The latter, mainly for the transport of oil, stone, and cement, are operated, so far as possible, with privately owned wagons, of which there are currently over 18 000 in service, designed to the requirements of the CM & EE, to the highest efficiency standards.

There still remained a substantial quantity of freight business in wagon-load quantities, too uneconomic to be tolerated but too valuable to be jettisoned. The BR Board recognized that its freight problem could not be solved by liner-trains and block trains only: if these services were to succeed, it had also to reorganize its wagon-load activity. A network of express air-braked freight trains was therefore introduced in 1972, with a Bristol–Glasgow service as the first experimental stage, expanded over the years into a nation-wide system, thereby completing the modern freight service pattern. The service was named 'Speedlink' in 1977. The local freight train, stopping to attach and detach small wagons at stations just a few miles apart, no longer operates. The heavy, long distance, slow-moving freight train, passing through two, three, or even more marshalling yards en route from originating to destination stations or depots, also now represents a much smaller proportion of the freight business.

Although at nationalization there were formidable obstacles preventing any immediate radical changes in wagon design to improve either speed of operation or payload capacity, there existed considerable scope for standardization of wagons over and above that already accepted for many years as essential to permit inter-company running. To this end, the Railway Executive set up the Ideal Stocks Committee, already referred to in Chapter Two. This Committee recommended that future requirements for freight traffic, operating as it then was in the traditional pattern, could be met by building wagons of 71 types, modified in detail to secure the maximum standardization of components, compared with the original figure of 480. The first wagons of the new type were built in 1951.

For reasons already explained, the scope for increasing wagon size, particularly for the conveyance of general merchandise, was limited. More latitude for the use of larger wagons did, however, exist for mineral traffic. Although the bulk of coal and other minerals was conveyed in

Fig. 8.9   A Speedlink train of air-braked vans hauled by a Class 47
diesel-electric locomotive (BRB)

16-ton wagons, all-steel coal wagons of 20-tons capacity had been introduced to a limited extent before the Second World War. Shortly before the Modernization Plan was announced, the BTC introduced a new design of coal wagon, the largest then capable of running on two axles in Britain, with a capacity of 24½ tons. Despite the difficulties attendant upon the introduction of such wagons, which involved considerable expenditure on the adaptation of terminal facilities and loading appliances, on and outside railway premises, the BTC's aim was that by 1974 half the coal-carrying capacity on the railways should be provided by wagons of this capacity. Initially, the 24½-ton wagons, which were fitted with vacuum brakes and screw couplings, made a fairly minimal impact upon the coal movement scene. In the first place, they were unable to enter many industrial premises because of inadequate clearances and incompatible loading and unloading facilities. Also, the staff objected, on grounds of safety and the extra work involved, to close coupling the wagons and connecting the brake pipes. Whilst the BTC's very ambitious aim was not precisely achieved, coal movement over the years has nevertheless largely been turned over to wagons of more than 20-tons capacity.

Concerted action by British Railways, the National Coal Board, and the Central Electricity Generating Board led to the introduction of block trains of coal to generating stations, conveyed in power-braked wagons of 26 and 32-tons capacity, to which detailed reference is made later in this chapter.

The great advantage of road transport for the conveyance of freight traffic is its ability to give a door-to-door service without intermediate handling. In order to counter severe competition in this market, the railways introduced their own door-to-door services during the years following the 1923 amalgamations by providing containers of various types, equally suitable for conveyance by rail or road vehicles and readily transferable from one to the other. The railways' own road vehicles collected and delivered containers at customers' premises for loading and unloading and took them to and from rail freight depots, the long distance part of the overall transit being undertaken by rail. There was a steady growth in the use of containers for a wide variety of goods but the wagons carrying them were conveyed like any others by the ordinary freight services.

As a means of exploiting the advantages of road/rail container transport and attracting new traffic to rail, the LMR introduced in 1959 an overnight express service between London and Glasgow, named 'Condor' – container door-to-door – at a charge per container irrespective of contents. The service utilized existing designs of containers, on vacuum-braked four-wheeled flat wagons, but was later re-equipped with bogie flat wagons – converted steel carriers – with a 35-ton payload capacity, capable of running at up to 70 miles/h, compared with 50 miles/h in the case of the conflats previously used. A similar service, which again concentrated on new traffics, was introduced as 'Speed-freight' between London and Manchester in April 1963. This service used 10-ton containers, of lengths 9 ft, 18 ft, and 27 ft, the last-named being suitable for the then maximum permitted length of road vehicles. They were constructed of aluminium and steel to maximize payload/tare ratio and were conveyed on standard 13-ton long wheelbase conflats.

Comprehensive studies of the freight situation, initiated in 1961, suggested that there was significant scope for BR to increase its share of the national freight transport market, and that some 16 million tons of potential new freight traffic would be suitable for conveyance by combined road and rail movement, thereby taking advantage of the low cost of trunk haulage by rail over medium to long distances for flows of traffic which, though dense in total, were composed of consignments too small in themselves to justify train-load operation.

Thus was the nationwide liner-train container service – to be known as 'Freightliner' – initiated. Planning of the Freightliner services had started in 1962, the intention being to link main centres of industry and population by fast, regular trains, composed of fifteen flat wagons capable of taking large containers constructed to the proposed International Standards Organization (ISO) cross-section of 8 ft × 8 ft. Apart from new traffics, the trains would also convey existing traffics which were unprofitable by normal wagon-load services. Payload capacity would be about 360 tons per train and the trains would operate at up to 75 miles/h.

Started under BR management in 1965, transferred to joint ownership with the National Freight Corporation under the 1968 Transport Act, and returned to sole BR control by the 1978 Railways Act, the Freightliner service is one of the great success stories of British Railways, not least in engineering terms. The first five routes were authorized by the Minister of Transport in 1964 and, although delayed by objections from the National Union of Railwaymen to free access to Freightliner terminals being granted to traders and hauliers to bring in their own traffics, the first commercial service ran on 15 November 1965, in this case a thirteen-wagon train between London (York Way) and Glasgow (Gushetfaulds). By 1968 the services covered a wide network in Britain and had also expanded into Belgium, with wagons conveyed by the cross-Channel ferry services to Zeebrugge. In that relatively short time, the engineers had designed and built the wagons to operate the services, had produced the containers, had planned and constructed the terminals, and had equipped them with the necessary handling devices.

In order to enable containers to the recommended ISO standard, 8 ft square in cross section, to be conveyed within the British loading gauge, the floor of the wagons designed for the Freightliner service had to be appreciably lower than standard. A prototype set of four bogie wagons, each 40 ft long with buckeye couplers and a floor height above rail level of 3 ft 1½ in, was built for preliminary trials. The load-carrying capacity of these wagons was, however, judged to be inadequate and an improved design was prepared. This had a 60 ft loadable length and a floor height of 3 ft 3½ in. Standard buffing and drawgear was fitted at the outer ends of the set, with a solid bar coupler between adjacent wagons. Three-piece cast steel bogies, with 2 ft 8 in diameter wheels, a modified version of the American 'Ridemaster' bogie, were provided, equipped with disc brakes controlled by a two-pipe air brake system with proportional load application. The Chief Civil Engineer accepted these wagons, subject to an axle load limitation of 17½ tons for vehicles operating at up to 75 miles/h, restricting the load-carrying capacity of the wagons to 51 tons. The wagons were designed to carry containers from 10 ft to 40 ft in length.

The original concept of the Freightliner was based essentially on a rail and road system, with little consideration being given to the handling of maritime containers. The first two years of Freightliner operations, however, coincided with a substantial increase in the use of containers for seaborne cargoes. There was consequently a corresponding demand for the transport of international shipping lines' containers, which in turn required greater strength in wagon design and improved facilities for lifting containers, and stacking them up to six high. Bearing in mind customer requirements and the need for compatibility with other container activities, a decision was taken in 1967 to modify all wagons to carry ISO standard maritime containers.

In the early 1970s there was strong pressure to introduce a larger size of container than the 8 ft × 8 ft cross-section international standard, by creating an additional standard height of 8 ft 6 in. Pressure to introduce this originated in the USA, where it had been a standard size for many years. This presented particular problems to BR, in view of its restricted loading gauge, but two new wagons (Lowliner 'A' and Lowliner 'B'), with dimensions as under, were designed to meet the new standard:

	Lowliner 'A'	*Lowliner 'B'*
Loadable length:	40ft	60ft
Height of floor:	2 ft 10 in	2 ft 9½ in
Wheel diameter:	2 ft 4½ in	2 ft 4½ in
No. of axles:	4	6
Axle load:	16 tons	14 tons
Gross weight:	64 tons	84 tons
Maximum payload:	48 tons	62 tons

In parallel with the development of these two new designs the Chief Civil Engineer instituted an inquiry as to the likely cost of increasing headroom on the routes mainly followed by such traffic. The ultimate decision was to carry out the required civil engineering improvements to the routes specified (see Chapter Nine), in view of the high cost of providing special wagons of low platform height. Only one prototype two-wagon set of each type was built and the design was not repeated.

If the advantages of the Freightliner were to be fully secured, meticulous planning of terminals was essential. Adequate stabling accommodation and storage space had to be available and facilities provided for the rapid transfer of train-loads of containers from rail to road and vice versa. A fundamental issue was the choice of transfer equipment and in late 1962–3 various existing systems were studied in order to establish the basic criteria to be met. This examination emphasized the advantages of an overhead lifting system; the need in particular for flexibility when dealing with a random range of containers on adjacent trains; and suitability for adapting to other uses, for example at combined wagon-load/container terminals. The light-weight design of box containers and the need to handle low-side open containers were important factors in determining initially the need for a system which lifted a container at points along its base.

In June 1963, a small group, including J. Ratter (Board Member) and H. Wilcock (Rolling Stock Design Engineer) visited the USA to inspect several types of lifting equipment. The Drott 'Travelift', used mainly for 'piggy-back' semi-trailer handling, was chosen as the most suitable equipment then available for British Railways purposes. The Drott Travelift is powered by diesel-hydraulic equipment and runs on heavy

Fig. 8.10   Work in progress at a Freightliner Depot (BRB)

duty large size pneumatic-tyred wheels. It straddles either two or three rail tracks and one roadway. It lifts containers by means of a four-point grappler, adjustable to deal with any length of container, with arms engaging in lifting points built into the container base. The weight of the appliance is such that a reinforced concrete roadway has to be provided over the full anticipated train length. Two of these cranes were ordered, one 36 ft wide for use in Glasgow and one 48 ft for use in London. Experience with these machines led to a Mark II version, modified to suit British requirements, and thirteen of these were built by Rubery Owen, under licence, for use at London (York Way), Glasgow (Gushetfaulds), Manchester (Longsight), Liverpool (Garston), and Aberdeen, covering the original Freightliner network.

Reference has previously been made to the adoption of the recommended ISO standards for container design and the decision to modify wagons to carry such containers. A change in the overhead lifting equipment was also required to enable containers to be lifted under their base or from the top corner castings. To meet this requirement, the CM & EE produced a new design of lifting frame, which could be used with any design of crane and permitting either bottom or top lift of any of the several container sizes and types in use.

The performance of the Drott Travelift was not wholly satisfactory, despite various modifications, and the Outdoor Machinery Section of the CM & EE Department therefore prepared a detailed specification for an electrically operated rail-mounted Goliath crane of 52 ft track rail span, a capacity of 30 tons and covering three rail tracks and one for road vehicles. Further developments of this 0–4–0 Goliath crane were the 2–6–2 and 2–6–3 Goliath cranes, for use at larger terminals. These provided lifting coverage over two vehicle roads, six rail tracks and two or three container storage roads. To deal with container traffic at the BR ports, transporter cranes were supplied by British industry and installed at Parkeston Quay, Holyhead, and Dublin.

In 1978, Freightliners became involved in a development in inland container handling techniques which could open up new markets among companies with private sidings or other nearby loading facilities. In conjunction with the Transport and Road Research Laboratory and Bath University, a company (Small Container Intermodal Distribution Systems), in which Freightliners have an interest, have developed a special steel pallet with telescopic legs, capable of lifting standard ISO containers carrying loads up to 22 tons, without the need for cranes or other heavy lifting equipment. The pallet (known as a SCID) is a simple mild steel rectangular box, measuring 20 ft × 8 ft × 6 in, which uses the power of an ordinary 24 volt vehicle battery to transfer containers from road to rail and vice versa. Road vehicles position the pallets and their containers over the railway tracks, the wagons are run in beneath them and the legs retracted to lower the pallets on to the wagons. The new system could open up new areas not served by main terminals and reduce train turn-round and lorry waiting times.

Before the Freightliner became accepted by British Railways as the best way of obtaining the advantages of rail and road transport in one combined operation, trials had been carried out with another method of obtaining the desired results. In 1957 a party of British Railways officers visited the USA to see railway development in that country over the past ten years or so. The party included H. R. Gomersall, a mechanical engineer who was at that time Planning Assistant to the General Manager of the Eastern Region. In the course of the tour, Gomersall visited the Chesapeake and Ohio Railroad and became interested in the 'Railvan' which they had been developing since 1952.

This was an 'amphibian' freight vehicle, designed to provide a simple method of transfer of freight between road and rail. The vehicle was simply a road semi-trailer, capable of running on both road and rail, the unique feature of which was the combination of pairs of retractable rail wheels and pneumatic-tyred road wheels on a single spring suspension system, operated by compressed air, which enabled them to be changed over in a matter of minutes. When running on rail, the front of one vehicle was coupled to the rear of the preceding vehicle, the whole train being a series of two-wheeled articulated vehicles, a specially designed adaptor truck being used to connect the leading vehicle to the locomotive. On road, the Railvan was coupled to a standard motor vehicle, in the same way as normal semi-trailers. To provide stability during the road/rail change-over, and during loading and discharging at customers' premises, legs similar to those on standard road trailers were provided. At main depots, a rubber-tyred 'spotter' vehicle was provided to effect the transfer of the vehicle from road to rail and vice versa. This vehicle also provided the compressed air to operate the wheel change-over mechanism. Terminal requirements were simple – a siding or loop with the ground made up to rail level and a small portable air compressor to operate the wheel changing mechanism at places where a separate spotter vehicle could not be justified, the work of transfer in such instances being undertaken by the road prime mover itself.

A British company – Pressed Steel – became interested in the Railvan's potential and acquired a licence to manufacture in Britain. A modified version, to suit the British loading gauge and the Construction and Weight Regulations for Road Vehicles, was designed by the BR Carriage and Wagon Development Unit at Darlington, in association with Pressed Steel. A prototype – a covered van – was built, in aluminium, in 1960, to become known in Britain as the 'Roadrailer'. Body dimensions were length 24 ft 7½ in, width 8 ft, height 8 ft 2 in, capacity 1570 ft³: payload was 11 tons and tare weight 5 tons, giving a payload/tare weight ratio of 2·2 : 1 – an improvement on conventional wagons at that stage. Automatic brakes were provided, vacuum for rail and air for road use. A

Fig. 8.11 The rocking beam and suspension details of the retractable wheels of the Road-Railer, showing the rail wheels lowered and the road wheels raised (Pressed Steel Co Ltd)

train of 75 Roadrailers was capable of operation at up to 70 miles/h.

In theory, the Roadrailer possessed positive advantages over containers on flat wagons: change-over from road to rail could be undertaken almost anywhere, at minimal cost in the provision of facilities; transfer from road to rail could be effected in about 2½ minutes and from rail to road in 1½ minutes; the body could be in any form required – van, open, flat, tipper, tank – to suit the needs of any class of commodity. The disadvantages of the Roadrailer were that, because of the wheel change-over mechanism, its cost was higher than that of a conventional container and conflat of comparable payload and that, without an adaptor unit, it was not compatible with any other form of rail vehicle. In that respect, at a time when the emphasis was more on wagon-load movement and the concept of train-load working was not so developed as it is today, this inflexibility was a serious matter. In today's circumstances it would be a less important factor.

After initial trials with the prototype, 50 further vehicles, with van and open bodies, were produced for more comprehensive testing on the Eastern Region. In due course a date was set for the inauguration of a service between London and Edinburgh. Before this date was reached, however, the train broke a coupling when running at speed and the opening of the service was deferred. Thereafter, there was a long spell when virtually no further progress was made. Opposition to the whole concept of the Roadrailer developed at BR HQ. The difficulties which were experienced in the early stages could have been overcome and the axle load, at around 16 tons, was well within the permitted range. The vehicles, with a three-point suspension, rode very well indeed. Be that as it may, the opposition to the novelty of the concept continued and customers, too, were reluctant to use the Roadrailer service. Persistent allegiance to conventional movement methods continued, irrespective of the time and cost advantages of the Roadrailer.

Despite further efforts in 1966 to popularize the Roadrailer, response was negligible and eventually the vehicles were taken out of service and, after a time, broken up. So ended the Roadrailer revolution. Its failure may have been due, at least in part, to its timing. It came into being at a time when containerization and the Freightliner were developing, providing the opportunity for the road/rail transfer of larger payloads than the Roadrailer. The relatively small payload of 11 tons was perhaps regarded as inadequate by road hauliers. If it had come earlier, before the container revolution, it might have been more acceptable. It could never, however, have become a success in maritime traffic, which is now the main element of Freightliner.

It is interesting to note that, although the Roadrailer concept was abandoned by both the Chesapeake and Ohio Railroad and British Railways, the idea has been taken up again in America, where a leasing company has arranged for 250 vehicles of this type to be built, to come into service towards the end of 1980. Time alone will tell whether, in the light of the urgent need for fuel economy, the Roadrailer will now prove to be more acceptable and successful.

The fundamental changes in the nature and operation of freight traffic arising from the Modernization Plan and the Beeching Report have depended for their success on the design and production of a new range of wagons, some for general use, others for special traffics. Five main types of standard continuously braked wagons were put into service:

(a) a two-axle coal wagon of 31 tons gross loaded weight (GLW), 21-ton capacity, mainly for servicing domestic coal concentration depots and industrial sidings, which has become the most widely used of the mineral wagon fleet;

(b) a two-axle covered van of 45 tons GLW, 29 tons capacity;

(c) A two-axle open wagon of 45 tons GLW, 31 tons capacity;

(d) a two-axle steel-carrying wagon of 45 tons GLW, 31 tons capacity;

(e) a bogie steel-carrying wagon of 100 tons GLW, 75 tons capacity, capable of adaptation to various types of load by the fitting of bolsters and/or cradles.

A two-axle mineral wagon of 45/50 tons GLW, 31 tons capacity, was also designed.

Additionally, a range of special-purpose vehicles has been developed for particular traffics. In 1970, a new design of long wheelbase van was built at Ashford for the conveyance of motor parts for Fords, between

Dagenham and Halewood. These vans are of 22 tons capacity, with four wide sliding doors to facilitate loading and unloading with fork lift trucks. In the late 1950s, car-carrying vehicles were also produced for the conveyance of cars from manufacturing plants to distributors. In the first instance, as a low-cost solution, these vehicles were produced by removing the bodies from redundant coaching stock and modifying them to form flats for motor car conveyance. Later, a small number of well-type double-deck car carriers was built by Newton Chambers for MAT Transport Ltd, equipped to run on European railways also, via the BR ferries.

In 1964 a new type of double-deck car transporter was designed, of which a prototype was built in less than eight weeks. It took advantage of the low load-carrying requirement in relation to length and utilized the principle of articulation, creating a unit of four wagons carried on five bogies – hence the name, 'Cartic 4'. The frame of each vehicle was lowered between the bogies, to make it possible to carry an equal number of cars on each deck. These wagons were designed specifically to suit Ford cars being manufactured at that time, particularly in relation to car height, but the dimensions of the Cartic 4 are well suited to the majority of the popular modern types of car.

Within the last two years, a study group comprising representatives of the British, French, German, and Italian railways has produced standard overall dimensions for new three-axle articulated and two × two-axle permanently coupled two-tier car carriers. Some modifications are neces-

Fig. 8.12   A Cartic 4 car carrier, allocated to Motorail services (BRB)

sary to achieve clearance within the British loading gauge. A feature of the design is that the pivoted end section of the top deck can be angled down to form a loading ramp.

Europe's first car-sleeper, for the conveyance of cars and their passengers, overnight between King's Cross and Perth, began in 1955, using existing bogie vans fitted with end doors for car loading. Later, fourteen of a covered version of the well-type two-tier car transporter were designed and built by Newton Chambers. The well was loaded and unloaded by an hydraulically operated lifting mechanism, which, however, proved to be so lengthy a process that it became the tendency to use the upper deck only. Later still, because of the expense involved in providing covered vehicles, with installed lifts, open two-tier Cartic-4 car carriers, capable of operating at up to 75 miles/h, were introduced into the services. Nowadays, what have since 1964 been known as 'Motorail' car carrying services operate over a wide network, particularly during the holiday season.

Block trains between collieries and power stations, devised to secure maximum utilization of locomotives and wagons, started to operate in 1965. Under this arrangement, trains of 28 permanently coupled four-wheeled wagons are loaded from overhead hoppers at collieries for dispatch to specific power stations. At the power station, the train travels over underground storage hoppers at a constant speed of 0·5 miles/h and discharges its load. The empty train then returns, straight away, to the same colliery for another load, hence the name 'Merry-go-round' (MGR) by which these trains are known. In the first instance, 21-ton wagons were used for this service, with manual opening and closing of the

Fig. 8.13 A Merry-Go-Round coal train from the East Midlands at Didcot power station, hauled by a Class 47 diesel-electric locomotive. Although developed for coal traffic, the MGR system has also been adopted to convey other commodities, such as gypsum to cement manufacturers (BRB)

hopper bottom doors, but later 26-ton wagons, capable of being increased to 32 tons capacity by the addition of body-side extensions, were developed. With these wagons, lineside equipment engages with the hopper door mechanism to provide automatic opening and closing. The wagons were designed to minimum body weight and, following intensive investigation into alternative materials available, thin gauge galvanized steel plate was specified as the most suitable and all wagons were so built, the first time this material had been used for wagon construction. Roller bearing axleboxes were fitted and a simple disc brake, acting on one wheel per axle, was developed for these wagons. Wheels of larger diameter than normal (3 ft 7 in) were fitted to satisfy the Chief Civil Engineer's requirements at that time for axle loadings. Special repair facilities were established at Burton-on-Trent and Worksop to deal with these wagons, on a preventive maintenance basis as far as possible.

Research is currently in progress into the remote control of the locomotives hauling MGR trains when discharging their loads at power stations, the objective being to enable the train to be operated as a conveyor belt under the control of the CEGB controller. This would eliminate the need for sustained concentration by the driver in observing signals during the unloading process and would also obviate the need for meal relief for him whilst at the power station. The system in mind uses track detectors for the communication link with the locomotive and has been installed for test purposes at one power station.

A problem at large modern coal-fired power stations is the disposal of

Fig. 8.14   A Presflo wagon: one of the earlier, small types, capacity 17 tons, built at Shildon in 1964 (BRB)

the fly-ash residue from pulverized fuel. Arrangements were made for this material to be sent by rail to various points for land reclamation and other purposes. There is, for example, a constant flow of fly-ash from West Burton and other Trent area power stations to disused claypits of the London Brick Company at Fletton, near Peterborough. For this purpose, 21-ton capacity 'Presflo' wagons were built.

Developed by the Carriage and Wagon Development Unit at Darlington in 1953 and first used for the conveyance of cement in bulk to railheads for onward distribution by road transport, the special feature of Presflo wagons – as their name implies – is the method of discharging their load. Compressed air fed in through perforated plates aerates and agitates the powdered contents, which flow from the wagon like a stream of liquid. Experience showed that the initial design of Presflo wagon, with a 20-ton payload and 13-ton tare, did not provide the degree of economy necessary and private builders therefore introduced an improved design of two-axle 45-ton GLW wagon, with a 32¾-ton payload in cement. Later still, a 100-ton GLW bogie wagon, carrying two cylindrical vessels of the same type as the two-axle 45-ton GLW wagon, with a total capacity of 78 tons, was produced. Similar types of Presflo wagons have been used for other powdered traffics – flour, salt, various chemicals, and pulverized fuel ash for the making of concrete.

Up to the early 1960s, virtually all tank wagons were four-wheeled, unbraked, of 35-ton GLW and 21-ton capacity, conforming to the 17½-ton axle load which was then the permissible limit. When the maximum axle load was increased to 22½ tons, on specified routes, two-axle 45-ton GLW tank wagons, in private ownership, were introduced for petroleum products, giving a payload capacity of 32 tons. In 1965, Metropolitan-Cammell were asked by Shell-Mex and BP to co-operate in the development of a bogie tank wagon of 90-ton GLW. The wagon had a tare weight of 26 tons and a load capacity of 64 tons – 20000 gallons, some 16 per cent more than the capacity of two 45-ton GLW two-axle wagons. In 1966, soon after the successful introduction of the 90-ton GLW wagon, the Chief Civil Engineer agreed to accept a 25-ton axle load for bogie wagons operating in train loads over specified routes and this led to the construction of 100-ton GLW wagons for petrol and oil traffics, with a payload capacity of over 70 tons.

In 1972, the development by private builders of a new friction-damped pedestal suspension permitted the construction of 50-ton two-axle tank wagons, which again are limited to train-load operation over specified routes, at a maximum speed of 60 miles/h. Similar wagons have also been built for private ownership for the conveyance of liquefied gases, chemicals, and other liquid products.

Several designs of hopper wagons have been produced – some railway but mostly privately owned – for aggregates from quarries, mainly to road construction railheads, lime, salt, and bulk grain, using air-assisted

Fig. 8.15   A 100 ton tank wagon (BRB)

gravity discharge. Capacities vary according to the requirements of the particular traffics. If required, aggregate wagons can be fitted with bottom doors which can give a variable rate of discharge to match the capacity of conveyor systems below the wagons. Large hopper wagons have also been built for the conveyance of ballast for the civil engineers.

The tendency has been to encourage the development of wagons specially designed to meet the particular needs of specific traffics. The railways themselves have, for example, developed pallet vans for the conveyance of palletized traffic; fertilizer wagons; timber wagons; steel coil wagons, with, if required, telescopic roof, which enables the complete roof and both sides to be opened up in three sections; tube wagons; and stainless steel covered wagons for the conveyance of atomic flasks. Articulated three-axle telescopic sliding curtain wagons of low platform height to provide maximum loading space are also becoming available for steel traffic, in particular to and from EEC countries. Apart from the pressurized tank and hopper wagons already referred to, privately owned 100-ton GLW wagons have also been developed for such traffics as fertilizers and iron ore. Private owners have also developed a 'Jumbo' covered bogie van 71½ ft long for the conveyance of automobile body pressings in Freightliner services to the Continent.

Liaison with private owners on the design and construction of their wagons is maintained through a Joint Technical Sub-Committee, set up in 1948, on which British Railways and private wagon owners, builders, and repairers are represented. It is chaired by a Design Engineer from the CM & EE Department – H. Wilcock was chairman for 17 years, from 1959 to 1976 – and its purpose is to promote technical developments associated with privately owned wagons. Perhaps its most outstanding achievements have been the development of designs for tank wagons for petroleum products and the drafting, in 1963, of proposals for the standardization of privately owned wagons. These cover the comprehensive requirements for the design of wagons acceptable for running on BR lines and are a basic work of reference for all private owners, builders, and repairers.

The features in the designs of the new wagons which have contributed most to meeting present day requirements have been the fitting of continuous power brakes, roller bearing axleboxes and new spring suspension systems, all of which together permit safe and reliable operation at considerably higher speeds than were acceptable in the past. Advantage has been taken of the higher axle loads now accepted by the Chief Civil Engineer to build wagons of increased carrying capacity with a greater payload/tare weight ratio.

Until the early 1960s, when the maximum axle load for wagons with 3 ft 1½ in diameter wheels was raised to 22½ tons, the limit had been 17½ tons, decreasing with reductions in wheel diameter. A further increase to 25 tons was agreed by the Civil Engineer for specific routes in 1966. Maximum speed was for some years limited to 60 miles/h for axle loads exceeding 17½ tons but in 1976 the Chief Civil Engineer accepted that specified wagons having approved suspension characteristics could operate with 20-ton axle loads at a speed of 75 miles/h.

The Modernization Plan recognized the need for improved service times and for better line occupation by narrowing the gap between the fastest and slowest trains, quite apart from the benefits which would accrue from improved wagon turn-round time and a reduction in the wagon fleet. This meant that a high percentage of the whole fleet would have to be equipped with continuous brakes. Reference has already been made in Chapter Four and earlier in this chapter to the setting up of the Power Brakes Committee and its recommendation that the air brake should be adopted as the future standard on BR. This recommendation was based on the outcome of trials which the Railway Executive had initiated in 1950, to determine the relative merits of the vacuum and air brakes for the operation of long and heavy mineral trains at speeds higher than previously acceptable. For the trials, about 800 16-ton coal wagons were fitted with continuous brakes – half with the standard vacuum brake and half with the Westinghouse air brake. The trials, over a total of 11000 miles, were mainly between Toton and Brent on the Midland main line, with trains of 70 wagons hauled by Britannia Class 7 locomotives, one engine for a train of 70 empties, double-headed for 70 loaded. The trials clearly indicated that the standard vacuum brake was inadequate for 70 loaded coal wagons, particularly in regard to release time, whereas the air brake met all that was demanded of it. Because of the operating difficulties which the Regional General Managers – with one exception – feared would arise during the change-over period, the recommendation of the Power Brakes Committee to adopt the air brake as the future standard was not accepted. The BTC decided to continue with the vacuum brake for all stock except electric multiple units, for which the air brake was already standard equipment. A programme, initially designed to cover a period of ten years, for fitting vacuum brakes to all freight rolling stock was put in hand, including provision for the maintenance and testing of the brake equipment at marshalling yards and goods depots, as well as in works and outstation shops.

At the time this decision was taken operating conditions could be summarized as 90 miles/h maximum speed for passenger trains and 60 miles/h for freight with a maximum load of 1500 tons. Four-aspect colour light signals, then being introduced on main lines, were spaced to give an average stopping distance of 3000 yards. The standard vacuum brake, as then existing, could meet the above conditions but it was at the limit of its performance and had no margin to cope with any further development in operating conditions.

The background against which the decision was taken in 1956 to retain the vacuum brake changed fundamentally during the next few years. The maximum speed of passenger trains was to be increased to 100 miles/h – in some cases even higher. Freight train speeds were to be substantially increased, with longer trains, possibly up to 2000 tons. With the growing emphasis on block trains in circuit working, liner trains with new wagons running at 75 miles/h, and the decline in wagon-load traffic, the operating problems during a change-over period would be much reduced. There was, moreover, to be a drastic reduction in the number of coaches and wagons required to run the improved services of the future. So favourable an opportunity to change to the air brake, technically superior, fully developed, and able to meet all prospective operating conditions, was unlikely to occur again. The whole question of the brake system to be adopted as the standard on British Railways was considered once more in 1963 by the Technical and Planning Committees of the Board.

Two courses were open to meet the new conditions – to change over to the air brake in its latest form for all new vehicles, or to develop the vacuum brake further, to provide two-stage braking for high-speed passenger trains, much reduced time of release on freight trains, and a variable load device to adjust brake force to the weight – loaded or empty – of freight trains. Any attempt to develop the vacuum brake to satisfy these essential requirements would have involved a long and expensive programme of work, a successful outcome from which was by no means certain. The BRB therefore decided to adopt the air brake as the future standard for all new construction. This was the right decision. In the opinion of some well qualified to know, it could, with advantage, have been taken some ten years previously.

The two-pipe graduated release air brake is the system adopted in Britain. Under this system, which separates the air-feed and control functions of the brake, a second pipe, continuous down the train, is introduced to overcome the basic weakness of the single-pipe arrangement, which is the relatively slow release of the brakes at the rear of long trains.

The introduction of power brakes on mineral wagons posed problems owing to the brake gear fouling the mechanism of wagon tipplers. To overcome this trouble, the practicability of fitting disc brakes instead of the normal tread brakes was investigated. A number of 24-ton mineral wagons were fitted with disc brakes, for trial purposes, in 1961. In this application, the brake pads were applied directly to the wheel, which led to some problems with cracked wheels. Thereafter, a modified design of disc brake was fitted, in 1964, to Freightliner wagons. Such brakes are now standard for all new two-axle and bogie wagons. First-cost considerations preclude the general conversion to disc brakes of older freight vehicles. With freight stock generally, the brake force in relation to weight is not sufficiently near to the limit of adhesion to justify additional expenditure on wheel slide protection.

A consequence of the decision to fit continuous brakes to the bulk of the wagon fleet was the need to replace the three-link couplings in general use on unfitted wagons. Fitted wagons were equipped with screw couplings or 'Instanter' three-link couplings. The Instanter coupling, which originated on the GWR and was used on their brake-fitted wagons, has a pear-shaped centre link which can be used either in the short or long position. The objective of using it in the former position is to achieve the relatively smooth shock-free operation of screw couplings in a simpler way. The Instanter couplings, as originally designed, were not entirely satisfactory. The centre links tended to stretch under load and were liable to jump from the short to the long position, thus defeating their object. It was decided therefore to use screw couplings. The design first chosen, which was fitted to mineral and steel-carrying wagons, was the UIC standard which, though stronger than the BR pattern, was also consider-

Fig. 8.16   The Instanter coupling: the right-hand wagon has Oleo buffers (BRB)

ably heavier and thus more difficult to handle. This disadvantage, and the delays caused by staff having to go between wagons to tighten or loosen the screws, were decisive in making this type of coupling unacceptable, both within British Railways and to their customers, such as the National Coal Board and the British Steel Corporation. An improved design of Instanter coupling was therefore evolved, greatly strengthened and with the shape of the centre link modified to eliminate the risk of this link jumping from the short to the long position. This is now the standard coupling for the bulk of BR's modern freight vehicles.

In the early 1960s, the question of fitting automatic couplers to British freight stock was considered, in parallel with a UIC proposal that they should be adopted generally by the railways of Western Europe. Design specifications to suit British stock and operating conditions were prepared, including, *inter alia*:

(a) the need for simplicity in action and robustness in construction;
(b) the curve radius which must be negotiable;
(c) the extent to which it must accommodate vertical and horizontal misalignment between one wagon and another;
(d) the ability to couple with passenger stock; and
(e) the need to ensure that, if accidental uncoupling took place, the brake connections must part in such a way that the fully automatic action of the brake was preserved.

The Dowty Group, in conjunction with the C & W Development Unit, developed an automatic coupler for drawgear and brake pipes but tests with prototype equipment on 100 wagons in 1958–9 showed that, although capable of satisfactory coupling at impact speeds of from two to eight miles/h, it was too cumbersome for general adoption and did not entirely meet safety of operations requirements. For broadly similar reasons, the UIC automatic coupler was also considered to be unsuitable for British use.

In Britain, the increasing tendency towards train-load and block train working, and the consequent reduction in the extent to which wagons pass through marshalling yards, make it unlikely that the high cost of automatic couplers could be justified for internal working. Furthermore, an automatic coupler has not, in fact, been adopted in Western Europe, although it is in use in some Eastern European countries. However, the design of all new standard wagons built by BR since 1966 provides for the later fitting of an automatic centre coupler, if required.

Heavier wagons, longer trains, higher speeds in service, and smarter working in hump marshalling yards all combined to emphasize the need for the development of an improved design of shock-absorbing buffer to withstand increased impact loads, thereby minimizing damage to wagons and their contents. To meet this need, an hydraulic buffer, produced by Oleo Pneumatics Ltd, was introduced into railway service in the early 1950s and is now a standard fitting on all freight stock. The heavy hydraulic damping which occurs reduces impact shocks by about 75 per cent.

The problems associated with the riding of passenger vehicles apply also, to perhaps an even greater extent, with freight vehicles. The load/tare ratio of passenger vehicles is lower than with freight vehicles, the increased range in the latter case making riding problems more difficult to overcome, particularly those relating to stability of movement of vehicles involved in high-speed services.

With the progressive increase in the number of diesel locomotives in service the rate of acceleration and average speed of freight trains increased, accompanied, unexpectedly, by an alarming rise in the number of derailments of four-wheeled wagons on plain track. It was necessary to impose strict limits on the maximum speed of many freight trains pending a solution of the problems involved.

All railway vehicles have a critical speed below which their swaying and rolling movements are determined by track features. Above the critical speed a continuous side-to-side 'hunting' oscillation occurs, caused by the forces acting between wheel and rail, limited only by the wheel flanges, slipping of the wheels, and bending of the axleguards. Typical examples of measured critical speeds for vehicles with tyres in new and partially worn condition respectively are: for 10 ft wheelbase covered vans, 40 and 25 miles/h, and for pallet vans, which were particularly prone to derailment, 28 and 19 miles/h. Critical speeds are determined largely by the characteristics of the spring suspension system.

In the days when the railway was populated with small four-wheeled wagons, and there were few pretensions towards speed in the freight services, wagons were fitted with leaf springs, with or without auxiliary rubber springs. In 1963, as a contribution to the insistent need for better riding of freight vehicles, British Railways adopted the UIC double-link suspension, which was widely approved and accepted on the Continent. It was not, however, generally successful on British short wheelbase wagons, due mainly to wear on the links and saddles, arising from the friction needed for lateral damping. Theoretical and experimental work undertaken by Dr A. H. Wickens, then Superintendent of the Dynamics Section of the Research Department, showed that vehicles fitted with this suspension were unstable laterally. Wickens' work also demonstrated that, by the choice of suitable suspension and other design parameters, four-wheeled wagons can be made to run stably at very high speeds. The critical speed of the pallet van can be raised from 19 to 108 miles/h, so that hunting oscillations would cease to be a limiting feature of performance.

Efforts over the next few years to develop a suspension which would improve ride performance and prevent derailments of four-wheeled wagons produced a sequence of new designs. They included a BR variation of the UIC double-link suspension, with a single, longer link and more precisely machined bearings, giving better control of friction and

Fig. 8.17   The long-link suspension, generally adopted for all four-wheeled wagons,
except those equipped with Taperlite suspension (see Fig. 8.18). Note the
brake discs fitted to the wheels (BRB)

reduced wear. This suspension, initiated by Koffman, was relatively cheap in first cost and, for this reason and also in view of its good performance was adopted for four-wheeled wagons.

One type of suspension developed by the Research and Development Division, for application on two-axle wagons, is the FAT 13 (Taperlite) suspension. Initially described as the HSFV5 (High Speed Freight Vehicle, Mark V) suspension, it has been under test on BR since the early 1970s. Tests carried out by the UIC Office of Research and Experiment in 1979 with this suspension on a BR covered van resulted in its being the only one approved by UIC for operating at speeds up to 93 miles/h. It incorporates a Taperlite spring, swing links, and viscous damping in both vertical and lateral planes. Wheelset yaw (or 'hunting') control is obtained through a rubber shear spring. Service experience indicates extended intervals between maintenance and tyre reprofiling, but a disadvantage of this novel type of suspension is its high initial cost.

A subsequent development is the 'Controlled Friction Taperleaf' suspension, a simplified version of the Taperlite, retaining some of the better features but eliminating the viscous damping. By this means, costs have been significantly reduced and a variant of the design, adapted to suit the UIC double link suspension, has been developed which can be fitted with minimal alterations to a large proportion of existing tank wagons, improving ride performance and the safe negotiation of any normal track irregularities.

Fig. 8.18   The FAT 13 (Taperlite) suspension, developed by the Research
and Development Division (BRB)

The arguments for and against bogie vehicles have centred around the question as to whether they will enable an increased payload to be carried at reduced cost. They have also been influenced by the fluctuating developments in the design of bogies and four-wheeled suspensions. Over the years, the engineers have done a great deal of work on bogie design, to produce improved performance, but until the early 1960s very little practical information was available to assist an analysis of the behaviour and thus to determine design requirements of bogies for high-speed freight vehicles. As a result of work carried out by the Research and Development Division, it is now possible to assess, from the design details, the critical speed at which unstable running is likely to occur. The analytical methods which have been evolved have been applied to the development of new forms of suspension for bogie vehicles, as well as four-wheeled wagons.

Mention had been made of the Ridemaster type of bogie which was initially fitted, in a modified low height form, to Freightliner wagons. This bogie was a conventional type of cast steel, three-piece construction, initially with rubber pads between the upper saddle type member and the main bolster. These pads were later eliminated, as it was found that lateral movement of the bogie was so small as not to justify their retention. In service, it was found that the vertical ride was not as satisfactory as was hoped and also that heavy wear occurred due to excessive bogie hunting. A change in the tyre profile and the adoption of rubber side bearer units produced a significant improvement in the riding performance of the bogie. Following a derailment, further modifications were made and in its final form this bogie was provided with traction bars for longitudinal restraint and variable vertical friction damping.

In the later 1960s interest also centred upon a French design of high-speed freight bogie, the UIC standard Y25C, which incorporated most of the features which, as a result of the scientific approach to design problems, had come to be accepted as essential – notably, load-proportional suspension damping and adequate bogie rotational resistance for stable running at high speeds, associated with one-piece bogie frames with sufficent torsional flexibility to permit negotiation of track twist, particularly in sidings and at terminals. In 1970, a Y25 design of bogie, modified to meet BR conditions and having a 25-ton axle load, was tested under a 100-ton GLW tank wagon and gave fully acceptable ride performance at speeds up to 60 miles/h, and, with a reduced load of 70 tons gross, up to 75 miles/h. These bogies were also fitted to the prototype Lowliner 'A' and 'B' wagons and a number of other new and rebuilt wagon types, including iron ore hoppers and bogie steel carriers, in the 1970s.

The CM & EE's design office also developed a freight bogie with a 25-ton axle load, incorporating all specified design criteria, and in which damping can be accurately catered for by the provision of friction-free suspension components, associated with hydraulic shock absorbers. This bogie, known as FG25, has a separate swing bolster on knife-edge links and is capable of satisfactory operation at speeds of up to 100 miles/h. Additionally, a number of bogie designs have been developed by private wagon builders for fitting to privately owned wagons.

A development towards improving the efficiency of the conventional three-piece bogie has been the introduction of cross-bracing, under which the wheel sets on a bogie are so connected diagonally that whilst they have

Fig. 8.19   A cross-braced bogie, currently under trial (BRB)

limited lateral movement in relation to each other they can move freely to 'steer' round curves. Such bogies, equipped with alternative soft and stiff primary suspension and with reduced secondary suspension constraints, have been tested under a modified Freightliner vehicle. The benefits of the anti-lozenging effects of cross-bracing are lower rail and wheel wear, a smoother ride and better curving performance. Evaluation trials are in progress on wagons built by BR Engineering Ltd for the Kenya railways.

Research in the field of bogie design, for both passenger and freight vehicles, never ceases and the next few years will undoubtedly see further improvements in design, to give even better riding characteristics, with reduced maintenance costs.

For reasons explained in Chapter Four, the Modernization Plan heavily over-estimated the need for investment in marshalling yards, although it must be said that, when the Plan was prepared, the proposals were appropriate to the freight services as they were then operated. At that time, it was considered that, with some increase in operating speeds, larger wagons, and some reduction in the number of goods depots and small marshalling yards, the pattern of freight working would continue on the same basic lines as in the past, with a preponderance of wagon-load traffic passing through marshalling yards *en route* to final destination. It was not for some years after the Plan was in progress that, with changing competitive circumstances and improved methods of assessing traffic flows, the policy of concentrating on train-load operations emerged, together with more selective acceptance of traffic in wagon loads. This change reduced the need for intermediate marshalling. Even later, computer-aided techniques, such as TOPS (Total Operations Processing System, dealt with more fully in Chapter Ten) reduced still further the need for large marshalling yards. The result of this failure to forecast with accuracy the freight future in 20 years time was unprofitable expenditure on a number of marshalling yards which, in the event, proved to be too many and too big.

The yards which were built or modernized were highly automated. Retarders – pairs of clamps which can be raised to grip wheel flanges with varying degrees of pressure – had been in use in Britain since the first installation at Whitemoor in the early 1930s. In those days, retarders were mainly hydraulically or electrically operated, the degree of retardation applied being varied according to the number of wagons in the group or 'cut', the types of wagons concerned and the distance they had to run to join up with wagons already in the sidings. The points to permit access to the various sidings were power-operated from the 'hump' cabin.

Over the years, however, various stages of automatic point operation and braking have been introduced. Most of the work of point setting to route wagons into the correct sidings is done by electronic means. An operator in the reception sidings notes the destination of each wagon, uncouples between each wagon or cut, and prepares a 'cut card' showing the siding into which each separate cut should be routed. He passes this information by teleprinter to the control tower, where a punched tape fed into a reader activates equipment to reset the points between each cut. Braking in most modern yards is by retarders, automatically controlled by a combination of radar and other electronic equipment which, in the few seconds after a cut comes over the hump, assesses its weight, speed, and rollability, and how far it has to run to buffer up to other wagons in the siding, and applies braking pressure accordingly.

Towards the end of the marshalling yard programme, the Dowty Group marketed a new device for exercising continuous control over wagons running into sidings, without the need for complex equipment to assess speeds, weight, and rollability. The Dowty automatic wagon control equipment consists of a series of closely spaced oil-fed hydraulic plunger units laid inside each running rail. Some of these are retarders only, but others are booster-retarders which accelerate or decelerate wagons as required to maintain their progress into the sidings. The wheel flanges depress the plungers in the units, the speed of depression governing whether the retarder should offer resistance to the wheel, or, if it is a booster–retarder, whether it should offer resistance or add to its speed on the up-thrust. The wagons are thus sent forward at a speed sufficient to ensure that they buffer up in the sidings without excessive impact.

The Dowty equipment was subjected to exhaustive trials at York, Hull Inward, and Goodmayes yards. It gave far more accuracy in the separa-

Fig. 8.20 Dowty marshalling yard equipment, showing retarder and booster-retarder units, with power lines to the latter. About 23 000 units were installed in Tinsley Yard (BRB)

tion of cuts, because of its stricter control of speed, thereby considerably reducing the number of occasions when wagons, due to their different running characteristics, were sorted into the wrong sidings. With the Dowty equipment, too, the hump did not require to be so steep, and construction costs were less. On the other hand, the installation was more expensive than an orthodox retarder system and oil consumption was very high. On balance, however, it was assessed that the savings which would accrue from the reduced errors in shunting justified the Dowty system. After the test operations, the system was first installed in the new Tinsley yard at Sheffield, Eastern Region, in 1965, and also at Bescot, LM Region. These early installations were hydraulically powered, but a later installation at Scunthorpe, Eastern Region, in 1972, was the first Oleo retarder system, in which the units are completely self-contained, needing no external power supply or control signals.

Whilst not strictly a matter directly associated with the engineers' contribution to passenger and freight services, it is perhaps not inappropriate to mention, at this point, the effect of the change in traction from steam to diesel and electric on the provision of breakdown equipment.

The introduction of diesel and electric locomotives, requiring to be lifted at their bogie centres, necessitated a new approach to rerailing operations, for which the steam breakdown cranes then in service were not entirely satisfactory. From the late 1950s there was a more widespread use of hydraulic jacking equipment for dealing with derailments, particu-

Fig. 8.21   The 45-ton steam crane allocated to Gorton Depot assisting in the renewal of a bridge at Aldham Junction, 21 October 1951. A distinctive feature is that the overhead wires for the MSW electrification scheme had to be drawn clear to enable the jib of the crane to operate (BRB)

larly when these occurred under overhead electric wires. At the same time, however, a programme of conversion of steam cranes to diesel operation, and the manufacture of new cranes, was necessary. The programme which was produced, based on an all-Regional assessment of requirements in 1969, since modified to take account of a reduction in the number of derailments, covers the following requirements:

Ten 75-ton steam cranes, already converted to diesel operation;

Five 45-ton steam cranes to be converted to diesel operation and capacity increased to the maximum extent possible with the existing structure, possibly to or approaching 60 tons;

Two 45-ton steam cranes, built to restricted Southern Region Hastings line gauge, to be converted to diesel operation and up-rated;

Two 75-ton cranes, diesel operated, already built; and

Six 75-ton cranes, being built by Cowans Sheldon to a new design, with telescopic jib, powered by 280 h.p. Rolls Royce engines. The first of these was delivered in 1978.

All the crane movements are hydraulically actuated. The great advantage of diesel operation is that cranes are now at instant readiness, compared with the unavoidable delays incurred in raising steam in the cranes previously used.

It is, of course, the mechanical and electrical engineers, by their

Fig. 8.22 A Cowans Sheldon 75-ton diesel crane lifting a Class 24 diesel locomotive at Doncaster (BRB)

involvement in the design, construction, and performance of loco-motives, coaching stock, and freight vehicles, who tend to be most in the public eye. The civil engineers and the signal and telecommunications engineers play a less public, but nevertheless equally important, role in the development of the passenger and freight services.

The civil engineer has always been involved in the provision and maintenance of track and structures to the required safety standards, and in the provision of other facilities to meet the requirements of the operators. In recent years, he has become even more deeply involved, in providing the track alignment and stability which permits the safe passage of high-speed passenger trains; in the strengthening of track to permit increased axle loads and to make possible the passage of faster and heavier freight trains; in the reconstruction or modernization of passenger stations; in the rebuilding of bridges to provide clearances for overhead electric traction; and in the planning and construction of marshalling yards and freight depots, to aid operating efficiency.

The work of the signal and telecommunications engineer, too, has been vital to the furtherance of the railways' development plans. Demands upon line occupation have necessitated the development of signalling systems which speed the passage of trains and which also help to economize in the costs of operation. On the freight side, computer-based information systems have been devised to give operators current knowledge of the traffic situation and thereby enable them to deal with traffic more effectively and with less equipment. Indeed, it is in the field of signalling, telecommunications, and information processing that perhaps the greatest technological advances have been made over the past 20 years.

These and other aspects of the civil and signal and telecommunications engineers' work are more comprehensively dealt with in Chapters Nine and Ten, but it must be emphasized here that their work makes as relevant a contribution to the passenger and freight services as does that of any other of the engineering disciplines.

CHAPTER NINE

Civil Engineering

THE role of the railway civil engineers in the United Kingdom has inevitably changed over the years since the first public railway emerged in 1825. Up to the end of the nineteenth century they were mainly engaged in the construction of new railways. That they built well and soundly is evident from the fact that many of their works, for example bridges, have been able, many years afterwards, to withstand much heavier traffic than could have been contemplated at the time they were first built. On the other hand, some structures, for example some major station buildings, have had to be rebuilt to cope with the traffic now passing. In the early 1900s their main responsibility was one of maintenance, until changing circumstances from the 1920s onwards, due to the development of road transport following the First World War, led to the need to withdraw services from, or reduce facilities on, uneconomic lines, a process which continued at an increasing rate until the 1960s. During this phase the civil engineers' maintenance responsibility, including the renewal of life-expired bridges, tunnels, and track, increased, combined with a relatively minor involvement in picking up track and demolishing old structures on closed lines, and a limited amount of work in connection with changes in traction and the construction of marshalling yards called for under the Modernization Plan.

Since the 1960s there has been an increased demand for route rationalizations and new construction, in connection with dieselization and electrification projects, and for new stations to be provided adjacent to major cities, such as Bristol Parkway, so that adequate parking space may be available for the ever-multiplying car. Indeed, for a relatively short period, there were high hopes of a requirement for planning and constructing high-speed railways from a new International Passenger Terminal at White City in London to a Channel Tunnel Terminal near Folkestone and from King's Cross to serve the then projected Third London Airport at Maplin. Alas, changing circumstances led the Government of the day to cancel these projects.

During the period following nationalization, therefore, the civil engineers have been involved in a varied programme of new works, whilst at the same time continuing their basic maintenance function and keeping pace with technological advances in equipment and with improvements in methods of working. It is in these various contexts that this chapter will attempt to indicate the progress which has been made since nationalization.

Reference has already been made in Chapter One to the limited extent of co-ordination which existed between the civil engineering departments of the four group railway companies before nationalization. There was a Railway Engineers' Association, chaired in turn by the Chief Engineers of the four companies, which discussed matters of common interest. Although valuable discussions took place and co-ordination was achieved on some major items, in other instances the Association's conclusions were in fact only regarded as recommendations, to be adopted or ignored by the companies as they thought fit. For instance, a recommendation which was not generally adopted was in relation to the weight of rail and type of fastenings to be used: three of the companies accepted the recommendation but the fourth – the Great Western Railway – continued its own previous practice.

After nationalization, a Civil Engineering Committee was established to succeed the Railway Engineers' Association and in the early days this was chaired by W. K. Wallace of the London Midland Region. It considered matters of common interest and also pursued issues of standardization raised with it by J. C. L. Train, as Civil Engineering Member of the Railway Executive and Head of the Civil Engineering Department. It was not until June 1962 that there was any real central control over civil engineering matters and even then it was slow in developing. Day-to-day responsibility still remained with the Regional Chief Civil Engineers. All design work was also done in the Regions, with the exception of standard permanent way details, for which responsibility for separate aspects was allocated to the Regions by the Railway Executive. Proposals were submitted to the Permanent Way Sub-Committee of the Civil Engineering Committee for comment and then passed to the Committee itself for authorization. This situation continued until 1969, when arrangements were made for detailed design of standard components to be undertaken at HQ, an arrangement which also applies to standard bridge design. Even now, the civil engineering function, whilst under the general oversight of HQ, has not been centralized to the extent which has taken place in mechanical and electrical engineering work.

On nationalization, the 95 lb bull-head (BH) rail, with coach screw fastenings, was in general use on five Regions, with 97½ lb BH rail, with through bolt fastenings, on the sixth (the Western Region), although experiments with the heavier rails and through bolt fastenings were in progress on some of the other Regions, in order to secure a more economic rail life in heavy wear situations. The BH rail had proved very satisfactory, particularly on sharp curves with check rails and for easy switch and crossing maintenance, but it came to be realized that the flat-bottom (FB) rail, in general use on the Continent and in America, but only in limited use in Britain, was stronger, weight for weight, and more suitable for use on lines carrying heavier and faster traffic. Being of stiffer design, it spread wheel loading over more sleepers, as well as permitting stronger fish-plated joints.

The first trials with FB rail were carried out at Cheddington, on the LMS in 1936, using a British Standard rail weighing 110 lb per yard. This initiative was followed by trials on other companies' lines. The LMS trials were extended in 1939, some of the new lengths being laid with the American Railroad Engineers' Association standard of 131 lb per yard. Abroad, FB rails were generally fastened direct to the sleepers by screws or spikes, where hardwood sleepers were in use. Where such sleepers were not used, and where traffic was heavy, it was the practice to insert rolled-steel or cast-iron baseplates between the rail and the sleeper. In the LMS trials, various combinations of baseplate and fastening were used, including cast-iron baseplates attached to sleepers by coach screws and wood ferrules, with the rail secured by a clip of malleable iron or spring steel, and cast-iron or cast-steel baseplates with three elastic spikes which secured both the baseplate and the rail. The locations chosen for the trials varied widely, to give as wide a range of conditions as practicable: for example, areas subject to heavy and fast traffic, in tunnels, on curves, near water troughs and near sea. Lengths of 95 lb BH rail were laid in adjoining lines in order to provide comparative information on wear. Trials using the 110 lb British Standard track were generally satisfactory but the American 131 lb rail proved to be less suited to British conditions.

Experience indicated that if the full economies of FB rail were to be obtained, some redesign of rails was necessary, particularly in the light of the likelihood that they would require to be used with concrete, as well as wood, sleepers. In conjunction with the other group railways and the railmakers, a new FB rail of 113 lb per yard, to give a substantially greater ratio of strength to weight of rail, was produced. Trials with these rails started in 1946 and continued for some time after nationalization, when a committee of Permanent Way Engineers was charged with the task of recommending the design of FB rail which should be adopted as the BR standard for running lines. The design evolved – 109 lb per yard for main lines – incorporated only relatively slight modification of the 113 lb FB rail, resulting from experience gained in maintaining the trial lengths. One important change was that the top surface of the rail was rolled to a radius of nine inches instead of the twelve inches previously used. Nine inches is the radius to which rails gradually wear and thus gives a better ride as soon as laid.

This rail became the British standard in February 1949 for use on category A and B lines – in broad terms, those subject to speeds of over 60 miles/h, as they became due for relaying. Since then, the classification has been progressively amended to Class A, 100–125 miles/h; Class B, 75–99 miles/h; Class C, 50–74 miles/h; Class D, 49 miles/h and less, with each classification being divided into four sub-categories according to the annual gross tonnage passing over the line.

In line with the new BR standards, the range of sections published by the British Standards Institution had also been amended and these were included in the revised BS 11: 1959, all the varied sections having the suffix A after the weight. In this range, the 110A rail was almost identical with the UIC 54 kg/m section and represented only a small change from the 109 lb FB rail. As these small changes – in the inclination of the sides of the head, the thickness of the outer edges of the foot and the radius of the crown of the rail head – were beneficial, and in order to assist exports, BR changed over from the 109 lb to the 110A lb FB rail in 1959.

In the years which followed, BR Research Department investigations into the causes of rail web failure in service, particularly at the fishbolt holes and the rail ends, indicated that it would be beneficial to thicken the web in the region of the neutral axis, which was near to the centre line of the fishbolt holes. This was done by making the sides of the web parallel from top to bottom and the small increase in weight arising changed the section from 110A to 113A, which was adopted as standard in 1968.

FB rail was higher in initial cost but renewal and maintenance costs were expected to be less. The 109 lb FB rail was assessed as 59 per cent stronger vertically and 136 per cent stronger laterally than the standard 95 lb BH rail and required less components in assembly, especially when elastic spikes were used to secure both rail and baseplate to the sleeper.

At nationalization, the softwood sleeper (mainly Baltic redwood or Douglas fir), impregnated with creosote, was the one principally in use in Britain. Tropical hardwood sleepers (notably Jarrah) were in limited use abroad and had been introduced into some areas of the United Kingdom even before the war, but they were more costly than impregnated softwood sleepers. A. K. Terris, Chief Civil Engineer of the Eastern Region from January 1955 to July 1965, was an enthusiastic proponent of the Jarrah sleeper but his colleagues in other Regions were not convinced of their superiority over concrete sleepers. The latter had been installed in various European countries from as long ago as the end of the nineteenth century. The first recorded installation in Great Britain was by the L & NWR in about 1910 but until the early 1940s the majority of installations were of small numbers of sleepers for experimental purposes and mostly they were unsuccessful. In 1941 the LNER laid in about half a mile of concrete sleepers, of various types, at Hitchin, but only prestressed sleepers and a heavy LNER design proved successful.

So far as British Railways are concerned, the concrete sleeper of today owes its origins to work commenced in the same year by the LMS, assisted by the Building Research Station. At that time, timber for sleepers was in short supply, as the majority had to be imported, and a home-produced alternative material was therefore sought. Although individual reinforced concrete blocks, both with and without flexible steel tie-bars, had been used under sidings and goods lines, their designs were unsuitable for higher class tracks and a single-piece rigid sleeper design was sought. A length of track in the down fast line at Cheddington was used for tests and the first range of concrete sleepers was installed there in 1942. As well as observing service performance, measurements were made of the loads applied to the sleepers as trains passed, and of stress in the concrete and the reactions of the ballast underneath.

The earliest of the sleepers installed were of ordinary reinforced concrete and were found to be unsuitable in structural properties to stand up under main-line traffic. However, the development of prestressed sleepers at this time, utilizing the load and stress measurements made in the track, resulted in a much more satisfactory design being evolved. This was first laid in at Cheddington in 1943, followed shortly afterwards by installation at other sites, including one at Forest Hill in South London which carried 180 electric trains per day.

It is of interest to mention that prestressed concrete for sleepers used in Great Britain comprises high strength concrete cast into a long line mould, through which pass high-tensile steel wires held in tension. When the concrete is sufficiently hardened and bonded on to the wires, they are cut at the sleeper ends and the external tension is released. This is transferred as compression to the concrete and termed 'prestress'. The main advantages of prestress are that a far higher external load can be applied to the concrete member before it cracks than would otherwise be the case, also that any cracks which do form under overload conditions will close on removal of the load.

As a result of the trials, concrete sleepers were coming into more general use at the time of nationalization, having by then been adopted by all four main-line railways. By the early 1950s, over two million sleepers of this type had been installed. Many of these sleepers are still in use, adapted for FB rail, after thirty or more years.

Both FB rail and concrete sleepers were coming increasingly into use in the late 1940s/early 1950s and consideration was at the same time being given to the introduction of continuously welded rail (CWR). New designs of concrete sleepers suitable for continuously welded FB rail had therefore to be considered and in this context two features were of particular significance – the prospect of a longer life from a concrete sleeper than from a timber sleeper and the assistance which the extra weight of a concrete sleeper would give to the stability of track laid in with CWR. The design and installation problems to be overcome were basically to

    (a) provide adequate strength of sleeper for the more arduous traffic conditions envisaged;

    (b) devise a system of fastening the rails to the sleepers which would be satisfactory from a mechanical strength point of view, easy and simple to instal when stressing and destressing CWR, require minimum inspection and maintenance, and have adequate life so that it did not limit the useful life of the sleeper itself; and

(c) meet the electrical requirement of reliably insulating the rails from the sleepers for track circuiting purposes. The introduction of nylon, which could be used for moulding insulating elements capable of withstanding wear and abrasion, was a vital new factor in the further development of the concrete sleeper.

As similar circumstances applied on overseas railways, a committee was set up by the International Union of Railways in 1952 to study the technical and economic aspects of all established types of concrete sleeper assemblies. The work included the laying of two test lengths of track in Europe incorporating sleeper assemblies of the types used on British and other railways. In the light of all the evidence that became available from these tests, British Railways decided that the monolithic transverse sleeper, prestressed with bond-anchored wires, and with simple elastic fastenings, was the most suitable type. From the structural point of view, however, a slight increase in strength, depth and number of wires was necessary for main-line service. Sleepers with 22, 24, 26 and 34 wires were manufactured, with depths up to eight inches, for extended trial purposes, and the design with 26 wires was adopted.

Since then, the quality of concrete sleepers has progressively improved, basically in the same form but with some detailed changes being made by the CCE, BR HQ, in close association with the manufacturers and the Research Laboratories at Derby. Concrete sleepers purchased by BR are obtained either from the Costain Concrete Co Ltd or from Dow-Mac Concrete Ltd. Both manufacturers have many years of experience and close technical liaison is continuously maintained with the Research and Civil Engineering Departments of BR. Concrete sleepers have a life expectancy two or three times greater than softwood sleepers and they also provide greater track stability to withstand the heavy loadings and faster and more intensive services now operating. Furthermore, the price relative to both softwood and hardwood sleepers has been greatly reduced until the situation has been reached that timber is only economical in special circumstances and in point and crossing work.

Developments in relation to FB rail and concrete sleepers, and, later, the introduction of continuous welded rail with its special requirement in regard to stressing and securing, led to a need for a new type of fastening to attach the rails to the sleepers. There were many different types in use and several of these were subjected to laboratory and track tests. They included one design by A. Dean, used on the North Eastern Region; one, the SHC (Spring Hoop Clip) type, first used on the Western Region and later also on the Eastern, London Midland, and Scottish Regions; and the Mills C. Clip, widely used on all Regions except the Southern.

Early in the 1960s it became apparent that the number of types of fastenings had to be reduced, as each required some difference in the design of the sleeper in the vicinity of the rail seating areas. The technical requirements for a low-cost rail fastening were therefore established – adequate strength, simple to install and remove, and needing minimum maintenance attention – and available designs were assessed against these criteria.

In 1959, the Eastern Region had introduced the Pandrol rail fastening on the East Coast main line, just south of Peterborough, on timber sleepers, and a design incorporating this fastening on a concrete sleeper was produced. Four malleable iron housings are cast into the sleeper, one on each side of each rail position. Spring clips are driven into each housing, with a nylon element keeping the gauge and providing insulation between each clip and the top surface of the rail foot, the latter resting on a resilient pad on the sleeper. The Pandrol proved to be a simple, ingenious, and most effective fastening. The spring steel clips can be quickly driven into place, and are as easily removed. It is resilient and thus unaffected by vibration, it will not work loose, and it prevents rail creep, that is, the tendency for rails to move in the direction of travel. It can be used, and re-used, on wood or concrete sleepers.

When this design had been proved, the number of standard fastening assemblies was reduced to two. Judged against the criteria laid down, the SHC and the Pandrol were selected in 1963 as meeting more of the requirements than the remainder and most concrete sleepers were provided with one or other of these fastenings. Neither of these two assemblies required nuts, bolts or screws. In 1965 the Pandrol became the single standard, the position it still holds, and its use has spread to many countries throughout the world.

Over the years, up to the late 1940s, normal rail lengths had increased from 30 ft and less to 45 ft, then to 60 ft and occasionally to 120 ft. At that time, the welding of rails up to 180 ft in length had only been adopted for experimental purposes or in circumstances where, for example, it was necessary to eliminate the hammering effect from rail joints.

Fish-plated joints in conventional track allow for expansion or contraction of the rails with temperature variations and initially there were considerable misgivings as to the ability to control the effects of expansion and contraction in longer rails. In this context, tests were carried out on the Southern Railway in 1938 with rails 180 ft long, micrometer readings of longitudinal movement being taken at 15 ft intervals every hour for 48 hours. As a result of these tests it was calculated that with any lengths of continuous welded rail, and with the temperature variations likely to be encountered in Britain, the maximum movement in the rail would be in the 150 ft at each end, the centre portion being under uniform compression, or, in cold weather, tension. In order to limit these stresses the rails are stretched when being laid to the length they would be at a temperature of 80°F and then firmly fastened down. This process is usually carried out by hydraulic jacks (tensors), although in earlier days the rails were heated by passing gas flames over them. The use of hydraulic methods has greatly increased the precision with which the work can be carried out, as well as reducing the time and cost of installation and replacement.

The advantages of CWR, due to the elimination of rail joints – track maintenance reduced by more than one-third, smoother and more comfortable ride, fewer rail end and fishplate failures and longer track life, less wear and tear on vehicles, and savings in fuel costs – were confirmed in trials on the LM Region between Nuneaton and Lichfield, by comparing performance over CWR on one line and conventional jointed track on an adjacent line. These trials also endorsed the findings of the earlier trials on the Southern Railway and the gradual introduction of CWR on the heavier passenger lines began at Crewkerne, Southern Region, in 1955, shortly to be followed by other lengths on most Regions as the track became due for renewal. In 1963 BR HQ defined the ten most important main-line routes for priority renewal in CWR. A standard code of practice for the installation and maintenance of CWR was adopted in all Regions in 1968, the fundamental requirements being that ballasting standards must be fully maintained, fastenings must be efficient, and rail stresses must be evenly distributed.

In the summer of 1969 the number of instances in which lateral distortion occurred in CWR, leading in some cases to derailments, showed the

Fig. 9.1   An adjustment switch in continuous welded rail. The rails are clamped at this point to prevent sideways movement. The short lengths of rail in the 4-ft strengthen the sleepers, to withstand movement. Pandrol fasteners fix the rails to the sleepers (BRB)

need for greater stability in hot weather and a searching analysis of the forces set up in CWR was initiated. This led to a revised code of practice being evolved and during the winter/spring 1969–70 a major programme of widening and raising the ballast shoulders and the restressing of rails to a higher stress temperature was carried out. In 1970 an arrangement was made with the Meteorological Office whereby morning forecasts are provided to Divisional Civil Engineers to give an early warning of very hot weather during which it is inadvisable to disturb CWR and to enable them to arrange additional patrolling. The measures taken were sufficiently effective as to reduce to a very large extent the CWR distortions which occurred in 1970.

Before laying in the track, rails are welded into 300 ft or 600 ft lengths (even occasionally longer) in depots, by electric flash butt methods. When in position on or alongside the track, welding is carried out by the Thermit process.

The increasing use of CWR reinforced the need to find rail steels with better wear and other properties, particularly to enable CWR to be laid on sharp curves and in tunnels. A joint development programme with the Research and Development Division and British Steel was therefore set up in 1968. A wear-resistant rail, made from austenitic manganese steel, has been in use for a number of years, particularly in locations where severe wear on sharp curves is a major problem. Until recently, two

Fig. 9.2   Thermit welding of CWR, showing a tensor in position (BRB)

factors have prevented the use of this special steel in CWR. First, the heat applied during joint welding imparted brittleness, and second, the much higher coefficient of expansion of austenitic manganese steel, compared with steels normally used in CWR, created excessive stresses in the rail with changes in temperature. The first problem was overcome by the development by British Steel and BR of a weldable quality of the special steel, suitable welding procedures being established in discussions with two specialist welding firms. The second problem, of high coefficient of expansion, is less serious where ambient temperature changes are small, such as in long tunnels. The first BR installation using the new steel was in the tunnel near Old Street Station, on the former Northern City line between Finsbury Park and Moorgate, now intensively used by GN suburban electric trains. Previously, despite the use of rail lubricators, rails made of the standard grade of steel were having to be renewed after very short periods of service. After several months of intensive service with the new rails there was no perceptible change in rail profile over more than half a mile of sharply curved track.

Before leaving the question of CWR, other points are worthy of brief mention, to indicate the progress which has been made since the welding of rails into long lengths was introduced. Formerly, insulated fishplates using fibre and nylon insulating elements and high-strength bolts were used. More recently, the glued joint, dispensing with the use of fishplates, has been introduced and is in general use with CWR. It requires less maintenance and has greatly increased the reliability of the joint under heavy traffic conditions and in cold weather, when the tension in the rail may be as high as 90 tons. Nevertheless, there is still an unacceptable failure rate of glued joints and the complete solution to the problem is the use of jointless track circuits. These have been in use for some years in CWR on non-electrified lines and recently circuits have been developed which can be used with electrified track (see Chapter Ten). These are now being installed as resources permit. Secondly, the problems initially experienced in maintenance, due to the need for rail replacements to be made at controlled temperature, are becoming less difficult, due to the development of hydraulic methods of stressing, to which reference has already been made. Also, research is in progress on means of overcoming the loss of ballast resistance in the lateral direction after tamping, by pre-loading the sleepers immediately following the tamper, in order to limit the formation of voids after traffic commences.

Before 1948, designs for switches and crossings had been evolved for 110 lb and 113 lb FB track and these were used as the basis of the standard designs using 109 lb FB rails. In both plain line and points and crossings it has always been the practice to incline the running rails at an angle of 1 in 20 towards the centre of the track, and this principle was continued in the first designs of switches and crossings for FB track. It had the disadvantage, however, that it involved applying twist, as well as bending, to the rails used in crossings, which often caused poor seating on the baseplates and overstressing of the rail fastenings, especially after heating during repairs by welding. It was therefore decided that new designs should be prepared with all rails in switch and crossing work placed vertically on horizontal seatings, thereby reducing the number, and simplifying the assembly, of the component parts involved. Other factors governing the decision to redesign switch and crossing work were the need to simplify and reduce the varieties of special baseplates, to standardize on the Pandrol fastenings, and to re-arrange the timbering in order to provide for easier mechanical maintenance by tampers.

In all crossings built up by bolting together lengths of rail and spacing blocks the continual passage of heavily loaded wheels causes some relative movement between individual rails and blocks. This in time leads to wear, loose and broken bolts, and variations in gauge and rail gap dimensions. In order to overcome this trouble crossings made in one piece of cast manganese steel have been widely adopted and have substantially reduced maintenance costs, particularly at large terminal stations where standard crossings could be life-expired within three or four years. The rate of crack propagation in this material is low and, therefore, the risk of sudden failure is considerably reduced. Some of the advantages of the monolithic crossing are obtained by using a 'semi-welded' crossing, in which the acute angle, or 'Vee', consists of machined rails of standard steel welded together.

Until the Second World War, it had been the practice to mount the chairs and baseplates for switches and crossings on softwood timbers but thereafter the quality of imported softwood deteriorated considerably. It was therefore decided to standardize on the use of Australian hardwood (Jarrah or Karri) timbers for all switch and crossing work. These timbers do not require creosoting, are virtually rotproof and give a life comparable to that of concrete sleepers. In plain line track, a resilient rail pad is inserted between the rail foot and concrete sleeper; similarly, the pad is used in crossing work between the rail foot and the baseplate, thus maintaining track resilience throughout a layout. The Pandrol rail fastening is also standard for crossing work.

In tests, it has been proved that high lateral shocks can be caused by contact between the backs of the wheel flanges and the sides of the check rails, placed opposite the nose of crossings to ensure that the wheel flanges take the correct side of the crossing. These shocks lead to poor riding, to high axle stresses, and to misalignment in switch and crossing layouts. The problem can be cured only by the elimination of check rails and to achieve this the movable or 'swing nose' common crossing has been developed. In this design, the nose of the crossing moves from side to side according to the direction in which the train is to pass and, as there are no gaps to cross, an unbroken path is provided for the wheels. In the case of one track crossing another, movable switch diamond crossings are now widely used on high-speed lines when the angle between the tracks is flatter than 1 in 7 or 8.

With the introduction of welded rails on concrete sleepers the track gauge (4 ft 8½ in) has been reduced to 4 ft 8⅜ in, in order to reduce the amount of play between the wheel flanges and the running rails, and thus produce steadier running.

One of the problems encountered during very cold weather is the tendency for points to be prevented by ice from closing fully, the signalling detection thus correctly preventing signals from being cleared. This causes considerable delays to traffic. In order to overcome this problem, long-life anti-freeze lubricants and switch heaters have been introduced.

There are two basic types of point heater – gas and electrically operated. Gas heaters are relatively high power units, which quickly raise the temperature of the switches, slide chairs, and stock rail above freezing point. This makes the gas system suitable for automatic control, with gas being burned only when it is required. A new type heater, thermostatically controlled, introduced for trial purposes on the Eastern and LM Regions in 1978, burns natural gas at normal pressure, thus eliminating any need for boosting.

Increasingly, however, electric heaters are being employed. There are two basic types – cartridge and area resistance. The cartridge type consists of standard heating elements, from 200 to 500 W, housed in metal tubes fitted into holes in the slide chairs. The area resistance method employs a non-metallic element, made from woven glass fibre covered with a deposit of fine graphite, thus producing an element that is thin, light, tough, and flexible. When an electric current is passed through it, the whole area of the material heats up evenly. The element – rated at only 100 W – is sealed and forms a strong flat sheet for fitting between the slide chairs and sleepers.

When the country does experience a spell of very cold weather, icing and blockage of points assumes quite serious proportions, although statistics show that, on average, only on very few days in a year are weather conditions sufficiently severe as to cause any great difficulty. Nevertheless, point heaters are being installed at an increasing number of locations throughout British Railways, (currently some 14000 sets of points are so fitted) whilst a number of old-style gas heaters are being converted to electric operation.

The quality and quantity of ballast under the track are extremely important in the maintenance of good line and level. The functions of ballast are

    (a) to distribute the load of traffic from the sleepers to the formation, without progressive settlements;

    (b) to permit drainage of the track;

    (c) to prevent lateral and longitudinal movement of the track; and

(d) to afford a convenient medium for packing the track to correct cross level and gradient.

In order to establish the necessary criteria for ballast able to withstand the destructive effects of heavy traffic and at the same time stand up to repeated cycles of maintenance tamping, the Research and Development Division undertook a widespread investigation, both in the laboratories at Derby and at selected sites under traffic in the country. As a result of the investigation, the mechanical properties of the ballast suitable and available for railway use have been established. It is essential that the ballast should have a high resistance to crushing and attrition, under the weight and vibration of passing trains, in order to avoid the creation of too much powder, which clogs the ballast and prevents good drainage. The granites, basalts, and metamorphosed limestones produce better results in this context than the normal limestones, which should only be used on less important lines. Blast furnace slag was used until the early 1960s on part of the East Coast line but this also proved to be unsatisfactory in modern conditions.

A main source of supply in the south is Meldon Quarry, near Oke-hampton, on the edge of Dartmoor. Quarrying there was started in 1897 by the London and South Western Railway. The quarry has been gradually expanded over the years until now it is one of the biggest in the country, producing over 350000 tons of stone a year. The production of

Fig. 9.3   Meldon Quarry: the Railway-owned quarry in Devon, the source of a high proportion of the ballast used in the Southern part of Britain (BRB)

ballast is the quarry's major activity but additionally it provides stone blocks for walling, washed aggregates for concrete, road stone, chippings, and an excellent stone dust for blanketing over clay formations. In the Midlands, a major source of supply is the other railway-owned quarry at Caldon Low in Staffordshire.

Before the war, the increase in the speeds of trains, and the higher traffic densities over certain routes, had highlighted the need for improved track standards, whilst at the same time reducing the time available for track maintenance work. In meeting this new situation, the LMS was in the forefront in introducing measured shovel packing for filling voids in the ballast under the sleepers. This system, first tried in Britain in 1934, provided for determining the amount of stone chippings required under the sleepers immediately below the rail, to eliminate vertical movement of the track under load. The method involved the use of sighting boards to determine the static error in rail levels over a given distance and voidmeters to determine the extent of the voids under the unloaded sleepers, which when depressed under load would increase that error. These measurements, added together, determined the quantity of stone chippings required under the sleeper to bring the rail up to its correct level. The system helped significantly towards improved maintenance and was adopted by all the main-line companies.

In the middle 1930s, the new science of soil mechanics was used in determining the stability of weak formations, embankments, and cuttings. One of the first applications was at Hildenborough on the Southern Railway in 1937, where clay coming up through the ballast was a constant source of trouble. The formation was dug out to a predetermined depth and replaced by concrete slabs, ashes, and clean ballast, with an ample drainage system. Since the war, this practice of 'blanketing' has been followed in many places on all Regions, but concrete slabs have given way to quarry dust, gravel or sand below the ballast. In the early post-war years, roofing felt was often inserted below the blanketing material to shed rain water into the drains but since the early 1960s it has been the practice to provide a layer of polythene sheeting in the middle of the blanket.

Before mechanical means of recording the condition of the track were introduced, the permanent way was visually checked by inspectors and gangers. Periodically, it was walked and 'marked' as to its condition, according to certain agreed principles and criteria, during track inspections by officers and technical staff from District or Divisional offices.

When higher speeds were introduced in the pre-war years, problems of track maintenance inevitably occurred, not the least of which was the question of standards for the alignment of curved track and its subsequent maintenance to the standards adopted. To assist in this work, the railways made increasing use of the Hallade track recorder, first introduced into Britain from France by the Great Northern Railway in 1922.

The Hallade recorder, placed on the floor of a coach, works on a similar principle to the seismograph and with four pens records on a roll of paper vertical and horizontal movements and changes in train speeds, whilst an operator-controlled button marks each quarter-mile post. Examination of these records, in conjunction with the track marking, greatly assisted in the maintenance of satisfactory track. The records were useful for establishing superelevation standards and the degree of cant deficiency which could be permitted on curves, to secure maximum passenger comfort. In the early 1940s the LNER produced a booklet of rules for 'Speed Curvature and Cant', which laid down the requirements not only for curves but also for transitions and for speeds through switch and crossing work. After nationalization, one of the LNER engineers concerned with the preparation of this booklet (M. G. Maycock) and J. C. Loach of the Research Department were charged with establishing a common set of rules for curve design and arranged a programme of tests using a Hallade recorder over a long series of specially adjusted curves on the Festiniog branch in North Wales. The rules which were then formulated on the requirements for superelevation, the form and dimensions of transition curves, and the permissible speeds through junctions still form the basis of current practice.

The measurements provided by the Hallade recorder could be affected by the riding quality and speed of the vehicle in which it was being

Fig. 9.4   A new junction being assembled in the lay-out yard at New Cross Gate, Southern Region, prior to dismantling and relaying on site at Shortlands Junction (1958) (BRB)

carried, unless, as became the practice on some Regions, it was always carried in the same vehicle. A more precise method of track measurement was therefore needed and during the 1950s/60s a number of Matisa Track Recording Trolleys was purchased. These were four-wheeled vehicles, with enclosed cabs, having pairs of small measuring wheels projecting on outriggers in front and in rear. These vehicles, which could travel at 20 miles/h, measured and recorded variations in cross-level, cant, curvature, alignment, and top level in each rail separately. They were provided with equipment which automatically sprayed paint on the track to mark irregularities requiring urgent attention.

The Chief Civil Engineer's Department has a comprehensive workshop organization, with workshops and smaller depots located throughout the railway. In addition to routine repairs to plant and equipment required for day-to-day maintenance of the permanent way, bridges, stations, and other buildings for which the department is responsible, the depots are mainly engaged in the preparation and assembly of new plain track and points and crossings. The policies of the four group companies in regard to the manufacture of permanent way components differed to some extent. Depots for creosoting wooden sleepers and manufacturing a wide variety of concrete lineside components were under the direct control of the Civil Engineer. Cast-iron chairs and baseplates were usually made in the foundries at one or other of the Locomotive Works, notably on the LMS at Horwich, where mechanized machine moulding continuous casting plants produced 50000 tons of chairs and baseplates a year. The Chief Civil Engineer of the Southern Railway, on the other hand, had his own chair foundry at the Permanent Way Depot at Redbridge, near Southampton, where also rails for points and crossings were machined and completely assembled and sleepers were creosoted. The Locomotive Works at Crewe, Swindon, and Gorton had point and crossing shops. With the general introduction of long welded rails, production lines for flash butt welding were installed at existing depots or new depots – Chesterton in the Eastern Region, Castleton in the LM Region, Dinsdale in the North Eastern Region, Motherwell in the Scottish Region, and Hookagate in the Western Region – were built to carry out this work. As previously mentioned, the length welded at depots was 300 ft but in time all depots were extended to 600 ft or longer, Chesterton being capable of dealing with the welding of 1200 ft lengths. These lengths, when loaded on to flat wagons, can negotiate sharp curves.

After the Second World War the rising costs of materials and labour, and the difficulty experienced in obtaining staff of the right calibre, combined with the urgent need to overtake arrears of maintenance which had built up during the war, emphasized the need for increasing productivity by the introduction of piecework schemes and the mechanization of civil engineering operations.

A limited number of piecework schemes had been introduced at civil

Fig. 9.5 Flash butt welding in process at one of the new welding installations (BRB)

engineering shops before the war, one of the earliest being in the GWR creosoting depot at Hayes. By the end of the war, work study principles were being increasingly applied outside the railways and in 1946 the Southern Railway employed consultants to advise on work measurement schemes for their concrete depot and stores at Exeter. The schemes were successful in reducing unit costs and were therefore extended to other concrete depots on the Southern Railway, and to the Permanent Way Depot at Redbridge for sleeper preparation, foundry work, and point and crossing manufacture.

These innovations were introduced by V. A. M. Robertson, then Chief Civil Engineer, but the greatest advances were made under his successor, F. E. Campion, who decided in 1950 to apply work study principles to permanent way maintenance operations. Trial schemes showed some promise of success and the first full scheme was introduced at Woking in 1954. Similar payment-by-results (PBR) schemes were developed in other Regions and the principles were applied to most operations of the civil engineering department by the early 1960s. The effect of PBR was to reduce manpower by 33 per cent and the staff remaining were able significantly to increase their earnings by greater productivity. For the first time, managers concerned with railway civil engineering work were able to plan the work-load and to check actual performance and costs by means of control data for each gang or task. The PBR schemes were, however, withdrawn in 1974, when, under a pay agreement with the Trades Unions, all bonuses were consolidated into the basic wage structure.

The mechanization of permanent way operations was initially confined to the use of powered hand tools and off-track plant. Later, the range of equipment was extended to include such items as rail benders, weld strippers, draglines for blanketing and earthworks, ballast regulators to grade track profile to exact requirements, hydraulic stressing equipment to pre-tension CWR, and Pandrol spike drivers and extractors.

With the integrity and safety of the track as their prime responsibility, the civil engineers were understandably cautious in moving away from their well proven manual methods of maintenance and renewal. With staff problems becoming more pressing, however, it became essential to introduce more sophisticated mechanical plant and equipment to the maximum extent possible for maintenance purposes.

One of the first of the big machines to be introduced was a Matisa ballast cleaner, used on the LM Region in 1948. It had an endless chain of small buckets threaded under the track on which the machine stood. This scooped up ballast into a high level hopper, from which it passed through sieves. The dust and dirt was passed by belt to either the lineside or wagons on the adjacent track and the good ballast was returned to the track. The machine excavated to a depth of around 12 inches below the sleeper and progress was about 40 track yards (130 cubic yards) per hour. More machines of this type, but with increased capacity, were purchased, as were similar machines made by Plasser-Theurer. They have since increased still further in size and capacity, the latest machines being self-propelled and capable of lifting and slewing the track after ballast cleaning operations. They have an output of around 400 cubic yards per hour.

In 1948 the North Eastern Region acquired a Matisa petrol-driven sleeper tamping machine, the first to be obtained for use on the railways of Britain. This was a self-propelled four-wheeled trolley with eight pairs of opposed tools which penetrated the ballast on each side of the sleeper and adjacent to the rails. The tools, vibrating at a high frequency, were drawn together, thus packing and compressing the ballast beneath the sleeper in the position in which it was most required. There was a trailer which could be man-handled to the side of the track, and a swivel platform under the machine so that it could be turned and run off the track clear of passing trains.

In the 1960s the mechanization of track maintenance was receiving much attention on the Continent, as well as in Britain, and more sophisti-

Fig. 9.6   A ballast cleaning machine (Anthony Florey)

Fig. 9.7   A ballast tamping and lining machine (BRB)

cated hydraulically operated machines were being produced to encompass more and more functions. From 1967 onwards automatic lining was incorporated into tamping machines, so that they could lift, line, and tamp simultaneously, thereby producing a more uniform and stable track than could be achieved by men alone. Later models also incorporated equipment for consolidating the ballast and for dealing with two sleepers simultaneously. Joint tampers and switch and crossing tampers – the latter a major advance – were also developed. The latest Plasser-Theurer lining and tamping machines, for both plain line and switch and crossing work, can deal with about 1250 yards of track an hour. Hand-held tampers (now all Kango electric type) are still in use, for switch and crossing tamping and spot plain line repairs. The supply generator is mounted on a large pneumatic-tyred single-wheeled frame to enable it to be moved along the trackside. Hand tamping is a slow and expensive process and is only resorted to when machine tamping is not possible or where the length to be tamped is short.

As the number of maintenance machines increased, the need arose for more rapid means of analysis of the track recorder traces, in order to ensure that the equipment was fully utilized and that priority was given to the more urgent maintenance requirements. As a result of liaison between the Chief Civil Engineer, North Eastern Region, and the Derwent Electronics Co of York, a computer was developed in 1965 for fitting to the Matisa track recording trolleys. Under this system, known as NEPTUNE (a name derived from the description 'North Eastern Electronic Peak Tracing Unit and Numerical Evaluator'), information recorded on paper rolls is analysed and is both printed out and visually displayed as figures, representing the general quality of each track parameter as the inspection takes place. In the early 1970s, the Eastern Region Chief Civil Engineer's Department at York (the Eastern and North Eastern Regions having in the meantime been merged) evolved means of reducing the work involved in examining record traces and NEPTUNE figures by pro-

cessing the tapes through another computer to give print-outs and sum-
maries of data relative to each parameter and geographical section of the
line concerned, together with a comparison with previous records.

In 1977, a new High Speed Track Recording Coach, designed jointly by
the Civil and Mechanical and Electrical Engineering Departments and the
Research and Development Division, came into service. This is a considerable advance on previous recording cars, inasmuch as it can record at
speeds up to 125 miles/h. The coach records the various track parameters
whilst running in normal train formations and prints out the information
in analogue form. A computer monitors the information, carries out an
analysis of the data and prints out for each 220 yards of track condition
factors in numerical form. It also prints out locations where set standards
for the more important parameters are exceeded. An automatically
triggered paint spray marks the location of any serious defects in the
track. The data recorded can be fed into a computerized system for the
planning of plant for on-track maintenance.

Before leaving the subject of track maintenance machinery, three other
units for specialized purposes must be mentioned – one for the detection
of defects in rails, one for the elimination of corrugations in rails, and one
for attention to the permanent way as a whole. The detection of hidden
flaws which may develop in rails is an important matter. During the initial
trials with FB rails, the LMS used a Sperry rail flaw detector, of American
design, which was able to detect rail fissures by recording variations in

Fig. 9.8   Inside a Track Recording Trolley, showing the NEPTUNE equipment. Irregularities
in the track, in the various parameters, are recorded on the paper roll in the centre of the
picture; irregularities over a certain level are displayed on the screen above the paper roll;
and the equipment on the left hand side converts the paper roll record into figures (BRB)

Fig. 9.9   The recording panel and video equipment in the High Speed Track Recording
Coach. The equipment records irregularities in the track at much higher speeds
than is possible with the track recording trolleys and may disclose inequalities
which may not be so apparent at lower speeds (BRB)

the magnetic field set up as it ran over the track. Subsequent developments have exploited the use of ultrasonic sound waves for flaw detection, in both hand-held and self-propelled equipment. A two-car diesel unit was brought into use in 1970 as a rail flaw detection train. This can detect flaws in rails whilst travelling at speeds up to 20 miles/h. Signals are received from ultrasonic probes sliding along the rail surfaces and, as the unit was originally built, this information was recorded continuously on 35 mm film. Analysis of these films, and the initiation of any necessary action, was a somewhat slow process and it has now been found possible to eliminate the film recording stage. Instead, in 1977, a small computer system was installed on the train, to analyse the information as it is received from the probes, defects detected being recorded, together with location information, on magnetic tape. This tape is then analysed by the main computer, which is able to translate the information back into picture and report form.

Shallow corrugations sometimes develop in the running surface of rails, at particular locations, and may do so again at the same place when new rails are laid. This phenomenon has baffled railway engineers and scientists for a long time and in recent years has become an increasing problem. A paper on the subject was read to the Permanent Way Institution in November 1979 by C. O. Frederick (Group Manager, Track, Research and Development Division), based on a technical memorandum issued by that Division.

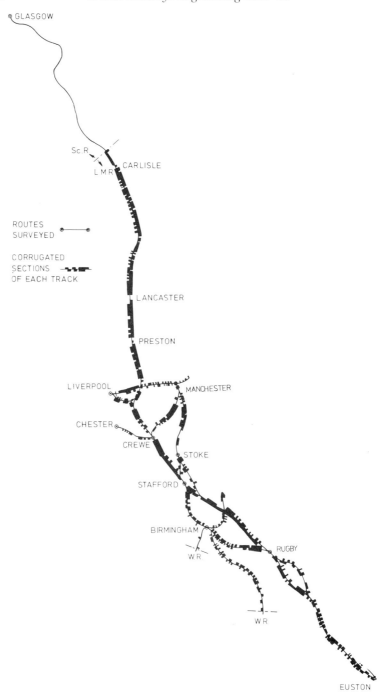

Fig. 9.10   The corrugation problem: the incidence of corrugations on the
West Coast main line (BRB)

A survey of the corrugation problem on BR, by means of noise measurement on service trains, revealed some strange facts – that when the survey was undertaken in 1974–5 there was a heavy distribution of corrugations on the West Coast main line of the LM Region between Euston and the Scottish border north of Carlisle (see Fig. 9.10); that the continuation of the West Coast main line from the border showed no corrugations whatever; that the York–Sheffield line of the Eastern Region was heavily corrugated but there were very few corrugations on the East Coast main line, although they have recently increased in number; and that all lines in the Southern and Western Regions showed evidence of corrugations occurring, with particularly heavy concentrations on the Reading–Taunton route.

The immediate effect of these corrugations is vibration, raising the noise levels in trains, giving rise to what is commonly known as 'roaring rails'. The vibration causes damage to the track through loosening of fastenings and deterioration of line and level. A rail grinding train developed by Speno International of Geneva is now used to grind out corrugations and pit marks in the running surface. It is equipped with 48 grinding stones, adjustable to any angle. The train runs at 4 miles/h when removing corrugations and can also be used to reprofile rails by grinding out the effects of side wear. The grinding train is now in use throughout the year and it is estimated that a 50 per cent increase in life-expectancy of rails will be achieved.

A. N. Butland, who was Chief Civil Engineer of the LMR from 1959 to 1962, before becoming CCE at BR HQ, played a significant part in the development of mechanized permanent way maintenance. It was he who was largely responsible for the development and expansion of the use of

Fig. 9.11   The Speno Rail Grinder. The sparks indicate where grinding is taking place (BRB)

machines, producing a system under which all plain track with good ballast conditions can be maintained by mechanical plant.

On British Railways, track is renewed mainly by complete relaying with new material. Approximately 600 miles of track are renewed each year. There is also a partial renewal programme of some 100 miles a year and the planning of the total programme is a formidable task. To make the best use of high cost resources a Computerized Renewal of Way System has been in use since 1975. The many dramatic advances both in technology and in work control processes which have taken place in the last 20 years have resulted in a reduction in the overall permanent way labour force by 60 per cent, a revolution in management control and, at the same time, a significant increase in track quality. An important factor in the planning of the day-to-day work of the reduced labour force is CAMP (Computerized Approach to Maintenance Planning). Besides enabling the engineers and supervisors to store information on work to be done and calculate work content, it enables the actual work done to be recorded for future analysis.

Other computer systems, including the Rail Flaw Detector Train (RFDT), the Civil Engineering Plant System (CEPS) and the Investment Budget Control System (IBCOS) are contributing to the effective maintenance of track. The next stage – the integration of these systems with a track data base – will provide all the details relative to any track section and produce information correlating work input and track quality, the frequency of various work types and the age of the track, the incidence of rail failures with axle loading and route tonnage, and many other comparisons yet to be defined.

The first record of track renewal by mechanical means in Britain was in 1932, when the LNER acquired a Morris tracklaying machine capable of renewal work with possession limited to the track being renewed. This machine was modified in 1957 for use in installing long welded rails on concrete sleepers with a renewal rate of 1400 yards in eight hours. Track renewal by the use of cranes was also carried out by the LMS, in the Peterborough area, in 1938, and the system was further extended during and after the war. The cranes used were generally steam operated, of six to ten tons capacity, very slow in operation and time-consuming in preparation for work. With the introduction of heavier track sections and concrete sleepers, diesel cranes of 10 to 15 tons capacity were obtained, and 35 to 40 ton cranes were available on loan from the Motive Power Department for particularly heavy lifts.

New track was pre-assembled into 60 ft lengths in specially laid-out depots. The method adopted on site was to have bogie wagons loaded with lengths of new track on the line to be relaid and one or two cranes on the adjacent line. When two cranes were used, one of them lifted out two or three lengths of old track and placed them on an empty wagon. The other crane lifted new track from the material train and placed it into the gap. This continued along the line, loading the old lengths on to the wagons on which the new track had been brought to the site. Complete possession of two tracks was necessary, but by this means it was normally possible to relay ten to twelve lengths (200 to 240 yards) of track in one hour.

The benefits which were secured from track renewal by crane – greater speed of relaying, shorter line possessions, shorter periods of speed restriction subsequent to relaying, pre-assembly of track under depot conditions by specialist staff, and current removal of old materials – emphasized the need for further developments in this area. The Divisional Engineer's staff at Purley, Southern Region, initiated development by designing a special tracklaying machine, capable of operation in tunnels, consisting of two hoists, 30 ft apart, powered by pneumatic winches, with arms projecting over the adjacent track. They were mounted on a 40 ft bogie wagon. A machine to this design was built for use in relaying the track in the 2611 yard Polhill Tunnel, near Sevenoaks, in 1948. The Western Region also, in 1949, produced their own version of a machine for relaying pre-assembled track. It consisted of two crane trucks with a central control vehicle, permanently coupled, and was an advance on the Southern Region machine. The first major work for which it was used was in the Severn Tunnel.

Since then, far more sophisticated tracklaying machines have been produced, some on the same general principles, but others occupying only the track being relaid. In the mid-1960s the Eastern Region

Fig. 9.12 The tracklaying machine developed by the Southern Region in 1948, operating from the adjacent line (BRB)

Fig. 9.13   A Thomas Smith tracklaying machine, requiring the
occupation of the adjacent line (BRB)

purchased two East German single-line gantry machines and a little later
the Western Region tried a variety of French designs. All of them required
modification to make them suitable for British use. They consist of two
self-propelled gantries with hydraulic hoisting machinery in the top
cross-member. They run on rails previously laid on either side of the track
at 10 ft centres, without fouling the adjacent line. Sections of track to be
renewed are lifted out and loaded directly into a materials train. The
ballast is then levelled before the machine places either a new 60 ft
panel of track with service rails, or, using a special beam, just the new
sleepers, in position and passes on to the next section of line. Another
machine follows and picks up the outer temporary rails and places them
on the sleepers, where they are secured to become the new permanent
way.

Recently a number of new twin-jib tracklayers capable of manoeuvring
into place a 60-ft long piece of track weighing 11·75 tons have been
purchased. The jibs can be power slewed, luffed and extended. Each jib is
capable of being operated independently of the other if so required.

A ten-year programme for the replacement of life-expired tracklaying
equipment is now in progress, the decision having been taken in 1975 to
modernize the fleet and make amendments in usage policies. Future
policy will be to restrict the use of jib cranes to switch and crossing work
and other miscellaneous tasks and to deal with plain line renewals by
tracklaying machines. When the decision was taken in 1975 it was estimated that the work-load would justify a fleet of 54 tracklaying machines,
129 single jib cranes and 17 single line gantries. The first orders within this
programme – for 28 tracklaying machines and 44 self-propelled rail-
mounted cranes, to be produced by Plasser-Theurer and Cowan Sheldon
Ltd – were announced in February 1976 and deliveries commenced in

1977. The tracklaying machines can travel at up to 65 miles/h in train formation and at up to 20 miles/h when self propelled.

It was always an important duty of the permanent way maintenance staff to keep the track ballast and cess substantially clear of weeds, which interfered with normal maintenance work, clogged ballast and restricted drainage. The work was carried out manually, and in the summer months up to 30 per cent of maintenance staff time could be spent on this task.

First trials with the use of chemical weed-killers on the railways of the UK took place in the early 1930s, following extensive trials in Canada. By 1938, all four main-line railways had weed-killing trains, using sodium chlorate as the weed-killer, with calcium chloride to reduce the fire risk, but only about 10 per cent of running lines were sprayed by these means. This situation continued until nationalization, since when there has been a progressive improvement in the design of the trains and the extent of treatment. By the early 1960s, virtually all running lines were being sprayed annually.

Until 1968, the slopes alongside the tracks were regularly cut, using hand, and later, mechanical, scythes, to prevent seeding and as a pre-caution against fires caused by sparks from steam locomotives. In 1968, due to the regular weed-killing programme and the phasing out of steam locomotives, it was decided that grass cutting as a general practice should cease, except in certain fire risk areas. This policy has resulted, over the past ten years or so, in an increasing growth of brambles and various saplings and some measure of treatment has had to be reintroduced, using adjustable sprays on the weed-killing trains or other means. In assessing the extent of the treatment to be given, a very delicate path has had to be trod between the views of the environmentalists, who are anxious to avoid the extermination of grasses, flowering plants and wild life, and the neighbouring farmers, who complain that pests from lineside areas do damage to their crops!

These are the major items of mechanical equipment which British Railways have produced over the past 30 years to help provide a track capable of withstanding the stresses created by very high speeds, heavier axle loads, and increased intensity of traffic, whilst contributing to the overall reduction in track maintenance and renewal manning levels.

Throughout their history, the railways have been seeking higher speeds and the civil engineers have been constantly engaged in upgrad-ing the track to meet this requirement. The imperative need to compete effectively with road and air transport has accentuated this demand for higher speeds, from 90 miles/h to 100 miles/h and now to 125 miles/h to utilize the capacity of the HST and the APT.

The first stretch of 100 miles/h track was introduced at Lolham, in the Eastern Region, in 1964, but it was not until later in the decade that 100 miles/h operation was regularly introduced. Electric working on the LM Region lines provided for speeds of up to 100 miles/h over considerable sections of the line, amounting to something over one half of the total mileage involved, whilst on the East Coast route the introduction of the Deltic diesel locomotives permitted similar speeds.

In March 1968, a report was prepared by the LM Region on their experience of 100 miles/h operation, so that this might be applied to future plans involving further increases in maximum speeds. The report indicated those areas of civil engineering which needed to be given special consideration in assessing the practicability and cost of introducing higher speeds over particular routes, namely:

(a) The effect of more intensive services, operating at higher speeds, on the incidence of rail failures.

(b) The effect on cant requirements of running high-speed passenger trains and slow-speed freight trains over the same lines.

(c) The likely need for improved clearances, largely in the spacing between tracks, in tunnels and alongside bridge abutments or retaining walls, and in the siting of tracks in relation to station platforms and buildings. Ideally, fast tracks should not adjoin platforms.

(d) The incidence of sharp curves was the most important limiting factor. Where practicable, with reasonable economy, this difficulty should be overcome by realignment, to secure easier transition curves. In order to avoid unnecessarily heavy expenditure on realignments, however, the first aim should be to consider the possibility of easing existing permanent speed restrictions.

(e) Stability of the formation on which the ballast was laid was the prime requirement for a high speed track. Formation stabilization involves the existence of satisfactory drainage.

(f) Quality and quantity of ballast was important. Experience to date with concrete sleepers mechanically packed indicated that the hard wearing quality of the stone might be of long term importance. Concrete sleepers under traffic were naturally harder on the ballast than were timber sleepers and the abrasion due to this and to the tamping process had more effect on limestone ballast than on the harder granite ballast. Less wear meant that there would be a higher percentage of recovery of good stone in ballast cleaning.

(g) So far as plain line track was concerned, prestressed concrete sleepers with modern spring clip fastenings had proved to be one of the most satisfactory track developments in recent years, and they were suitable for speeds higher than 100 miles/h without modification. From the maintenance viewpoint, the frequency of packing of sleepers was dependent on the degree of settlement which took place under the sleepers. It was reduced by increasing the number of sleepers from the equivalent of 24 to a 60-ft length to 26 and even 28.

(h) The most difficult track to maintain, and the part giving the least satisfactory ride, was that passing through switches and crossings. A great deal of attention had been given to designing more satisfactory details, resulting in swing-nose and switch diamond crossings.

(i) Main lines of the future would be maintained by on-track machines, which had already shown that they could produce a more uniform and longer-lasting top and alignment than the older manual methods. Men, however, would still be required for the maintenance of fastenings, fittings, and joints, as well as various lineside jobs. The possession pattern for maintenance work on high-speed lines was a key matter. Future timetabling and diagramming of trains on high-speed lines should be so planned that for any sections of track there was an agreed period of time, say three to four hours in the twenty-four, when maintenance needs had first call on track possession – naturally at a time when traffic needs were least critical.

The basic necessity for the satisfactory operation of a high-speed service is to ensure that the correct relationship between the vehicle and the track is achieved – that is, the relationship between the destructive effects of the vehicle and the ability of the track to withstand them. The correct relationship can only be obtained by ensuring that the design of the traction and rolling stock, especially as regards axle load, unsprung weight on axles, and suspension, and the design of the track go hand in hand. The civil engineer must be fully aware of the operating requirements for the service and the behaviour of the traction and rolling stock to be built to provide it. He can then be in a position to indicate the extent to which the track, as it at present exists, can meet requirements and, if not, what improvements are necessary to bring it up to the requisite standard, and at what cost. That cost must then be weighed against the commercial, operating, and mechanical and electrical engineering advantages of the proposed service, to decide whether or not it would be economic to go ahead with it. The need might arise to redesign the traction and/or rolling stock to avoid excessive cost in civil engineering works, which might or might not in turn necessitate an adjustment in the high-speed service proposals.

Inevitably, trains running at 100 miles/h and over must have some adverse effect on the track, although perhaps less so than heavy axle loads. In fact, isolated faults, which develop regardless of speed, and may indeed be caused by slower freight trains, often determine the frequency of maintenance cycles. Nevertheless, high speeds involve more frequent maintenance, because less general deterioration in the track is permissible and without the mechanical aids which are available it would be impracticable to produce and maintain a railway capable of carrying services operating at 125 miles/h and beyond. It says much for the progressive nature of permanent way engineering thinking and planning that the BR Board was able to adopt a forward-looking high-speed policy without civil engineering design and practices having to be radically revised. The comprehensive works which had been carried out on the main routes in the 1950s and early 1960s – remodelling of track layouts, introduction of CWR with pre-stressed concrete sleepers and ample ballast, the adoption of Pandrol clip fastenings, and the deep excavation of weak formations to ensure uniformly good ballasting and drainage – generally met the requirements for higher speeds, up to 125 miles/h for passenger trains and 75 miles/h for freight, without undue difficulty or excessive expenditure and therefore reduced the track work which had to be undertaken when the High Speed Trains were introduced. One aspect of track design which may take some years to resolve is the effect upon the rail itself of high speeds, freight traffic with 25-ton axle loads, and high total tonnage passing over the route. There is evidence that these factors may lead to the development of faults thought to be due to fatigue in the steel structure. The new rail flaw detector car will assist in finding the answer to this problem. This aspect apart, British Railways can face the extension of high-speed services, to the present maximum level of 125 miles/h, with confidence in the adequacy of their track, but whether speeds or axle loadings can develop much further, without large-scale civil engineering works, is a matter still under examination.

Since the mid-1960s, as part of a project promoted by ORE, the Research and Development Division at Derby has been investigating the possibility of providing a continuous concrete apron in place of the conventional sleepered support. The outcome of their work – known as PACT (Paved Concrete Track) or 'slab track' – consists of a continuous concrete slab on which the rails are fixed. It eliminates sleepers and ballast, facilitates the accurate alignment of rails and significantly reduces maintenance and hence line possessions. This form of track is most suitable for use in tunnels and on viaducts.

The first trial lengths were installed for experimental purposes at Radcliffe-on-Trent, near Nottingham, in 1969, and at Duffield, north of Derby, in 1972. In 1975 urgent work had to be undertaken in Mountfield Tunnel, near Robertsbridge, between Tunbridge Wells and Hastings on the Southern Region, to prevent further deterioration of the formation and the footings of the tunnel. The geological conditions were such that it would have been unwise to remove the support to the tunnel walls by digging beneath the tracks. To overcome the problems a slab track was provided through the tunnel, laid on a reinforced concrete base which was extended up to the tunnel walls to provide cross strutting. A length of slab track was also installed on part of the new electric main line in Glasgow in 1974, to facilitate the provision of electrical clearances in the Eglinton Street tunnels. As part of the Greater Glasgow PTE scheme, the former Glasgow Central Low Level line – now the Argyle Line – most of which is in tunnel, has been reinstated. The track is of paved construction in the tunnels, only the approaches from Rutherglen and Partick Hill being normal sleepered track. Slab track is also being installed on about 1¼ miles of track where the Bedford–Moorgate line passes underneath St Pancras station and the LT Circle Line.

The concrete slabs laid at Radcliffe were cast using an adapted slip-form paver, as used in the construction of roads. The trials there proved the feasibility of the concept and the ability to achieve the right degree of accuracy of track surface. A special paving machine was then designed by Messrs Robert McGregor and Sons Ltd, to fit the BR structure gauge, and was delivered late in 1970. Further trials were conducted at Radcliffe in 1971, laying in curved track and switch and crossing layouts. The trial length at Duffield (1·8 miles) was laid in a main line for test under higher speed conditions.

With rising speeds, the need to provide and preserve a very high quality of alignment and top level, with minimum interference to train operation, for maintenance purposes, is urgent. Slab track fulfils this need, but the high cost of installation, even taking into account the low maintenance costs subsequently incurred, does not justify the general provision of slab track at present. There is also the problem of the long possessions which are needed for the concrete to set and develop strength.

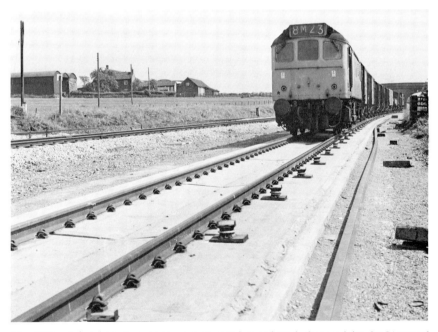

Fig. 9.14 A freight train entering experimental paved track designed for the Liverpool Underground scheme, laid on the Radcliffe-on-Trent test line, in 1972. Supports for conductor rail can be seen alongside the line.

Fig. 9.15   The special paving machine, designed for the BR structure gauge, at work on the laying of slab track at the entrance to Mountfield Tunnel, Southern Region, 1975 (BRB)

Asphalt offers a major advantage over concrete as a base for ballastless track construction in being available for traffic immediately after laying and rolling, without the need for the hardening time associated with concrete. Material costs are, however, higher and some form of precast construction is necessary to carry the rails. Nevertheless, test lengths were installed at Radcliffe in 1974 and at the approach to West Street Tunnel in Glasgow – within which slab track was laid – in 1975. Performance of these trial lengths has been satisfactory but, again, cost, and the problems involved in handling large quantities of asphalt in tunnels, is an obstacle to universal adoption.

Chapter Seven referred to the inter-departmental collaboration which is essential to the planning and execution of an electrification project. With overhead electrification, the civil engineer is primarily concerned with four aspects:

(a) Alterations to the track to suit the new service and to improve operation by remodelling junctions, building flyovers or burrowing junctions, re-aligning curves to ease speed restrictions, and simplifying layout by removing redundant sidings and connections.

(b) Design and supervision of construction or modernization of stations, maintenance depots, power supply control rooms, and other buildings.

(c) Alterations to, or reconstruction of, bridges and other lineside structures to obtain the mandatory electrical clearances from live overhead equipment. In this context, it is the railway overbridge which presents the greatest difficulty in obtaining clearance. The usual methods employed are the raising or reconstruction of the bridge deck, the lowering or slewing of track inside arches, or a combination of the two. Whether overhead clearance is obtained by lifting the existing superstructure or lowering the tracks, or by reconstruction, depends upon the type and condition of the existing bridge and the nature of any track improvements involved. Many bridges with flat decks would be lifted, unless their condition was such that they would in any event require to be reconstructed within the next ten years, and unless the road profile over the raised bridge would be worsened to an extent which would be unacceptable to the Highway Authority, in which case a new deck of reduced construction depth might be provided. A significant part of the cost involved can be in alterations to services – water, gas, electricity – carried by the bridge. Where the clearance at an arch bridge has to be improved, there is very little alternative to demolition of the arch.

(d) Approval of design of overhead structures: design and erection, jointly with the CM & EE, of such structures on bridges, on viaducts, and in tunnels.

Third-rail electrification projects present the civil engineer with a somewhat more straightforward task, although there is still the need to secure that track layouts meet likely future operational requirements and that formation and track can withstand the new form of service. If the current collector shoes on the trains are too close to the girders, some steel underbridges may have to be modified, but the civil engineer is spared the extensive bridgeworks involved in overhead electrification. On the other hand, the erection of more lineside substations is involved and additional refuges have to be provided in tunnels for the safety of men working on the track. The civil engineer is also responsible for the installation and subsequent maintenance, to the CM & EE's requirements, of the conductor rail.

This brief description of the main functions of the civil engineer in relation to electrification projects applies generally to all such schemes. Most schemes, however, involve especially big tasks, or encounter particular problems, within the broad roles outlined. Some of those met with in past schemes are referred to below.

The Liverpool Street–Shenfield electrification involved lengthening three large bridges in the immediate vicinity of Liverpool Street and extensive alterations in track layout at Liverpool Street station itself.

Station reconstructions included the provision of surface platforms for interchange of traffic with the London Transport Central Line at Stratford. A flyover was built near Ilford to take the suburban lines over the main lines and a new single line was provided for two-way working between Bow Junction and Stratford.

On the Wath–Dunford Bridge section of the MSW electrification a new problem arose in the design and erection of overhead equipment structures. For about 11 miles of the route the tracks are laid on ground which is liable to subsidence owing to colliery workings. Provision had therefore to be made in the designs for future subsidence and the problem was overcome by providing adjustable structures, enabling the overhead equipment to be raised, as tracks were raised following subsidence, in order to maintain the correct wire height. The major civil engineering tasks on this route were, however, the construction of a double line tunnel at Woodhead and a single line tunnel at Thurgoland. Traffic passed through the Pennines, between Woodhead and Dunford Bridge, via two single line tunnels, 3 miles 22 yards long. The first of these was completed in 1845 and soon proved to be a bottleneck. The second was opened in 1852, connected with the first by 25 manholes. Both tunnels were stone lined and built on an incline rising towards Dunford Bridge of 1 in 200. The proposals for the electrification of the MSW line pre-supposed that the two single line tunnels would be renovated for use by the new services but the rate of deterioration of the tunnels, chiefly because of the disappearance of the mortar from the joints in the stone lining, combined with the heavy steam-hauled traffic then passing, made it impracticable for the engineers to keep pace with the repairs during weekend possessions of the line, which were all that could be granted at that stage. The position was such that in 1946 it was decided to give the engineers absolute possession of each tunnel in turn over a period of nine months, so that repair work could be pursued continuously, day and night, thus necessitating single line working through one tunnel and the diversion of a heavy volume of traffic via other routes. In the event, even this generous possession was inadequate for the necessary repairs to be encompassed and as further operating disturbance could not be tolerated it was inevitable that a new tunnel should be built and the old ones abandoned.

Three different schemes were investigated – the construction of one new single line tunnel and repair of one of the existing; two new single line tunnels; and a new double line tunnel. In terms of cost, the proposed new double line tunnel was the cheapest and a recommendation to that effect was approved by the LNER Board, Parliamentary Powers being obtained in the LNER Act of 1947. The new tunnel, the longest on a main-line railway to be constructed in Britain in the twentieth century, was started in February 1949 and completed in 1953. It is of double line arch construction, concrete lined, and is 3 miles 66 yards long, with a maximum width of 27 ft. It was planned to rise at 1 in 129 from the Woodhead end for about two miles and then fall towards Dunford Bridge at 1 in 1186, to permit two loose-coupled trains in the tunnel at the same time, and with a parabolic curve 800 ft long at the summit. The works involved remodelling the approach tracks at both ends, the construction of new platforms and station buildings at both Woodhead and Dunford Bridge, two new signalboxes, a new overline bridge at Dunford Bridge, a new underline bridge at Woodhead and the replacement of houses which the new line of route, slightly to the south of the old tunnels, caused to be demolished.

A pilot tunnel was first driven (completed in May 1951) and then opened out, steel arches being inserted two feet or so apart, where necessary to support wet shale. Rock was loosened by blasting and the broken rocks loaded into skips which were moved out of the tunnel on narrow gauge track and tipped into road vehicles for depositing at selected places on the moors. For the concrete lining, mobile steel moulds were built up and concrete pumped between the moulds and the rock face to give at least 21 inches thickness. The steel supporting arches were left in. The construction of the tunnel was completed in October 1953.

The other new tunnel, at Thurgoland, between Wortley and Penistone, was a less challenging task. It was an essential preliminary to the electrification of the line, due to the impossibility of obtaining sufficient clearance in the existing double line tunnel for overhead equipment for two tracks.

Fig. 9.16 Woodhead Tunnel: The Dunford Bridge portal, showing the structure supporting the overhead equipment (BRB)

A project to open out the tunnel was too costly and it was therefore decided to drive a separate tunnel for the down line, converting the existing tunnel for single line working in the up direction. The new tunnel, constructed on a 40 chain curve, is through hard sandstone, with thin layers of shale extending into it from above. To support any unstable areas ribs of old rails and steel plating were inserted under the concrete lining. The tunnel was driven from each portal. The headings met on 9 January 1948 and the tunnel was opened to traffic on 3 October of that year.

On the severely graded Worsborough Branch two masonry arch bridges had to be replaced. They were rebuilt with prestressed concrete beams. As considerable subsidence was to be expected in the area, the bridges were so designed that their superstructures could be jacked up to a new level when required, jacking pockets being left in each masonry abutment.

On the London–Tilbury–Southend line a number of major tasks were involved in the period 1957–62. One was the construction of a new flyover near Barking to carry boat trains between Tilbury and St Pancras and the heavy and growing freight traffic to and from North Thames-side. This work, which was completed in January 1959, involved the building of a structure a quarter-mile in length, with a gradient of 1 in 80, on land made available by temporary diversion of the running lines. A second task was the construction of a dive-under below the main lines just east of Barking station and a second flyover just west of the station to carry the west-bound District Line service, thus permitting cross-platform exchange for the very large number of passengers who daily change trains at Barking. This part of the work was finished at the end of 1959 and eliminated heavily used level crossings at the east end of the station. Other works included the erection of a signalbox; the reconstruction of the station buildings, at both street and platform level; the construction of two new underline bridges; and the provision of new sidings for District Line trains. These works were accomplished without inter-

Fig. 9.17   Barking Flyover, completed in 1959, to carry boat trains and freight traffic over the suburban lines to be electrified (BRB)

ference with traffic operations, mainly by careful staging to permit of the maximum advantage being taken of night and weekend possessions.

The major civil engineering features of the GN suburban electrification, completed in 1978, were the construction of a flyover at Welwyn Garden City and the renewal of a flyover at Holloway. The track was lowered through several tunnels to obtain the necessary clearances. Practically all switch and crossing work was renewed and the track was substantially realigned for 125 miles/h running. The tracks in the two single line, sharply curved tunnels from Drayton Park to Moorgate were completely relaid and reballasted.

At King's Cross a new circulating area and travel centre were provided, with new interchange facilities with London Transport lines. The track layout in the station and its approaches were remodelled, the outer suburban services being concentrated on the west side, via a flyover. The work in the station area was complicated by the very restricted space between the ends of the new platforms and the entrances to adjacent tunnels and by the existence of the Regent's Canal cast iron aqueduct. A high proportion of specially designed trackwork was necessary. A particular task was the replacement of the train shed roof, which consisted of two arches, each spanning four platform lines. These arches, when constructed, were the largest in the world.

Civil Engineering for the electrification of the LM Region main lines from Euston was directed by R. L. McIlmoyle, Assistant Civil Engineer, and in-

Fig. 9.18   The honeycomb structure embankment at Elton, designed to facilitate dealing with an abnormal rate of subsidence (BRB)

volved the strengthening of the road bed by deep ballasting, improvements in drainage, and the realignment of curves, to permit of 100 miles/h running; the transposition of tracks between Armitage, Rugeley, and Colwich; the remodelling of the junctions at Colwich and Norton Bridge; the construction of a diversion and new tunnel at Kidsgrove; and the reconstruction or raising of over 700 bridges, including nine spans of a twelve-span road bridge at Crewe. Additionally, some 1400 yards of tunnel, in a number of locations, had to be opened out or enlarged to provide clearances. An unusual task was involved with the Elton Viaduct over the River Wheelock, three miles east of Crewe, which suffered from the effects of brine extraction from the ground, causing an abnormal rate of subsidence. Some 20 years earlier all the spans but one had been removed and replaced by an embankment but the remaining span needed to be attended to in the course of the electrification works. An ingenious way of solving this problem was devised, as an alternative to lifting the bridge every few years. An embankment constructed of reinforced concrete pipes, five feet in diameter, and placed in layers to form a honeycomb structure, was built to replace the bridge span. The old bridge sank at a rate of eight inches a year and the intention is that a new layer of pipes will be added every seven years or so to compensate for the subsidence of the new embankment.

Other major tasks on the Manchester, Liverpool, and Birmingham routes were the demolition and reconstruction of stations, including

Fig. 9.19   The entrance to Coventry Station, before reconstruction (BRB)

Fig. 9.20   The new Coventry Station, by night, reconstructed during the
electrification of the lines out of Euston (BRB)

Euston, Manchester Piccadilly, and Birmingham New Street. The rebuilding of Euston station had been under 'active' consideration for
more than 50 years before the work was finally approved. The station was
completely reconstructed between 1962 and 1969, with a new track layout
in the station and its approaches, longer platforms, a larger concourse
with improved passenger facilities, and a multi-storey underground car
park. Building operations were made particularly difficult by the existence of the London Transport underground station, the foundations of
existing and previous buildings, and underground services and piping.
The reconstruction unfortunately involved the demolition of the famous
Doric Arch at the station entrance (built in 1837) and Hardwick's equally
well-known Great Hall (built 1846) which formed part of the original L &
NWR offices. With the reconstruction, it was intended to build offices
over the station for letting but planning permission was refused as a result
of the prohibition then in force on the erection of new office accommodation in London. It was not until 1977 that a change in public policy made it
possible to begin the erection of office accommodation in front of the
station.

Manchester Piccadilly station, formerly London Road, was originally
constructed piecemeal by three separate railways – L & NW, Manchester, Sheffield and Lincolnshire (MS & L), and MSJ & A. It was
completely rebuilt in 1960 in association with 50-cycle a.c. electrification.

Fig. 9.21 · An aerial view of the approaches to the rebuilt Euston Station (BRB)

There were some complications, due to two d.c. electric services – MSW and MSJ & A – also using the station. These were overcome by terminating the MSJ & A services at Oxford Road station. Extensive track works outside the new station were necessary and a considerable amount of heavy bridge works was also involved. The associated reconstruction works at Manchester Oxford Road station, in 1960, included the first, and so far the only, major laminated roof timbering on British Railways.

Birmingham New Street station was completely reconstructed in 1965 to accommodate the new electric services and the Western Region trains which formerly ran into Snow Hill station. A co-operative scheme was evolved by BR, Birmingham Corporation, and a development consortium, to provide for shops, offices, and entertainments on a 7½-acre concrete slab over the station. A major civil engineering task was the partial reconstruction of a four-span bridge over the tracks.

The Weaver Junction–Glasgow electrification involved considerable work in bridge reconstruction to permit realignment of the track to accommodate higher speeds and to provide increased clearances. Extensive track rearrangements were necessary between Gushetfaulds, Polmadie, and Rutherglen. An unusual task was the reconstruction of the aqueduct, just north of Weaver Junction, taking the Duke of

Bridgewater's Canal over the railway. The centre pier of the aqueduct was removed to facilitate the slewing of the track and the canal width was reduced from 40 ft to 20 ft. The canal had to be kept open for traffic during the reconstruction and the new aqueduct was constructed over the part of the canal which was to remain and lowered into position on previously prepared bored piles.

In order to permit increased track possessions on this route, a number of ground-worked facing crossovers were installed, so that traffic could be diverted from one track to the other. Many of these were subsequently removed but some still remain, properly signalled, to facilitate maintenance work.

The Glasgow suburban electrifications presented relatively few troublesome civil engineering problems, the most difficult task being the Newton Street tunnel on the Glasgow–Gourock line, where both rock excavation and tunnel relining were required to provide the requisite clearances.

The Kent electrification involved a large range of track improvements and widenings, the enlargement and redesign of strategic junctions, platform extensions, and the laying of some 160 miles of conductor rail. Large-scale track renewals in CWR were carried out before the electrification of the Waterloo–Bournemouth route and considerable work was also involved in alterations to stations. For the first time in any such project network analysis and critical path scheduling techniques were used to interweave the activities of the various engineering disciplines into an intricate but efficient plan.

Over the years, the problems faced by civil engineers in the punctual execution of works directly involved in an electrification project, and in associated rationalization works, have become increasingly difficult. Every facet of the work has been subject to internal scrutiny, to ensure that only essential work is carried out, whilst at the same time the engineers have been urged to achieve completion as early as practicable, to secure as rapidly as possible a return on the investment involved. The closure of alternative routes has made it impracticable, in many cases, to divert trains, to permit of the granting of longer track possessions, and the elimination of loops and sidings has meant that it has not always been possible to stable works trains near the scene of operations. At the same time, a declining locomotive stock has meant that fewer locomotives have been available for works trains. The reduction in the number of motive power depots has meant that fewer high capacity breakdown cranes have been available for heavy civil engineering lifts, and those which have been obtainable have probably had to travel longer distances to site. The reductions in, and shortages of, manpower has made the manning of works trains, and the provision of look-out men, more difficult, quite apart from the effect which shortages of qualified technical staff has had upon the planning of projects.

Road improvement schemes – for example, the widening of bridges – increase the civil engineering work-load when electrification projects are in progress. Local Authorities are always consulted when such works are contemplated and delay is liable to be imported into what is in any case usually a very tight programme.

The Modernization Plan referred to the need to eliminate permanent speed restrictions and improve the track to facilitate main-line speeds of 'at least 100 m.p.h.', where conditions permitted. Since then, schemes for improving a number of the main lines have been carried out, not merely to fulfil the promise of the Modernization Plan but, beyond that, to permit of the operation of the 125 miles/h High Speed Trains.

On the East Coast main line, works undertaken since the late 1950s have included the remodelling of the layout at King's Cross, Newark, Doncaster, Durham, and Berwick; the realignment of track to ease curves at a number of intermediate points; the rationalization of point and crossing work in the vicinity of Grantham and the rebuilding of platforms on a new alignment to permit 100 miles/h running through the station. An additional running line over a five-mile section between Pilmoor and Alne, north of York, has been provided and a diversion in cutting at Newton Hall, near Durham, has raised a speed restriction from 55 miles/h to 85 miles/h. The cutting for the new alignment, completed in 1970, was excavated some years earlier, in readiness for the diversion, the spoil being used to raise the level in the new Tyne Yard, constructed in 1959–60.

Fig. 9.22   The flat crossing at Retford, before the dive-under was constructed to eliminate conflicting movements (BRB)

Fig. 9.23   Work nearing completion on the line taking the Manchester–Sheffield–
Lincolnshire route beneath the East Coast main lines at Retford, looking west
and showing the new platforms (BRB)

Track widening between New Barnet and Potters Bar, involving the construction of three new tunnels, of an aggregate length of one mile, was carried out in 1958–9, in order to increase line capacity. The construction of the new tunnels was relatively straightforward, the main claim to recognition being that they were the first BR tunnels to be built with precast concrete segments. Sharp curves alongside the River Ouse at Offord, south of Huntingdon, have been eliminated to permit of 100 miles/h running. The track was slewed up to 40 ft, involving building out the embankment into the river.

Peterborough station has been reconstructed. In 1973 the reverse curves through the station were straightened out, the previous speed restriction of 20 miles/h being raised to 105 miles/h. Conflicting running facilities through the station which, combined with the speed limit, caused East Coast expresses several minutes extra time on each run, were completely eliminated. Later stages of the work have included the replacement of temporary station buildings by a large covered concourse, travel centre, modernized passenger facilities, and new administrative offices.

At Retford, in 1965, a new dive-under was constructed to eliminate the flat crossing of the East Coast main line and the Manchester–Sheffield–Lincolnshire line, which had always been a source of delay, particularly to trains on the latter route. Later, the East Coast tracks through the main-line station were realigned for high-speed running and a new down side platform was provided.

Two other developments affecting the East Coast main line are not directly related to its modernization to permit of high-speed running. Reference has already been made, in Chapter Eight, to the adoption of the international standard 8 ft 6 in maritime container. Inability to convey these containers over the East Coast route, owing to loading gauge restrictions, inhibited Freightliners from participating to the fullest extent possible in import/export container traffic. This difficulty has been over-come by lowering the tracks in two tunnels, to give the necessary clearance: at Stoke, five miles south of Grantham, 880 yards long, and at Peascliffe, three miles north of Grantham, 967 yards long. Work on these two tunnels started in September 1978 and was completed early in 1979. It was the original intention similarly to lower the tracks in the 267 yard Penmanshiel tunnel, between Berwick and Dunbar. Work on this started in January 1979 but collapse of part of the tunnel roof during the course of the work led to the tunnel being abandoned and a diversion being constructed round it. The diversion, 2½ miles long, which involved a very large amount of rock excavation (250 000 cubic yards) was completed in August 1979, five months after the accident and six weeks ahead of schedule, a very considerable achievement and a credit to all concerned.

The development of the new Selby coalfield involves the diversion of a stretch of the East Coast main line in the Selby area – the first major

Fig. 9.24　The approach to Paddington Station prior to remodelling in 1967, in connection with the installation of multiple-aspect signalling (BRB)

length of double-track main-line railway to be built this century. This is necessary to enable the National Coal Board to extract a thick seam of coal from beneath the existing line, an operation which would cause serious subsidences and drainage problems. It will be of 125 miles/h standard and must be completed by the time NCB operations reach the existing route, which is expected to be in the early 1980s. The proposed fourteen-mile diversion will leave the present route at Temple Hirst (five miles south of Selby), running north-west to cross and connect with the Leeds–Selby–Hull line at Hambleton. The new route then turns north to join the York–Leeds–Sheffield line near Colton (six miles south-west of York). An advanced type of laser-based surveying instrument is being used by the engineers planning the route – the first of its kind to be used on railway work in the United Kingdom. The instrument combines a one-second theodolite and a 3200 yard distance meter, both connected to a microprocessor which controls the measurements and calculates the results. Readings relative to slope, horizontal distance, and horizontal and vertical angles are electronically recorded, converted to punched paper-tape form and fed into the computer for the automatic production of drawings.

In the 1960s/early 1970s the Western Region carried out a number of projects to remodel and rationalize track layout, with major blanketing and drainage schemes, coincident with the introduction of multiple-aspect signalling or station alterations. Major track alterations at Padding-

Fig. 9.25   The remodelled layout at Paddington, showing the LTE lines segregated on the right hand side (BRB)

ton, in the early 1930s, had provided for what were virtually two separate stations. Platforms 1 to 4 could be used for departures only and platforms 7 to 11 for arrivals only, platforms 5 and 6 being the only ones signalled for two-way working. Platforms 13 to 16 were used for suburban services and were shared with LTE trains. In the late 1960s a major scheme for resignalling the eleven miles from Paddington to Hayes gave the opportunity to carry out a complete remodelling of the track layout at Old Oak Common and the approaches to Paddington, to provide for in and out working to all platforms, an additional relief line out of Paddington station, complete segregation of the LTE lines, simplification of switch and crossing work in cast manganese on Jarrah timbers and the raising of the speed restriction between Paddington and Royal Oak from 10 miles/h to 25 miles/h.

In the 1960s a flyover was erected and the main lines between Newport and Magor remodelled, placing the relief lines to the south of the main lines so that coal and iron ore trains could approach the Spencer steelworks from Newport without having to cross the latter. The east and west approaches to Newport station were simplified. Track and station layout alterations were made at Swindon in 1966–8, involving the closure of the down side island platform, the lengthening of the up side island platform and the construction of a bay line platform at the west end for use by diesel multiple unit services to and from Gloucester. The track layout, allowing for two-way working in the station area, was among the first in Britain to utilize the new range of vertical 4 ft 8⅜ in FB switches and crossings. The permissible speed over the main lines at Swindon was later increased from 90 to 100 miles/h.

In 1969–72 a major rationalization and development scheme was carried out in the Bristol area. The former Midland route from Westerleigh Junction to Bristol was closed and the track layout at Temple Meads station remodelled. A new station was built at Bristol Parkway, six miles from Temple Meads, to provide Inter-City passengers with extensive car parking facilities, which could not be provided in Bristol itself.

It was decided in 1972 to replace the two Gloucester stations – Central and Eastgate – by a single station on the former site. This scheme had advantages in so far as accessibility to shopping areas, the elimination of heavily used level crossings, and the release of land for development were concerned. It does, however, involve all Bristol–Birmingham trains which call at Gloucester reversing in the new station.

Prior to the introduction of the 125 miles/h HSTs on the Western Region main lines from Paddington to Bristol and South Wales, a number of other alterations were carried out to track layout and alignment. Later, in 1978, as part of the Reading to Westbury multiple-aspect signalling scheme, the layout at Newbury was remodelled and the tracks east of the station were slewed and relaid.

Works which have been carried out in Scotland include new facilities to permit the closure of Princes Street station in Edinburgh and St Enoch and Buchanan Street stations in Glasgow. Double track has been restored between Blair Atholl and Dalwhinnie and passing loops provided on the Highland Line between Stanley Junction and Inverness, to cater for increased traffic arising from the exploitation of North Sea oil.

Since nationalization, many stations have been either completely reconstructed or modernized, or have received 'face lifts' of varying extent, incorporating, where appropriate, the re-equipment of public rooms, the redesign of inquiry offices, and improved booking halls and circulating areas. Some of the major station reconstruction projects have already been described. Space does not permit of reference to many others but perhaps mention should be made of two particular projects and of the reconstruction of Southern Region terminal stations in London.

At Bradford, the old Exchange station was a ten-platform terminal station. Trains entering the station passed under a bridge which carried a main road on a large single steel span. South of the bridge, at a lower level, was the old Bridge Street Goods Depot, which had been closed and sold to Bradford Corporation. A scheme for a bus/rail interchange station was developed jointly by BR and the Corporation and implemented in 1972–5. Under this scheme, the station has been reduced to four platforms, the bridge replaced by an embankment and a new bus depot built on the site of the goods depot.

In the early 1970s it was decided to establish a new International Exhibition Centre near Birmingham. To serve the new Centre, and Birmingham Airport, a new station – Birmingham International – was built, 8½ miles from Birmingham New Street and was opened in January 1977. The five platforms are connected by stairs and escalators to the main station concourse, whence a footbridge leads directly to the central area of the Exhibition Centre.

Since the Second World War, a number of the London termini of the Southern Region have been extensively reconstructed. The first of these was Holborn in 1958. The old buildings were entirely demolished and a new booking office and public facilities constructed, with a high-rise block of office accommodation above.

During the war, the glass was removed from the famous high arched roof of Cannon Street station, resulting in the unprotected ironwork becoming badly corroded. Between April 1958 and January 1959 this was taken down, in itself a major engineering feat. In 1960–65 the old office building over the entrance was demolished and new multi-storey offices were built over modern passenger facilities. The platforms were lengthened as much as the proximity of the bridge over the River Thames would allow. The station was closed for five weeks in 1973–4 for extensive alterations to the track layout. It is interesting to note that the planning for the major reconstruction in the 1960s included a car park and a helicopter station on the new roof, but both ideas were dropped. The car park project proved to be too expensive and the high chimney stack of Bankside power station was too near for the helicopter scheme to be adopted. Part of the roof of the new station was, however, built to the required strength before the schemes were finally withdrawn.

The next station to be reconstructed was Blackfriars, in 1973–7. The station was completely rebuilt, with improved passenger facilities, better interchange arrangements with LTE, and office accommodation for rental. The office block scheme is the only one of its kind to be financed and managed by BR. The reconstruction involved the removal of one, the repair of another, and the rebuilding of three of the five bridges serving the area. The rebuilt bridges included the main railway bridge over Queen Victoria Street and the viaduct which supports the station platforms over other streets. The section of the office block over the LTE lines has been supported on rubber bridge bearings to lessen the vibration from trains. Virtually the only reminders of the former station are the engraved stones which adorned the entrances to the old station, showing fifty-four towns and cities – including Berlin, Marseilles, St Petersburg, and other overseas destinations – which could be reached by train from Blackfriars. These stones now ornament the walls of the new concourse.

There have been two separate schemes to ease operational problems and at the same time provide modern passenger facilities at London Bridge. The first, started in 1972 and completed in 1976, involved extensive track alterations over about 150 single track miles to eliminate a notorious bottleneck at Borough Market Junction. A new flyover and high-speed crossover between Hither Green and St Johns enables trains serving Charing Cross and Cannon Street to be segregated. A new power signalbox has been provided. The second scheme, formally opened in December 1978, has involved the complete reconstruction of the station itself. The main buildings were destroyed during the 1940–41 blitz and had not been replaced. A rebuilding scheme was prepared in the 1950s, incorporating a sky-scraper office block but planning permission was forestalled by a private development nearby. The project now carried out is a modification of the earlier proposals and includes the roofing over of the adjacent bus terminal.

A major programme of improvements at Victoria is now well in hand, for completion about 1985. It includes considerable track relaying, in association with the resignalling scheme referred to in Chapter Ten, and an enlarged concourse, with improved passenger amenities, including a new travel centre for Continental passengers.

In the Scottish Region, the track layout at Edinburgh Waverley was considerably simplified and platform lengths and widths modified in 1978, during a major resignalling scheme.

The railways of Britain have reached an age when an increasing number of the bridges have had to be extensively repaired or rebuilt to

Fig. 9.26 Aerial views of Cannon Street Station, before and after reconstruction (Aerofilms Ltd)

meet modern conditions of speed, loading, and service frequency. This factor, combined with the raising or reconstruction of bridges to provide clearances for overhead electric wires, has meant that in recent years there has been a heavy programme of bridgeworks to undertake.

Railway bridge engineers have over the years amassed a considerable fund of knowledge of the cost and behaviour in service of the various designs of bridges and of the materials used in their construction and international collaboration has been helpful in this context. Routines have been developed for the inspection and safety assessment of bridges and procedures evolved for repair or renewal, with minimum interference with traffic.

To assist in encompassing the additional work which has arisen in relation to bridges in recent years, a constant watch has been kept on the development of techniques and practices for the repair or replacement of existing bridges and the erection of new bridges. More modern instruments and methods of measuring stresses in structures are available than in the past. Decisions can thus be taken more rapidly as to whether repair or reconstruction is necessary. Stresses in bridges can be measured by vibrating wire strain gauges or displacement transducers feeding information in digital form direct to computing equipment; laser beams can be used for movement detection within fine limits; and overall structure displacement can be detected by photogrammetry.

The building or rebuilding of railway bridges involves different considerations from those relating to the building of other bridges. Heavy and frequent rail traffic can rarely be diverted for any appreciable length of time and commercial considerations dictate that it be interrupted or delayed to the minimum possible extent; a closure of an alternative route leads to more intensive traffic on remaining lines, so the number and lengths of possessions must be reduced and speed restrictions minimized; problems arise from electrification (particularly by the overhead system), high speeds, and heavier axle loads; and environmental considerations inhibit noisy operations such as pile driving, especially at night. The result is that the design of a bridge is very largely dictated by acceptable ways of construction in the site conditions prevailing.

In cases where the structure carrying the railway is the only part requiring renewal this is usually carried out on the old abutments, unless the Local Authority requires to widen the road underneath. In the latter circumstances, new abutments are built in deep trenches behind the old ones, the track being carried over the excavations on temporary joists. Subsequently, the old structure is removed, usually by cutting it up with oxy-acetylene torches into suitable pieces for lifting out by crane, and the new one is put in by crane or, more frequently, rolled in on trestles after erection alongside the line.

The extension of the national motorway programme has involved the construction of a number of new bridges, over and under the railway,

Fig. 9.27 Rolling in the Clacton dive-under bridge, Ardleigh, 28 May 1961. The 1200 yard long dive-under enables down Clacton line trains to run on to the branch without interference with main-line trains (BRB)

some of steel, others of reinforced or prestressed concrete. Design varies according to site conditions. For overline bridges, the excavation and piling for the abutments are kept far enough back from the track to avoid the imposition of speed restrictions and the superstructure is lifted in by crane. When under the line, the method employed is usually similar to that referred to above for the replacement of an old bridge on widened abutments and a speed restriction can rarely be avoided.

Some examples of bridgeworks which have involved special features may be of interest.

Kingsferry Bridge is situated about four miles from Sittingbourne, Southern Region, and provides the only rail and road access over the River Swale to the Isle of Sheppey. The present bridge was opened in 1960 and replaced a Sherzer rolling lift bridge built about the turn of the century. The old structure was particularly susceptible to damage by shipping, resulting in frequent closure for repairs. The new bridge has a span which remains horizontal whilst being lifted at the towers at each end. In 1½ minutes, a clear height of 95 ft above high water level can be given. The lift span is 125 ft long and 50 ft wide, to allow a single line of railway and two lines of road traffic. When the bridge is lowered after having been open to river traffic, the action of locking it in position with electrically operated bolts reconnects the signalling circuits and the return traction current path via the running rails. Flashing lights are provided for the control of road traffic. Overall control is from a permanently manned

Fig. 9.28   The reconstructed Grosvenor Bridge, over the River Thames,
from the upstream side (BRB)

cabin in one of the towers, with radio and telephone contacts to ship and shore. The two main piers are connected by a service tunnel beneath the river, containing all railway and statutory services.

The Grosvenor Bridge over the River Thames, carrying all trains to and from Victoria station, comprised three separate structures, built side by side in 1859, 1865, and 1901. With the increase in weight and frequency of trains, maintenance became extremely costly and in 1958 it was decided to renew the bridge. Normal traffic had to be kept moving all the time. Fortunately there was a clear width right across the bridge where, many years previously, there had been a platform for Grosvenor Road station and this space was used to accommodate a track. The new structure, 910 ft long, was therefore designed so that the steelwork for one line could be erected for the whole length of the bridge, whilst adjacent tracks were moved sideways, making use of the spare space. Thus the full service of trains was kept running. As the structure for one line was finished, the adjacent track was moved on to it, so enabling the next stage of the steelwork to be erected. The old bridge had a flat steel deck but the new tracks are ballasted. This added to the weight and the river piers had therefore to be underpinned. Whilst the work was in progress, two navigation spans were kept open for the Port of London Authority. A service girder, 220 ft long, positioned a few feet above rail level, was used to support the old arches whilst they were cut up for removal. New half-arches, assembled at a site down-stream, were floated up to the bridge and lifted into position by the service girder. For the four river spans, 44 arch girders were erected. The work was started in May 1963 and completed by the end of 1967.

The Britannia Bridge over the Menai Straits between the Welsh mainland and Anglesey was built in 1850 by Robert Stephenson and carried the Irish mail service to Holyhead. It consisted of two rectangular tubes of wrought iron, with a wooden decking over each tube to protect the metal from the heat of the sun in summer. On 23 May 1970 tarred wood inside one of the tubes was set on fire by two young trespassers on the railway and the tubes were damaged so severely that the bridge had to be closed

Fig. 9.29   The Britannia Bridge, over the Menai Straits, before the fire (BRB)

Fig. 9.30   The reconstructed Britannia Bridge, before the top
deck roadway was added (BRB)

Fig. 9.31   The new Britannia Bridge, with the top deck roadway completed (BRB)

to traffic and rebuilt. A new bridge, of lattice steel arch construction, has been built. At the request of the Secretary of State for Wales, the design was strong enough to accommodate, at a later date, a three-lane roadway over the railway. The design was also such that the new structure could be used in dismantling the old ironwork. Work began on the bridge in September 1970 and it was reopened to rail traffic in January 1972. Work on the roadway over the bridge started in October 1977 and it was opened by HRH the Prince of Wales in July 1980.

In order to serve a new potash mine at Boulby in North Yorkshire, it was necessary to reinstate part of the former Saltburn–Whitby line between Skinningrove and Boulby. A major obstacle was the road crossing at Carlin How. As the original railway alignment was now occupied by the rebuilt coast road, the reinstated railway was forced by its new alignment to cross the road at an angle of 15°–20°. Construction of an embankment would have been both difficult and costly and it was decided to carry the single track railway on an eight-span viaduct, with a total length of 510 ft and a maximum height of 30 ft above ground. The two centre spans are each 74 ft long and the six side spans each 60 ft long.

The whole of this area of North-East Yorkshire is covered with boulder clay which, on the site of the bridge, was proved by boreholes to a depth of 100 ft below ground. 'Boulders' varying in size from inches to several feet and weighing up to ten tons occur in this material and two such were encountered during construction. For this and other reasons it was decided to use what was in 1970 a relatively novel form of construction. Large 6 ft diameter piles were bored, one supporting each pier, the pile continuing as a 5 ft 6 in diameter column above ground level to terminate in a cross-head supporting the superstructure of prestressed, pretensioned concrete beams. All the piers are of this form except for the centre pier, supporting the two 74 ft spans, of steel plate girder type. This centre pier consisted of two columns, on either side of the road, with a steel box girder cross-head spanning the road and supporting the superstructure. This method was adopted to overcome the problems caused by the very acute intersection angle. The bridge was designed to carry the standard railway loading and the principal traffic consists of 100-ton bogie hopper wagons. There is a speed limit of 30 miles/h, due primarily to the tight curves and steep gradients on the branch.

In 1975 it became necessary to renew the wrought-iron bridge over Beith Street, near Partick Hill, Glasgow. The situation was complicated by the fact that the Greater Glasgow PTE's Transclyde scheme was in progress at the time and this called for the resiting of Partick Hill station to form an interchange with the city underground. This in turn necessitated slewing a considerable length of track by about 27 ft, with the result that the new bridge could not be put in the exact position of the old. The slewing of the track and the installation of the new bridge had therefore to be programmed for the same weekend. Work on the bridge started in

November 1977, when the contractors began the construction of the new reinforced concrete abutments and wing walls on a foundation of concrete piles. In the spring of 1978 the steelwork for the bridge was brought to the scene, for assembly on four rail-mounted trestles to facilitate subsequently rolling into position. Concrete was poured in to form the floor, making a total weight, of steel and concrete, of 800 tons. On the Friday of the weekend for which the work was scheduled, the overhead wiring was isolated and slewed and the old bridge was demolished. By the Saturday afternoon it was possible to start to roll in the new bridge over the 90 ft gap between the abutments, using two electric winches with steel hawsers attached to the rail-mounted trestles. Inside 15 minutes, the bridge was poised directly above its final position, the structure was jacked up, the trestles rolled out, the jacks lowered and the bearings welded.

At Lyne, between Virginia Water and Chertsey, the M25 motorway passes under BR tracks at an angle of 28 degrees. An angle as sharp as this obviously introduces many undesirable complications in the design of a bridge and affects the method of erection. It was possible, however, in this case, to divert the existing line round the site. This enabled the new bridge to be built in its final position, with the result that rail traffic was interrupted on only two occasions, for the connection and disconnection of the deviation line. At the majority of sites, of course, this form of construction is seldom possible, as the extra working space is rarely available.

Fig. 9.32   The rail bridge over the proposed route of the M25 motorway, at Lyne. The pylons supporting the cables rise 72 feet above the edge beams (BRB)

A series of feasibility studies, of construction in steel and concrete and combinations of both these materials, was carried out before a decision was taken to adopt a prestressed concrete cable-stayed bridge, which was found to meet all the economic, aesthetic, and structural requirements. It is the first time in Europe that this type of bridge has been used for railway traffic. The structure, some 350 ft long, is founded on a thick layer of fine silty clay sand, which enables normal reinforced concrete spread footings to be adopted for both the abutments and the mid-support girders. From the deck, above these piers, rise two reinforced concrete towers, to which are anchored the upper and lower stay cables. The two main spans, continuous over the centre supports, are formed of prestressed concrete edge beams with a reinforced concrete deck between. The deviation line was constructed in 1976 and bridgeworks, started in April 1977, were completed in February 1979.

The twenty-one approach spans of the 405 yard curved Landore Viaduct over the River Tawe – two on the Neath side and nineteen on the Swansea side – were renewed in 1978–9. The spans, varying in length from 30 to 74 ft, consisted of wrought-iron plate girders, with timber decking beneath the tracks, and were replaced by steelwork. The main river span of 147 ft was redecked and strengthened in 1960 and did not require replacement, although some repairs were carried out to the steelwork. The two tracks were dealt with separately, trains in both directions using the remaining line in the meantime. All the major work was carried out whilst traffic was operating, the railway only being closed on Saturday nights/Sunday mornings to enable temporary girders to be inserted to strengthen the eastbound track while the other was demolished. The pier supporting the viaduct on the west side of the main Swansea–Neath road, which comprised masonry beneath the westbound line and steelwork beneath the eastbound line, had the steel supports replaced by reinforced concrete. The renewal of the viaduct enabled the speed restriction over it to be lifted from 20 to 40 miles/h, and made it suitable for the passage of the heaviest freight vehicles, which had previously been prohibited.

So far as tunnels are concerned, the railway civil engineer nowadays is chiefly involved in their maintenance. In many cases, the mortar between the bricks has deteriorated after well over a century of smoke from steam locomotives and the seepage of water containing injurious salts dissolved whilst percolating through the ground. Deep repointing or pressure grouting behind the brickwork is often sufficient, but sometimes the entire replacement of one or two rings of bricks is necessary. This work can only be done during a possession of the line, usually at night, and it is therefore a slow process. In a few tunnels, the foundations of the side walls are not sufficiently deep, so they tend to move inwards as a result of the pressure behind the walls. Cross-strutting beneath the track then becomes necessary and once again the work requires possession of the line.

In some cases, repair work would have been so extensive and the interruption of traffic so serious that tunnels with relatively shallow cover have been opened out, as in the case of Broomhouse tunnel between Chesterfield and Sheffield in 1968. The same method was considered for the Corbridge Tunnel between Newcastle and Carlisle, but a soil mechanics investigation showed that the tunnel would have become unusable during the earth removal process, and it was therefore decided to build a by-pass, which was completed in 1962.

In the 1950s, as part of the Modernization Plan, a large-scale programme of marshalling yard modernization and construction was carried out – an issue already referred to more fully in Chapter Eight. From the civil engineering point of view, the construction of marshalling yards is generally a big but fairly straightforward job, consisting mainly of earthworks and track laying, with some associated building work.

An unusual civil engineering task was the installation of a Travolator between the London Transport platforms at the Bank station and those of the Waterloo and City line, an underground railway operated by the Southern Region. Since 1898 this line has carried an increasingly large number of commuters during the morning and evening rush hours. At the city end there was a 300 ft long sloping tunnel between the platforms and the London Transport concourse to which it led. The upward traffic moved so slowly that the platforms were not clear by the time the next train arrived from Waterloo. In 1955 it was decided to instal travolators in a new sloping access tunnel. The rubber belt, which replaces the steps of an escalator, usually runs at 120 ft per minute along a gradient of 1 in 7 and

Fig. 9.33   The city platform end of the Waterloo and City Line travolator (BRB)

clears the platform before the arrival of the next train. In the morning peak, both strips of the travolator run up to the Bank station exit. In the evening, one strip runs each way. Over 20000 passengers are dealt with each way per day, concentrated in about 1½ hours in the morning and again in the evening. Work on the installation, including the excavation of the tunnel, and the provision of circulating space and machine rooms at either end, was completed in August 1960.

All the Regional Chief Civil Engineers are involved, to some extent, in work at ports and on sea defences. A considerable item in the civil engineering budget is for dock and harbour maintenance. Apart from dredging in certain of the harbours – a recurring commitment – most of the railway ports have been modernized to some degree or almost completely reconstructed since nationalization.

Civil engineering work at ports has included the construction of 'roll-on/roll-off' facilities for road vehicles. The first such installation was provided by the LMS at Stranraer in 1939. This has since been renewed and similar facilities have been provided at Newhaven, Parkeston Quay, Folkestone, and Fishguard. At the same time, passenger and freight

Fig. 9.34   'Roll-on/roll-off' facilities in use at Newhaven (BRB)

facilities have been modernized at the ports. At Dover, a new hoverport was brought into operation by the Harbour Board in 1978, the longest and most modern of its kind in the world. A direct rail link to the hoverport is being developed.

Experience both before and since nationalization has often demonstrated the need for the railways to provide adequate sea defence and flood prevention measures. A particularly difficult place is Folkestone Warren, an area of undercliff between Folkestone and Dover, two miles in length, which has for centuries been the scene of extensive landslides – and over which the railway pioneers built a line, opened in 1844. Since then, a number of slips has occurred. A serious landslide in 1915, when the greater part of the Warren was involved in a bodily movement towards the sea, caused the line to be closed until 1919. Further slips in 1937 and 1938 led to the initiation of a major investigation into causes and possible remedies, an investigation which was halted by the Second World War and not resumed until 1948. During the next two years, the general conditions of stability in the area were fully investigated. Geological evidence deduced from 25 test borings, coupled with comprehensive soil tests, enabled the pattern and effects of past landslides to be studied, and the likely benefits of various lines of remedial action assessed. The investigations showed that the major slip surface was on the Gault clay underlying the chalk cliffs, and in 1948 a programme of stabilization over this area was commenced, consisting of sea defence works, repairs to existing drainage headings, and the driving of one new heading.

The sea defence works, undertaken over the period 1948–56 included building two walls at right-angles to an existing sea wall, 200 ft long and 400 ft apart. A front wall with a stepped face was then constructed at the seaward end between the two walls to form an enclosed area, the walls being approximately 14 ft high and 12 ft wide. This area was filled with chalk excavated from the cliff adjacent to the railway line, from a position where it would improve stability. The filling after consolidation was protected by a concrete raft laid in slabs and suitably reinforced where necessary.

At a point one mile west of Whitstable, the London to Ramsgate line runs for about a quarter of a mile within 100 ft of the sea and some 20–30 ft above it. The railway is constructed on a sloping clay formation which has for many years been subject to slipping. Even before the First World War, some protective works had to be carried out, but they were largely demolished by high tides and gales in the later 1930s. From then until the Second World War a very close watch was kept on the condition of the sea wall, until the erection of beach defences by the military authorities made it impracticable to do so. In 1945, severe gales and high tides led to the sea breaking through the wall in five places over a distance of 200 yards. More damage occurred in 1946 and the decision was then taken to carry out permanent defence works, in advance of the existing line of the wall. Further along the same route, the East Coast floods in January 1953 broke through the sea wall, flooding an area stretching up to five miles inland. The railway was on an embankment, four or five feet high, a few hundred yards from the shore and the track and ballast were washed away for a length of over half a mile. The Kent Rivers Board, responsible for sea defences, by agreement with Campion, Chief Civil Engineer, Southern Region, immediately started to build a chalk embankment about 15 ft high on the seaward side of the railway to protect it and the grazing land beyond, until the slower work of permanent protection could be completed.

The same floods caused widespread damage on the other side of the Thames estuary to Eastern Region lines. Individual incidents were less serious but there were many more of them and careful organization was necessary to deal with them all with minimum interference to traffic. Considerable repairs had to be carried out to some station buildings. Some three years previously, serious floods had occurred further north along the east coast, in Northumberland, when severe rainstorms washed away track and destroyed seven bridges on the main line and feeder routes. On this occasion the East Coast main-line services were interrupted for some time.

The cancellation by the Government of the Channel Tunnel project in 1975 deprived the civil engineers of a challenging task which would have exercised all their ingenuity and experience. It would have been a wide-ranging task, involving the building of several miles of new high-speed railway, the construction of bridges and tunnels, and the erection of new terminal buildings.

The development of the plans for the tunnel, and the method of operation, are referred to more fully in Chapter Fourteen. So far as the civil engineering involvement was concerned, the final plans catered for two single line tunnels, with a service tunnel between them. The tunnel diameter was dictated by the requirement to carry lorries in covered wagons and was designed at 22·6 ft. The overall length of the tunnel, portal to portal, was 32 miles. The running tunnels were to be interconnected by ducts every 275 yards, allowing air to circulate round the trains, and by adits to the service tunnel at similar intervals. Approach gradients and curvature were specified to be suitable for speeds well in excess of 100 miles/h, although for capacity reasons this speed was unlikely to be exceeded. Track within the tunnel was to be CWR on concrete slab base. Final designs incorporated precast tunnel invert sections with longitudinal rail beams, cast in situ by slip-form paver, giving continuous rail support.

On the British side, BR were proposing to build a new railway, largely independent of existing Southern Region lines, from the London area to the tunnel terminal at Cheriton, Folkestone, suitable ultimately for speeds up to 185 miles/h, and capable of taking trains of the larger Continental gauge. British Railways' planning strategy, therefore, was concerned with providing additional route capacity suitable both for present speeds and future very high speed operation. Some 74 miles of new double track railway was involved, of which 31·5 miles would be on a new alignment, including 11 miles in tunnel. It was proposed to site the new London passenger terminal at White City, where there would be good connections with the Midlands, the North, and the West, and with the rest of London via the Underground railways.

These plans, however, were judged to be too elaborate in the financial climate then existing. This fact, combined with the environmental objections to the proposed new high-speed railway, caused this part of the project to be abandoned in November 1974. Two months later the British Government decided to withdraw from the entire Channel Tunnel project. Recently, however, new and modified plans for a tunnel have been developed and these are referred to in Chapter Fifteen.

Proposals for the high-speed railway which would have been required for serving a Third London Airport on largely reclaimed land at Maplin Sands were by no means as far advanced as those for the Channel Tunnel route, at the time these two projects were cancelled. The intention was to introduce a frequent service of high-speed trains to and from King's Cross, using a specially constructed route beyond the immediate environs of London and working into the various terminals of the airport. The opportunity may come again if the expansion of Stansted as the Third London Airport is eventually authorized.

Such is the story of civil engineering developments on British Railways since nationalization. It is a story of solid achievement in developing the permanent way to meet changes in forms of traction, in speeds of operation and in vehicle weights and to facilitate the signal engineering advances to which reference will be made in the next chapter; in the development of mechanical methods of assessing track conditions and of carrying out maintenance and renewals; in the provision of new stations; in bridge and tunnel construction and maintenance; in the modernization of port and harbour facilities; and in resisting the encroachment of the sea upon the railway. Outstanding above all else, however, is the improvement in efficiency and cost effectiveness in the maintenance of the permanent way, which has taken place at the same time as the increased speed and weight of traffic has occurred: a record in which the Civil Engineers take pride.

The achievements in civil engineering may be less obvious to the travelling public than is the case with some of the other engineering disciplines – for example, new forms of traction and new types of rolling stock produced by the mechanical and electrical engineers, or modern signalling and information display equipment installed by the signal and telecommunications engineers. Nevertheless, the contribution of the civil engineers has been of equal importance in providing the high quality permanent way upon which the modernized railway runs, without which developments in the other engineering techniques would have been wasted – if indeed they could have taken place at all.

CHAPTER TEN

Signal and Telecommunications Engineering

I T is in the field of railway signal engineering that the greatest technical advances have taken place, starting in the years following the First World War and progressing at increasing tempo since the late 1950s. The physical exertion involved in the movement of semaphore signals and points, by mechanical means, and the visual check on the operation of the equipment, has gradually given way, as capability and finance have permitted, to a system which, by the utilization of electronic devices and miniaturization of equipment, permits the operation of signals, points, and train describers over long distances. The change has reduced operating costs by the elimination of a large number of signalboxes and has provided for safety checks on the occupation of the line and for the relay of service information to management, staff, and passengers.

Such a change in the character of the signal and telecommunications engineering function, and particularly the continued advances in the development of electronic equipment, has inevitably necessitated a parallel change in the calibre, education standards, and training of staff employed in the department. The installer and lineman of the pre-Second World War era, requiring only relatively little technical knowledge, has given way to one needing the knowledge and skill to install and maintain equipment as complex, and as subject to progressive development, as any coming within the responsibility of any of the railway engineering disciplines.

The early railways demonstrated the need for quick communication between stations and junctions, as well as a means of conveying instructions to engine drivers by which they could regulate their approach to such places. From these necessities sprang what became known by the generic term 'signalling'.

In 1843, a system of partial interlocking was introduced at Bricklayers Arms on the South Eastern Railway and, thereafter, further developments in signalling equipment took place, largely by private manufacturers. In 1856 a system of mechanical interlocking of manually operated signals and points was patented by John Saxby. Edward Tyer had, in

1851, established the first business expressly devoted to the production of electrical signalling apparatus, perhaps his best known invention being the electric tablet system for single-line operation, introduced in 1878 following a serious accident on the Norwich–Yarmouth line in 1874. Others also entered the industry and built up a constantly improving means of protecting and accelerating rail traffic – a process which still continues more than a century later.

Signalling – the means by which traffic movements on the railway are controlled – has three main objectives. The first – and initially the only – purpose is to achieve a high standard of safety in operation, by regulating the flow of traffic in such a way as to ensure that there is an adequate interval of space between following or converging trains. The need for regulation for safety purposes was recognized early in the development of railways and the semaphore signal was evolved and first put into use at New Cross on the South Eastern Railway in 1841. Secondly, the intention is to translate the instructions of the traffic controller into the position of points on the ground and the appropriate signal aspects. Thirdly, as a later development, the objective is to secure the minimum time between trains – the 'headway' – as a means of permitting the passage of as many trains as practicable over a stretch of line within a given period. The achievement of these objectives – safety, routeing, and maximum track capacity – involves a study of proposed train speeds and densities over a route before a signalling layout and equipment plan can be finalized.

The safety aspects of signalling are clearly defined in Ministry of Transport 'Requirements for Passenger Lines and Recommendations for Goods Lines in regard to Railway Construction and Operation'. The 'Requirements' represent the standard practice of British Railways, formulated following discussions between Ministry officials and railway officers, and since the earliest days there has been no attempt to legislate on methods to be adopted in advance of these having been discussed between the parties concerned and proved in practice. The regulations thus evolved relate, *inter alia*, to the siting and indications of stop and distant semaphore signals, on running lines and at junctions; the siting and interpretation of three- and four-aspect colour-light signalling; the provision of signal-post telephones; automatic train stop and warning systems; the siting and operation of points; interlocking of points and signals to ensure that conflicting movements cannot occur; the maintenance of the block system of working, which provides for an adequate space interval between following or converging trains – either by the use of three-position block telegraph instruments and signalling bells or by track circuits; signalling at public road crossings; and methods of controlling traffic movements over single lines. All these various requirements are incorporated, as appropriate, in instructions to the relevant staff, through such documents as 'Arrangements for Train Signalling by Block Telegraph', the BR Board's 'Rules and Regulations', the 'Appendix to the Working Time-table' setting out exceptional working methods to be adopted at particular places, and instructions relative to operations at individual signalboxes.

Restrictions on the distance of manually worked points from the signalbox (initially 250, later 350, yards) and the regulations governing the block system led to a need for signalboxes at frequent intervals, and often for several signalboxes at complex junctions and major stations and yards. The introduction, some 80 years ago, of electrical control of semaphore signals and of points worked by electric motors enabled some extension of the range of signalbox operations, a process which was accelerated between the end of the First World War in 1918 and nationalization 30 years later. It was during this period that significant advances were made in signalling methods and practices, including the widespread introduction of colour-light signals, first with power-operated lever frames and later with electrical relay interlocking, and the extension of track circuiting, all of which contributed to extending the area of control of individual signalboxes, leading to the elimination of some boxes and much-needed economies in costs, as well as greater operating safety and efficiency.

Semaphore distant and stop signals, which were the main means of control on the railways for broadly the first century of their operation, had many disadvantages. They had to be sited, wherever possible, to give a sky background to the arm by day. This was impracticable in many cases and sighting boards, or white-painted surfaces, had often to be provided behind the signals instead. By night, the signal lamp, usually oil-burning, was inefficient, and for best results had to be at the driver's eye level – something of a problem, very often, in relation to the sky background required for daylight sighting and leading to the provision of co-acting arms and lamps, giving a signal aspect at two different heights by day and by night. Semaphore signals and oil lamps were particularly difficult to see during fog or falling snow and 'fogmen' (usually permanent way staff) had to be employed at all distant signal posts to warn drivers, by detonators, when signals were at caution.

The introduction of colour-light signals was a tremendous step forward, providing, as they do, light beams of sufficient intensity for both day and night viewing, even during the adverse weather conditions which had previously necessitated the use of fogmen. The replacement of isolated semaphore distant signals by colour-lights was a particularly valuable first step on many semaphore-signalled main lines. Although in some cases, notably on the GWR, there was an attempt to relate colour-light signalling to the same two- and three-aspect indications of semaphore signals, all four companies eventually adopted a common system of multiple-aspects, based on the recommendations of a committee of the Institution of Railway Signal Engineers, set up in 1922 to investigate the advantages and disadvantages of three-aspect signalling. The committee, in its report published in 1924, was opposed to the adoption of three-aspect semaphore signalling but was in favour of three-aspect colour-light signals, with red as the danger ('stop') aspect, yellow for caution ('be prepared to stop at next signal'), and green for line clear ('next signal at green or yellow'). The committee also recommended the substitution of yellow for red on the arm and in the light of semaphore distant signals. It suggested, too, that on intensively used lines with colour-light signalling a fourth aspect – vertical double yellow – should be introduced, to provide an adequate braking distance and to indicate 'be prepared to pass the next signal (single yellow) at restricted speed'. The fundamental difference between multiple-aspect colour-light signalling and semaphore signalling is that, in the former case, a definite indication is given by every signal of the aspect which is being displayed by the next signal ahead. The adoption of multiple-aspect signalling leads to improved line capacity by increasing the number of sections into which a line can be divided, without increasing, and even by decreasing, the number of signalboxes. The first three-aspect installation was introduced between Marylebone and Neasden in the 1920s.

The block system of working was first used at Clay Cross tunnel, between Derby and Chesterfield on the North Midland Railway, in 1841. Under the system, a signalbox was provided for each block section and train movements depended on the signalman actually seeing the train pass his box. The distance of signals from signalboxes was thus limited, whilst Board of Trade (the responsible Government Department prior to the formation of the Ministry of Transport) regulations stipulated that points must be within the sight of the signalman, so that he could check their satisfactory operation. Each block section extended from the last stop signal of one signalbox to a point 440 yards beyond the first stop signal of the next box ahead, with, other than in exceptional circumstances, only one train being allowed in the section at one time. Communication between boxes was by three-position block telegraph instruments and single-stroke train signalling bells, using a standard code of rings for each class of train or for conveying particular advice or instruction.

Track circuiting was first introduced in Britain at the turn of the century, as a signalling safety precaution, on the London and South Western Railway, between Andover and Grateley, in association with semaphore signals. Track circuits were originally battery operated but mains operation, with emergency or stand-by equipment, was later developed for outlying installations, with full power operation at larger installations. The expansion of track circuiting between the wars revolutionized signalling and provides one of the basic features of modern signalling systems. Track circuits indicate on an illuminated diagram in the signalbox which sections of rail are occupied. With multiple-aspect colour-light signalling they also exercise direct control over signal aspects and prevent the movement of points until it is safe for them to be changed.

Rails forming a track circuit are insulated from the rest of the track and, unless continuously welded, must be bonded together with wire at joints to form a low resistance path for an electric current which flows through the rails to actuate a relay which is normally energized when the track is clear. When a train enters the track-circuited section, the axles provide an alternative low resistance path for the current, the major part of which is diverted from the relay, which becomes de-energized. The occupation or otherwise of the track circuit is thus detected and, by means of contacts on the relay, circuits controlling signals and points are either 'locked' or 'free'. It is thus not possible for a signalman to clear a signal controlling entry to an occupied track circuit or to operate points whilst a train is occupying the section concerned. In automatic colour-light signalling areas, relays set each signal to danger as a train passes on to the track circuit. When it passes off the circuit, the signal returns progressively to yellow, double yellow (if provided), and green.

Electrical relays, which have been in use for well over 60 years, are vital to modern signalling and are the agency by which the whole function of control is exercised, being responsive to the condition of track occupancy, the existing position of points and signal aspects. They are of a type unique to railway signalling, since if they fail they must 'fail safe', in common with the circuits to which they are connected. Over the years, they have progressively been reduced in size and various designs have been developed to meet particular requirements.

In the early 1900s, means were developed of operating points by power – electrically, pneumatically or, for a time, electro-pneumatically – from mechanical or power frames. With power operation, the limitation on the distance from the signalbox at which points may be operated was removed, providing the set of the points was electrically detected and indicated in the signalbox and the track at the points was track-circuited.

The earliest power frames followed the general structured pattern of mechanical frames, the points and signals being operated by levers assembled in a straight line, with mechanical interlocking. The levers served merely to open and close electrical contacts, the functions themselves being operated electrically or by electrically-controlled compressed air motors. Virtually no physical effort was required to operate the levers and it was therefore possible for them to be miniaturized to a length of around six inches. One of the earliest installations of this type was in the Crewe station area, in 1900, the signals being operated by solenoids and the points by electric motors. It followed the introduction by the Great Eastern Railway, in 1898, of the first electro-pneumatic installation at Bishopsgate, operated in this case by handles, rather than levers. A further development was the introduction of electrical in place of mechanical interlocking, the levers merely serving as switches through which the operating circuits are controlled. Thus, the main reason for mounting levers in a rigid frame, which was essential with mechanical interlocking, no longer applied. With what became known as relay interlocking, the levers could be replaced by switches, incorporated in an illuminated diagram of the layout covered, or on a separate miniature panel, having the same relative positions thereon as the functions themselves out on the track. The switches were the equivalent of the levers to the signalman, but the relays for the various functions were the real controllers and took the place of the levers from the engineering standpoint.

Power frames had, generally, individual levers for points and signals: that is, one lever per function. Some early relay interlockings followed this principle but it was soon appreciated that the system lent itself to operation on a route basis. Following trials with a small prototype installation at Didcot, the first large-scale route-control system in Britain was installed at Newport, GWR, in 1927, where two station boxes were equipped with route-setting lever frames, whilst retaining the existing points and semaphore signals, converted to electric operation. The GWR did not pursue the system, but later the LNER took up the idea of route control of signals and points, but with interlocking provided in the electrical circuits of the operating controls instead of mechanical interlocking, thereby opening the way to operation by small thumb switches, mounted in groups on a much more compact panel. The pioneer installation of any magnitude on this system – there had been a very small installation at Goole just before – was at Thirsk, as mentioned in Chapter One. It was initiated by A. E. Tattersall, Signal Engineer of the LNER, who earlier, as Signal Superintendent to the Chief Engineer of the GNR, had been responsible for the introduction on a fairly large scale of power-operated points and signals and for the reversible working and three-position signalling through Gasworks Tunnel near King's Cross. The Thirsk scheme provided a thumb switch at each signal location on the panel, for each possible route between chosen pairs of stop signals on the panel layout. The turning of the switch, providing all controls were clear, caused the particular route to be set up on the ground, the signal to be cleared and the clear indication to be repeated in the correct position on the panel. Similar systems were later installed at Hull and Northallerton. In the initial installations, on the passage of a train, the signal was returned to red and the route switch was replaced to normal by the signalman. In some later installations, however, automatic restoration of the route switch took place on the passage of a train. Point control switches were provided for emergency working, arranged in rows along the top or bottom of the panel.

An alternative arrangement to the individual route switches, which occupied considerable space on the panel or console, was for a circular dial to be provided at the signal locations on the panel. This dial had as many positions as the number of routes involved.

A number of large schemes embodying the general principles described were brought into operation before the Second World War, among which may be specially mentioned the East Coast main line between York and Northallerton in 1934. Additionally, there were many small and relatively inexpensive economy schemes, which had the effect of speeding the flow of traffic and/or eliminating signalboxes. Such schemes included the provision of outer home signals, with track circuiting, to permit the acceptance of second train by a signalman whilst a preceding one was still in the area of control of the box, for example in a station platform; the provision of advanced starting signals, with track circuiting, to permit the approach of a second train into a station before the preceding one had moved into the next section; the provision of intermediate block home signals, manually operated or automatic, with track circuiting, thus permitting the closure of an intermediate signalbox, originally installed to give an additional block section; and the provision of intermediate block home signals with sidings connections operated from ground frames, manually operated but with adequate electrical controls on the levers to safeguard train working.

The Second World War interrupted further extension of the installation of modern signalling. At its outbreak, a number of schemes had been planned, and even started, but in most cases completion had to be deferred until after the war. Some of these schemes were associated with electrification projects, as, for instance, Liverpool Street/Fenchurch Street–Shenfield. The alternative system referred to above, using circular dial switches, was installed on the Liverpool Street–Bethnal Green section in 1947, and was of special interest. Apart from constituting part of one of the largest areas in Britain to be equipped with power-operated colour-light signalling, it marked the adoption of the panel system at a London terminus carrying an unusually dense suburban traffic, for the first time – a fundamental change in signalling practice over a route of this kind – and provided the opportunity to compare panel and power frame operations under heavy service conditions. Under the scheme adopted, the new signalbox at Liverpool Street controlled 318 routes, the multi-position route-setting switches at each signal location being capable of taking up any one of eight positions. The operation of the last running position switch completed the route and cleared signals, providing all points were correctly set and detected, all facing shunt signals were off and all track circuits clear. The other signalbox included in the first stage of this scheme, at Bethnal Green, was similar in design but less extensive.

The second stage of the Liverpool Street–Shenfield resignalling, covering Stratford, Bow, and Mile End, was operated on the 'Entrance-Exit' (NX) system and the third stage, up to Shenfield, on the 'One Control

Switch' (OCS) system. Both these systems are referred to again later. In all, on the Liverpool Street–Shenfield route, 12 new route relay signal-boxes replaced 33 mechanical boxes.

Other schemes interrupted by the war were not associated with electrification. One such was for resignalling in the York area. Eight mechanical boxes were to be concentrated in one all-electric installation, covering 800 possible train routes and controlling 18 miles of running lines, plus 5½ miles of loops, sidings, and platform lines, and linking up with previous resignalling to Northallerton and Darlington. Work was resumed in 1946 and the project completed in 1951, providing, at that time, the largest route relay interlocking system in the world.

The situation at nationalization may therefore be summed up as follows. Multi-aspect colour-light signalling, with continuous track cir-cuiting, was the general practice for new installations on main lines and others bearing heavy traffic. Large concentrated layouts were being operated in more and more cases from power signalboxes, with automatic and semi-automatic colour-light signalling on intervening sections of, for the most part, plain line, or lines with a limited number of point connec-tions. Such connections were usually released electrically from a power signalbox or, occasionally, from ground frames which also controlled the

Fig. 10.1 The new signalbox at Wilmslow, LM Region, with relay room below. This power box, like the ones at Sandbach and Manchester (Piccadilly) has single switch (OCS) console type of operation, with separate illuminated diagrams. Later boxes have push-push Entrance-Exit type consoles, sometimes with separate illuminated diagrams (BRB)

Fig. 10.2   The OCS control panel at St Pancras (BRB)

protecting signals. On the LNER, route relay interlocking was incorporated into the system.

The NX interlocking system referred to above was first introduced at Brunswick on the Cheshire Lines Committee railway in 1937. Under this system, the setting up of the route was effected by turning a switch on the panel at a point corresponding to the commencement of the route and by pressing a button at the point representing the end of the route. The apparatus then automatically performed all the necessary operations to set up the desired route and clear the relevant signals. This system is now generally adopted for all modern signalling installations but, except on the Paddington–Swansea route of the Western Region, the switch controlling the entrance to the section has been replaced by a button, involving what is known as a 'push-push' operation. On that route, progress in resignalling has been rather quicker than on most other through routes and the 'turn-push' method originally adopted has been continued virtually throughout.

The OCS system provided separate switches for each route but mounted them on a console fixed below the main panel, keeping the switches so far as possible immediately below the relevant signal positions on the panel. This system was also installed at a number of locations and on a number of routes, including the York area, St Pancras, and during the electrification of the Crewe–Manchester line, in the 1950–60s.

Although much had been done to extend the area of control which could be exercised from one signalbox, the state of technical development had, up to the Second World War, still imposed limitations in this context. Each power signalbox circuit was operated over individual insulated conductors, generally also with separate return wires. The number of conductors required was therefore high, and thus costly. They were, in general, concentrated in multi-core cables and ran underground or on lineside supports. Physical protection of the cables was both necessary and difficult, and costly to provide. As the scope of operation increased, so did the diameter of the conductors, to limit the voltage drop in the circuits. Thus there was an economic limit to the area which could be controlled from one signalbox. At nationalization, this limit was of the order of seven miles.

Technological advances in the electrical and electronic fields during and after the war, fostered by the avowed intention of the 1955 Modernization Plan – to install the most modern methods of controlling rail traffic, to secure both efficient operation and the highest degree of safety – led to greatly accelerated developments in railway signalling and progress in the various areas concerned is now considered.

In a paper to the International Engineering Conference held in September 1975 to celebrate the 150th Anniversary of the opening of the Stockton and Darlington Railway, A. A. Cardani, Chief Signal and Telecommunications Engineer, British Railways, reported progress with the installation of modern signalling in the United Kingdom. At that time, some 9375 single track miles (approximately 40 per cent of the BR network) had been modernized. In the process of modernization, and the simultaneous rationalization of the network, a reduction of over 6000 signalboxes had been achieved. By the end of 1978, some 47 per cent of the total single track mileage of 22 000, that is something over 10 000 miles, had been equipped with modern signalling. At that time, 34 power boxes were in operation, but there still remained 2399 manually operated boxes.

Also, the area of control which could be vested in a modern signalbox had continuously increased. The size of area is not entirely dictated by technical limitations and other factors influence the extent of control which can be introduced. These include the ability to plan and implement a project within a reasonable time-scale, the traffic pattern over the lines in question and other works which may be in progress at the same time – for example, electrification.

Nevertheless, at the time Cardani wrote his paper in 1975, there were still 240 signalboxes, out of a total of 3000, associated with the track mileage which had been modernized. Of these 240, about 40 could be considered to be major control centres for the future. An examination of the then existing network indicated that the signalling control of more than 90 per cent of the system might ultimately be possible from about 70 signalling centres, each one controlling an average of 300–325 miles. The balance of the system would consist of lines with a low traffic density and therefore commercially not justified for resignalling with the same degree of control.

The rate of progress towards bigger areas of control is illustrated by reference to successive projects. At the time of the LMR main-line electrification from Euston in the mid-1960s it was possible to extend the area of control to as much as 59 route miles. The Derby power box, constructed in 1969 as part of the Derby, Nottingham, Trent, and Birmingham resignalling, controlled 78 route miles. By the time electrification was extended to Carlisle and Glasgow, increasing confidence in the ability to extend the scope of control led to the introduction of even larger areas. Three new boxes were provided on the LM Region – at Warrington, controlling 62 route miles; at Preston, 114 route miles; and at Carlisle, 104 route miles. The new box at Motherwell, in the Scottish Region, controls 124 route miles

The London Bridge resignalling, covering the approaches to three terminal stations, as well as a section of the South London inner suburban area, and completed in 1975, placed 47 route miles under the control of the new box. The Victoria resignalling, planned to be completed in 1983, will control 103 route miles of track.

The King's Cross suburban electrification required one new power-operated signalbox at King's Cross, controlling 83½ route miles from King's Cross and Moorgate to Sandy on the East Coast main line, to Royston on the Cambridge Branch, and the Hertford Loop. The full

Fig. 10.3   The Entrance-Exit type console and panel in Preston power box, controlling 114 route miles, 263 single track miles, of railway (BRB)

Fig. 10.4   An inner suburban electric multiple unit train enters London Bridge
beneath a colour-light signal gantry (BRB)

Inter-City and suburban services require the King's Cross box to handle around 830 trains a day. At the height of the evening peak, 60 trains are monitored on the panel simultaneously. A feature of the panel is automatic working facilities on certain signals, easing the signalman's workload by allowing following trains to pass over the same route under automatic control instead of setting the route up afresh after each train.

When the box was linked to a similar box at Peterborough, in late 1977, the two were the only signalling control centres on the East Coast main line south of Doncaster, 156 miles from King's Cross, controlling over 140 route miles of track between them. Eventually, on the East Coast main line, only seven boxes will control 400 route miles – namely, King's Cross, Peterborough, Doncaster, York, Darlington, Newcastle, Edinburgh. The rationalization and resignalling project currently approaching completion in East Scotland includes a power signalling centre at Edinburgh Waverley which will, when the scheme is completed in 1981, control the largest area on BR – from the English border, through Edinburgh, across the Forth Bridge almost to the River Tay, and westwards from Edinburgh to a boundary roughly half-way to Glasgow and Motherwell, a total of 221 route miles. Figure 10.5 illustrates the area to be covered by the Edinburgh Waverley box.

Table 10.1 below summarizes the situation for selected boxes.

The longest continuous routes on BR, controlled by power boxes, with progressive train describers all the way, are the Western Region route

Table 10.1   Mileage Controlled by Selected Signalboxes and
Manual Boxes Replaced

Signalbox	Region	Year of commissioning	Mileage controlled		Manual boxes closed
			Route	Single track	
King's Cross	E	1977	83½	260	57
Peterborough	E	1972	59	176	20
Doncaster	E	1979–80	180	350	61
Rugby	LM	1964	59	159	23
Saltley	LM	1969	90	210	49
Derby	LM	1969	78	178	43
Trent	LM	1969	74	209	62
Warrington	LM	1972	62	145	51
Preston	LM	1972–3	114	263	87
Carlisle	LM	1973	104	210	44
Motherwell	Sc.	1972	124	278	68
Glasgow Central	Sc.	1960 (Extended 1973)	27	68	26
Edinburgh	Sc.	1979–81	221	435	64
West Hampstead	LM	1979–81	70	270	31
Feltham	S	1974	70	138	39
London Bridge	S	1975	47	147½	16
Victoria	S	Target 1983	103	267	37

from London to Swansea (191 miles) and the inter-Regional cross-country route from Sheffield to Swansea (234 miles). Table 10.2 gives details of the boxes on these routes, with total route and single track miles controlled and the number of boxes replaced.

The development of the larger control areas arose through the operators' awareness of the value of centralized control and confidence in the ability of the signal engineers to adapt technical innovations to this purpose. One factor which made larger areas of control feasible was the development of two reliable remote control systems, first tried in the Wilmslow, Sandbach, and Manchester Piccadilly boxes in association with the Crewe–Manchester electrification in 1960. One system – time division multiplex – involves the use of synchronized scanning equipment at each end of the remote control link to detect changes in signal input at the other end of the link. In the other system – frequency division multiplex – a multiplicity of electrical signals at different frequencies can be transmitted simultaneously over one circuit between the control point and remote interlockings many miles away. This development reduced cable costs and made it economical to control remote interlockings over distances of 50 miles or more.

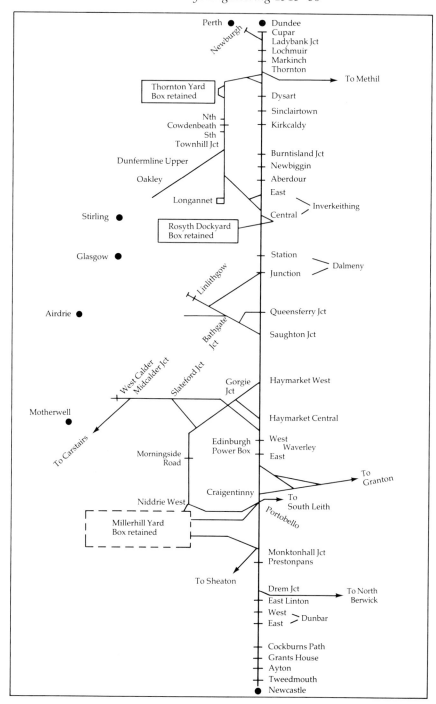

Fig. 10.5   Edinburgh Waverley Power box: a diagram illustrating the area of control (BRB)

Table 10.2 Signalboxes on London–Swansea and Sheffield–Swansea Routes

Signalbox	Region	Year commissioned	Mileage controlled		Manual boxes closed
			Route	Single track	
Paddington–Swansea					
Old Oak Common (Paddington)	W	1968 (Extended 1977)	13	70	14
Slough	W	1963	19	70	15
Reading	W	1965 (Extended 1979)	104	272	43
Swindon	W	1968	70	135	27
Bristol	W	1970–71	114	254	56
Newport	W	1962 (Extended 1968)	45	125	26
Cardiff	W	1966	31	90	41
Port Talbot	W	1963 (Extended 1973)	71	163	40
Total: 8	—	—	467	1179	262
Sheffield–Swansea					
Sheffield (Stage I)	E	1973	23	69	17
Derby	LM	1969	78	178	43
Saltley	LM	1969	90	210	49
Gloucester	W	1968–9	95	182	49
Newport	W	1962 (Extended 1968)	45	125	26
Cardiff	W	1966	31	90	41
Port Talbot	W	1963 (Extended 1973)	71	163	40
Total: 7	—	—	433	1017	265

The train describer also plays a vital part in the effectiveness and degree of centralization of traffic control achievable over large areas of dense traffic networks. In this context, it is of considerable interest to note that the track circuit, first developed in 1867 but not brought into service in the United Kingdom until 1902, is still the vital equipment which locates the train in the system and provides the basic element for train protection and control.

Under the block system, the description of the train next on line is passed from box to box by bell code and is restricted to a broad indication of the type of train – express passenger, stopping passenger, express freight, ballast, etc. When track circuiting and electrically-operated signalling were developed, it became possible to have a number of trains

Fig. 10.6   Remote control: time division multiplex equipment (BRB)

on a stretch of line between signalboxes and to replace the absolute block system. This fact emphasized the need for a means whereby a series of trains could be 'described' to the signalbox in advance, and for a method of storing descriptions for display as earlier trains cleared the section.

The first such system – largely mechanically-operated and inflexible in use – was introduced by the Metropolitan District Railway before the First World War, but there was relatively little further development until the later 1920s. In November 1928 a paper presented to the Institution of Railway Signal Engineers suggested that a new type of train describer, requiring only one pair of wires between signalboxes, should be devised. Two manufacturers produced prototype equipment which was subjected to service tests on the Southern Railway. The equipment ultimately chosen was installed on the Brighton line, in conjunction with electrification and resignalling, in 1933, the solution to the problem having been found in the use of telephone type techniques and equipment.

When train describers were first introduced the descriptions were passed from box to box by the signalman at the starting point pressing one of a number of buttons on a panel, each appropriate to a particular type of train and destination. A corresponding visual indication was displayed to the signalman at the next box down the line, who, in turn, passed the description forward. The equipment usually permitted three consecutive descriptions to be on display at any time, with provision for storing additional descriptions up to the maximum number of trains likely to be in the section simultaneously.

Continuing developments in electronic technology have now made it possible to design train describer installations to operate automatically. A system on these lines was first used in the York resignalling scheme. In it, a description, once initiated, is sent forward automatically and is switched over to the appropriate instrument when a train changes from one line to another. The installation at York was linked to adjacent signalboxes and introduced a feature which at that time represented a new departure for Britain, in the form of display. Instead of merely indicating the order in which trains are approaching, the display is so arranged that the information giving the class and destination of the train is illuminated on a panel showing the actual signal which the train is approaching, the indication moving forward in step with the movement of the train. Once the code giving the description, destination, and direction has been set up on the appropriate line by the signalman, the apparatus works automatically, being controlled by the passage of the train over the track circuits and past signals. By watching the passage of the indications along the line of route on his illuminated diagram, a signalman can make a reasonable assessment of the speed of the train and can judge whether time exists for any local conflicting movements without introducing delay to the major train.

It is interesting to note that, long before modern train describers were introduced, there was one line in Britain on which a unique description system was in operation – the London, Chatham and Dover Railway. Signalboxes on this line were not equipped with standard block instruments, but instead were provided with what in effect were single needle telegraph instruments, each with a bell which sounded once for every beat of the needle on incoming signals. The ordinary block codes were transmitted by beats of the needle and the bell rang accordingly in the adjacent box. When this process was completed, the train concerned was described by further beats to right or left, on the basis of the single needle alphabet.

A system of train description – first introduced on the Western Region, in a rather different form, in 1958 – was adopted as standard throughout BR in 1961. The basis of the system is a four-digit code, identifying all trains in the working timetable, as under:

1st digit: a figure, denoting the class of train;

2nd digit: a letter, specifying the route of the train, or, if a local train, the district in which it is operating;

3rd and 4th digits: figures, identifying the particular train in the working timetable.

Digital general purpose computers, with suitable peripheral equipment to link up with the signalling relay equipment, are used to progress the codes through the system. In addition, the computer enables a range of ancillary functions to be exercised through the train describer system and these will be referred to later. In future, it is possible that trains will report themselves into the system. Techniques for this already exist and are employed on the Victoria Line of the LTE. However, for main-line operations the economics of the situation do not at present justify the cost of such a system.

Before the last war, passenger information on display at stations was normally restricted to finger boards or manually-operated indicators informing passengers of the platforms of departure of their trains. Indeed, some of the smaller ones still use finger boards and some of the indicators referred to still exist, even at important terminal stations. The pre-war railways introduced, in the late 1920s, loud-speaker announcements at major stations and also installed manually-operated train arrival boards, indicating the train, platform of arrival, and minutes late. In August 1951 the LMR took this latter aspect a stage further, when they installed apparatus at Euston to inform passengers in a new arrival bureau of the running of incoming trains. Information on train running was received at Willesden telegraph office and was relayed to the arrival bureau at Euston. The information was also passed to the station announcers, for relay over the public address system.

The development in the 1960s of the computer-based train describer system has enabled very much more sophisticated methods of display to be introduced. The computer collects data on train running by reacting to the operation of push buttons on the panels of main and fringe signalboxes and by responding to the actual passage of trains through the signalling area. From the information thus collected, the computer determines to which display points each item of information should be sent and generates signals which enable the information to be displayed automatically, in appropriate form, on platform indicators.

The train describer system installed at London Bridge station, Southern Region, in 1976, includes all the latest developments in this field of technology and is the largest such installation in the world. The equipment also incorporates a computer-based Master Timetable System (MTS), which is gradually being expanded as other resignalling schemes are introduced on the SR. MTS monitors the times at which trains pass various locations – signals, track circuits, points – and controls passenger information by automatically working 'next train' indicators on station concourses and platforms. If trains run out of sequence, the computer sets the indicators and alerts station staff. Information generated by the system can be retrieved through visual display units (VDUs), for the benefit of operating or other interested staff. The Victoria train describer system, which will be operated by microprocessors, will be linked into the system.

Information in regard to the working timetable, up-dated daily to take account of special trains or other changes in service, is stored in another computer at Regional HQ. This information is continuously compared with movement information generated through the train describer equipment to produce a print-out of all trains more than a predetermined number of minutes early or late.

In 1962–3 a system of train reporting was introduced on the Fenchurch Street–Upminster–Shoeburyness section of the LT & S line, linked to the train description apparatus. Under this, the time each train passed 12 selected points was relayed to the Fenchurch Street Control Office and automatically recorded by electric typewriters. Subsequently, the Southern Region linked more sophisticated equipment to its train description apparatus to actuate electronic teleprinters which made a permanent record of traffic movements from minute to minute, replacing the manual records previously maintained. By 1970, train describer equipment regularly included provision for the automatic transmission of information on train running to other centres, the first such equipment being in use between Dartford Control and Divisional Control at Beckenham.

The new Rugby signalbox also introduced, on an experimental basis, automatic train recording facilities, using the train description equipment in conjunction with a teleprinter, enabling train running information at selected points to be relayed to control rooms. Later, the West Coast main-line electrification provided the opportunity for installing an all-electronic system under which train descriptions are automatically stepped forward from signal to signal and transmitted to the next box at the appropriate time, data storage and processing being carried out by a small general purpose computer. The use of a computer permitted a further advance in train reporting on the LM Region.

For many years, the traffic control system of the former LMS, and of the LM Region following nationalization, provided for the reporting of trains passing a number of points on the line, corresponding to those at which passing times were specified in the working timetable. The reports were originally made by telephone and later by teleprinter. Either method necessarily involved a certain time lag, which has been eliminated by a system of automatic reporting, actuated by the train description apparatus which transmits, instantaneously, the times at which trains enter upon the track circuit at each signal. A tape record is thus produced of all train movements within the area of each signalbox, indicating, minute by minute, the time of transmission, the signal number from which it is made, and the timetable reporting number of the train.

The information so collected is automatically disseminated to the Regional Control Office at Crewe and to Divisional Controls and other signalboxes concerned. The computer can be interrogated from some receiving points for further information. The system has been adopted in subsequent installations.

The introduction of widely spaced boxes removes the ability which previously existed of signalmen observing any irregularity in the running of trains and quickly stopping them for examination. By means of the automatic train reporting system, however, regulators in the power boxes so equipped are able to maintain a check on the running of trains at selected points in their control areas, information which is useful in deciding whether or not to 'loop' a freight train to allow an express to overtake.

The LM Region system of train reporting was designed to permit of regulation over long stretches of line, as distinct from the more localized regulation, in an intensively occupied area, required of the Southern Region system.

The modern computer-based train describer, apart from being the means whereby trains are advised forward from box to box, is in fact the key system with which an extensive range of devices for the conveyance of information to railway staff and the public is associated – passenger information displays and public address systems, automatic train reporting, platform optimization, input of timetable changes, and, when fully developed and justified, train regulation and control and automatic route setting.

In October 1978 the Eastern Region introduced apparatus at King's Cross, for trial purposes, which enables passengers to obtain service information quickly. The system is based on a small microfilm computer which stores information about journeys to and from 48 other stations served from King's Cross. By the operation of push buttons on TV type display units located in the public area of the Travel Centre, information can be obtained as to train services for inward and outward journeys, on the desired day of travel. This is one example of a number of possibilities which BR is currently pursuing, for means of conveying information to the public.

The advances which have taken place in signalling and telecommunications techniques have not been associated particularly with the system of traction employed. From the operator's point of view, there are almost identical installations working with both d.c. and a.c. electric traction and on non-electrified lines. The decision to use a high-voltage 50-cycle a.c. electric traction system did, however, introduce two major problems for the signal and telecommunications engineers, namely

(a) consideration of the conditions to be fulfilled in the transmission of both traction and track circuit currents in the rails; and

(b) the interference with communications circuits owned by the railway and with the national system of the Post Office, as well as the effect on railway signalling circuits.

Previous experience in Britain with 50-cycle traction showed that the interference problem would be severe, a fact confirmed by events in other countries which had adopted a.c. traction at varying frequencies.

So far as the first issue was concerned, the introduction of 25 kV a.c. traction led to particular problems with interference to track circuits. In the process of resignalling on the LM Region main lines various designs of track circuit were introduced. The first units on what was, in effect, a large-scale trial installation on the Styal line consisted of 75-cycle double-rail a.c. track circuits, approximately 1100 yards long, with d.c. single-rail overlap track circuits 220 yards in length. After completion of the Crewe–Manchester line, however, it was decided, both for economic reasons and to facilitate the bonding of structures, that d.c. single-rail track circuits should be used generally throughout, except in limited areas where, in addition to the 25 kV 50-cycle traction system, other electrical factors had to be considered. Early installations at Manchester London Road, where 1500 V d.c. traction was also in use, and at Crewe, where there were significant d.c. stray earth potentials, used 83⅓-cycle single-rail a.c. track circuits. Precautions were taken to ensure that the track relays received current which was free from contamination by the 50-cycle traction supply. Because of the 630 V d.c. fourth-rail traction system immediately adjacent to the 25 kV a.c. lines between Euston and Watford, 83⅓-cycle a.c. track circuits are also used in certain areas on this line.

The conversion of the Liverpool Street–Southend–Chelmsford lines from 1500 V d.c. to 25 kV a.c. presented a particular problem. As the change-over in traction system had to be made overnight, the simplest possible solution was sought. It was recognized that it would be impracticable also to change the track circuit equipment overnight and it was therefore necessary to devise a system which could be progressively changed over under d.c. traction conditions. The difficulty was overcome by converting the signalling power system to 83⅓ cycles, with protection against false operation by the 50-cycle traction current.

In regard to the second problem – induced electrical interference – the flow of large single-phase 50-cycle a.c. traction currents along the overhead contact wires creates alternating electrical and magnetic fields of sufficient magnitude as to induce harmful voltages in lineside signalling and telecommunications power supplies. The question of interference was considered at the earliest stages of planning, with full regard to the directives of the International Telegraph and Telephone Consultative Committee on the protection of circuits against the harmful effects of induced voltages from high-voltage power lines.

So far as signalling cables are concerned, protection is given where necessary by the use of frequency-discriminatory circuits or immunized relays. In regard to telecommunications, ideally special equipment should be designed and provided for electrification schemes but this is not economically practicable and efforts are therefore directed towards limiting the induced voltages, so that standard telephone exchange and transmission equipment may be used. Three methods are employed on BR, to protect apparatus and personnel from induced voltages. One method requires booster transformers to be provided in the power circuit feeding the motive power units. These booster transformers are arranged to cause the greater part of the return current to flow through the running

Fig. 10.7   The installation of signalling and telecommunications cables alongside the track
is undertaken by the use of specially-equipped wagons (BICC)

rails or, more effectively, through a return conductor provided specially for the purpose. As a result, the voltages induced in neighbouring cables may be less than one-tenth of that induced when no booster transformers are provided.

With the second method, the telecommunications cables are so constructed that their cores are substantially screened from the magnetic field that induces a voltage in them. Screening is provided by the use of a high-conductivity aluminium sheath, earthed at 1000-yard intervals. The screening can be further improved by the addition of steel tapes. With the third method, the cables may be left open to the full effect of the disturbing influence from the a.c. traction current, but special devices can be provided in the cable circuits to act as barriers to the induced voltages. They prevent more than a small fraction of the voltage from reaching the terminal apparatus or personnel working on the terminations of the circuits.

The British Post Office telephone system, with a nation-wide network developed over a long period, includes a number of basically different designs of exchanges using a number of equipments of different vintages. These exchanges are inter-connected by an extensive network of circuits, largely in unarmoured lead-sheathed cable. It will be apparent that the electrification of BR routes, using a high-voltage a.c. system, at such a late stage in the development of the telephone network must cause extremely serious interference problems, unless induction is limited to values which do not give rise to noise and functional interference. In the case of the line from Crewe to Manchester, a detailed study on a theoretical basis showed that without suppression at source some 1600 circuits could be adversely affected. Further examination showed that similar conditions could arise elsewhere. The difficulties would have been mainly due to magnetic induction but in some areas – notably on the Colchester–Clacton line – it was found that noise could also occur due to harmonic voltages in the contact wire system. Open wire lines close to the railway were affected, as also were telegraph circuits and television reception. In such cases, the lines have either been placed in a metallic-sheathed cable to give effective screening or have been diverted.

As a generality, the cost of providing immunization of signalling and telecommunications equipment is included in electrification projects, and, where appropriate, an amount is included for the immunization of equipment on associated lines not currently proposed for electrification but where it is considered to be a sensible and economical provision for the future.

The introduction of electrification from Euston to Manchester, Liverpool, and Birmingham led the LM Region to initiate an investigation into the effects of train running at speeds up to 100 miles/h. The report, issued in March 1968, commented that, whilst the signalling system itself was quite capable of dealing with trains running at this speed, the apparatus physically connected to the track was very liable to wear and damage due to the additional vibration which arose in such circumstances. The slightest fall in track maintenance standards resulted in excessive deterioration, which was particularly apparent when equipment was fixed to the rails, switches or sleepers. As an example, the single core conductor wiring in point machines initially caused trouble, as vibration severed the single core, and these had to be replaced by flexible multi-core cables.

Over the years, difficulties have been experienced with track circuits owing to the breakage of track circuit bonds at rail joints, and of cable connections to the rails, and these increased as the general level of train speeds rose. Increases in breakages as speeds increased to 100 miles/h were estimated at around 20 per cent in the case of track circuit bonds and 50 per cent in cable connections to rails, although it was accepted that the problems with the bonds would be lessened to a great extent by the introduction of continuous welded rail, which could eventually eliminate the need for them. The incidence of track circuit failures due to the breakage of cable connections was accentuated by the use of mechanical tamping machines – a problem which has been overcome, to some extent, by greater care in fitting, in the first instance, and by disconnection when tamping takes place.

The universal use of track circuits and the increased problems these brought in the field of track maintenance, promoted considerable interest in the search for a design of continuous, or jointless, track circuit, which, unlike the conventional track circuit, does not require insulated joints to be inserted in the rails. It should be stressed that, so far as the signal engineer is concerned, jointless track circuits have no advantages. They are more elaborate and complicated than the ordinary jointed track circuit, and are thus more costly to produce and less reliable in operation. The benefit of the jointless track circuit accrues to the civil engineer, due to the elimination of joints in continuous welded rail and thus to the reduction in track maintenance costs. Overall, jointless track circuits are advantageous to install if the savings in maintenance costs exceed the extra cost of the track circuit equipment. The increased safety potential by the elimination of the joints is a further benefit.

Close headway working over busy lines requires fine limits of control and therefore a larger number of short track circuits than would be needed on less intensively used lines. The provision of frequent insulated rail joints to separate the track circuit sections in such lines would be even less acceptable to the civil engineer. Techniques which enable track circuits to be separated without the use of insulated rail joints have been known for many years and, on non-electrified lines, such track circuits are widely used. For some years, however, the search for a jointless track circuit suitable for use on electrified lines went unrewarded. The normal jointed track circuit can be used on electrified lines, providing the signalling power supplies are compatible with the traction supply. With d.c. electrification, therefore, track circuits use alternating current; with a.c. electrification, they use direct current or alternating current not harmonically related to the traction frequency. This simple solution is not applicable to jointless track circuits, however, as there is only a limited number of frequencies, within the limits of the basic traction frequency, which can be selected without risk of being affected by the presence of harmonics in the traction current.

A number of jointless track circuits have been developed which, although in use overseas to some extent, have been found to be incompatible with BR electrifications. Eventually, however, a design was developed – GEC Reed jointless track circuit – which works on a single frequency and has been proved to be satisfactory in use with continuous welded rail in electrified areas. This is currently being installed, as resources permit, pending the development of a more economic solution. One possible alternative is the ML Engineering TI (Traction Immune) circuit, developed in the early 1970s. This circuit, based on a French design, operates on two frequencies, but this has not so far proved to be superior to the Reed jointless track circuit. A further possibility is being investigated by the Research and Development Division which is carrying out a study to determine the optimum form of track circuit signal and receiver for providing safe and reliable track circuits on continuous welded rail in electrified areas. These studies are not yet complete.

Increasing speeds have accentuated the difficulties of obtaining adequate margins between trains for testing equipment, particularly where signalboxes have a fairly small area of control. This has resulted in inquiries having to be made of up to three or four signalboxes in order to obtain adequate time to carry out tests without delaying trains. The problem is less acute where power signalboxes control greater lengths of line.

The demand for speeds in excess of 100 miles/h has led to even greater problems. British Railways adopted, as a standard, a curve (known as the W curve) relating speed to stopping distance. This is in general use for resignalling projects with line speeds up to 100 miles/h and affords signal-post to signal-post braking, on the level. The curve indicates that, at a speed of 100 miles/h, the braking distance required is 6690 ft, which means a deceleration rate of 1·098 miles/h per second. For a train travelling at 125 miles/h, to stop in the same braking distance, a deceleration rate of 1·7 miles/h per second would be necessary. If the deceleration rate from 125 miles/h was to remain the same as from 100 miles/h, a braking distance of 10420 ft would be necessary. In the event, it was found that the High Speed Train and the Advanced Passenger Train, travelling at a speed of 125 miles/h, can achieve the higher deceleration rate and can comply with the W curve. These trains can therefore be utilized safely, at their higher speeds, on existing 100 miles/h routes, particularly in the light of the added protection given by the Automatic Warning System, further developed to cope with trains running at the higher speeds mentioned. In order to avoid penalizing higher speed trains on the move, and thereby causing unnecessary delay, a modification of the signal aspects governing diverging movements at certain junctions has been introduced. This has been achieved by allowing signals to display a flashing yellow aspect on the approach to a junction set for a divergence.

There is, however, little doubt that 125 miles/h is about the maximum from which it is possible to pull up with confidence, and with only disc brakes, in the distance allowed for 100 miles/h operation. Any increase much above 125 miles/h, say up to 150 miles/h, would demand further developments in the braking system, possibly supplemented by some form of cab signalling. Subsequent demands for yet higher speeds could entail a more radical change in the signalling system, possibly towards total automatic train control, although it is possible that needs might be met by the provision of a speed indication in the driving cab when line conditions permit the train to travel above 125 miles/h. When not in receipt of such an indication, the driver would be required to conform to the lower normal speeds and signals. Such a system is attractive for its simplicity relative to full automation.

The ability of the APT to negotiate curves at higher speeds than con-

Fig. 10.8   A transponder in the track about to be passed over by an express passenger train hauled by a Class 86 electric locomotive. Equipment in the driving cab at each end of an APT energizes the transponder, a pre-set coded signal is transmitted to on-train processor units, and the maximum permitted speed at which the train may approach a curve or junction is displayed on the driver's control console (BRB)

ventional trains has led to the installation of equipment on the London–Glasgow West Coast route which advises a driver in his cab of what his speed round a curve should be, if this differs from that of the normal hauled train. The system, code-named CAPT, uses about 500 passive coded transponder units fixed at intervals between the rails which, through train-borne microprocessor equipment, can provide cab indications of permitted maximum speeds (but not signal indications) and can lead to a substantial increase in both maximum and average speeds, with minimum adjustment to signalling installations. A transponder is a package of electronic equipment which is normally inactive and needs no external lineside power supply. It is activated by an inductive signal transmitted from a passing train by an under-floor aerial below the traction unit. Energy is thereby generated in the transponder to provide power to the solid-state circuits which create coded signals for transmission back to the train. The return messages are converted to a visual display on the driver's control panel of the speed limit at each particular location. Each transponder can only transmit fixed information set up in the electronic equipment by the manufacturers. In order to ensure the integrity of the information displayed, the microprocessors are duplicated and cross-checked. The equipment will only be installed on other routes if APT services are extended to them.

A factor which needs to be taken into account is the effect on line capacity of increasing train speeds, and the consequent widening of the gap between the slowest and fastest trains. Because of the closure of minor lines and the transfer of their traffic to the main routes, line occupation on the latter has increased. Higher maximum speeds of passenger trains have increased the difference between their speeds and those of the slowest freight trains. The commercial desirability of interval passenger services has limited the possibility of increasing line capacity by running trains in speed bands. Future signalling must be designed to give the desired line capacity without the expense of heavy engineering works, such as additional running lines. There will be an increasing requirement for two-way signalling, both for capacity reasons and to reduce the impact of a failure on following trains.

In the years up to and immediately following nationalization, consideration was given to the introduction of Centralized Train Control (CTC) – the remote control of signals and points at passing loops on single lines from a central control point – on certain routes in Britain, particularly in Scotland. The system was first introduced in the United States of America in 1927, as a means of reducing costs and delays in transit inherent in traditional forms of single line control and to improve safety where previously points were hand operated. The system was developed and introduced in other countries overseas and was reported to be completely reliable. In Britain, however, there was little evidence to support or counter arguments for such installations. Indeed, single lines in Britain were relatively short compared with overseas and did not normally have passing loops except at stations and depots, where local working was generally under the control of the station master or other supervisor, through ground frames released by the controlling box. The scope for the economic introduction of CTC was therefore less than in other countries.

Nevertheless, the Modernization Plan assumed that financial cases for CTC over certain routes would be forthcoming and referred to the fact that remote control of points and signals from a central point, over considerable route mileages of line, offered significant advantages, as compared with conventional methods of signalling. The Re-appraisal of the Plan, issued as a White Paper (Cmd. 813) in July 1959, stated that CTC would be introduced on a number of routes, totalling some 170 miles, over the next five years, enabling long stretches of single line, with intermediate passing loops, to be controlled from one signalbox.

In the event, virtually the only real CTC scheme which was authorized was between Craven Arms and Llandovery (60 miles) on the Central Wales line but this project was later cancelled. A modified form of CTC was introduced on the eight-mile branch line from Sittingbourne to Sheerness, Southern Region, with control vested in a new box at the former point. In general, however, it was found that the economics of other routes proposed would not support the heavy expenditure involved in installing CTC. Instead, a less expensive tokenless block system was developed for the operation of some of the surviving single lines. This method of operation, introduced in 1967, provides a means of checking the entrance of trains into a section and their arrival at the other end and eliminates the traditional crossing point exchange of tokens. In the first instance, the system relied on the operation of treadles at the section entrance and exit, but control is now exercised through track circuits. The system has been installed in a number of places, notably in Scotland, but, as a generality, it is now the practice to install conventional colour-light signalling, appropriate to the traffic conditions over the branch.

Automatic route selection, whereby the setting of routes can be based on the train describer system, was first introduced at Woking in 1969, to operate Pirbright Junction. The system in this instance was based on the use of first-generation electronic train describer equipment – that is, a train describer which does not operate through a computer. With such a system, route setting decisions are made by electronic circuity alone. A system of this nature has limited application, in both facing and trailing directions, according to the operating circumstances in the area, but the

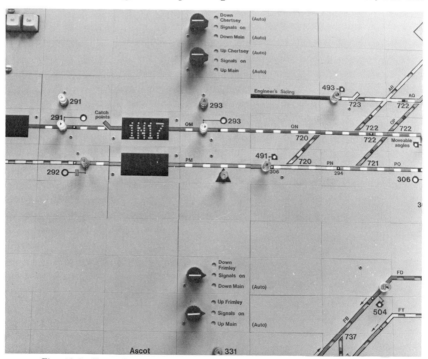

Fig. 10.9   Train describer indicators on the panel in the signalbox at Ascot.
Switches provide for automatic working of signals on the main lines and the up
and down Chertsey lines (BRB)

advent of computers as the basis of train describers removes the constraints imposed by circuit complexity. Facing junctions can be operated using train descriptions as an index to the required junction setting for each train and conflicting junctions can be operated, in timetable sequence, 'first come, first-served', or any other procedure which might be established. The new limits to the application of the system are the ability to specify a set of rules and the ability to set up file handling procedures for stored train information.

In the operating circumstances in heavily trafficked areas, automatic application of such a system, based on the working timetable, has some disadvantages, largely due to possible out-of-sequence train running at junctions, but even if this necessitates occasional manual intervention the effect must still be a significant reduction in the work-load on the signalman.

Facilities for automatic route selection will be installed where this can be shown to be advantageous, but in general they can only be justified in heavily worked areas, and then only after careful assessment of the operating benefits to be derived.

In order to take full advantage of the principles of electronic remote control, and bring really extensive sections of the railway under the direction of a single control installation, miniaturization of interlocking relays and control equipment, to reduce costs and the size of the control panel in the power boxes, is essential.

A further development has been the use of what is known as 'geographical circuitry', in which standard relays are arranged in the relay room in a manner corresponding to the actual relative positions of the signals and points which they control. The following are some of the advantages obtainable by the use of geographical circuitry in the conditions obtaining in Britain:

(a) A saving in time because the manufacture of a number of standard relay sets may be ordered immediately a contract has been let and before wiring diagrams are available.

(b) The wiring of the sets is undertaken at works in strictly controlled conditions by ͻmi-skilled or unskilled staff.

(c) The testing of the standard sets can be automated, with saving in time.

(d) Fewer installation staff are required on site.

(e) Multi-core cables, with plug connectors, are used to a much greater extent in relay room wiring than with conventional circuitry, leading to a considerable saving in time.

(f) Changes may be effected more simply and rapidly than with any other system by the rearrangement of relay sets and multi-core cables.

As a consequence of the drastic reduction in the number of signalboxes from which the passage of trains can be observed, and the distance from

Fig. 10.10   Geographical interlocking equipment in London Bridge
signalbox relay room (BRB)

them at which points may be operated, hot axle-box detectors and point heaters have been widely installed. Although considerable improvements have been made in the design and construction of axle-boxes, hot boxes do occasionally still occur. For this reason, it has been necessary to install equipment at appropriate points alongside the track to detect, by infra-red radiation, actual and incipient hot boxes, and to transmit the information electronically to a visual display unit in the controlling signalbox. The equipment, which operates through lineside scanners, can differentiate between left and right journals of wheelsets, detect more than one box running warm on one wagon, count the total number of axles on the train and identify the position of hot boxes. Since 1960, when the decision to introduce hot box detectors was first taken, the equipment has been installed at over 100 locations on the railway. The development of point heaters has already been referred to in Chapter Nine.

The signal and telecommunications engineers were very much involved in the design, development, and installation of the lifting barrier type of level crossing, installed from 1961 onwards. This subject is fully dealt with in Chapter Twelve. A further development in relation to protection at level crossings was introduced in May 1977 when the Southern Region installed BR's first level crossing signalling control system, with closed-circuit TV console and illuminated track diagram

Fig. 10.11   A close-up of hot axle-box scanning equipment installed in the track (BRB)

with train describer, at Barnes in south-west London. Two crossings are controlled from the main signalbox panel and three from the CCTV level crossing console in the same box. The system was designed and engin- eered by BR staff. Assembled in the signals and telecommunications workshops at Wimbledon, the new unit has switches for screen wipers and view selectors and an emergency link by barrier telephone for motorists, as well as monitor and crossing signal controls. In the Don- caster resignalling scheme, the new box will control seven level crossings, two on the main panel and five on a separate CCTV console. Such an

Fig. 10.12   'Servolarm' hot axle-box indicator panel installed in the signalbox (BRB)

arrangement reduces the work-load on the signalman. The Feltham box, on the Southern Region, had, for example, ten crossings controlled through the main panel.

Means of communication with the drivers of moving trains have been the subject of consideration and experiment for many years. Prior to nationalization what was in general terms called 'Automatic Train Control' was really the only means of conveying to drivers information regarding appropriate signal indications and even this was in operation in only isolated areas, apart from on the GWR main lines. Since then, a system more properly known as the 'Automatic Warning System' has been extended to virtually the whole of the railway. It is primarily a safety function of the signalling system and is therefore referred to in greater detail in Chapter Twelve.

Since nationalization, and the increase in train speeds and traffic densities, thoughts have increasingly turned towards the development of means of contact between a control centre on the track-side and moving trains, both for the display of signal indications in the cab and for the purpose of two-way speech, and as long ago as 1950 the possibilities of electronic links between track and train, based on radar techniques, were being explored. At that time, however, the problem arose of confining the pulses to individual tracks, as well as involving large numbers of relatively delicate valves in the apparatus.

In the early 1970s a train control project was being considered by the BR Research and Development Division. Its objective was the development

Fig. 10.13   Closed circuit TV cameras watching a level crossing. These are the 'eyes' of the signalman controlling the crossing from a signalbox some distance away (BRB)

Fig. 10.14 Junction Optimization Technique (JOT): prototype equipment in Glasgow Central signalbox. The VDUs show a suggested pattern of working at junctions to minimize delays to traffic (BRB)

of a comprehensive system of communication and control of train movement, involving data and speech transmission to and from moving trains. The function of the control system was to improve quality of service and to secure operating economy by increasing punctuality and utilization of track, rolling stock, and staff. The system was divided into a number of separate modules, compatible with each other and with existing signalling installations. Thus the total system could be introduced gradually in the most cost-effective way, to match the varying needs of the railway at different locations.

The basic module is an optimization technique for train sequence and platform occupation in complex junction and station areas. This is achieved by the inclusion of the working timetable, track layout features, platform working, and other information usually required by the signalbox controller in the regulation of traffic, into the train describer computer, to enable it to assess the location of all trains approaching a junction or station. The computer can then process and continually update the information and if traffic operations become out of phase with the timetable the signalman, by keying into the system, is offered, on a VDU, a suggested pattern of working which would cause minimum delay to traffic. An application of this kind – known as Junction Optimization Technique (JOT) – could have considerable potential for extension within the existing signalling system. Simulation studies carried out at the time the system was developed suggested that it could produce a significant reduction in delays in busy commuter areas. A two-year evaluation of JOT began at Glasgow Central in January 1978, the objective being to show whether computer-optimized decisions can be relied on. The results of this evaluation are now being studied, to establish whether there would be advantage in similar installations elsewhere, either at terminals or heavily worked intermediate stations. The major difficulty met with in reaching a decision is the setting of criteria by which to judge whether JOT, which can put forward propositions open to acceptance or rejection, can in fact do better than the signalman himself, if he is well trained and fully conversant with operations in his area. Further reference is made to this technique, and to the even more sophisticated Train Regulatory Advisory System (TRACE) in Chapter Eleven.

Various methods of track to train communication have been the subject of research and trial in recent years. There was 'wiggly wire', an inductive coupling system between coils mounted beneath the trains and two insulated wires laid between the running rails, which was developed to provide signal aspect and other communications in the driver's cab. Such a system would have been expensive and subject to vandalism, without giving balancing advantages in present operational circumstances, and would have added to the civil engineer's maintenance problems. A new form of automatic warning system – again referred to in Chapter Twelve – was also developed for trial between Bournemouth and Totton on the Southern Region. This was the 'Signal Repeating Automatic Warning System' (SRAWS). This provided a visual indication in the driver's cab of the next signal ahead, if within 275 yards of it, and an indication of the signal just passed until within 275 yards of the next signal. The system could be extended to provide continuous cab signalling without modifying the train-borne equipment and a two-way telephone between the driver's cab and the signalbox could be added, using the same communication link. After comprehensive trials, this system, like 'wiggly wire', was abandoned, but the research which had been undertaken led on to the development of a special purpose train-borne computer, for use in connection with high-speed operation, to monitor train speeds and indicate track information to the driver. Trials with this system on test track near Derby and in the Manchester area are referred to in Chapter Eleven.

By the mid-1970s, two systems – the inductive loop system and a system of radio communication from radiating transmission lines – were in the process of development and evaluation, jointly by BR and contractors. The former system utilized cables, initially unscreened, laid between the rails in a loop, so that the magnetic field coupled continuously with pick-up coils on the trains. Transmission quality varied and was adversely affected by weather conditions, and experiments are continuing with different types of cable. The other system – using radiating cables – is referred to again later.

The planning and implementation of signalling improvement schemes has been a major task within the railways, frequently hampered by shortages of staff with the right educational and training background, and by the generally somewhat spasmodic release of capital investment. For several years after nationalization, the planning of resignalling projects continued on a Regional basis, with little or no central co-ordination, except where they were to be associated with electrification schemes. In 1965, however, when A. W. Woodbridge was Chief Signal and Telecommunications Engineer at BR HQ, it was decided to introduce a National Signalling Plan, with the object of ensuring better use of staff, equipment and finance, and to secure progress in accordance with a proper programme of priorities. This plan, now known as the 'National Signalling Assessment' is periodically revised. Over the past 25 years or so considerable progress has been made in the introduction of multiple-aspect colour-light signalling, continuous train detection by track circuits, and progressive train description. So far, about half of the network has been modernized. Work continues on the remainder and may well accelerate, if resources permit, but it still remains a very long-term programme.

The revolutionary developments which have taken place in railway signalling are plain for all to see. Hidden from the public gaze, but of no less importance, are developments in the supporting telecommunications.

The BR telecommunications system is the largest and most comprehensive private network in the British Isles and it ranks highly anywhere in the world. Its evolution has not always been easy and many problems of organization and technique have had to be resolved to bring about the national system which has emerged.

In order to appreciate the span of the system it is necessary to go back to the situation at the time of nationalization, when BR inherited four separate telephone systems belonging to the former companies. These had all been developed independently, over a period of years, and offered little scope for expansion into an integrated system. During the time of the four main-line companies, some progress had been made in the cabling of open wire telecommunications circuits and in the installation of more modern, but still generally manually operated, telephone exchanges. Many miles of pole and wire route still remained, however, and the single-needle morse telegraph system, first used between Paddington and West Drayton on the GWR in 1839, was still widely in use. Very considerable extensions to the railway communications system had been made during the Second World War, 21000 miles of wire and 429 circuits being added to the pre-war network. The traffic control telephone systems had been given special priority in this expansion. As an example, a modern traffic control telephone system was brought into operation by the LNER at Edinburgh in October 1946, with selective calling to stations and signalboxes and a number of automatic extension connections to the local railway switchboard. Comments made by A. Moss, Signal Engineer of the LNER, in his Presidential Address to the Institution of Railway Signal Engineers in March 1948 – that it might not be too optimistic to envisage an automatic network of telephone and telegraph facilities, covering the whole of BR, and that the use of electronic devices might be possible in these contexts – were indicative of the way the thoughts of the engineers were turning at that time.

The resignalling project at York, completed in 1951, included provision for three comprehensive telephone systems, for normal and emergency use – operational circuits to traffic controls and adjoining signalboxes; signal-post circuits; and maintenance circuits. Apart from connections to control offices and other signalboxes, the operational system provided communication between the box and any station in the signalbox area. All running signals, except in the immediate vicinity of York station, were equipped with signal-post telephones, to enable drivers to contact the signalbox in case of emergency or delay. The third telephone system, for maintenance purposes, had a separate switchboard through which lineside loudspeakers, at half-mile intervals, could be operated, to contact linemen and others working on the track.

The Modernization Plan added fresh impetus to the development of the telecommunications system, although it was not specific as to the particular aspects to which main attention should be directed. The Reappraisal of the Plan, in July 1959, summarized the progress which had been made and indicated the general direction of development over the next five years. It called attention to the developments which had taken place in the use for railway purposes of v.h.f. radio, CCTV, and facsimile telegraphy. As to the next five years, technical advances, including developments in electronics, were expected to enable modernization to go ahead more rapidly and more cheaply. Manual telephone exchanges and omnibus circuits would be replaced by auto-exchanges, including local and trunk dialling, and increasing use would be made of facsimile reproduction and teleprinters. As an example, a new exchange to be provided at York would afford subscriber trunk dialling facilities with new exchanges at Middlesbrough and Newcastle, possibly by means of a microwave link. Subscriber trunk dialling would also be provided at new exchanges at Hull and Leeds. One thousand miles of open wire routes would be replaced by cabling.

The micro-wave link in the north-east was in fact the first such privately owned and operated telephone system in the country, providing subscriber trunk dialling for some 3000 railway telephones between York/ Leeds and Newcastle/Berwick-on-Tweed. The system was adopted because improvement in the internal on-demand subscriber trunk dialling service was urgently required and the annual costs incurred by a micro-wave system appeared to be less than those of any conventional cabled system. The link was introduced in 1964 but is now obsolete and will in due course be replaced by cabling.

Progress in the development of cables and means of insulation and immunization has played a major part in the provision of modern telephone and telegraph facilities and equipment. Generally, cables cater for long- and short-distance telephone circuits and provide the necessary conductors for the operation of traction supervisory and remote control systems. They are carried in line-side routes, usually of surface concrete troughing. These accommodate the cables required for railway signalling, as well as for trunk and local telecommunications facilities. In these circumstances, it has been found to be economical for the railway to install and maintain its own trunk cable network, rather than rent high quality circuits from the Post Office.

In the middle 1960s the British Railways Board initiated a study into the issues involved in installing a national telecommunications system which would provide all the facilities required for a modern business organization. As a result, in 1969, J. F. H. Tyler, then CS & TE at BR HQ, produced the Railway National Telecommunications Plan, its principal objective being to provide an automatic trunk dialling network between all business centres on the railway, as well as a good basis for data transmission services. In outline, the plan comprises some 50 main trunk-switching telephone exchanges, situated at strategic locations. In addition to the arrangements made for internal calls on the railway network, access is provided to and from the Post Office public telephone system. At present, all the switching equipment used in the automatic telephone exchanges is of the step-by-step electro-mechanical type, as is widely used by the Post Office in their public exchanges. The Post Office conditions regarding signalling and transmission standards have been observed. The railway system is now virtually complete, except for some peripheral additions which need to be made.

Electrified lines have required two additional telephone systems. One connects the electrical control rooms to stations, maintenance depots, substations, signalboxes, and plug-in points along the track. The other provides the essential control and supervisory functions for the power supply and distribution network. The pairs of wires over which the supervision and control of the power supply are performed are contained in the telecommunications cables but the supervisory equipment itself is provided by the CM & EE's Department. The increasing use of radio telephony, however, may in the future make it unnecessary for an electrification telephone system to be provided.

A telegraph switching system was introduced into the Southern Area of the LNER as early as 1938, to provide the facility of a direct service between wayside stations and to accelerate and raise the efficiency of the telegraph services generally. In the post-war period teleprinter equipment was gradually introduced, to replace the old single-needle telegraph system, but it was not until 1962 that a modern switching system began to emerge. In that year the LM Region established an electronic telegraph switching centre at Crewe, designed initially to link major centres and HQ, but with the ultimate objective of extending it to all the large depots and stations in the Region. The installation – known as STRAD (Signal Transmission, Reception, and Distribution) – has a capacity of 90 incoming and 90 outgoing channels, and was the first fully automated electronic installation in commercial service in Britain.

The equipment is designed to receive teleprinter messages and re-transmit them in the correct order of priority, in accordance with instructions transmitted as part of the message. Messages received for outgoing channels which are engaged or temporarily closed are stored and re-transmitted in correct priority and time sequence when the required channel again becomes available. Storage is available for approximately 300 average length messages on a magnetic drum, providing what is in effect essentially a short-term store, to meet the needs of peak traffic periods. Long-term storage, to meet the requirements of telegraph offices which close at night, is also provided, in the form of a magnetic tape machine, with a capacity of 3000 average length messages.

The development of the teleprinter network was another area requiring central co-ordination and a National Teleprinter Plan, complementary to the plan for the national railway telephone system, and covering the whole of BR, was therefore prepared. Under this, a total of 420 teleprinters throughout BR will be connected to a teleprinter message switching exchange at Blandford House, near Marylebone Station in London. This switching centre is now ready and the connecting-up process should be completed in 1980.

For a good many years the major railways of the world have been pursuing the development of systems to collate and process information on the various railway activities, to assist management in planning and controlling the use of resources, both human and physical, to meet the objectives of the organization in the most effective and economical way possible. British Railways have been as much involved in this activity as any other railway in the world and developments in train description and train control, already referred to, provide evidence of the progress made in this respect. A paper read to the Chartered Institute of Transport on 11 November 1974, by D. M. Bowick, then Chief Executive (Railways), BR Board, traces the development of computerization within BR, in relation to accountancy and paybill systems, personnel statistics, and production planning.

By far the most comprehensive data-based system to be introduced on BR, however, is TOPS – Total Operations Processing System. This is a computerized freight information system designed to help BR to revitalize its freight business. Its adoption developed out of a growing realization of the vital need for improved means of controlling the movement of rail freight – particularly the less than train-load element – and the utilization of the resources involved, if the reduction in freight volume which had taken place over the years was to be halted and reversed, and the costs of freight movement reduced. In 1967 a major planning exercise was launched to evaluate the principal alternatives available to management. The outcome – Freight Plan 1968 – indicated that a mixed train-load/less than train-load system, with a reduced requirement for terminals and marshalling yards, produced what were likely to be the best results for the freight business as a whole. Such results were dependent on a significant improvement in service quality, with better utilization of rolling stock, which could only be achieved by the introduction of a computerized system of control of resources and regulation of traffic.

The shortcomings of the freight business had been evident for some years and a number of projects had been evolved, during the earlier 1960s, to assist in eliminating some of the problems which had arisen. There had been a computerized system, known as Continuous Progress Control, in the Cardiff Division of the Western Region, using telephone contacts, which had assisted in controlling the wagon position in that area; a new system of freight rolling stock control was introduced at BR HQ, again involving telephone contacts, to secure better wagon utilization; and the Eastern Region had introduced a system of Advance Traffic Information, under which information on the composition and movement of trains was passed from yard to yard, using two-way radio within the yards and teleprinter and telex contacts between yards. All these helped towards some alleviation of the freight problem but the real need was for a fully comprehensive system which could take account of all the factors influencing the efficiency of the freight business – better rolling stock and terminal utilization, improved service quality, better service of information to customers, better matching of traffic to resources – and provide currently information which would enable managers to exercise better control over the business.

Systems in operation on overseas railways were investigated but only one – TOPS, operated by the Southern Pacific Railroad in America – came near to matching up to the British requirements. The system comprised a computerized database, with a filing system continuously up-dated from all significant points on the railway as to the location and state – loaded, empty or 'for repairs' – of the whole of the wagon fleet. Detailed examination confirmed that the system could be adapted to British conditions and outline plans were prepared. Over the next few months, those concerned with the development of the project – operators, computer experts, signal and telecommunications engineers – had the task of persuading top management, the BR Board, and the Department of the Environment that a control system was essential to the survival of the BR freight business and that TOPS was the system which

Fig. 10.15   The TOPS computer room, showing the monitor console of the 'on line' computer. The tape units in the background are used for storing 'historic' information. 'On line' data is contained in 32 disc packs, each capable of storing 100 million characters of information (BRB)

should be introduced. The project was finally authorized in October 1971 and its subsequent development and implementation, with the help of Southern Pacific staff and their American consultants, took four years.

The information required by the system is essentially the status and location of each wagon. Information is fed into the main computer through terminals at all the 150 or so Area Freight Centres (AFCs) established at marshalling yards and principal freight depots. An extensive and reliable data transmission network is an essential requirement for the successful operation of the TOPS system and it is in this context that the CS & TE has been heavily committed. The network must provide a highway for the rapid transfer of information between the AFCs and the main computer at Marylebone, in London. It was fortuitous that, for some years prior to the decision being taken to adopt the TOPS system, a substantial development in telecommunications had been undertaken on BR to provide a national network of line communications to meet the railways' telephone, telegraph, and data transmission requirements. It was fortuitous, too, that the National Telecommunications Plan had been initiated, to weld these developments into a co-ordinated programme. When the National Telecommunications Plan was conceived there were no large-scale data communications projects under development, but the telecommunications engineers realized that this requirement would grow in the future and some provision was therefore made in the plan for this purpose. In the event, the decision to adopt TOPS made it necessary to review the data transmission provision in the plan and, in certain areas, to incorporate additional facilities.

In pursuing the telecommunications requirements for TOPS, some organizational problems arose. The CS & TE at BR HQ is responsible for equipment standards and the development and co-ordination of national plans. The actual work on the ground is the responsibility of the CS & TEs in the Regions. The order of priority accorded to particular aspects of the plan was based, for the most part, on Regional operational requirements, as decided by Regional management. When the TOPS project was conceived and developed, however, it was recognized that, if the work was to be carried out within the tight time-scale which had been set, it would need to be wholly controlled from HQ. A team was therefore set up, under W. K. H. Dyer, to plan the transmission requirements; to research, design, test, and commission equipment; to settle priorities; and to oversee the actual progress of the work.

One thing is quite certain: TOPS could not have been implemented, at least until some years later, had it not been for the relatively advanced stage of the National Telecommunications Plan. In one respect, however, the plan, as drawn up and modified, did not match up to the high standard required by TOPS. It included the retention of the microwave radio link between York and Newcastle. It was found, in practice, that this link was insufficiently reliable for data transmission of the quality required by TOPS and Post Office lines were therefore rented for the conveyance of the TOPS information, pending the provision of BR cabling.

It is essential for any on-line computer project involving long-distance communication circuits to have an effective and versatile control. All TOPS data circuits are routed through the Communications Data Centre, which is adjacent to the central computer, and which monitors the operation of the equipment and the messages which flow through it. The team led by Dyer was responsible for a great deal of the original design work on equipment installed in the TOPS system, including the Data Centre. The Centre is staffed on a 24-hour basis and provides both a means of switching either lines or equipment to ensure continuity of operation should any part of the line system fail, and a rapid means of diagnosing the precise area of failure.

Telecommunications engineering involvement in the TOPS project also covered local communications. Whereas the data input/output terminals are sited in yards and depots, the telecommunications network interconnects principal centres of administration sited adjacent to large passenger stations. Local lines were therefore required to provide a transmission path from the data terminals into the trunk system. Over the years, the railways had developed a complex of local lines, some open wire, some cabled. They had been installed from time to time to meet miscellaneous requirements and their qualities and characteristics varied enormously. Some of the lines had been in use for many years and although they were giving admirable service their electrical characteristics were not consistent with the modern trunk networks. To have

Fig. 10.16   The TOPS Communication Data Control centre, through which all the messages between TOPS terminals and the central 'on line' computer are monitored and converted to computer 'language' (BRB)

installed a local network specifically for TOPS would have been prohibitively expensive. The network was needed to provide the essential links and furthermore had to be as reliable as the trunk lines and equipment. Existing local lines had to be pressed into service to meet the new burden of transmitting vital data and a considerable amount of engineering work was involved in bringing them up to the required standards. Teams of engineers were sent out, over the whole of BR, to investigate local facilities and equipment. An exhaustive examination of the lines and cables was carried out, adding and replacing as necessary, and when the engineers were satisfied that the best possible circuits had been identified between the data terminals and the trunk exchange, they applied, for an extensive trial period, artificial data over the circuits to confirm their suitability. TOPS offices also rely, to a large extent, upon getting their local information by telephone. This requirement greatly increased the use of local communications and involved adding extensions to exchanges in various areas. All these additional requirements had to be carried by the same distribution cable networks. Furthermore, a great deal of internal yard and depot communication was needed to provide information from the lineside, involving the provision of portable radio equipment and facsimile apparatus.

A further possible communications development within TOPS, considered at one stage but since abandoned, was the use of television at marshalling yards for the verification of inwards trains, with the pictures being transmitted to a receiving instrument in the AFC. There was some difficulty at first in obtaining a clear picture when trains were travelling at more than walking pace, but although this problem was overcome it proved impracticable to establish a viable scheme, including staff economies, for the general introduction of TV verification.

The basic justification put forward for the adoption of TOPS was to improve freight transits and thereby benefit the railway's revenue position; to improve wagon utilization and thus reduce the size of the wagon fleet and the costs of maintenance, modification, and new construction; and, by the combination of these factors, to secure better train loads and improved marshalling yard, terminal, and train working, leading to further savings. The system has been justified on these grounds alone – there was a total reduction of 38 per cent in fleet size by the end of 1978 – but it has been, or will be, extended to provide for other uses, including locomotive allocation, control, and maintenance; cripple wagon control; planned preventive maintenance of wagons; control of coaching stock. In all these further developments, the telecommunications engineers are, or will be, closely involved.

The growing demand for data transmission facilities led at one stage to the view that it might be necessary to develop a National Data Plan, compatible with the new teleprinter system, and designed to rationalize the provision of terminal and communication equipment for all data projects and to meet planned on-line computer activities in the future. In the event, data transmission techniques have developed so rapidly with the advent of the microprocessor that it has been advantageous to adapt existing computer networks to a much greater extent than was originally thought practicable to match emerging data needs.

Reference has already been made in Chapter Eight to the involvement of the signal and telecommunication engineer in the control of shunting in marshalling yards and, earlier in this chapter, to the interest in the development of communication between track-side and locomotive cab, both for cab signalling and two-way speech purposes. Indeed, the interest in the latter aspect goes much further back than nationalization. The first recorded instance of train to land telephones was in Canada in 1930 and telephones were installed on selected Continental trains used by business executives before the Second World War. During the war, as a further safeguard against the breakdown of essential fixed communications, a complete radio network was built up in Britain, with 42 fixed stations and 40 mobile rail or road sets. These had facilities for intercommunication, not only between centres on each railway, but also between radio stations operated by all the railways.

First experiments in v.h.f. radio communication were between the control tower and shunting engines in marshalling yards, suitable equipment for this purpose having been developed shortly before nationalization. Whitemoor up marshalling yard was selected early in 1949 for the first application of radio-telephony to practical railway operation in Britain. This was part of an extensive programme of trials sponsored by the Railway Executive in the application of radio to both traffic and engineering operations. A radio transmitter was provided in the control tower, with remote control in the foreman's cabin, and mobile equipment was installed on the first of four diesel-electric shunting locomotives to be fitted. The system was designed to reduce the unproductive time inherent in earlier means of communication between ground control staff and shunting locomotive drivers. It was likely to be of particular value in conditions of fog and snow. Transmission was usually between the foreman's cabin at the hump and the shunting engines but facilities were provided for the point controller in the control tower to break in and speak to drivers in an emergency.

Early in 1950 the General Electric Company designed a low power v.h.f. radio transmitter and receiver for use by railways and in other places where some rough usage might be expected. This was a 15/20 W frequency-modulated transmitter/receiver in a light-alloy case and was capable of selectively calling a large number of stations by a two-digit dialling system. It was demonstrated on a diesel shunting locomotive at Willesden. Around the same time, too, the experiments were extended beyond the bounds of the yards and on to the running lines, but at that stage it was found that distance, particularly where tunnels intervened, weakened the radio signals, unless relay stations were installed at appropriate points along the route. There were also experiments on the Eastern Region with radio-telephony as a link between traffic controllers and the drivers of a small group of diesel locomotives used on tripping wagons between the London area yards.

Later developments reflected considerable interest in the use of radiating co-axial cables to provide v.h.f. and u.h.f. communication. The range of natural radio propagation in tunnels is very poor – only a few hundred yards at most. One way of overcoming this problem is to use a cable from which the required radio signals radiate rather than from a conventional aerial. The special design of cable concerned is sometimes known as a 'leaky-feeder' because, when fed with radio signals at one end, it leaks small amounts of energy all along its length to be picked up by nearby mobile aerials. This principle can be used on railways to provide a continuous communication link to moving trains, by allowing receivers on the trains to detect the small amounts of energy radiated from a cable laid alongside the track. This technique can also be used with free space radio systems to fill in areas of difficult reception caused by geographical obstructions such as stations, tunnels, cuttings or valleys. The efficiency of the system depends very materially on the composition and screening of the cables chosen and a comprehensive field test programme was carried out by BR scientists and engineers, in conjunction with manufacturers, to evaluate the performance of many different designs of radiating cable.

Fig. 10.17   Telephone and operating console in driver's cab, for communication
with signalman and guard (BRB)

Since the late 1960s there has been significant progress in the development of voice and data transmission between a fixed point and a moving train, at relatively acceptable cost. The requirements to be met by a signalbox to train radio system have been defined as two-way speech between signalman and driver and between signalman and guard, via the driver and the train intercommunication system; the ability to limit communication to a particular train; the transmission of coded running instructions using VDUs; signalbox announcements to passengers via the train public address system; general calls by the signalman to all trains in his area, if required; and the extension of the facility to other telephones on the BR network. Radio communication is a pre-requisite of one-man operation.

A pilot scheme is to be introduced at King's Cross, with one of the Great Northern inner suburban electric multiple-unit trains, which operate in a restricted area with a number of long tunnels. The system operates in the u.h.f. band, where interference from electric traction is minimized, through a number of fixed transmitting and receiving stations located at the track-side. Radiating cables are used in tunnels, with repeaters in long tunnels where this is necessary to maintain the strength of the signal.

Direct signalbox to train radio communication can displace the signal-post telephone system and has other potential uses – for example, service monitoring, emergency reporting, and even as a basis for a signalling system over lightly used lines in conjunction with strategically placed transponders.

The growing demand for radio communication has led to the introduction of yet a further plan – the National Radio Plan. The plan is in two phases, to meet two major needs. The earlier phase provides for a blanket coverage of the railway system with a v.h.f. radiation network to give radio-equipped lineside and road-borne staff inter-connect arrangements to the general telephone network. The later phase of the project makes provision for the fitting of radio in the driving compartments of traction units, as described.

The first element of the National Radio Plan was introduced at Euston in 1977. It will be extended as far as Rugby in 1981 and to the North-East London and Tilbury areas of the Eastern Region as soon as possible thereafter. In Scotland, the Edinburgh and Glasgow suburban areas and the West Coast main line are now covered by a radio network of ten base stations controlled from the Glasgow Queen Street telecommunications centre. Portable and mobile radio sets enable technicians and lineside staff, such as permanent way gangs, to maintain a constant two-way telephone link, though they may be working miles away from the nearest telephone. The drawback to the system is again that radio reception is poor in tunnels and cuttings and behind obstructions, and before the Scottish Region network could become fully operational reception 'black spots' had to be identified. The task of charting radio reception along miles of railway in Central and Southern Scotland appeared formidable but it was accomplished in a matter of days by the use of IRIS ('Messenger of the Gods') a mobile laboratory operated by the Research and Development Division. By running along every line within transmission range of a base station, IRIS was able to supply data to pinpoint accurately all the locations where the radio signal was weak or non-existent.

IRIS is a converted railcar and ten-foot long aerials protruding horizontally from the buffers at either end enable her to simulate a man standing on the track using a portable receiver/transmitter. The base stations are energized as IRIS comes within range at speeds up to 70 miles/h and her recording apparatus automatically locks on to the correct frequency. A continuous signal emitted by the base station is passed into a field-strength measuring system and distance travelled is noted by a tachometer, whilst a technician seated in the driving cab makes a running commentary on the train's whereabouts. Simultaneously, the procedure is followed in reverse: IRIS transmits her own own continuous signal via the appropriate base station to the control panel at Glasgow Queen Street. Engineers can thus determine signal strength at that end. When the data are examined, the black spots can be tabulated for dissemination to the staff.

Present-day signalling schemes, both in terms of size and technical innovation, are far more complex than would ever have been thought of in the first years after nationalization. At the time this trend started to emerge, it was considered that the associated problems could be contained by an increase in the work force, both in design and development and in implementation. It soon became apparent, however, that this was not the complete answer and other methods of increasing design productivity were tried before attention was turned to the pros and cons of computer-aided techniques. The possibility of preparing signalling circuitry on a computerized basis was initially investigated by signalling contractors in the late 1960s, with the first tentative steps in production being taken about four years later.

There are three other main areas, apart from production, in which the computer can be utilized by the designer in the railway signalling field. The first is in relation to routine engineering tasks, such as the design of transformers and other equipment, and calculations as to power distribution requirements. The second category is the one-off design or feasibility study. Over the years, subjects investigated within this category have included jointless track circuits and wagon rollability and braking characteristics in marshalling yards. The third area of work is a computer check upon design, rather than computer-aided design, and can include simulation of the wiring at a particular installation with a view to the elimination of human errors. A particular benefit of checks of this nature is that wiring schedules can be prepared by the computer and extensive use of this facility has been made, with significant advantages in installation accuracy.

The employment of the digital computer in railway signalling design is still in its early stages. Undoubtedly, as the advantages of standardization are increasingly recognized and achieved, the influence of the computer in this field will grow. At the same time, the computer must not be regarded as the be-all and end-all in future design practice. Despite its advantages, human involvement in the generation of ideas and in planning the function which the computer can perform must continue to be accorded its full measure of importance in the design process.

Such is the rate of development in the electronics field that any record of achievement in signal and telecommunications engineering is almost certain to be at least in part out of date by the time it has passed through the publishing processes. Some developments in the future will depend upon need. If, for example, a vital commercial need arises for passenger train speeds of 150 miles/h or more, then no doubt means of cab signalling will be developed to meet the new requirement. Even now, as a step towards meeting a requirement of this nature, a pantograph which could operate at up to around 185 miles/h is in the process of development by electrical engineers: there is no reason to think that signal and telecommunications engineers could not come forward with a matching development. Again, developments in micro-processing, already involved in the supervisory control of electrification schemes, enabling large areas to be operated from one control room, will inevitably be an increasingly important factor in signal and telecommunications engineering.

There are suggestions that signalling control panels are too costly to install and occupy too much space and that they should be replaced by VDUs, which have already been used with some success in some areas for the display of selected information to signalmen, traffic regulators, platform staff, and the public. Experience has shown that VDUs with associated keyboards, to present coloured displays of certain types of information, are suitable for use as control consoles for rapid transit lines and in areas where traffic is comparatively light, but as yet they are not regarded as a practicable alternative to the control panel in complex control areas, except for displaying advisory information which only requires occasional reference. Optical fibre telecommunications systems, which transmit signals in the form of light pulses along thin glass strands instead of electric signals along metal conductors, and therefore give improved protection against inductive interference, are particularly beneficial in high capacity communications systems. Such systems could, however, involve high cost in the premature replacement of communication systems which are not life expired and are likely to be viable only in relatively few instances at the present time. Nevertheless, in the case of both VDUs and optical fibre communication systems, changing circumstances or further technological developments could produce an entirely different reaction.

Automatic Train Operation is already a practical proposition: automatic driving, with a traffic regulation system, can provide energy savings and improved operating benefits. Technological developments which have taken place, and are taking place, mean that the concept of the fully automated railway is no longer the nebulous thing which it was when talked about fifteen or more years ago. The timetabled working of trains along fixed tracks makes it that much easier to apply automation to the railways – an issue referred to again in Chapters Twelve and Fifteen.

CHAPTER ELEVEN

The Contribution of Technological Research and Development

RAILWAYS in Britain have been major users of industrial research during much of their existence. One of the world's first industrial laboratories was established at Crewe Works in 1864. Early in the twentieth century Churchward's determination to incorporate the latest technological developments into Great Western mechanical engineering practice made Swindon appear like one great laboratory complex. Until comparatively recent years, the research activities were, in effect, a service to a number of departments. It was what would be termed 'defensive' research in today's language, in that it was concerned with the application of scientific procedures to the improvement of existing railway practices. It could range from testing paints or fabrics for durability to the detection of fatigue in metals, the examination of the combustion process in locomotives or improving the riding of rolling stock. It was evolutionary in its character.

What is now called 'offensive' research is concerned less with the evolutionary development of existing railway practices, or the testing of materials, and more with the search for better systems. If we accept these definitions, then the scientific work which was applied to the development of the locomotive, whatever the form of traction, was defensive in its nature in that it was always seeking to improve on a known technology. Research and development entered the offensive, or more revolutionary, category when it began to question the technology itself. The two categories of research have co-existed since the wheel revolutionized methods of surface transport on land. George Stephenson did much to advance the evolutionary development of Trevithick's revolutionary application of the steam locomotive to rails. It was intended that the atmospheric railway, developed by Clegg and Samuda, would supersede the locomotive and thereby permit lighter forms of track and bridges to be used. The facts that Robert Stephenson rejected the system and Brunel found it to be a costly failure, do not deny that the atmospheric railway was one of the revolutionary, or offensive, types of Victorian research and development.

It was not, however, until the 1960s that the offensive research effort within railways in Britain was given the resources to take its place alongside the defensive research activities. In the early 1960s scientific research accounted for about 0·1 per cent of railway working expenses. Within a decade, the proportion had risen to over 0·6 per cent. Greater resources were then being made available for research in general and, in particular, for exploring in more revolutionary ways the technological boundaries of the railway as a system of transport. This increased spending included certain projects funded by the Department of Transport in the interests of national transport research. 'R and D' had come of age!

By the end of the nineteenth century there were eleven laboratories owned by the pre-amalgamation railway companies. The emphasis was in the field of chemistry and the work was concerned mainly with the investigation of locomotive feed water, lubricants, the calorific value of coal, and protective finishes; or the examination of goods to meet the requirements of the commercial departments. Most of the engineering research work was carried out within the civil and mechanical engineering organizations. The laboratories at Crewe and Horwich were well known for their metallurgical research and Sir Henry Fowler's work, particularly on nickel steels, achieved world wide application in wider fields than those of railways alone. Work on materials testing and development was generally carried out by materials inspection organizations within the engineering departments and had attained a very high level of efficiency on the four main-line Companies before nationalization.

There was also co-operation between the Companies in research activities. In 1924, the four groups combined in asking the British Non-ferrous Metals Research Association to undertake research into the wastage of copper firebox stays in locomotives. Another interesting example of co-operative research took place in the 1930s on the problem of the air resistance of trains. Both the LMS and the LNER were rivals in developing high-speed passenger services between London and Scotland, but neither had the proper equipment to evaluate the effects of streamlining and other measures to improve levels of performance at high speeds. The two Companies made joint use of the wind tunnel facilities at the National Physical Laboratory, one of the several research establishments under the control of the Department of Scientific and Industrial Research. Models of the trains used by both Companies were used for the tests, which showed that 29 per cent of the air resistance experienced by a ten-coach train was accounted for by the engine and tender. The tests also showed that 25 per cent of the power of the locomotive at 60 miles/h was absorbed in overcoming air resistance, even without wind effect. The streamlining of the trains used on both East Coast and West Coast routes was derived from this work. In his design of the 'beaver tail' observation car at the rear of the LNER's Coronation, Gresley showed that he was compensating for the 50 per cent additional

Fig. 11.1   Following air resistance tests in partnership with the LNER, the LMS Company
built its own wind tunnel at Derby (NRM)

resistance of the last coach over the coaches immediately preceding it: a
fact brought out by the tests.

Another area of collaboration between the Companies and the Department of Scientific and Industrial Research was in the work of the Bridge
Stress Committee, which was formed in 1923. Each of the Companies was
represented by a civil engineer, and the object of the Committee was to
study the resonance effect on bridges of locomotive hammerblow due to
the reciprocating parts being partially balanced. The findings of the
Committee, published in 1928, were accepted for the purpose of railway
bridge design in many parts of the world.

The LMS was the only Company within the four main-line groups to
co-ordinate and concentrate research work within a separate Scientific
Research Department. In 1928 a committee was formed with the purpose
of recommending the best means of encouraging scientific research within the Company. The committee drew attention to the need to provide
some systematic means of bringing to light problems ripe for investigation. The main problems for early attention proved to be the maintenance costs of rolling stock, and fuel economy. The new department
was established in 1931 by Sir Harold Hartley, who took the title of
Vice-President (Works and Ancillary Undertakings) and Director of
Research. It employed about 60 science graduates within its total com-
plement of some 150 men and women. Its work was guided by an
advisory committee, which included scientists of international eminence
and a scheme was introduced for the temporary interchange of the

Company's research staff with those engaged in academic work. It is of interest to note how the LMS described its newest department:

> . . . the department is the scientific consultant of all branches of the railway; it obtains information, gives advice or conducts investigations on probably a wider range of subjects than any research organization in the country, and a great advantage is its independent position.

Sir Harold Hartley contributed an article to *Modern Transport* on 11 June 1932, in which he described in some detail the early work of the LMS Scientific Research Department. Some of the activities would have been carried out in the engineering departments on the other Companies. One example coming within this category was the research carried out in the 1930s into the combustion process in the locomotive firebox. Indeed, the Chief Mechanical Engineer's department of the LMS did not find it easy to share what it considered to be its own responsibility in this field with the research worker. This particular episode did, however, have a happy ending. Stanier, who was Chief Mechanical Engineer at the time, employed his usual tact and delighted Hartley by sending him a personal letter to say that the practice recommended by the Scientific Research Department would reduce the Company's locomotive coal bill by 5 per cent.

T. M. Herbert took charge of the new department from the beginning and continued to be in control of a railway research organization for over thirty years. He was a mechanical engineer with a strong academic

Fig. 11.2   Hartley House, Derby. Headquarters of the LMS Company's Scientific Research Department in the 1930s (BRB)

background and successfully overcame the initial antagonism resulting from a separate department taking on work previously done within the organization of the Chief Mechanical Engineer. Along with a number of his successors Herbert was, however, generally to find relationships with civil engineers easier than those with mechanical engineers. Perhaps, this experience has had something to do with the nature of the work and the manner in which it has influenced the respective attitudes of the civil and mechanical engineering departments.

While the LMS had initiated a separate department for research, the other Companies carried out their research activities within those departments requiring the research work. The Southern, for example, had separate research groups, with specialized staff within the departments of the Chief Mechanical and Electrical Engineer and the Chief Civil Engineer. Reference has already been made to the research and testing work jointly undertaken by the LMS and LNER Companies in the air resistance study. A great deal of research data was exchanged between the Companies, but the only co-operative research organization to be established then did not deal particularly with scientific matters. Reference is now being made to the Railway Research Service, which was set up in 1923 in conjunction with the London School of Economics. Although this Service issued a Bulletin on railway research and development on a worldwide scale, it was primarily an intelligence centre covering all railway activities.

It was only to be expected that the development of the steam locomotive should be of almost obsessive interest to the mechanical engineer. George Stephenson was involved as early as 1818 in making a device to determine how hard a locomotive pulled; so helping to overcome the competition of the horse and the stationary engine. By 1837, I. K. Brunel, Charles Babbage, and Daniel Gooch had produced a true dynamometer car, which doubtless helped Gooch to improve on Brunel's reputation as the designer of mediocre locomotives. Increasingly sophisticated dynamometer cars were later introduced by a number of railway companies. All tests carried out on the line had, however, the disadvantage that the quality of the results was affected by weather conditions, operating circumstances, and the nature of the route. The locomotive testing station was designed to avoid the shortcomings of tests on the line, and reference has been made to the Swindon and Rugby installations in Chapter Five.

The Transport Act of 1947 both empowered the British Transport Commission to engage in research and required it to obtain the approval of the Minister of Transport to the lines upon which it decided to act. This acknowledged the Minister's interest in research but was much less positive than, for example, a later situation in the Federal Republic of Germany where legislation committed the Minister to ensure that the equipment and installations of the German Federal Railways accord with technical developments and are continuously improved. This is not only a direct encouragement to engineering research, but virtually an assurance that the results will be seen to be applied.

Hurcomb was not the kind of Chairman to overlook any clause in the 1947 Act, and within its first month of life the Commission decided to review the research organizations in the undertakings which it had inherited by asking a committee under the chairmanship of Sir William Stanier to submit a report. The committee proposed that a Transport Research Consultative Council should be formed and that the Commission should appoint a Chief Research Officer. The Minister of Transport duly agreed the proposals and Dr H. E. Merritt, formerly Technical Director of David Brown Tractors Ltd, was appointed to the position of Chief Research Officer in May 1949.

Merritt's task was not an easy one. He was required to supervise and co-ordinate the whole of the research activities throughout the Commission's Executives. Although a mechanical engineer with special expertise in motor vehicle transmissions, he was a newcomer to the world of public transport. His contributions to the literature of research were of particular elegance and he did what he could to co-ordinate research work. The Railway Executive had a research and development establishment of 300 people working in ten laboratories throughout the country. Furthermore, T. M. Herbert had been in charge of the Scientific Research Department of the LMS since 1931 and was appointed the Executive's Director of Research in August 1949. He was unlikely to regard the supervisory role of the Commission as being of a penetrating character. Under the formidable leadership of F. A. A. Menzler, the London Transport Executive also had a well-developed research organization and looked for no guidance from Commission sources.

The Railway Executive's research facilities were not integrated into one department until 1 January 1951, when the research and scientific testing of the other Regions were amalgamated with similar activities on the London Midland Region. These consisted in the main of the six chemical laboratories outside the former LMS Company, along with the two research organizations which had been established in the mechanical and civil engineering departments of the Southern Railway. The mechanical component of the Southern contribution was particularly strong in carriage and wagon matters, while the civil component moved from Wimbledon to Derby to form the core of British Railways research work on soil mechanics.

The new organization was made up of seven divisions, concerned respectively with engineering (under T. Baldwin), physics, chemistry, metallurgy, textiles, protective coatings, and operational research. With the exception of T. H. Turner from the LNER, who took charge of metallurgy, a former LMS man headed every division. The Operational Research Division worked from London, but the rest were located in

Derby, with a subsidiary engineering laboratory at Ashford on the Southern Region.

Although R. A. Riddles had overall responsibility for the research activity within the Railway Executive, he does not appear to have regarded it as anything more than a service to the engineer. Indeed, there is no mention of the word 'research' at any point in his presidential address to the Institution of Locomotive Engineers on 16 November 1950 with the title of 'Nationalization and the Mechanical Engineer'. This attitude was, however, little different from that of the Railway Executive as a whole in its early days. There seemed to be so much urgent work to do in the shortest possible time that research, whether concerned with commercial, operational, or engineering objectives could have the effect of inhibiting action. And the Executive was certainly not timid in the matter of taking action. The Commission would have sometimes preferred a little less action and rather more thought.

As in the case of railway motive power, mentioned in Chapter Two, there was a gulf between the attitudes of the Commission and the Railway Executive on the subject of research. In the case of research the difference in attitudes was of much less moment, although frustrating enough to Merritt. Hurcomb, as Chairman of the Transport Research Advisory Council – as the Consultative Council was later termed – wanted the Commission to be seen to be exercising some supervision over research activities. The Executive, although more concerned with other priorities itself, saw little purpose in the Commission involving itself with the subject. In November 1953 Elliot, who had succeeded Missenden as Chairman of the RE, made mention of his research responsibilities in giving an account of his stewardship to the Institute of Transport. The fact that the Director of Research reported direct to the Chairman instead of to the Member for Mechanical and Electrical Engineering, as in the early days of the Executive, showed how the attitude to research had evolved in British Railways.

The Transport Research Advisory Council met infrequently, but its members made many informal visits to the research establishments of the Executives. There is no doubt that the Council deepened the knowledge available within the different scientific disciplines, but there was some difficulty in reconciling the opinions of those who took a long-term view of railway engineering development and those whose main concern was to get new equipment into service. Even after five years of nationalization many passengers were still travelling in carriages which had been in service during the time of the First World War. In these circumstances, the production of new equipment, which would permit an overloaded railway to keep working, naturally took precedence over ideas of innovation in the list of engineering priorities. This conflict between short-term and long-term considerations is confined neither to research activities nor to railways alone and is normally resolved by the interplay of a number of factors, including the organizational methods adopted, changing circumstances over time, and the attitudes of the personalities involved. All these features have been present in the development of research in British Railways, but the point to be made clear at this stage is that the short-term considerations clearly exerted the greater influence during the earlier years.

The Transport Research Advisory Council had, as would be expected in these circumstances, a very limited influence on the course of railway research. Neither did the Research Co-ordination Committee make much impact. This body met monthly under Merritt's chairmanship with the purpose of co-ordinating research activities and avoiding the duplication of work in common areas. Herbert, and his opposite numbers in the other Executives, took part in these meetings. They reviewed progress in both scientific and operational research and made recommendations as to how the necessary work should be accomplished. As the main part of the Commission's research resources were with the Railway and London Transport Executives, Merritt could make very little progress without their co-operation. What progress that was made came mainly in such areas of chemical research as lubricants and protective finishes, which were matters of common interest to all the Executives. As if to compensate the Commission's Chief Research Officer for having no organization of his own, the Railway Research Service was transferred to his control. As this was confined to railways, and was an information service concerned more with commercial and operating than engineering matters, it would have been more logical to keep the body within the Railway Executive's organization.

In 1950, the first issue of *Transport Research Quarterly* was published by the Commission's Chief Research Officer. The aim of this publication was to promote a better understanding of research amongst its users and, at the same time, to develop a sense of unity between the research activities carried out within the Commission's undertakings. There was certainly a need to create the sense of unity: within the Railway Executive alone, the Engineering Division was only one of seven divisions spread over many locations. The new publication succeeded in promoting a better appreciation of the many aspects of research amongst users and gave those who were working in research an indication of what was being done elsewhere. On the other hand, the monthly meetings of the Research Co-ordination Committee proved to be a more direct channel of communication and the Transport Research Quarterly ceased publication in 1952. Although the Commission played a role in both stimulating and co-ordinating research, it was only when the railway activity was separated from the Commission's other undertakings in the 1960s that rail engineering research achieved its real thrust.

Merritt left the Commission at the end of 1951 and was replaced as Chief Research Officer by C. C. Inglis, formerly Deputy Chief Engineer at the Ministry of Supply's Armament Design Establishment. He was an electrical engineer with some early overseas railway experience with a firm of consulting engineers, although a newcomer to the Commission's service. Inglis was clearly not satisfied with the part being played by research in railway development, but he had little opportunity to make much impact until the Railway Executive was abolished in 1953. His relations with Riddles and Herbert were not of the happiest and the situation was not helped by what Inglis considered to be an unduly heavy influence of former LMS practice in the railway research organization.

It should be remembered, however, that some useful work was done in the early 1950s, particularly in respect of the problems of adhesion and the riding qualities of vehicles. Under both Merritt and Inglis further progress was made in liaison with the universities and other research organizations, including the Department of Scientific and Industrial Research. Included in this extra-mural work was a study concerned with the load–strain characters of pre-stressed concrete units, and another where Imperial College made a study of the problems associated with the icing of conductor rails on electrified services.

The individual Regions running electric services tended to devise their own de-icing solutions, but the Research Department had the role of developing the chemicals which were used. Another area where the chemist came to the assistance of the engineer was in the field of protective coatings, where the name of F. Fancutt is well remembered. The paints laboratory of the former Southern Railway moved to Derby along with the soil mechanics section to join the research headquarters of British Railways. A. H. Toms was well known to civil engineers for his contribution to the knowledge of soil mechanics. Another important contribution by the chemist was in the treatment of locomotive feed water, where T. H. Turner was very active over many years. Chemical research was later to play an important role in the treatment of cooling water for diesel locomotives.

Unification of the railways had not so much changed the course of railway research as it had enabled the available resources to be allocated to more effective purpose. It will be remembered that in the 1930s the LMS and LNER had to enlist the help of the National Physical Laboratory in connection with their air resistance tests. New equipment was slowly becoming available to British Railways, including a new wind tunnel which was brought into use at Derby in 1953. The range of engineering research and development was now widening. It included, for example, the behaviour of continuous brakes on heavy mineral trains and the associated problems of types of couplings, the over-heating of wagon axleboxes and the design of oleo-pneumatic buffers on wagons. These activities involved both the mechanical engineering and research departments. On the civil engineering side, permanent way studies were related particularly to track fastenings, concrete sleepers, and the longer term metallurgical work on the wear and fracture of rails.

It was only to be expected that the publication of the Modernization Plan at the end of 1954 would give a considerable boost to the railway research and development effort. Research staff resources were now augmented. Also, a limited number of design studies and development contracts were put into the hands of manufacturing industry. The Research Advisory Council was subjected to new pressures, and it was at this stage that the Technical Development and Research (TD and R) Committee was established. With a number of mechanical, electrical, and signalling studies placed with manufacturers, the work carried out within British Railways itself was now laying particular emphasis on civil engineering problems. To the work on concrete sleepers and their fastenings were added studies of rail joints and rail sections with the use of strain gauges, photoelastic, and mathematical techniques: the stability of long welded rails and the problems of stress in old bridges.

The Technical Development and Research Committee (referred to in Chapter Four) soon recognized the need to re-structure the research and development activities of the railway in order to meet the modernization requirements. In November 1954, or shortly before publication of the Modernization Plan the Commission appointed the Chief Engineers (R. C. Bond, J. H. Fraser, C. W. King, A. E. Robson, and S. B. Warder) and the Director of Research (T. M. Herbert):

> . . . to examine and report on the facilities for, and organization of, railway development work.

As the task was concerned only with the railway activity of the Commission, the role played by Inglis appears to have been on the sidelines, but he put to the group views which had been expressed to him by the Regional General Managers.

The group reported in May 1955. Their report firstly defined the different levels of research and development. These were described respectively as normal technical progress, the development stage, and research itself. Secondly, the report listed a very impressive list of all the development work currently in hand in each of the engineering departments. Thirdly, it listed the research projects currently in hand.

It was the fourth aspect which was, however, of particular interest because this recommended the establishment of three new development units, i.e.,

(i) A Carriage and Wagon Engineering Development Unit to provide facilities for the design and manufacture of experimental and prototype equipment. The location of the unit would be at Darlington.

(ii) A Locomotive Performance and Efficiency Development Unit to establish and maintain a continuous analysis of the technical and economic performance of diesel locomotives on all Regions of BR. The location would be at Derby.

(iii) A Signal Engineering Development Unit to provide facilities for the design and manufacture of experimental equipment and to supervise its testing in service. This unit was to be located in London but it never developed on the same scale as the mechanical engineering units. One or two projects were remitted to manufacturing industry for development.

The Chief Electrical Engineer was already carrying out development work in conjunction with the electrical contractors and the British Electrical and Allied Industries Research Association.

The new Development Units were the responsibility of the engineering departments. The overall control of the work was with the responsible Chief Officers on the British Railways Central Staff, but the units themselves were integrated with the Regional engineering departments. This arrangement seems to have worked very well.

In addition to the Development Units it was recommended that better test track facilities should be provided so that trials could be carried out to establish the riding qualities of vehicles, and their effect on the track. The new test installation, involving four miles of track near Derby, was the first of its kind in Europe and was the responsibility of the Research Department. At the same time a prototype, self-propelled, coach was built for the purpose of measuring and recording the condition of the track throughout British Railways. The Research Department maintained contact with the Development Units through the engineering officers on the British Railways Central Staff. It was at a later stage (1969–70) that the Melton Mowbray–Edwalton line was converted into another, and longer,

Fig. 11.3   The Old Dalby Test Track, showing the control centre and workshop (BRB)

stretch of test track, as part of the Advanced Passenger Train development programme. It became known as the 'Old Dalby' Test Track.

In 1957 the Research Department acquired its own digital electronic computer (an Elliott 402) to assist in the solution of scientific and technical problems. This was the first of a number of computers within the Department which could be applied to complex structural calculation. By 1963, when the equations involved in the study of wheel/rail dynamics had been formulated, the calculations were shared between the Elliott 402 and computer resources outside British Railways. The contribution made by the computer in widening the scope of railway research in Britain has been of fundamental importance.

In the late 1950s the Research Department had not only acquired new facilities which would greatly increase the scope of its activities. The attitude to research was changing, and it was decided that speculative research work should now be allocated its own share of resources. The Department had clearly consolidated its independent status and its relationships with the engineering departments were to enter a new and sensitive stage. A programme of what has already been described as offensive research could not now be far away. In effect, this programme had to await the 1960s before being able to get into its stride. By then further new facilities would be available and the British Transport Commission would be replaced by the British Railways Board with subsequent re-shaping of attitudes and the railway system itself. Meanwhile, there

Fig. 11.4 Early research with the fibre-glass/PTFE section insulator at Wilmslow, Cheshire, in 1954. A pantograph trolley running from a 'live' to 'dead' section of test rig overhead equipment to determine the burning effect of the electric arc (A. H. Emerson)

was ample research and development work in connection with the implementation of the Modernization Plan to keep engineers in all departments fully occupied.

A great deal of the research effort had for example to be directed towards the solution of problems emerging from the swelling flood of diesel and electric traction. Steam locomotives, with their reciprocating parts partially balanced in the wheels, had always made their impact felt particularly on bridges. The newer forms of traction had comparatively little effect on bridges but their small diameter wheels were having a more severe effect on rail joints. In addition, the higher speeds being achieved with electric and diesel traction were accentuating the need for new bogie designs and having a disturbing effect on short wheelbased freight wagons. The question of freight wagon derailments will be considered in the next chapter.

Research in the electrical engineering field was concentrated in two main areas. One was concerned with the complex problems of pantograph and catenary. The other was related to the continued use of d.c. traction motors on the new 25 kV a.c. lines and was to lead to significant weight and cost savings in electric locomotives.

In the signalling area a development contract was placed which resulted in the world's first electronic signal interlocking system. This was installed at Henley on Thames in the Western Region in 1961, following co-operation between BR signal engineers, Imperial College of Science and Technology and Mullard Equipment Ltd. A further electronic interlocking installation, manufactured by the Westinghouse Brake and Signal Company Ltd was introduced in 1963 at Norton Bridge between Stafford and Crewe on the London Midland Region. Another project which had its roots in the late 1950s was an automatic wagon recording system, designed to register and transmit the identification numbers on passing freight wagons.

In mid-1961 the Technical Committee at Commission headquarters reviewed the course which research and development should take in the next five years and in the longer term. The Heads of Departments and Regional General Managers expressed their views. R. C. Bond, then Technical Adviser, made clear the attitude of the engineering departments at that time. In short, this was that the main contribution of research and development in the short term was to help operators and engineers to reduce maintenance and operating costs and to improve substantially the reliability of the existing rolling stock and equipment. Other matters for immediate attention were the heating of diesel-hauled passenger trains and the outstanding decisions on the braking of freight trains. In the longer term Bond referred to the speeds which were envisaged when the Modernization Plan was first published, i.e., average speeds for express passenger trains of 75 miles/h with maximum speeds up to 120 miles/h according to route and average speeds for freight trains of 45 miles/h with a maximum speed of 60 miles/h. He advocated that the costs of achieving these passenger train speeds should be established and that a study should be made of optimum speeds for freight trains.

Early in 1962 Bond was again making his views on research and development plain as he was becoming concerned about the planning of the programme. He emphasized that the only object of research was to increase revenue and/or reduce costs and was clearly of the opinion that there was a situation developing which required careful control by a body involving the interests not only of the research and engineering departments but also representing the commercial, operating, and financial points of view. His experience of working with the Scientific Research Department on the LMS had alerted him to the sensitive situation existing between a separate research department and the engineering departments in the grey areas of evolutionary development. There was a new element in these views which was to be a cardinal – and almost unique – feature of research in British Railways. Research was no longer to be thought of as a service to any particular department but to British Railways as a whole. In quite another context it is of interest to observe that the Regional General Managers were to be included in the proposed control body. Bond was putting forward his views in February 1962 with the decentralization of 1953 nearly a decade away, but realized all too clearly that any lack of Regional involvement in the decision-making stage could result in lack of interest at the stage of implementation.

In the late 1950s it was evident that the physical equipment available for research and development was inadequate for the task. The need for a new engineering laboratory had been recognized at the time of publication of the Modernization Plan and the necessary development was begun. The scheme was delayed by the financial position of the Commission at that time and the consequent commitment of all available resources to the elimination of steam traction. Meanwhile, the digital computer acquired in 1957 – the first to be installed in Western Europe for railway scientific and engineering applications – was housed in a temporary building in Derby. At the same time there were two further research and development innovations. Spectrographic analysis of diesel locomotive engine sump oil (which had been the research task of S. Bairstow) became standard practice throughout British Railways and trials began of disc brakes fitted to passenger carriages.

In 1959 the Commission authorized the building of the new engineering laboratories at Derby, but another year was to pass before the scheme was approved by the Minister of Transport. No doubt, the Minister's decision was assisted by the Report of the Parliamentary Select Committee in July 1960, which took the view that the Commission would gain by spending more money on research.

Engineering research, development, and testing within British Railways had never been the exclusive preserve of the Derby laboratories.

Regional activities were co-ordinated, but had not lost their vitality. As would be expected from the inheritors of the Great Western tradition, which cherished its own standards regarding weight of rail, depth of wheel flange, and vacuum brake pressure, the Western Region retained a strong research capacity. The locomotive testing plant at Swindon was now working largely to a co-ordinated programme laid down by the Locomotive Testing Committee created by the former Railway Executive while the reports prepared in the Region's Civil Engineering Laboratory bore the legend 'British Transport Commission'. Even so, the Western Region's research activity had a personality of its own.

Under the guidance of M. G. R. Smith, the Region's Chief Civil Engineer, this laboratory began a large testing programme in 1953. In 1961, it produced a report entitled 'Experiments on the Stability of Long Welded Rails', which was concerned with the stability problem associated with the use of long welded rails and the precise functioning of the various factors involved, particularly regarding longitudinal movements due to thermal forces. The results of this study confirmed the earlier findings of the Southern Railway from their site measurements at Hildenborough in 1938. A young civil engineer, D. L. Bartlett, who had been very closely associated with this Western Region study, was appointed Assistant Director of Research under T. M. Herbert in 1960. Later, as Director of Research (Engineering), Bartlett was to be responsible for the development of the new Engineering Research Laboratories at Derby.

The new laboratories were opened by HRH Prince Philip, Duke of Edinburgh, on 14 May 1964, or one hundred years after the opening of the first railway laboratory at Crewe Works. It was appropriate that the new buildings (which earned a Civic Trust Award for Dr F. C. Curtis, the Commission's Chief Architect and A. H. Cantrell, Chief Civil Engineer of the Southern Region) were on the opposite side of the road to laboratories built by the former LMS Company, named after Sir Harold Hartley, and opened by Lord Rutherford in the 1930s.

At the time of opening, the British Railways Board (which replaced the British Transport Commission in 1962) clearly had in mind its commitment to re-shaping the railway system and concentration on main trunk routes when it included in the brochure produced for the opening ceremony the following down-to-earth view of its research responsibilities:

> The major objectives to be achieved with the aid of research and by the more rapid adoption of advances in the technology are:
> (a) Reduction of the cost of providing and maintaining routes of adequate quality.
> (b) Increased route utilization by improved signalling and train control.
> (c) Increases in train size and pay-load.
> (d) Safe high speed operation of large trains.

(e) Improved performance and reliability for all equipment, accompanied by savings in capital and maintenance costs.
(f) Cheap terminal handling of freight. In particular, cheap road/rail transfer of freight which must be road borne at one or both ends of transit.
(g) Avoidance of damage to freight.
(h) Improved passenger comfort.

By the exclusion of any reference to speculative research the Board reflected its concern with financial viability as its dominating priority. The physical re-shaping was, however, being accompanied by a wider re-shaping of ideas about the future of the railway. The commercial revolution was in full spate by the mid-1960s and the results of the new commercial research were known to those engaged in engineering research. Fortunately, this was a reversal of the situation when the Modernization Plan was being drawn up in 1954 and investment was planned for a railway which was later to be shaped into a new commercial environment. It was inevitable that the major research objectives outlined by the Board with such apparent clarity would be pursued in an imaginative manner with the help of the Research Department's increased resources.

By this time the Department had been re-organized and had three main divisions. These were Engineering Research, Electrical Research, and Scientific Services. Operational Research and Commercial Research were not within the Research Department and by 1968 were to form the nucleus of the Board's new Planning Department, before being involved in later changes.

The new facilities available to the Engineering and Electrical Research

Fig. 11.5   General lay-out of the Railway Technical Centre at Derby (BRB)

Divisions were of a very high order when introduced in 1964. They became part of the Railway Technical Centre, which was extended in 1967, 1970, 1971, and 1975. The Centre houses staff concerned not only with research, but also mechanical engineering design and development, workshops, and supplies. The creation of the Centre has greatly facilitated the transition of projects throughout the stages from research through design to development and manufacture. Also, it has brought scientists into daily contact with engineers and so benefited mutual understanding. This unique blend of theoretical and practical expertise made Derby a focal point for world-wide interest in railway technological development.

The new laboratories owed much to the persistence of Inglis and the support of Robertson. The opening ceremony took place during Beeching's time as Chairman of the British Railways Board and during the year when Inglis retired. The twelve years as Chief Research Officer had begun with many difficulties for Inglis, but had ended with the realization of one of his main objectives.

From 1962 Inglis was assisted by Dr Sydney Jones, who joined the Research Department when Herbert retired. Jones, who succeeded Inglis in 1964, was a scientist with a background in defence research work and electrical engineering. He felt strongly that railway engineering would benefit from an injection of the modern scientific techniques with which he was very familiar. In particular, he sought agreement to start a new investigation into the causes of vehicle instability and bogie riding. This proposal was not welcomed by the Chief Engineer (Traction and Rolling Stock), who carried out his own development work on bogies, as has been described in Chapter Eight. Eventually it was agreed that there should be a fundamental investigation carried out into wheel/rail interaction by the mechanical, civil, and research engineers. This was to have very fruitful results.

In the mid-1960s a deep division existed regarding the purpose and use of research in British Railways engineering. J. F. Harrison, as Chief Engineer (Traction and Rolling Stock) was heavily involved with such problems as standardizing main-line diesel designs, absorbing the English Electric Deltics into the fleet and technological evolution in a number of fields. A. N. Butland, Chief Engineer (Way and Works) – it will be remembered that engineering titles at this time reflected a strongly European influence! – hardly felt the need for the help of the Research Department unless it confirmed his own views, expressed with such vigour, on the permanent way of the future. Those who were present when Jones was in disputation with these two engineers well remember the occasions, as neither of them found it easy to suffer even wise men gladly when in pursuit of departmental objectives.

In effect, the Chief Engineers thought that the efforts of the Research Department should either be associated with these objectives or engaged in pursuing the possibilities of the less conventional forms of guided transport which were attracting a great deal of public attention at this time. Jones, however, felt very strongly that the traditional system of steel wheel on steel rail had a great deal of untapped potential if it were only to be subjected to fundamental re-thinking. If these opposed views had been held by weaker personalities, the results could have been unfortunate in any industry in comparable circumstances. In British Railways the debate was creative in that the engineers involved were stimulated to achieve results either by the process of evolution or by returning to first principles. What none of the parties concerned could have realized at the time was the extent to which their involvement in the work on wheel/rail dynamics would prove to be the very basis of further railway technological advancement. Jones and his team had a deep conviction in the potential value of this fundamental investigation in particular, and in scientific methods in general. Otherwise, criticism, and even ridicule, of research proposals which sometimes appeared naive to the traditional mind could have had a withering effect on their work. It was also fortunate for the research activity that Jones became a Member of the British Railways Board in 1965 as this focused more attention on research than it had ever enjoyed in previous years.

Now that Derby possessed such a large and advanced centre of research, Jones had the task of attracting a team of the right calibre. It was not only necessary to seek out highly qualified staff; they had to be provided with the management environment which would give them the opportunity to develop their work. Bartlett left Derby in 1965 and later became Managing Director of the Board's subsidiary company British Rail Hovercraft Limited, of which Jones was Chairman. S. F. Smith, who had been involved with gas turbine development at Rolls Royce, became the new Director of Engineering Research and a number of other engineers were recruited around the same time to spearhead the engineering research effort at Derby. At British Railways Board Headquarters, Dr K. H. Spring, formerly an electrical engineer with the Central Electricity Generating Board, became Headquarters Research Manager and, later, Head of Research.

With new laboratories available, more engineers recruited and objectives set by the Board, the scene was set for a determined assault on the research priorities. The main factors in determining the research priorities were, as R. C. Bond had outlined in 1962, to increase revenue and/or reduce costs. This was an advance on the emphasis placed more on cost reduction alone by the LMS in the 1930s, but did not go as far as the research responsibilities set out by the British Railways Board in 1964 when the new laboratories were opened. Passenger comfort, high speed operation, and the optimization of railway route capacity were examples of specific targets for research. The situation was now changing, in that while most of the existing research work would continue, more initiatives would be taken in wider fields to explore the technological horizons of steel wheel on steel rail in the achieving of these objectives. The commercial attitude was no longer one of looking to technology to protect the rail share of the market: it was geared more towards the maximum use of technology in expanding the profitable sectors of the market. This was the opportunity, therefore, for both the commercial and the engineering research approaches to move from the defensive into the offensive area.

The interaction between wheel and rail was now the top item on the list of offensive research activities. It had been a source of interest – sometimes anguish – to engineers since the very dawn of railways. The arrival of the Research Department's own computers had prepared the way for the mass of mathematical calculations which were needed, but the course of the studies altered following the recruitment of A. H. Wickens in 1962 from the aircraft industry to take over the work on vehicle dynamics. The work was now aimed at an understanding of the dynamics of vehicle riding in the belief that this would lead to better vehicle design criteria and possibly identify the important features of track construction. It was soon evident, that it was the vehicle and not the track that, in general, limited railway performance. The Advanced Passenger Train (APT) as a concept was directly derived from this work on wheel/rail dynamics, and was designed to exploit the revenue of the existing main-line route system of Britain by improving the speed and comfort of the service to the passenger at minimum cost. In addition to this more dramatic result of the

Fig. 11.6   Part of the Vehicles Laboratory at the Railway Technical Centre, Derby (BRB)

wheel/rail studies, there have been a number of other developments resulting in better suspension systems on conventional vehicles, reduced vehicle maintenance costs, and lower track maintenance costs.

It is important to remember that the APT did not emerge fully formed from a scientific mind and that studies of vehicle riding did not begin with the opening of the new engineering laboratories. The work on vehicle dynamics was, however, developed on a more scientific basis from 1963. A 'linear' theory of the lateral stability of the four-wheeled vehicle was developed. The adequacy of this theory in predicting the behaviour of vehicles was demonstrated by a closely related series of tests using analogue computers, digital computers, model roller rigs, full-scale roller rigs, and track testing. These tests culminated in the production of a four-wheeled vehicle which rode stably with worn wheel profiles on a roller rig at 140 miles/h and on the track at the line limit of 90 miles/h.

The form of the APT was taking shape while the work of producing the four-wheeled vehicle which would be stable at high speeds was also in progress. By 1967 it was known that, to meet the commercial objective, a passenger train had to be made available which would run over the existing tracks and cut the fastest current journey times by one third. Today's APT has been described in Chapter Seven but, to achieve these objectives, the engineering research requirements were:

(a) High power-to-weight ratio and good braking performance which would permit high but smooth rates of acceleration and deceleration.

(b) The ability to curve at high speeds with no flange contact and to run stably at high speeds on straight track with worn wheel profiles. The initial service trains would have a top speed of 125 miles/h with a design capability of 150 miles/h and a 'development stretch' up to at least 200 miles/h, given suitable track alignments.

(c) A tilting suspension designed to maintain passenger comfort on curves. Speed on curves has always been decided by passenger comfort: not by the risk of overturning. The tilting suspension enables existing curves to be traversed at higher speeds without discomfort and with complete safety.

With evidence becoming available that the engineering research within British Railways was producing results of real significance to a wider world of transport, Jones began to seek financial support from outside BR itself. After some months he gained interest from a number of sources of some influence, including Lord Zuckerman, the then Scientific Adviser to the Cabinet. During 1968 agreement was reached between the British Railways Board and the Ministry of Transport for joint funding of the APT, which would cover the development of an experimental train along with the design and production of two prototype trains. Among the later extensions to the Engineering Research Laboratories at Derby was an Advanced Projects Laboratory in which the experimental (known as 'E') train was assembled, using the combined resources of the Railway Technical Centre and the BR main workshops. This laboratory had full facilities for the roller rig testing of the two power cars and also of components, such as transmission and brakes. It was also possible to make use of the Old Dalby high speed test track between Melton Mowbray and Nottingham. This test facility is equipped with both jointed and welded track, along with a typical selection of main line curves and gradients.

It has earlier been described why the APT began its experimental life powered by gas turbine engines and then switched to electric traction. It has also been explained that the diesel-electric High Speed Train (HST 125) was introduced as a means of closing the unacceptable gap between the speed potential of the locomotive hauled Inter-city train and the APT. It was possible to incorporate some of the research findings from the development work on the APT into the technologically more conventional HST 125. For example, the HST's bogies, suspension and aerodynamic design represent the result of a close association between research, design, and development staffs involved in the two projects. From 1973 onwards, the APT became the development responsibility of the Chief Mechanical and Electrical Engineer.

The next chapter will describe how the theory of vehicle dynamics was applied to the solution of a problem threatening railway safety, due to the derailment of short wheel-based freight wagons. The high quality of the research contribution in the field of railway vehicle dynamics was recognized in 1977. In that year the McRobert Award, administered by the Council of the Engineering Institutions was shared between British Railways Board and Westland Helicopters Limited. This award is made annually 'where in the opinion of the Council, an outstanding contribution has been made by way of innovation in the fields of engineering or the other physical technologies . . .' The names of Sydney Jones, K. H. Spring, A. H. Wickens, A. O. Gilchrist, and M. Newman were associated with the work and the MacRobert Award lecture was given on 21 February 1977 with the title 'Railway Vehicle Dynamics – A Practical Theory'.

The train control programme was another major part of the offensive category of railway engineering research. The logic of railway signalling has much in common with the wider science of digital arithmetic, and signalling had much to gain from the burgeoning development of electronic computers. Chapter Ten has described how train control grew from the basic conception of a number of block sections controlled by visual signals; later supplemented by mechanical methods of interlocking designed to ensure safety at points and crossings; also by track circuits to detect the presence of a train. More recently – and as will be explained in Chapter Twelve – these control devices were supplemented by an automatic warning system, which automatically applied the brake if the driver did not observe the audible indication given to him in the cab. .

The Research Department's work on train control can be traced back over a number of years, although its history does not go so far back as that of vehicle dynamics. The concept of full train control started from the proposition of continuous two-way communication between track and train mediated by electro-magnetic inductive coupling between sensors on the locomotive and a continuous conductor laid between the tracks. Such a system permits the driver to know at all times the state of the track ahead, and gives him warning also of permanent and temporary speed restrictions. In the ultimate it provided the possibility of completely automatic driving; the speed at any point being limited by the most restrictive condition, whether determined by the train ahead, track conditions or the performance of the train itself. The system also provides a central control point with continuous information of the positions and speeds of all trains within a specified area. In this situation it is possible to adhere to an optimum traffic pattern, and the position can be newly optimized if there is any departure from the planned operation.

During the late 1960s practical work on the train control concept led to the development of a series of systems. After the necessary development work by manufacturers on track conductors, also on train-borne miniature computers and other components designed in the Derby laboratories, the results of the research into train control systems were tested in different locations on British Railways. Chapter Ten has referred to the Junction Optimization Technique (JOT), introduced at Glasgow Central to give the signalbox staff current advice on how to deal with trains following a departure from the planned working. A more advanced version of JOT, known as Train Regulation Advisory Control (TRACE) has been developed to deal with a multiplicity of problems over a dispersed geographical area, such as, for example, those in London controlled from London Bridge or Victoria.

The BR Automatic Train Operation (BRATO) was tested in service on the Crewe–Manchester main line near Wilmslow. It was a track-to-train system designed for more complicated train patterns than commuter type services. It is possible that this system will be enhanced to receive instructions from JOT and TRACE so that automatic operation to optimal parameters can be achieved. A much simpler form of automatic system has been designed for the remote control of locomotives hauling 'merry-go-round' coal trains between colliery and power station.

The development of the APT Control System (CAPT) now installed throughout the West Coast Main Line between London and Glasgow preceded BRATO. CAPT includes track mounted transponders and train-borne microprocessor equipment as a means of providing the driver with a display of permitted speed at any point on the journey. It enhances the conventional signalling and automatic warning system by permitting the driver of the APT to exceed the line speed limits applicable to a conventional train. The limitations of the conventional signalling system at present preclude APT being operated at its designed maximum speed, which is in excess of 150 miles/h. Chapter Ten has described the system.

It has been seen how the research activities concerned with vehicle dynamics and train control methods have led from one new development to another. For example, the experience accumulated on the design of suspensions from the dynamics studies has been of great value in the development of new designs including the Mark III carriage, the HST 125 and the Class 56 diesel-electric freight locomotive. High speeds and/or heavy loads have, in turn, required consideration to be given to comparable developments in the technology of braking. The hydrokinetic brake was initially developed to meet the requirements of APT. Again, the attainment of maximum tractive effort in relation to weight on driven wheels has created the need for detailed studies of adhesion. Many solutions have been tried, including the application of several different chemicals and a method of cleaning the rail surface, but the most successful development to date is the high-speed sander. Studies have shown that water is the more critical factor than oil, which was previously thought to be the main cause of low adhesion.

The results of engineering research have improved the prospects for further main-line electrification. Much work has been directed towards improving the performance and reliability of the existing type of equipment and to reduce the costs of its maintenance. On the traction side, the

Fig. 11.7   The Tubular Axle a.c. Induction Motor (BRB)

main development has been in heavy current electronics and thyristor control, particularly static invertors for induction motor control. The Tubular Axle a.c. Induction Motor (TAIM) generated world-wide interest when it was first produced in 1977 as it eliminates much of the equipment associated with conventional motors, and also has potential as a very efficient rheostatic or regenerative brake. Another traction development has involved the lightweight electric battery. A very promising design of cell has been produced at Derby for the sodium-sulphur battery and this is another step towards the ability of electrically powered trains to operate away from electrified routes.

The dynamic behaviour of both pantograph and catenary systems has long been an area of major research activity in order to solve the problems of collecting power at higher speeds from the existing overhead systems; also in developing future systems. Novel methods such as energy collection without physical contact between wire and pantograph, have also been researched. Some of the most valuable work has been in improving the performance of insulators, particularly where high pollution conditions are experienced. The reductions made possible in the clearances required between the live, and other, parts of lineside structures have had a very favourable impact on the costs of electrification. Facilities available to the electrical research team at Derby have included the test coach (MENTOR), which can run at up to 150 miles/h, and a dynamically scaled overhead line installation on a research track. This line installation has enabled test trains running at speeds of, say, 90 miles/h to produce in the equipment being tested the effects of running at twice the speed.

The requirement placed on engineering research to increase train speeds and loads has created the need for higher standards of track maintenance. On the other hand, the other requirement to optimize the use of the tracks has had the effect of reducing the time available for maintenance. Fortunately, civil engineering research and development over the years has helped to prepare for this situation. Before nationalization in 1948 the Companies had begun the work which was later to cover almost every aspect of railway track. The list includes soil mechanics, blanketing methods, the switch to flat bottom rails, choice of steels, the stability of continuously welded rail, rail end stressing, concrete sleepers, better track structure, and the mechanization of maintenance methods.

With this impressive background of the continuous development of the permanent way, it was to be expected that the Research Department's Track Laboratory would seek to build on earlier work by developing a method of construction which would virtually eliminate track maintenance costs. The result was Paved Concrete Track, known as PACT and described in Chapter Nine. The use of pre-cast concrete slabs is another form of track without ballast, which has been under investigation.

Metallurgical investigations into steel rails, welding, and fracture behaviour have long been a major research activity in connection with

Fig. 11.8   The dramatic effect of the deliberate application of heat to rails during tests on
the Old Dalby Test Track. Less than one quarter of a second separated
these two pictures (BRB)

conventional track systems. The quality of the measurement of track geometry has been greatly increased by the introduction of new equipment such as the NEPTUNE trolley, the TRIM mobile laboratory and the High Speed Track Recording Coach (HSTRC), which can be attached to any inter-city train in routine service.

Many of the bridges, tunnels, and buildings which have to be maintained by the civil engineer were built over a century ago, and are today being subjected to stresses beyond the expectations of the original builders. The engineers at that time did not have available the scientific techniques of structural analysis which are well known today. Research studies have assessed the performance of a variety of types of structures as well as examining methods of maintenance and re-conditioning. A special technique has, for example, been devised for the protective coating of the Forth Bridge – that apex of painting endeavour – and protective measures have been developed for new bridges which have proved more effective than paints alone. Among these measures are surface grit blasting and aluminium spray techniques.

The science of aerodynamics has come a long way since the LMS and LNER initiated their air resistance experiments. In particular, the aerodynamics of vehicles moving at high speed close to the ground is a highly complex subject. Considerable experience has now been gained, particularly in tunnels, which has assisted the development of high speeds and contributed to the conservation of energy at these speeds. The importance of aerodynamic considerations is illustrated by the fact that they account for some 70 per cent of the drag experienced by a conven-

Fig. 11.9   Stanton Tunnel, on the Old Dalby Test Track used for aerodynamic tests (BRB)

tional train travelling at 100 miles/h, compared with about 30 per cent attributable to rolling resistance.

Other areas where research and development have been expanding the technological boundaries within which a guided system of transport works relate to accoustics, non-destructive testing, plastics development, linear motors, and non-contact suspension systems (there is a magnetic levitation test track at Derby). There is good reason for the work of the British Railways Research Department increasingly to be recognized as part of Britain's transport research effort. The Department of Transport's annual reports on Research and Development describe the activities which are carried out by British Railways, but funded by the Department. British Railways' research is almost equally divided between basic (i.e., offensive) research and research as scientific support to the different parts of the railway. The Government contribution currently amounts to approximately half the cost of the basic research, or about one-quarter of the total BR research budget.

Research is a form of enterprise with a high risk element. If this were not the case there would be little incentive to any innovative development. Sometimes, the outcome of engineering research has been disappointing. One example arises with regard to freight wagons, where the investigation of the structure of the wagon underframe involves the problem of damage caused by shunting operations. The oleo-pneumatic buffer was designed to lessen the effect of impact, and attention was then directed to improving the methods of retardation in marshalling yards. The Dowty line of individual retarders proved to be a great step forward in this field, but arrived at a time when, for commercial reasons, it was decided to concentrate on train-load working with the consequent demise in Britain during the early 1960s of several large marshalling yards. Again, the original four-wheel wagon suspension design that emerged from the wheel/rail dynamics studies was too expensive for profitable freight operations and had to be produced in a simplified form in order to be commercially acceptable.

Both cost and timing were drawbacks associated with the train control system known as the Signal Repeating Automatic Warning System which will be described in Chapter Twelve. These examples of research and development work, in both vehicle and train control fields, illustrate the importance of endeavouring, as far as possible, to anticipate change and for the marketing requirements to be made known to the research engineer through the constant interchange of ideas. It is to be emphasized, however, that while an engineering development may sometimes be too early or too late for it to make the maximum commercial impact, the research experience can often prove to be of great value in another area.

If it is to be successful research must be inter-dependent as an activity rather than independent of all supervision, or dependent on sponsoring departments. The experience in British Railways was that when research was a departmental service it did little more than bring scientific method to the aid of evolutionary change, although this does not diminish the value of the results. It meant that they were confined to the area of defensive research. When, however, the research effort was given a more independent status in the 1960s, it is unlikely that it would have made such progress as it did in wheel/rail dynamics or train control without firm support at Board level. The point at which real progress began to be made was when it was recognized that the two groups of professionals – the traditional railway engineers and the innovative scientific engineers – were in partnership, irrespective of the department in which they were located.

The remarkable achievements of research in British Railways have been due to the skilful partnership which was evolved between engineering in its academic and practical forms. The Railway Technical Centre at Derby has provided a unique opportunity for bringing together the skills of the Research Department, the development expertise of a department with railway working responsibility (that of the Chief Mechanical and Electrical Engineer) and the manufacturing capacity of British Rail Engineering Limited. The project itself, and not its departmental associations, is now what really matters.

The inter-dependence between research and wider engineering activities is reflected in the membership of the Research and Technical Panel, which now guides the research effort of British Railways. Its chairman is I. M. Campbell, Vice-Chairman (Rail) of the British Railways Board and Chairman of Transmark, the Board's international consultancy company. With him sit I. D. Gardiner, Managing Director of British Rail Engineering Limited, Dr K. H. Spring, Dr A. H. Wickens (now Director of Research), W. W. Maxwell, Chief Executive of London Transport Railways, and the Chief Engineers at BR Headquarters responsible for civil, mechanical, and signal engineering (i.e., M. C. Purbrick, K. Taylor, and A. A. Cardani respectively). The Panel also includes two eminent scientists from outside the industry: Professor Sir Hermann Bondi and Sir Eric Eastwood.

The role of the manufacturer of railway equipment in the field of research and development has been very considerable, but requires its own story to be told. The place of British Railways within the wider world of railway research will be considered in Chapter Fourteen.

CHAPTER TWELVE

The Pursuit of Safety

S AFETY can be described only in a negative way as being freedom from the state of danger. As danger in some form is always present in any activity, absolute safety is unattainable. Because it is unattainable, the pursuit of safety will continue to be one of the engineer's most dynamic activities. The closer that transport moves towards absolute safety, the harsher will be the operational and financial penalties of every incremental advance. The challenge to the railway engineer has always been in attempting to achieve the advance without incurring the penalty.

The aim of the engineer has been to devise equipment which, combined with high standards of discipline in the observance of safety regulations, will progressively eradicate the causes of accidents. In achieving this aim he has been constrained by cost, the technological limitations of the day, the need to keep railway traffic moving, and the lack of agreement between former railway managements on the actual techniques to be adopted for universal use.

Public opinion has always been the ultimate regulator of transport safety. On the one hand, public opinion abhors accidents but, on the other, would not today tolerate the restrictions, such as speed limits on road or rail, which would be low enough almost to eliminate injury to life or limb. Not only are acceptable levels of safety swayed by emotional rather than rational factors, but the British public appears to tolerate different safety standards on road and rail. According to Lt-Colonel I. K. A. McNaughton, Chief Inspecting Officer of Railways in the Department of Transport, in his paper 'The Price of Safety' delivered as the Sir Seymour Biscoe Tritton Memorial Lecture to the Institution of Mechanical Engineers on 17 January 1977, a railway accident rate equivalent to that on the roads of Britain 'would imply an accident rate more than 10 times higher than at present, with six or seven significant train accidents every day and perhaps two accidents as serious as Moorgate each year.'

There are several reasons for different safety standards on road and rail. One is the high value placed on the personal mobility provided by the motor car. Another is that the individual road unit at risk is smaller and, therefore less newsworthy than the larger numbers involved in a train.

Most important of all, however, is that the discipline and engineering integrity, which have become associated with a railway, in themselves create the expectation of safety. Public reaction to the fire in the Penzance to London sleeping car train at Taunton in July 1978, or to the collision at Hassocks in the December of the same year, show the extent of that expectation and the likely impact on public opinion if incidents of this kind were to occur several times in one day. The railway safety record in Britain has been improving over recent years and any worsening would be no more tolerated by public opinion than it would be countenanced by railway management. The British rail safety record not only is good, but is expected to be good.

It is important to remember that this record has not always been good. The opening of the Liverpool and Manchester Railway in 1830 was marred when William Huskisson MP was fatally injured by Stephenson's *Rocket* and Joseph Locke's driving skills could not compensate for the locomotive's being without brakes. Later, Queen Victoria herself was to write to Gladstone's Government and express her concern on the matter of railway safety and to reflect the state of public alarm. Legislation in 1840 (Lord Seymour's Act), together with the amending Act of 1842, set the

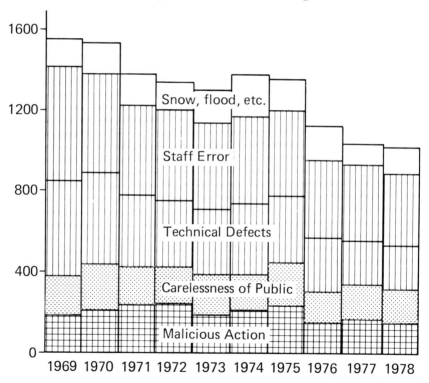

Fig. 12.1   Train accidents in Britain 1969–1978, showing the declining proportion caused by staff error and technical defects (HMSO)

safety machinery in motion by establishing a department of the Board of Trade with the special duty of supervising the activities of the railway companies. Official accident records were kept from 1840. One year later, the Board of Trade was exerting its new authority and recommended the better training of locomotive drivers. Like those men who first handled the controls of motor cars or flying machines, they sometimes took a sporting view of transport. Human error and lack of proper co-ordination in those early days were all too frequently accompanied by inadequate equipment and the failure of materials. The Bromsgrove and Hemerdon accidents in 1840 and 1849 respectively resulted from boilers bursting, while broken wheel tyres accounted for the accidents at Southall in 1847 and Dixenfold in 1853.

Perhaps the most important railway safety aspect of the 1840 Act was that it resulted in the appointment by the Board of Trade of Inspecting Officers of Railways. This led to the creation of the Inspectorate, now responsible through its Chief Inspecting Officer of Railways to the Minister of Transport. The functions of this Inspectorate in respect of British Railways are:

(a) The statutory approval of new works on railways carrying passenger traffic.
(b) Accident investigations, including the holding of formal inquiries.
(c) The giving of technical advice to the Minister on general railway matters.

The existence of the Inspectorate has done nothing to diminish the safety responsibilities of the railway itself. The Inspectorate's recommendations for passenger lines and requirements for goods lines must be met before new railways are opened, but it is not responsible for the safety of operation or of railway works after the inspection has been completed. Neither are the recommendations made by Inspecting Officers following accidents enforceable on railways, although they have rarely been rejected, at least in this century. Tribute should be paid not only to the unique contribution of the Inspectorate to railway safety, but also to the partnership established between it and the railway engineers and operators in the shaping of safety recommendations. It is of interest to remember that I. K. Brunel opposed the concept of the Inspectorate, but George Stephenson welcomed it.

Most of the early contributions to railway safety have been mentioned in earlier chapters, particularly in the growth of signalling practice and when discussing engineering research and development. It is useful, however, to enlarge on their safety implications and to introduce some chronological grouping. The basis of railway safety was established in the 1840s. Not only was safety brought within statutory supervision, but some important developments arrived on the signalling scene. In 1841, space-interval block working was introduced and proved to be safer than the time-interval system. In the same year was invented the detonator, which could be placed on the rail to give an audible warning of danger to approaching trains. One of the early contributors to railway safety was C. H. Gregory who, also in 1841, introduced the first semaphore signal. Two years later, he introduced the first form of wired interlocking between points and signals at Bricklayers Arms Junction in South London, but Saxby's system, fitted at Kentish Town in 1856, marked the beginning of reliable mechanical interlocking.

In the 1870s, the positive tappet interlocking lever frame designed by the Stevens brothers and Tyer's needle block system established the foundations of modern signalling safety. It was also in the 1870s that the mechanical engineers made a significant contribution to safety through advances in methods of braking trains. Today, it is difficult to believe that passenger trains travelling at speeds of 60 miles/h had to rely only on brakes applied on the locomotive tender, or in special vans at either end of the train, unless the train happened to be fitted with new equipment such as Webb's chain brake, or the Smith non-automatic vacuum system. It was, for example, not until 1876 that any of the Great Northern Railway's fast-running single driver locomotives designed by Stirling had any brake other than a hand brake fitted to the tender. During brake trials held on the Midland Railway at Newark in 1875, the automatic continuous brake proved its efficiency and was destined to replace other systems.

If the trials in 1875 proved the efficiency of the automatic continuous brake, its necessity was to be confirmed in 1889. On 12 June in that year eighty-five lives were lost at Armagh on the Great Northern Railway of Ireland when ten carriages of an excursion train fitted with the non-automatic type of vacuum brake ran backwards down a gradient and collided with a following train. This accident helped to determine the shape of the Regulation of Railways Act of 1889, which proved to be the most momentous year in the history of railway safety in Britain. The Act made the automatic continuous brake compulsory on all passenger trains in Britain. It also made compulsory the interlocking between points and signals along with the introduction of the absolute block system of signalling. All these cornerstones of British railway safety were already being shaped, but the Armagh accident created the demand for urgent action. No other railway accident has ever been followed by so many significant developments, but it will later be seen that there has been a strong correlation between major mishaps and the great steps forward in the evolution of railway safety measures.

The second half of the nineteenth century also saw a progressive reduction in failures of materials, which had been a serious cause of accidents on early railways. Boiler explosions had been reduced in number following the introduction of John Ramsbottom's locomotive safety valve, which could not be adjusted by a driver to increase steam pressure beyond the safe limit. More exacting boiler tests, along with the replacement of iron by steel in boiler construction, had also made their contribution. Wheels, tyres, and axles improved in quality, and the new process of shrinking forged or rolled steel tyres onto wheels dramatically reduced tyre failures. Rails also greatly improved in quality in the 1870s. By then, the use of timber for the main structure of large bridges had ended, and by 1890 cast iron had been replaced by wrought iron or steel. The collapse of the Tay Bridge in 1879 had confirmed some of the doubts about the use of cast iron raised following the less dramatic Dee Bridge accident in 1847, which temporarily tarnished the engineering reputation of Robert Stephenson.

With the arrival of the twentieth century there was a noticeable change of emphasis in railway safety. Examination of the reports of the Railway Inspectorate shows an increasing pre-occupation with the mitigation of the effects of accidents rather than with their causes. The Act of 1889 had created the foundations of safety, and it was now necessary to concentrate on refining equipment and working methods. It can be seen from the reports that growing importance was attached to the elimination of gas lighting in trains, to more robust rolling stock, and to better designs of buffers and couplers. General standards of signalling, staff discipline, and materials had by 1900 reached a standard which was an example to the rest of the world. In 1901, for the first time since records began, not one passenger lost his life in a railway accident in Britain.

Much of the credit for this high standard of safety must be awarded to the absolute block system of signalling, which had proved to be very effective in keeping trains apart on the same section of line. Similarly, the automatic continuous brake and interlocking between points and signals had more than justified their cost. There was, however, one weapon which was missing in the armoury of safety. This was a form of 'interlocking' between trains and signals, which would not permit a train to pass a signal in the danger position. The Hawes Junction mishap in 1910 confirmed the need for the electric track circuit to give a positive reminder to the signalman of track occupation. The Aisgill accident in 1913 showed that further safeguards were necessary and stimulated interest in automatic train control (ATC). This was to become the subject of much argument and experiment, and will be considered in later paragraphs.

Having considered the development of railway safety in Britain, and before considering the contribution made by engineers since 1948, it is appropriate to summarize what safety on railways requires. There are three groups of requirements. First, there is the primary requirement which predicates high standards of discipline by the staff in observing regulations, and a high degree of reliability in the case of equipment. Discipline is assisted by a comprehensive rule book and meticulous observance of the rules. Reliability of equipment needs sturdy construction to standards which often involve weight and cost premiums as part of the price of safety. The 'fail-safe' characteristic of railway signalling equipment is an example of the extent to which safety measures have been taken.

Second, although railways are a guided system which is inherently safe if these staff and equipment requirements are met, the primary stage requires to be supplemented by a series of devices which can intervene if staff and/or equipment prove fallible. Amongst these devices are the absolute block system of signalling, the interlocking of points and signals, the automatic continuous brake, track circuits, runaway catch points, treadles depressed by passing vehicles, axle counters, hot axlebox detectors, automatic train control, emergency regulations, and the careful scheduling of equipment inspection.

Third, there are the precautions necessary to minimize the effect of any accident which the primary and supplementary groups have failed to prevent. These include the design of rolling stock to minimize the effect of impact, where the all-steel vehicle, the buckeye coupling, and the use of safety glass along with fire resistant materials have made their contribution. The development of railway safety has been characterized by the absorption into the primary group of the other two stages as they have progressively emerged.

Reference has already been made to the Railway Inspectorate within the Ministry of Transport, and to the lecture delivered by the Chief Inspecting Officer of Railways on 17 January 1977. In his lecture, Lt-Col McNaughton described the relationship between the railway and the Inspectorate as resting on the following principles:

(i) The responsibility for the safety of operation of a railway must rest with the railway company.
(ii) Once a railway has been opened, the railway company is responsible for maintaining it to the standard necessary for safety.
(iii) The Government cannot be held responsible for the safety of structures designed and built by railway companies.

A railway line in Britain does not operate until the Inspectorate declares it safe, which is another example of the 'fail-safe' principle. If a bridge on that line were to collapse shortly after being opened (as happened in the case of the Tay Bridge Disaster) the responsibility would lie with the railway and not the Inspectorate. It is the responsibility of the Inspectorate to determine the cause of an accident after holding an official inquiry. What is reportable as an 'accident' can range from a major collision involving many casualties to an individual passenger bruised by a carelessly opened carriage door, and the inquiry procedure is not involved in every case. All cases are, however, recorded and classified under the following headings:

Collisions and derailments

Fires

Failures

Level Crossing Accidents
Trespassers
Movement accidents
Non-movement accidents

The inquiries into accidents and the subsequent reports by the Railway Inspectorate have created a background of case law, which has formed a frame of reference of great benefit to the progressive improvement of rail safety in Britain. Although the engineer is concerned with the elimination of all types of accident, he has been particularly involved with the first four of the above categories and they form a suitable basis for considering the contribution which he has made.

Collisions have always been the most dramatic of railway mishaps. The cause is usually the result of an error made by a train driver or a signalman. Collisions have been declining over recent years, due primarily to developments in signal engineering which have already been described. In effect, the very success in Britain of the primary rail safety system, and its secondary developments, was a reason for automatic train control (ATC) not becoming standard equipment throughout the country until comparatively recently. There have always been deep-seated objections to the introduction of any equipment which could be considered to sap the degree of vigilance exercised by those responsible for rail safety. Even the introduction of the telegraph was resisted on these grounds, and ATC was regarded in the minds of some engineers and managers as likely to weaken the driver's contribution to safety. Time has proved these views to be wrong. Although it could be claimed that one or two serious accidents occurred on lines equipped with ATC (including that in 1940 on the Great Western at Norton Fitzwarren), the list of accidents which would probably have been avoided if it had been in operation is much longer. It included the serious collisions at Welwyn Garden City in 1935, Castle Cary in 1937, Harrow in 1952, and Lewisham in 1957. In 1952, Lt-Col G. R. S. Wilson, Chief Inspecting Officer of Railways, estimated that 10 per cent of the accidents in the previous forty years, which had been the cause of formal inquiries, might have been prevented or mitigated by ATC.

Until ATC was introduced, the signalman had more equipment to protect him against making errors than was enjoyed by the driver of the train. A number of devices had been introduced over the years to maintain the vigilance of the driver, particularly under single manning conditions. The 'Dead man's handle' on electric trains, which required constant hand pressure to be applied to prevent a brake application, was an early development. More sophisticated vigilance control mechanisms were later designed, including the example on the electric locomotives running over the Manchester–Sheffield–Wath route, of a button which had to be pressed by the driver at intervals no longer than one minute. These devices did not, however, alert the driver to the position of the signal which his train was approaching and this could only be done by visual observation, detonators placed on the track, or ATC.

ATC, although a widely used abbreviation, was never an accurate way of describing a number of methods, ranging from cab signals to automatic stop devices, designed to lessen the risk of a signal being passed at danger. Today, the use of the term automatic train control is even less appropriate, as it more correctly describes systems using electronic equipment to control the starting, stopping, and speed of trains. During the 1950s British Railways switched to the more suitable term 'Automatic Warning System' and the abbreviation AWS will be used in this chapter to describe all applications previously referred to as ATC.

AWS has a long history as, from comparatively early days, railway engineers experimented with methods of producing audible or visual signals in the cab of the locomotive. The aim was particularly to assist drivers in locating signals in foggy conditions and to avoid the use of fog-signalmen, although colour-light signalling was later to overcome many of the fog problems. The Boult system of transferring signals to the locomotive by means of magnetic effects was patented in 1893 and introduced experimentally on the Great Northern Railway. Another limited example of cab signalling was the Miller system introduced in 1903 on the Western approach to Woodhead Tunnel. It was not sufficiently robust to survive Pennine weather conditions and was not extended.

Britain's first practical installation of cab signalling dates back to 1896, when Raven's mechanical contact system was introduced on the North Eastern Railway. It involved a pendulum lever on the locomotive, which was struck by a lineside stop co-acting with the running signal whenever the signal was not in the clear position. A whistle was also sounded, but no brake application was made. Later, as Chief Mechanical Engineer of the North Eastern, Sir Vincent Raven brought in an electrical development of his mechanical system. This was taken to the extent of providing a route indication in the cabs of locomotives running over some sections of the line.

Another sophisticated system, which by 1922 covered forty route miles on the suburban lines running out of Marylebone Station in London, was known as 'Reliostop' and was developed by the Great Central Railway. The Company's Signal Engineer, A. F. Bound, and Chief Locomotive Draughtsman, W. Rowland, were associated with patenting the system. With Reliostop a driver approaching a distant signal would hear a warning siren and a partial brake application would be made. If the distant signal was showing the caution aspect, the siren would again be heard, and a brake application made on approaching the stop signal. A stop signal passed at danger would result in an irrevocable full brake application.

There were many adherents in Britain to the view that safety standards would suffer if drivers came to rely on aids to the strict discipline of visually observing signals. They drew attention to the fact that railways in a number of countries with far worse safety records than those in Britain were being compelled by legislation to introduce some form of AWS. This attitude was not based on opposition to a new form of equipment, but on the belief that a driver using it would become less alert in observing the line in front of his train. After all, it could be argued that as the main purpose of AWS was to assist in locating signals, colour-light signalling would give a very effective return from any investment in safety. Gresley was one of those who subscribed to this view and, after his appointment as Chief Mechanical Engineer to the LNER in 1923, the AWS installations on former North Eastern and Great Central lines were removed. The busiest sections of line which had lost their AWS equipment were, however, early candidates for colour-light signalling. The fact that some Tyneside enginemen grumbled at the loss of the Raven equipment (sometimes termed 'my little friend in the cab') must have strengthened Gresley's conviction that he was restoring vigilance standards to the footplate.

From the beginning of the century, the Great Western Railway had taken a very different view. Not only did the Company believe in AWS: it developed its own system and extended it throughout its main-line network. After experiments going back to 1902, a system of audible cab signalling was introduced on the double-track Henley Branch early in 1906 and on the single-line Fairford Branch (where the distant signals were removed) later in the same year. By 1908 the system was introduced on the main line between Slough and Reading and by 1938 some 1850 track miles had been equipped.

The Great Western system of AWS was, therefore, well established when the Companies were nationalized in 1948. The equipment included a steam whistle in the locomotive cab, normally kept shut by an electro-magnet fed from a battery. Operation of the system depended upon contact between a shoe mounted under the locomotive and a ramp placed between the rails in advance of each distant signal. The ramp was connected to a low-voltage electricity supply and was energized, or not, depending on whether the signal was in the clear or caution position. Passage of current from an energized ramp to the locomotive circuit maintained the whistle closed, prevented a brake application and rang a bell to indicate that the signal was clear. If in the caution position, the electro-magnet on the locomotive became de-energized, thus allowing the whistle to sound until cancelled by the driver. A visual indication was also incorporated in the system at one stage but, not proving worthwhile, was removed.

The Great Western form of AWS was, basically, an audible cab signalling system applicable at distant signals. Around the time of the extension of AWS to Paddington in 1912 the system was modified in order to include a brake application. The steam whistle was replaced by a siren, through which air was admitted to the train brake pipe when the shoe made contact with a de-energized ramp, and the brake was gradually applied until cancelled by the driver shutting off the siren. Another modification to the Great Western system came later with the introduction of four-aspect colour light signalling, when it was shown that it was possible to distinguish between double yellow and green aspects. This was achieved by the addition of an electrically controlled air intake horn, which sounded immediately before the siren when a double yellow aspect was encountered. This modification, however, served only to illustrate the capability of the system to deal with changing needs, and was not generally introduced.

The Western Region of British Railways inherited, therefore, a reliable form of AWS which had proved adaptable to changing circumstances. It had undoubtedly contributed to the Great Western's above average record for safety, even when judged by the high standards of railways in Britain. Already installed in one Region, it could well have been extended to the others. It was not generally considered, however, to be the ideal system for the future because of its reliance on mechanical contact between the locomotive and track equipment.

Another system had been developed in Britain where magnetic induction had replaced physical contact, and went under the name of Strowger–Hudd (Strowger was the employer of Hudd, the inventor). The Hudd system was tested at Wraysbury on the Windsor branch of the Southern Railway in 1930, and on 28 July 1931 it was officially demonstrated at Byfleet on the South Western Main Line. The Company decided that AWS did not offer advantages equivalent to those which would result from the progressive introduction of colour-light signalling on its very densely occupied tracks.

The interest in the Hudd system was then taken up by the LMS Company. Shortly after A. F. Bound took up the position of Signal Engineer on the LMS, he was faced with the problem of dealing with an increasing number of commuter trains between London (Fenchurch Street) and Shoeburyness on the former London, Tilbury and Southend line. It was decided that the alternatives were either a full installation of colour-light signalling or the introduction of AWS. The colour-light option was ruled out because of problems with power supply and the high cost of the track circuiting required. Bound had been personally involved in the introduction of 'Reliostop' on the Great Central, but the Ministry of Transport committee examining AWS recommended that mechanical contact systems should not be used. This recommendation also convinced him that the Great Western system should not be used, although the LMS found little fault in a test installation on the Duffield–Wirksworth branch. In 1935–6 Bound was in touch with Hudd, who was retained as a consultant to the LMS Company. The system took a long time to develop, partly due to the familiar objections to AWS in principle, but due also to the unavailability in the mid-1930s of sufficiently strong permanent magnets. After a long series of trials, the Hudd scheme came into full operation between Gas Factory Junction in East London and Shoeburyness on 1 January 1948. After the serious collision on the LNER at Castle Cary, between Edinburgh and Glasgow, in 1937, the LMS and LNER had agreed jointly to develop the Hudd system. The LNER had actually acquired the necessary equipment, when the Second World War ended the contribution which that Company would have made to the work.

Unlike the Great Western form of AWS, the Hudd system was designed on the magnetic induction principle, with no physical contact between track and train. Like the Great Western system, it was associated with the distant signal. If this signal was at caution, a permanent magnet between the rails, by inductive action with a receiver on the locomotive, sounded a horn and began a brake application. A visual indication was also provided. When the signal was clear an electro-magnet between the rails was energized, allowing the horn to sound for a short time only and preventing a brake application. The driver could take control in the caution situation by silencing the horn and taking over the braking control.

There was also a third system in proved operation in Britain. The automatic train stop system had been used on London Transport lines for many years and was well known to British Railways engineers. It was used on the Euston–Watford line of the former LMS and on the Southern's Waterloo–City underground line. Also, main-line locomotives working over London Transport lines were fitted with the necessary equipment. It had been developed originally by the Metropolitan Railway and was based on a trip mechanism at stop signals. When the signal is at danger a pivoted lever on the track is in the operative position, where it strikes an angle cock and applies the brakes on a train which fails to stop. The system is effective, but particularly suited to London Transport conditions. It was considered to be less appropriate for adoption on the main lines of British Railways, with their greater variety of speeds and types of train.

After referring to the major forms of AWS installed in Britain, it is appropriate to take stock of the different attitudes adopted towards this aid to rail safety by the four main-line Companies. The GWR was well satisfied with its mechanical contact system. On the other hand, the SR considered that it would get better results from extending colour-light signalling than from any system of AWS. Both the LMS and the LNER showed little interest in AWS until the later years of the 1930s, and neither Company would have welcomed a mechanical contact system. It looked as if there could ultimately be a situation which would be similar to the struggle between the air and vacuum forms of automatic continuous brake. There was, however, a major difference. While the automatic continuous brake was a statutory requirement since 1889, there was some ambivalence within the Railway Inspectorate of the Ministry of Transport on the need for AWS. In his report following the accident on the Midland Railway at Aisgill in 1913 the Chief Inspecting Officer referred to the existing forms of automatic train control and cab signalling. He clearly had some doubts about the efficacy of the systems available, but considered that the Companies should unite in fuller experiments. He certainly showed little enthusiasm for the Great Western's audible cab signalling, but it must be remembered that this was at the time when the brake application was being grafted on to the system. Given another year's experience of the modification, a more positive recommendation could well have been made that all Companies should adopt Great Western practice. If so, it is likely that the Companies would have complied and British Railways would have inherited a standard system of AWS. Instead, the Companies went their own ways and the outbreak of the First World War created priorities greater than AWS experiments.

In the 1920s the views of the Railway Inspectorate hardened in favour of AWS. In 1922 and 1927 the Minister of Transport set up committees to review the matter. The 1927 review (chaired by Sir John Pringle, then Chief Inspecting Officer of Railways) was concluded in 1930. It recommended greater use of AWS and, while emphasizing the importance of the Great Western developments, considered that the Hudd system should be tried under working conditions. It also stressed the need for more penetrating signal lights, and it was this feature which was favoured more than AWS by all Companies, except the Great Western who opted for the extension of AWS. The recommendations of 1930 were not, therefore, as positive as those made by the Chief Inspecting Officer after the accident which occurred in 1928 at Charfield, on the LMS main line between Gloucester and Bristol. On that occasion it was strongly advocated that the Great Western system of AWS should be adopted throughout the country. Apart from Hudd's early work on the Southend line, little progress was made, however, until the Castle Cary accident on the LNER in 1937 turned intention into action. The LMS and LNER Companies agreed on the joint development of an inductive system but, for the second time, war intervened to postpone further work on AWS.

The British Transport Commission's first annual report appreciated the Railway Executive's concern to improve railway safety, although noting that the standard was already very high. The reference to AWS appeared to retain a hint of that long-felt reluctance to introduce any equipment which could possibly relax vigilance standards. It read:

> But the ideal is a system of warning control, of a type that is not prohibitively expensive, is simple in operation, does not give the drivers a false sense of security and can be adapted to the various signalling systems already in being.

After referring to tests of various warning systems which had been carried out on a section of track in the London area, the report went on to say:

> After demonstration runs and discussion, it was agreed that the most satisfactory system would be one which provided:
> (i) a location advice at a semaphore distant signal in the clear position and at a colour-light signal at green; and
> (ii) a distinct audible warning, with brake application, at all signals showing a caution aspect, including colour-light signals at yellow or double yellow.
> It was also agreed there need be no audible warning at signals showing a 'stop' aspect, as the men were content to rely upon locating stop signals after receiving a warning and an automatic brake application at the preceding caution signal. This brake application would be capable of being re-set from the engine cab.

As these requirements could be met by both the Great Western and the Hudd systems, it would have been possible to select either as the standard for adoption throughout British Railways. The Great Western system had the advantage of already being installed throughout one Region, but Hudd did not rely on the contact method which many engineers considered inferior to the inductive approach. In this aspect, experience has probably proved them right as any contact system would have had difficulty in operating reliably in the 1970s at speeds within the design capacity of the Advanced Passenger Train. The Railway Executive clearly recognized the greater potential of the inductive approach. Having made this decision, it was then necessary to produce a form of AWS which would meet the system-wide needs of British Railways for many decades. At the same time, the ideal AWS equipment had to take into account early experience of the Great Western and Hudd systems, while not overlooking the resources already invested over a number of years and currently making their contribution to safety in the Western Region. In 1951, the Railway Executive set up a committee with a remit to devise a system which would incorporate the following features:

(i) An inductive link between vehicle and track.
(ii) The equipment on the vehicle to be as in the Great Western system, but modified to work with the inductive link.
(iii) The provision of no visual indication

The committee carried out its work under the leadership of J. H. Currey, a signal engineer who had earlier worked with Hudd on the introduction of AWS to the London, Tilbury and Southend line. Use was also made of the same laboratory at Bow Works where the earlier work had been carried out. Currey and his team had difficulty in working strictly to the remit, and the only feature to be preserved intact at the end of the day was that relating to the inductive link. The Hudd receiver and the Great Western cab apparatus did not work well together, and the

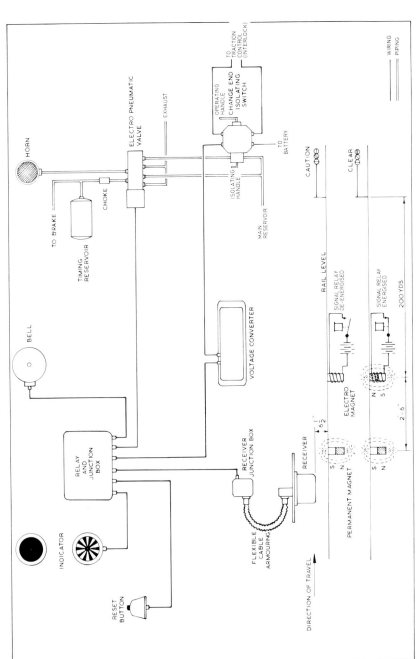

Fig. 12.2 Diagram showing the working of the BR standard automatic warning system (BRB)

modified GW cab equipment gave insufficient braking with the braking methods experienced on the Eastern Region. In 1952 some ideas were sketched out for a new approach, which was basically a development of the Hudd system. At the same time, however, there had to be considerable modification to the original type of Hudd magnets. Account had to be taken, also, of signalling developments (including the expansion of multi-aspect signalling), which were in their infancy when both the Great Western and Hudd methods were being introduced to railways still controlled mainly by semaphore signals. An experimental installation of the proposed new track apparatus was brought into use over fifty miles of the Down main line between New Barnet and Huntingdon on the former Great Northern section, and prototype receiving equipment was fitted to 54 locomotives. Monthly reports on the working of the equipment were made to the Minister of Transport, and periodical meetings were held between the Inspecting Officers and Currey's committee. The team was within nine days of putting the final design into service when, on 8 October 1952, three trains were involved in the most serious collision in the history of railways in England. This was the Harrow disaster, and was to give a considerable impetus to the AWS programme.

There were, however, considerable problems to be overcome in the development of the British Railways Automatic Warning System, and every stage in that development was subjected to very thorough test procedures. Although refined in many ways, the final scheme emerged closer to the Hudd system than was ever envisaged when the committee was given its remit in 1951; it even included the visual indication which was expressly rejected in the remit. Although Currey was in charge of the development of the system under the leadership of J. H. Fraser, Chief Signal Engineering Officer, and Lt-Col G. R. S. Wilson, Chief Inspecting Officer of Railways, took a close interest in its progress, civil engineers, mechanical engineers, the operating department, and some of the men who would have to work daily with the system shared also in what turned out to be a very successful result. It was very significant that a number of Western Region drivers, well used to the form of AWS designed by the GWR, were very favourably impressed by their first experience of the new standard system.

The first section of line to be equipped with the new British Railways AWS was the 105 miles of the East Coast Main Line between London (King's Cross) and Grantham. The Minister of Transport's provisional approval of the system was given on 6 April 1956. By the end of 1978, 4771 route miles had been equipped and the whole of the Great Western system replaced. The work had been carried out either through annual AWS investment programmes, or as integral parts of re-signalling schemes. Within the 1980s it is anticipated that over 2000 further route miles will be equipped, and so complete the programme based on the current criteria of route selection for AWS. These criteria allow priority to

Fig. 12.3 The receiver on a locomotive equipped with the BR standard automatic warning system about to pass over the track inductors (BRB)

be given to lines with passenger traffic, or where high traffic density, high speeds or prevalence of fog are experienced.

The Southern Region has always presented a special problem in connection with AWS. The Southern Railway had rejected AWS with semaphore signals in the 1930s in favour of multi-aspect colour light signalling. It was considered that the frequent audible warnings which would be received in the cab when running on close headways in suburban services could result in cancellation of the warning becoming a reflex action on the part of the driver. If so, safety would be put at risk by the system. On the other hand, the densely occupied Southern routes had a particular claim on AWS, as had been so grimly emphasized by the Lewisham collision in 1957.

The decision was, however, taken to introduce the BR standard equipment on the Southern Region, and by 1963 the system was working satisfactorily with steam traction between London (Waterloo) and Bournemouth. The extension to electric trains presented an entirely different problem, which was associated with magnetic fields. This was overcome by fitting the train receivers on the vehicle frames rather than

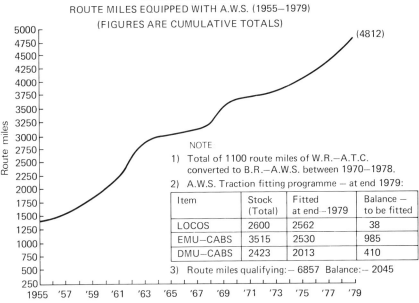

BRITISH RAILWAYS
ROUTE MILES EQUIPPED WITH A.W.S. (1955–1979)
(FIGURES ARE CUMULATIVE TOTALS)

NOTE

1) Total of 1100 route miles of W.R.–A.T.C. converted to B.R.–A.W.S. between 1970–1978.

2) A.W.S. Traction fitting programme – at end 1979:

Item	Stock (Total)	Fitted at end–1979	Balance – to be fitted
LOCOS	2600	2562	38
EMU–CABS	3515	2530	985
DMU–CABS	2423	2013	410

3) Route miles qualifying:– 6857 Balance:– 2045

Fig. 12.4 Progress of the installation of the Automatic Warning System on British Railways, 1955–1979 (BRB)

on the bogies of the electric multiple unit trains, and this required greatly increased strength in the magnets. By 1964 the Chief Inspecting Officer of Railways gave formal approval to the use of the BR system with electric trains running on third-rail tracks, and the system was introduced when the Waterloo–Bournemouth line was electrified in 1967.

Meanwhile, the problem of introducing AWS to closely signalled, high density lines was being approached as part of the wider research and development work on train control systems. The Southern Region took a keen interest in these developments. The result was the Signal Repeating Automatic Warning System, which has been described in Chapter Ten. This new system came closer to automatic train control than any earlier form of AWS and proved to be very suitable for Southern conditions. There were, however, three main reasons for not adopting it. It was three times as expensive as the standard BR system. It needed another year or two for further development before going into production, and AWS had already been delayed long enough on the Region. There was also a compatibility problem. Vehicles fitted with Signal Repeating AWS could operate with the standard AWS track equipment, but vehicles fitted only with the standard equipment would not work on tracks fitted with signal repeating AWS. Plans were made for the equipping of some Southern routes with each system, but Signal Repeating AWS was reluctantly abandoned in 1976, when it was decided to install only the BR standard system on the Southern Region. The installation of the standard system on the Southern re-commenced in 1974, and will proceed concurrently with the modernization of the Region's signalling. It is anticipated that the work will be completed by the mid-1980s.

The concern shared by many engineers and operators that AWS would reduce the vigilance of men on the footplate has not been justified in practice. Anybody who has travelled in the cab of an express train at high speed through thick fog, and contrasts the experience with a similar journey on semaphore signalled track not equipped with British Railways AWS, knows the value of the system. Over a wider field, reference has already been made to the development of more complete train control systems than were ever envisaged in the growth of AWS. Safety remains the essential ingredient in any train control system, however much it may be directed towards the optimization of the use made of the railway route system.

Although buffer stop collisions are generally so much less dramatic than collisions between trains (now so much more remote under AWS conditions), they account for nearly forty per cent of all passenger casualties in train accidents, although most are of a minor character. Some accidents are caused as a result of passengers on commuter trains alighting before the train comes to a stand. With doors controlled by the guard of the train this type of mishap would not happen, and power-operated sliding doors were used by the LMS in the 1930s. It has been for commercial and operating, rather than engineering, reasons that swing doors have been retained so long on many commuter services, particularly those south of London. British Railways policy is now to fit power-operated doors to all new suburban carriages. It will also apply to all main-line services operated by APT and to the recently designed Class 210 diesel-electric multiple unit.

One buffer stop collision which was outside the category of minor accidents was in 1975 at Moorgate, at that time on London Transport's Northern Line. Since that tragic, and exceptional, accident an automatic speed checking control was brought into use at Moorgate, now the City terminus of the electrified Great Northern line suburban services. It is also being introduced on the Waterloo and City Line of the Southern Region and at all underground terminal stations of London Transport. The system depends on timing devices triggered by track circuits, or treadles, and ensures that trains have sufficiently reduced speed before the train stop, and any related signal, moves into the clear position. Figure 12.5 illustrates the working of the system.

In order to avoid a buffer stop collision due to a driver mistaking his position on approaching a surface terminal station, British Railways introduced another new measure. This requires the final signal on the approach to a clear platform line to display a single yellow aspect and to be accompanied by the appropriate AWS warning. Along with the Moorgate innovation, it again underlines the dynamic character of safety

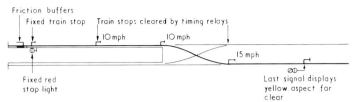

Fig. 12.5 Diagram of the 'Moorgate' type of control for underground terminal stations. Train speeds must be reduced to the prescribed levels before the timing relays release the train stops (BRB)

precautions and the continuing search for new measures to prevent the almost impossible happening which could pose a threat to railway safety.

The most potentially disastrous type of railway collision has always been associated with two trains meeting each other on a single line. The railways of Britain have maintained an exemplary safety record on single lines since 1921, when the Abermule accident showed that even the safest forms of mechanical and electrical devices are not proof against an almost unbelievable sequence of human errors. On single lines in Britain the absolute block system is supplemented by additional safety devices to avoid the possibility of a head-on collision. Most British Railways single lines use the electric key token instrument, developed from Tyer's invention in the 1870s, but a tokenless block system was introduced in 1967 and is now used in a number of locations, including the main line between Salisbury and Exeter.

Derailments have also been declining in number on British Railways, although not as fast as collisions where track circuits, colour light signalling, and AWS have been such favourable influences. Derailments range from very minor incidents, possibly involving a single wagon which is soon rerailed, to being the potential cause of a major collision. For that reason, they have always been considered as very serious matters.

During the 1960s a situation developed which was to cause considerable concern to British Railways. This was the problem of the increasing number of derailments occurring to the short wheelbase four-wheeled wagons in the freight fleet. While the derailment investigation procedures in the era before the Modernization Plan had been successful in determining cause and departmental responsibility, the technology had now become more complex. Increased speeds and axle loads, welded track, and mechanical track maintenance were stretching the railway closer to its technical limits than ever before. There was one piece of equipment which was giving evidence of not being compatible with the new conditions. This was the same small wagon which had held back the efficiency of freight movement over so many years.

The derailment problem with these wagons began to manifest itself in the mid-1960s, and by 1969 it accounted for 75 per cent of all significant train accidents. The particularly perturbing feature was that the mishaps were occurring on plain line, without the contributing complications of points and crossings. The immediate causes included minor wagon and track defects as well as traction and braking shocks. More serious was evidence of unstable motion at high speeds, due to a basic incompatibility between the conventional short wheelbase wagon and modern operating procedures and forms of traction. Higher train speed was not, however, the only reason for the derailments as fast freight trains conveying this type of wagon had been running at speeds of 60 miles/h for many years.

The commercial implications of removing the offending wagons from service were unthinkable, as such an action would have brought much of the railway freight business to a stand. The safety implications, however, were very grave as one serious derailment on a main line with fast passenger trains in the vicinity could have had disastrous results. The Board had to act quickly and took the decision immediately to impose speed restrictions and to remove some of the oldest wagons from the fleet.

As a longer term measure, British Railways decided on a multi-disciplinary approach which would explore the fundamental reasons for the derailment of these wagons – which often occurred at low speeds – and develop the technology appropriate to the type of wagon required by British Railways under modern conditions. It was clear that the restrictions at many freight terminals, which were a legacy of earlier days, would not allow an early switch to be made to the large wagons used on many other railways. On the other hand, it was expected that much could be done to improve the four-wheeled wagon's efficiency within the constraints imposed on BR.

Early in 1966 a Derailment Service was formed within the Engineering Division of the Research Department at Derby, and its engineers were given the task of investigating the problem. The work was carried out both on the ground and in the laboratory. Flying squad teams were formed and arrived on the scene as soon as possible after a derailment. Members of the Service were present at the inquiries into the accidents and also gave formal evidence at the inquiries held by the Railway Inspectorate. They were not involved where the reason for the mishap was self-evident, the decision on research participation being taken by the Operating Department.

The volume of detailed analysis of derailments available to the Derailment Service enabled it to study the mechanism of derailment as distinct from the determination of cause. An extensive body of knowledge of derailment technology became established. Collective analysis then made it possible to compare groups of derailments and so identify mechanisms and causes which would be very difficult to determine for an isolated case. There had been little published work in this field until I. G. T. Duncan (who was Superintendent of the Field Trials), J. B. C. McCann, and A. Brown presented their paper 'The Investigation of

Derailments' to the Railway Division of the Institution of Mechanical Engineers on 12 December 1977. This paper described the causes of flange climbing, longitudinal shocks, and mechanical or track failures as major contributors to derailments. The work of Duncan and his colleagues also brought out the relative effects of design and maintenance conditions in relation to specific wagon types and their derailing characteristics. It was confirmed that rain had a part to play in reducing derailments, as wet rails can limit flange forces during hunting and are rarely, if ever, associated with flange climbing.

As the equal distribution of the weight of the wagon and its contents on the wheels was important to the avoidance of derailment a wheel weight comparator was installed in the Western Region in 1972. The purpose of this equipment was to detect inequalities in the distribution of weight and it was originally intended to have ten comparators distributed throughout British Railways. Owing to difficulties experienced in the integrity of the information given by the machine and an improvement in the derailment situation, the equipment was not developed and the comparator was taken out of service after about a year's use. A more permanent contribution towards the solution of the wagon derailment problem was the introduction of the Total Operations Processing System (TOPS) by British Railways. With the help of this system it is now possible to produce details of the wagon miles run by every type of wagon on BR and so have records currently available of the incidence of derailments to link with different wagon designs.

By 1970 the results of the attack on the wagon derailment problem were to be seen, and the number of incidents had passed its peak. Since 1970 derailments per freight train mile fell by 42 per cent within six years. In addition, the work on wheel/rail dynamics, which had been going on concurrently with the derailment investigations, made its own contribution to future freight wagon design. A new four-wheeled wagon design capable of speeds up to 75 miles/h (depending on axle load) had been produced at Derby, and is referred to in an earlier chapter.

The new derailment investigational technology and wheel/rail dynamics studies had emphasized, *inter alia*, the importance of design in the elimination of component failures. The effects of failures of vehicle components responsible for broken axles or loose tyres have been reduced by computer aided design developments, proper maintenance, and testing procedures to detect incipient fractures. The incidence of hot axleboxes has been reduced by better bearings, and hot axlebox detectors have been introduced, particularly with re-signalling schemes, to replace the diminishing opportunities for visual detection of over-heated boxes.

It has also been possible to reduce the incidence of broken rails or rail buckling induced by heat. The risk of the broken rail has been reduced by ultrasonic testing and by the changeover to continuously welded rail, where any breaks normally occur at welds, or as transverse fractures. This type of break is potentially less of a threat to safety than the rail-end failure. Also, a track circuit failure usually gives warning of these situations on continuously welded track. It was found that the introduction of the diesel locomotive increased the problem of wheelburn and the resultant risk of rail fracture. Wheelburn is caused by excessive wheel slipping, and is overcome by the installation of wheel slide protection devices.

Reference has already been made to the research and development work in metallurgy dating back to the days of the former Companies. Fatigue failure exercised engineers from even earlier days of railways. By the early 1920s the Association of Railway Locomotive Engineers (ARLE) had commissioned the National Physical Laboratory to undertake work on their behalf on the problem of spring failures. By 1964 the British Railways Research Department possessed at Derby the largest fatigue testing laboratory in Western Europe. It was now possible to institute fatigue testing by using computers in the field of fracture mechanics and in the development of design data from fatigue life predictions.

The British Railways Materials and Inspection Division is located at the Railway Technical Centre. The Chief Resident Engineer (S. Wise in 1980) responds to the Chief Mechanical and Electrical Engineer, but works on

Fig. 12.6   Fatigue Bay in the Engineering Test Hall at the Railway Technical Centre, Derby (BRB)

behalf of all the engineering departments. The Division tests, for example, rolling stock and components for the CM & EE, rails, rail fastenings, sleepers, and steel for bridges on behalf of the Chief Civil Engineer and electrical relays for the Chief Signals and Telecommunications Engineer. It has also carried out work for railways outside Britain.

The major contribution made by the Materials and Inspection Division is in non-destructive testing. Here the Division not only carries out its own work, but also trains engineers in testing techniques to be applied in their departmental work throughout British Railways. It also has particular expertise in welding, and tests materials for fire resisting qualities. Thanks to the Division's testing methods on rails and axles, the threat to safety arising from breakage in service has been reduced to an insignificant level.

The railway carriage has not always been the safe vehicle which it is today. The public demand for better protection against injury in road accidents has become increasingly vocal in recent years, particularly since Ralph Nader brought out in 1964 the first edition of his book *Unsafe at any speed*. There was a time when there was cause for concern regarding the protection offered by a carriage in a railway accident. The crashworthiness of the early carriage was of a low standard. By the end of the nineteenth century, the continuous automatic brake and the absolute block system had greatly reduced the accident rate, but the accidents that did occur often reduced the wooden vehicles to matchwood. After his experience in the Staplehurst disaster in 1865, Charles Dickens wrote 'No imagination can conceive the ruin of the carriages' and a very similar description could have been applied forty-one years later to the Salisbury derailment of 1906.

The emphasis in railway safety has always been in the prevention of, rather than the mitigation of the effects of, trains being involved in accidents. It is of interest to note in this connection that although a railway line has to be certified as safe by the Railway Inspectorate before being allowed to open for traffic, the Inspectorate has no jurisdiction over rolling stock construction, except on tube lines.

By the time that the British Railways Mark I series of standard vehicles had been designed in 1950, railway carriage construction had passed through the following stages, which had progressively made their contribution to railway safety:

1. Wooden underframe and body.
2. Steel underframe and wooden body.
3. Steel underframe, steel exterior panels, wooden body frame, interior partitions and lining.
4. Steel underframe, bodyframe, and exterior panels. Wooden interior partitions and lining.
5. All-metal construction, with some interior partitions, linings, and finishings in plastics material.

These stages in the progression to safety were by no means clear cut. For example, the Lancashire and Yorkshire Railway had built some all-steel coaches in 1916, while some wooden bodied vehicles were made for the LNER in 1939, some years after building a number of earlier carriages in steel. The view taken by Gresley was that the wooden body had the greater capacity to absorb the impact, and that in all-steel vehicles passengers could be 'like peas in a drum'. He placed great faith in the rigidity provided by the buckeye coupling as a major contributor to passenger safety. This provided another example of how engineers could sincerely hold different views on how the available resources could be used in the pursuit of safety. The wisdom of the British Railways decision to combine the all-steel vehicles with the buckeye coupling has been demonstrated for the combination has given good evidence of its crashworthiness on several occasions.

A combination of wooden carriage bodies and gas lighting contributed to the list of casualties in the accidents at Clapham Junction (1892), Hawes Junction (1910), and Aisgill (1913). As far back as 1881, the Pullman car 'Beatrice' on the London–Brighton run was equipped with electric lighting; the first such installation in the world. By 1914, all major British railway companies had accepted electric lighting as standard in new carriages.

Although the use of steel has given structural strength and reduced the risk of fire, which has also been less likely since the elimination of gas lighting, fires have occurred since both these safety measures were introduced. The incidents at Penmanshiel in 1949, at Beattock in 1950, and at Huntingdon in 1951 showed the need for greater fire resistance in upholstery and interior finishes. The necessary improvements have been introduced with the help of research and materials inspection techniques. The Taunton fire in 1978 occurred in a sleeping car built eighteen years earlier. The incorporation of today's fire resistant materials could have reduced the effect of the fire, but the prime cause was the stacking of linen on top of a heater. This illustrates the never-ceasing need both for the staff to observe the rules and for the engineer to design out any threat to safety, however unlikely.

In the designing of vehicles to reduce the effect of collisions, the railway mechanical engineer has had two main objectives. One has been to preserve, as far as possible, the train as a unit and prevent the telescoping of one vehicle by another. The other has been to provide sufficient structural strength in the construction of the carriage itself in order to prevent the possible crushing of its occupants. There have been some ingenious devices to achieve the first objective, including the example of anti-telescoping steel teeth built into the ends of some Great Central carriages. By far the most successful, however, was the combination of buckeye coupler and the Pullman type vestibule connection between adjacent vehicles, which was responsible for reducing the effects of the

Castle Cary collision in 1937. The second objective was achieved through the substantial strengthening of the carriage shell through progressive research and development. The Mark I vehicle and all subsequent carriage designs of British Railways incorporate as safety features the buckeye coupler, the Pullman type vestibule along with all-steel construction and a very high resistance to end loading stresses. The derailment which occurred on the East Coast Main Line, when an HST 125 was travelling at 75 miles/h illustrated the success of this policy. The train remained upright.

Reference has been made more than once to the problem of the type of freight wagon inherited by British Railways. The wagon which was fitted only with a hand brake always presented a special safety problem. Not only was there a risk from vehicles breaking away, but the provision of catch points in otherwise plain track has created its own difficulties for both civil and signal engineers. Although the automatic continuous brake has made a substantial contribution to the safety of train working, the handling of both the heavy screw couplings and brake hoses has increased the need for staff to work between wagons at terminals and in marshalling yards. There was some resistance to carrying out this work, particularly by staff in some private sidings, and the engineering readiness to extend the automatic continuous brake throughout the wagon fleet had to be tempered by the traffic realities. The ideal operating answer was obviously the automatic coupler and a coupler was designed by Dowty Industries to meet the requirements of British Railways. Since that time, BR freight operational patterns have involved a progressively declining requirement for the shunting of wagons, while the design of a standard automatic coupler has become a prominent feature of European railway co-operation. In this context it will be considered in Chapter Fourteen.

Reference has already been made in Chapter Four to the history of the automatic continuous brake on the railways of Britain. It was made a statutory requirement on passenger trains in 1889 and the vacuum system predominated after the amalgamations of 1923. In 1955, engineering opinion favoured a switch to the air brake but, due to difficulties anticipated by a majority of the Regional General Managers in the transitional period, the vacuum system was confirmed as the standard. In the early 1960s it was known that the vacuum brake was approaching the limits of its performance. It was evident that it would have difficulty in coping satisfactorily with passenger train speeds above 100 miles/h and a freight train load in excess of the 1500 tons which was considered the maximum required at that time. It was certainly clear that some expensive development work would be needed to coax higher performance standards from the vacuum brake, while it was possible to benefit immediately from the continuous development which had been applied to the air brake. BR engineers were well aware of the work which had been done in the braking studies carried out in Continental Europe under the auspices of the International Union of Railways, and the manufacturing industry also had world-wide development experience. Their belated decision to standardize on the air brake did, however, enable British Railways to adopt the most modern system available, which incorporates a second, main reservoir pipe down the train. This decision, taken in 1964, not only provided for the safe operation of faster and heavier trains with existing types of signalling, but also made it possible to use compressed air in a variety of ancillary equipment, including power-operated doors, lifting facilities, and air-sprung bogies.

Consideration has already been given to the threat to safety posed by wagon derailments but the contents of the wagon can also present a safety problem. Wagons used for the conveyance of dangerous goods by rail have always been subject to special construction techniques as well as carefully designed operational regulations. Since British Railways were formed in 1948 it has been necessary to provide for a whole new range of commodities in the dangerous goods category, including a variety of chemicals and the nuclear flasks. Over 50 million tonnes of goods classified as dangerous are carried by BR every year under procedures agreed in detail with the Institute of Petroleum, the Atomic Energy Authority or the Chemical Industries Association. The United Kingdom Hazard Identification System (UKHIS) was made mandatory by BR for tank cars carrying dangerous goods at a time when it was only a voluntary requirement on vehicles travelling on public roads.

There have been progressive, and significant, improvements made in the design and construction of tank cars both by private industry and by BR . One of the main hazards is the possibility of an accident resulting in a

Fig. 12.7   A train of 100-ton GLW cryogenic tank wagons. These wagons resemble a giant vacuum flask, with near perfect vacuum between inner and outer skins. One of the loads carried, liquid nitrogen, boils at −196°C (BRB)

tank being penetrated by a coupling hook or broken rail. Shielding of the barrel is a major form of protection against this type of mishap. It is, however, in possible fire engulfment of rail tank wagons where the main danger lies, not only on the railway itself but also to the neighbouring community. The North American railways have had dramatic experiences of this type. Indeed, a serious fire was caused in 1973 at a private petroleum depot in Langley, West of London, by the irregular movement of a train which was still coupled to discharge pipes. This was a human error which no wagon design could have prevented and led to the requirement that the train should not be moved until a written 'Certificate of Readiness' had been presented to the guard. The engineering attention given to the design, construction, and maintenance of tank cars, combined with well maintained track, has been a major contribution to the very good safety record enjoyed by BR in the carriage of dangerous commodities.

Another recent development which could have been expected to threaten safety standards, at least in the public mind, is the increasing speed of trains in Britain. It has been a great source of satisfaction to BR engineers that the general increase in speeds over recent years has not been accompanied by any increase in the number of accidents in which speed itself has been a contributory cause. In effect, the reverse has been true and when speed has been judged to be the cause of a derailment, it has been due to excessive speed in a restricted situation rather than to the maximum speed laid down for the line. Within the last decade AWS has been involved to supplement the usual precautions taken to ensure the observance of speed restrictions. Following the derailment at Morpeth in Northumberland in 1969, warning of a permanent speed restriction has been given by the use of a permanent AWS magnet, as well as the lineside indicator, whenever the line speed is 75 miles/h or more, and the speed reduction required is at least one-third. The Nuneaton derailment in 1975 emphasized the need for similar measures at locations with temporary speed restrictions, and temporary installations of magnets are now made in these cases. It is of interest that concern was expressed in some quarters regarding the use of AWS in these circumstances. The grounds were twofold. First, it would divert resources from other safety measures. Second, it would weaken the force of the regulations requiring drivers to note the speed restrictions in force before beginning the journey by studying the weekly notices, and lessen the discipline of observing the visual indicators in advance of the restriction. This echoes earlier diverging views on the pursuit of safety, which have persisted since the arguments over the suitability of the electric telegraph as a safe form of signalling communication.

In October 1970 tests were made at Cheddington, on the West Coast Main Line to establish the effect of high-speed trains when passing other trains standing on adjacent lines and also on passengers who were on the

Fig. 12.8 High Speed Test Train at Chedington Station in October 1970 (BRB)

platform as the trains passed them at speeds up to 125 miles/h. A loco-motive was specially fitted with an air-smoother extension to the cab, while full-sized models of passengers and pieces of luggage were placed at varying distances from the edge of the platform. The experience gained in these tests was put to practical use when the HST was introduced into service.

Further developments brought about by higher speeds include the flashing yellow aspect installed at facing junctions on certain high-speed routes, and described in Chapter Ten. The BR standard system of AWS proved to be reliable at speeds in excess of 100 miles/h. When, however, the HST involved sustained running at 125 miles/h, it was necessary to ensure that the distance travelled during the period of grace before the brake application was not too long to prevent the train being brought to a stand before reaching the stop signal. Modifications were, therefore, introduced into the sensing element in the receiver on the traction unit so that it would respond positively to the shorter pulses experienced with increasing speeds. The AWS equipment is now capable of dealing satis-factorily with any speeds which may be experienced within the current design capacity of the Advanced Passenger Train, i.e., 155 miles/h.

The mechanical engineer has enabled the HST 125 to be stopped within the braking distance available to the conventional train travelling at a maximum speed of 100 miles/h. This has been achieved within the exist-ing signal spacing with the assistance of disc brakes and wheel slide prevention devices.

While the AWS system will now accommodate train speeds of up to 155 miles/h, the existing signalling system on British Railways currently presents problems with regular operation of these speeds. The Advanced Passenger Train incorporates a number of features which will enable it to achieve its designed level of performance. It is fitted, for example, with hydrokinetic brakes and also with the CAPT system, which gives a continuous indication in the cab of the maximum speed permissible at any point on the line. Meanwhile, the APT is not being scheduled to exceed 125 miles/h until both the engineering aspects, and the question of the passenger's tolerance to higher deceleration rates, have been fully resolved. There is always an engineering price to be paid for incremental increases in speed consistent with incremental increases in safety.

It is not only in connection with increased speeds that safety measures have had to take on a new dimension. Electrification has brought its own safety considerations. The problems which had to be overcome in connection with the introduction of the 25 kV a.c. system, and the limited clearances available with the British loading gauge, have been described in Chapter Seven.

Up to this point safety has been concerned with trains in collision with other trains or other incidents concerned only with the railway. There is always a potentially greater threat to safety when road and rail cross on the level as they are subject to different degrees of safety discipline. The protection of level crossings in Britain was originally determined by the Regulation of Railways Act of 1845, which remained unaltered in its statutory authority on crossing procedure for well over a century.

Fig. 12.9   A manned level crossing, interlocked with railway signals and with swinging gates. As required by legislation dating back to 1845 and referred to as a 'creaking anachronism' in the 1960s (HMSO)

The 1845 legislation required all public level crossings (some 4000 in the 1950s) to be equipped with gates which close alternately across the road and rail. Furthermore, all gates had to have an attendant. Where the gates were at a signalbox the staffing problem was less serious than elsewhere, but there were cases where gates were manned around the clock for the sole purpose of dealing with a very small number of crossing movements. This was at a time when labour was getting scarcer as well as more expensive and the mechanized road user of the 1950s was much less tolerant of level crossing delays than his counterpart in the nineteenth century.

The first real development in 100 years was when the British Transport Commission was permitted by its private Act of 1954 to replace, in specially approved cases, crossing gates by lifting barriers. It was still necessary, however, to provide the attendants at the crossings and there was little benefit to the road users. The significance of the 1954 legislation rested in the future potential for power operation offered by the lighter rising barrier when compared with the swinging gate. This feature was to bring British practice closer to the type of automatic and remotely operated level crossings which already existed in Continental Europe.

In 1956, the Minister of Transport agreed that it would be profitable to study level crossing protection methods in some of these European countries where regulation had not been so close as in Britain. In that year, a party consisting of two Inspecting Officers of Railways, two highways engineers, a British Railways operating officer, and E. G. Brentnall, then Assistant Signal Engineering Officer on the BR Central Staff, visited Holland, Belgium, and France. The terms of reference given to the party included the requirement:

> To make recommendations in principle and detail on the conditions under which Continental practice might be adopted with advantage to economy for the protection of public road level crossings on British Railways, having due regard to the safety of road and rail traffic.

The party soon recognized the different legislative frameworks in Britain and the countries which they were visiting. Speaking generally, Britain was unique in statutorily requiring the railway to fence in the line and to provide attendance at public level crossings, as required in the Regulation of Railways Act of 1845.

The party's report (*Level Crossing Protection*, HMSO 1957) recognized the need for a fundamental change in outlook in Britain as to the purpose of protection at level crossings. It considered that automatic and remotely operated crossing equipment 'might be adopted at selected British locations after satisfactory trials'. The Automatic Half Barrier (known as AHB) as developed in Continental Europe was thought to have proved to be a success. It was very encouraging to note the party's finding that automatic operation was more reliable than manual operation and no less safe. Also, it was shown to be of substantial benefit to road traffic and resulted in economies to the railways. Trials of automatic operation in Britain were recommended.

Section 66 of the British Transport Commission Act, 1957, allowed the experiment of installing automatic crossing protection to begin in Britain. As, however, the experiment was limited to locations where the daily motor traffic did not exceed 1000 vehicles and the maximum speed of trains did not exceed 60 miles/h, the rate of implementation was slow with only two automatic crossings introduced within the next four years. The first was at Spath on the subsequently abandoned Leek–Uttoxeter branch line and the second was at Marston, between Bletchley and Bedford.

Subsequent relaxation of the restrictions made it possible for British Railways to draw up a plan for the conversion of 1500 level crossings to automatic operation at the rate of 150 new installations a year. This plan was well on course, and 207 conversions had been completed, when something happened to bring the programme to an abrupt halt.

On 6 January 1968, a massive road transporter carrying an electrical transformer weighing 120 tons had come to a stand on the Automatic Half Barrier (AHB) type of level crossing at Hixon, between Stone and Norton Bridge in Staffordshire, when it was struck by a Manchester to London express travelling at 75 miles/h. The almost irresistible force met the near immovable object and eleven people on the train were killed. As his own Department had been so closely involved at every stage in the development of the AHB, the Minister of Transport ordered an independent judicial inquiry instead of the usual accident inquiry by the Railway Inspectorate. It was the first time that this procedure had been invoked since the collapse of the Tay Bridge in 1879.

The inquiry into the Hixon accident extended over 40 days, but all further installations of AHB's were stopped from the date of the accident. It was established that the immediate cause of the disaster was the failure of the transporter driver to carry out the proper procedure and the AHB was not faulted as a piece of level crossing protective equipment. It was evident, however, that the introduction of the AHB had greatly increased the level of responsibility required from the road user from that required when simply waiting for a manned barrier to be opened. Although the Ministry had made the procedure clear to road users and BR had done much to inform local people, including lectures to schools (one of the first AHB's had instructions posted in both English and Italian as there were Italian workers in a nearby factory), there were communication gaps in the understanding of the procedure to be followed at AHB crossings.

The paradoxical outcome of the inquiry was that while it was recommended that the programme of conversion to AHB installations should be accelerated, the process virtually came to a stand. The signal engineering changes included in the Hixon recommendations were not of a major character and could have been introduced without technical difficulty. They related mainly to the warning time cycle associated with the lowering of the barriers before the arrival of the train, the inclusion of an amber aspect in the road warning lights and improved telephone communications. It was the listing of new requirements regarding the road profiles and sight line conditions at level crossings which effectively halted the installation of the AHB in Britain for over a decade.

With little progress now possible in the replacement of the traditional gated crossing and the more modern manually controlled barriers (known as MCBs) by the AHB, the signal engineers of British Railways now had to turn to other developments. One major outcome was to eliminate the need to provide attendants at MCBs by introducing remote control from the nearest signalbox and monitoring operations through closed circuit television. Two other types of protected level crossing were very limited in their application as they were confined to roads with low traffic density, and required the train either to stop at the crossing or proceed at very low speed. One of these types is the locally monitored automatic open crossing (abbreviated to AOC(L)), which was first introduced to Britain in 1963. The other is the miniature red/green warning light system (MWL), where the barriers are opened by the users themselves.

Some ten years after the Hixon accident the situation on British Railways was that the gated level crossing (referred to in the Hixon report as a 'creaking anachronism') still existed at 1123 locations, so accounting for 56 per cent of the total number of 2000 protected level crossings. There were 498 manually controlled barriers (MCBs) and of these 97 were subject to closed circuit television monitoring. The number of AHBs had increased to 233 from 207 on the day of the accident. In the two categories with very limited application there were 58 automatic open crossings and 88 crossings with miniature warning lights.

It can be said that the course of level crossing protection in Britain was influenced by the Hixon accident as surely as the Armagh disaster confirmed the requirement for the continuous automatic brake, Hawes Junction emphasized the need for the electric track circuit, or Harrow underlined the urgency of AWS. The Hixon case was, however, in a very different category as it illustrated not so much the need for any new safety devices as for the road users' responsibilities in the situation of the AHB to be fully observed. It was reasonable, therefore, that some years should be allowed to elapse before the instigation of a further major review of level crossing procedures. This allowed the road user to become more familiar with the regulations and for railway experts, as well as highway engineers, to consider any detailed improvements that could be made in level crossing protection practices.

Early in 1977 a working party was set up by the Department of Transport and British Railways 'to consider ways in which methods of level crossing protection can be further developed in Great Britain, taking into account the cost and the need to maintain an adequate and publicly acceptable standard of safety – and to make recommendations'. K. E. Hodgson and T. W. Craig were the two British Railways signal engineers in the working party, which published its findings as *Report on Level Crossing Protection* (HMSO London) in 1978.

The Working Party visited the Netherlands, French, West German, and Swiss Railways during its investigations. It contrasted, for example, the 700 AHBs installed yearly in France with the one or two installed in Britain, and pointed out that British Railways since Hixon had little incentive to consider them. It also drew attention to the paradox in that gated level crossings seem to be fully accepted by users in Britain 'despite their having a higher accident rate than modern types of crossing protection.' At the same time, attention was drawn to the fact that 'although AHBs on the European mainland are usually cheaper than ours, they are no less safe.' It appeared that the scene was being set for a number of proposed changes.

Over eighty recommendations were made by the Working Party. One was 'That gated crossings should be replaced by modern alternatives at all level crossings on public roads.' Another would reduce the warning time cycle associated with the lowering of the barriers closer to the pre-Hixon standard, so reflecting an increasing concern regarding the impatient road user being tempted to zig-zag round half barriers in the lowered position. It was also recommended that the legal requirements in Britain, particularly the statutory authority required for the closure of unnecessary level crossings, should be rationalized.

The Working Party's recommendation of particular interest to British Railways' future plans was the simple statement that there should be 'A ten-year programme to modernize some 100 crossings a year.' In his Presidential Address to the Institution of Railway Signal Engineers in April 1979, K. E. Hodgson (Signal Engineer (New Works) at BR Headquarters and a member of the Working Party) indicated how the conversion work would affect the number and types of crossing. The position in respect of the 2000 protected level crossings would be as shown in Fig 12.10. The figures relating to the future situation take account of ten fewer protected level crossings than existed in 1979.

The recommendations made in the Working Party's report were approved before the end of 1979, with minor exceptions, by the Minister of Transport (Norman Fowler MP). The Minister has asked British Railways for a programme covering the replacement of up to 1000 gated crossings with automatic crossings within the next ten years. By the end of 1981, the first installations of the proposed Automatic Half Barrier level crossings, incorporating certain modifications, should be in service and existing AHBs will progressively be converted to meet the new require-

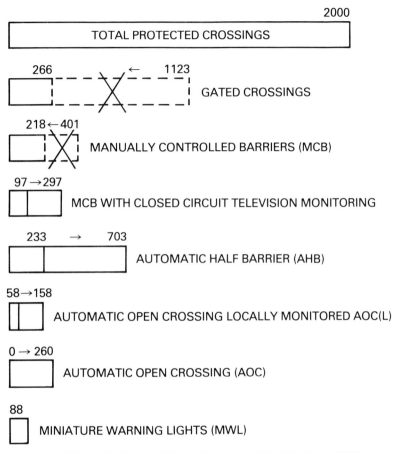

Fig. 12.10 Protected Level Crossings on British Railways (IRSE)

ments. British Railways enters the 1980s, therefore, with the Minister's support for the view that replacing many level crossings of the gated type originally required by the legislation of 1849 will improve safety, as well as saving manpower and money.

The main part of this consideration of the pursuit of safety by the engineer has been concerned, firstly, with aspects which are generally within the control of the railway and, secondly, where the road user must take some responsibility not only for his own safety but also (as the Hixon accident showed so tragically) for those who travel on the railway. In both these categories the engineer can make (and has already made) a very substantial contribution. In other areas his contribution is more limited. Although the civil engineer cannot relax his efforts to provide fencing protection, the problem of the vandal and the trespasser is one that rests mainly outside the engineering field.

Staff safety on railways is much less satisfactory than the position

Fig. 12.11   Automatic Half Barrier Crossing of the type which will be introduced on British Railways in the 1980s (HMSO)

regarding passengers, although the gap has been narrowed since the turn of the century. The Railway Employment (Prevention of Accidents) Act of 1900 gave the Board of Trade power to make rules which would reduce the risks incidental to railway work. A series of rules, introduced in 1902, made it mandatory to observe basic safety precautions, although these were already in force on some companies. The rules included the provision of power brakes on all locomotives, the guarding of point rodding, and warning arrangements for men at work on the line.

Since 1901 the overall fatal accident rate to railway staff in Britain has improved fivefold, but the railway is still a hazardous place of work compared with most other types of employment, particularly for those whose work takes them on, or near, running lines. Higher speeds have added to these hazards. The time taken for a train moving at 100 miles/h to travel a quarter of a mile after the listener has heard the warning signal is 7·8 seconds. For a train travelling at 125 miles/h the time lapse is reduced to 5·8 seconds.

With rising levels of speed, the civil engineer's permanent way staff are particularly at risk. More effective acoustic warning devices have been introduced to warn men on the track of approaching trains. High speeds have also required specially designed cab windows to be introduced in order to give adequate protection to the driver. The cab window on HST 125 can withstand an impact equivalent to that of a 2 lb brick hitting it at 190 miles/h.

Electrification has required its own safety measures, including live line protectors and isolation procedures. These procedures involve the use of radio equipment, as well as a revised method of the traditional written authority. The mechanical engineers of British Railways have also had the problem of getting rid of blue asbestos, now declared a safety hazard, but once used extensively in railway applications. Many other measures to improve safety of railway staff have been the subject of engineering developments, but none can take the place of a disciplined devotion to BR safety rules by those who go about their daily work on the railway.

What is the cost of safety on railways? At first sight it would appear odd that the costs of the safety measures taken by British Railways are not available for inclusion in this story. There would be little difficulty in assembling the costs of the elements of safety such as signalling, AWS, level crossing protection, or the fencing of the line. Other elements such as the 'fail-safe' feature of railway equipment or the safety aspects incorporated in the Mark III coach would be difficult to isolate from broader cost groupings, but could be estimated. The significant fact is that the price of safety is not regarded as being of the same importance as the pursuit of safety. This does not mean that the price of safety has been ignored. Most new safety devices have been measured against existing practices from the standpoints both of technical efficiency and of the relative value for money of the alternatives as contributors to rail safety.

That is why every advance has been accompanied by such lively debate. British Railways would be failing in their duty today if they did not seek ways, especially on little used lines, of providing high standards of safety at lower cost. As McNaughton wrote in his earlier quoted Tritton lecture, delivered on 17 January 1977:

> Except in the identifiable areas of the main network not yet brought up to present-day standards, there can be little justification for additional expenditure on safety grounds alone and, in my opinion, there is now a need for a careful re-examination of the traditional safety requirements, as they are applied today to the remainder of the system, to establish whether they are still making a measurable contribution to railway safety. In particular, if rural branch lines are to survive at all, such a review is an urgent necessity.

The signal engineers of British Railways have made a critical re-examination of safety methods on the little-used lines and have achieved some considerable savings. One particularly interesting break-through in this field was on the Central Wales line, where Post Office STD telephones with ex-directory numbers replaced the traditional block instruments. This solution was not operationally suited to the Inverness–Wick line in Scotland, where the use of radio links has avoided expensive new cable communications. Similar arrangements will probably be introduced on other little-used lines, but many worthwhile schemes will have to await the investment resources, which are currently about half the level which the engineers would require to modernize the whole of the BR signalling system within a practicable time scale.

It is important to remember, however, that the achievement of a modern, economic signalling system throughout British Railways is a vital element to its successful future, but the underlying objective continues to be the pursuit of safety itself.

CHAPTER THIRTEEN

The Locomotive and Carriage and Wagon Workshops

IN the early days of the railways in Britain few if any of the many separate railway companies which were created could afford to maintain their own workshops for the construction and major maintenance of their locomotives and rolling stock and therefore had to rely on private industry for these functions. For a variety of possible reasons – lack of understanding of and clarity in the initial specifications as to the performance requirements of the locomotives placed on order; mistakes in interpretation of specifications; unsatisfactory workmanship in construction and subsequent maintenance; preoccupation of contractors with work for other customers; and lack of capacity to meet the high level of new construction demanded by the expanding railway system – the results of private purchase and maintenance were not particularly satisfactory. When, therefore, in the later 1800s, many of the small railways amalgamated together to form larger companies the opportunity was taken in many instances to establish workshops where maintenance to improved standards could be concentrated, and, in certain instances, new construction could be undertaken.

This developing situation is demonstrated by a passage written by Joseph Locke, Chief Engineer of the Grand Junction Railway in the mid-1800s about Crewe Works, which opened in 1843, the same year as Swindon.

> At an early period, the Grand Junction Company bought all their locomotives from manufacturers. . . . But the engines were, necessarily, in need of constant repair, and an establishment was formed for that purpose (first at Edge Hill and later) at Crewe. Then arose the question, whether this establishment could not be advantageously used, not only for the repair, but also for the construction, of engines. The plan was tried . . . and the cost was found to be much less than the price they had formerly paid.

There is every reason to believe that the experience of other companies was similar, as they became large enough to support a workshops organization.

Each subsequent phase of amalgamation necessarily led to the rationalization of workshops facilities and following the amalgamations in 1923 the four group railways, in their turn, pursued a similar policy. Quite apart from the steps they took to reduce the number of designs of locomotives and rolling stock, they directed their attention to three main issues:

(a) The concentration of specific manufacturing processes at a single Works, when the volume of a particular activity made it economic to supply several Works from one source. To dispense with an entire Works raises many problems, social as well as financial, but to close a shop which is uneconomic is more easily arranged. The group Companies found that some processes were readily amenable to concentration at one of the several Works which amalgamation brought under single control. Apart from the GWR, on which the question of concentration did not arise because Swindon was virtually their only manufacturing Works, the group companies achieved a wide measure of manufacturing concentration.

(b) Standardization of methods of manufacture and repair whereby uniform workshop practice was introduced at a number of Works having common activities not suitable for concentration. Many locomotive and rolling stock components, though basically similar in pattern, were often produced by different methods at different workshops. Often, no one method was demonstrably superior to another, but where the method of manufacture at a particular Works produced an article as good as, or better than, the same

Fig. 13.1   The Locomotive Erecting Shop at Derby, c.1930. A partially completed steam locomotive is being moved by overhead crane to another part of the shop (BRB)

article produced elsewhere, and at a lower cost, it was obviously sensible to apply that method at other Works. The use of the best techniques available, over as wide a field as possible, was developed within each group Company.

(c) Concentration of output, particularly new construction, at fewer Works having the best facilities. Concentrating processes made possible some contraction in the space and staffing requirements in the workshops as a whole, a process which was further aided by a steady reduction in the numbers of locomotives and rolling stock owing to better availability and utilization under group Company conditions. An early consequence of the amalgamations was therefore the restriction of new building to the larger and better equipped Works within each group, and later, as stock decreased in variety and number, a few of the smaller Works engaged only in repairs were closed altogether. These included

Gateshead (locomotives) and Dukinfield (carriages and wagons) on the LNER – both partially reopened after the war to deal with arrears of repairs;

Stoke (locomotives, carriages, and wagons), Plaistow (locomotives), Newton Heath (carriages and wagons), and Crewe (carriages) on the LMS;

Brighton (locomotives) on the Southern Railway – reopened in 1943 mainly for new construction work;

Melton Constable on the M & GN Joint Railway; and

Highbridge (locomotives, carriages, and wagons) on the Somerset and Dorset Joint Railway.

There was also a continuing contraction in the number of works engaged in new construction. With regard to locomotives, at the turn of the century, twenty-four railway works built locomotives; there were seventeen at the time of the 1923 amalgamations; on nationalization, only ten were so engaged.

Tables 13.1 and 13.2 list the workshops which were in operation on nationalization:

Table 13.1   Locomotive Works at Nationalization, 1 January 1948

Region	Works	Output (1947)		No. of staff
		Repaired locomotives	New locomotives	
ER/NER	Darlington (i) Doncaster (i) Gorton (i) (ii) Stratford (iii) Gateshead (iv)	2809	32	11639

Region	Works	Output (1947)		No. of staff
		Repaired locomotives	New locomotives	
LMR	Crewe (i) Derby (i) Horwich (i) (v) Bow (iii) Rugby (iv) Leeds (iv) Bristol (iv)	3402	113	15169
ScR	Cowlairs (iii) St Rollox (iii) Inverurie (iii) Kilmarnock (iii) Inverness (iv)	1557	—	5329
SR	Eastleigh (i) Ashford (i) Brighton (i) (vi) (See also note (vii))	816	18	4106
WR	Swindon (i) Wolverhampton (iii) Caerphilly (iii) Barry (iv) Bristol Bath Road (iv) Newport Ebbw Jct (iv) Newton Abbot (iv) Old Oak Common (iv) Tyseley (iv) Worcester (iv)	1474	60	7443
	Total	10058	223	43686

Notes:
  (i) All classified repairs and new building.
 (ii) Used for new construction if programmes for new building exceeded capacity of Darlington and Doncaster.
(iii) All types of classified repairs but no new building.
 (iv) Subsidiary works, doing classified repairs, other than general repairs.
  (v) Re-opened for new locomotive construction in 1943, after being closed for new work in 1931.
 (vi) Re-opened in 1943 for new construction.
(vii) Classified repairs also carried out at eleven running sheds (Bournemouth, Bricklayers Arms, Eastleigh, Exmouth Junction, Feltham, Guildford, Hither Green, New Cross Gate, Nine Elms, Salisbury, Stewarts Lane: output of repairs 1947, 195: total staff, 800).

Table 13.2   Carriage and Wagon Works at Nationalization, 1 January 1948

Region	Works (i)	Output						No of Staff
		Carriages		Wagons		Containers		
		Repaired	New	Repaired	New	Repaired	New	
ER/NER	Doncaster Stratford Temple Mills Gorton and Dukinfield York Shildon Faverdale Walker Gate	14012	207	132308	5620	5420	295	11058
LMR	Derby Wolverton Earlestown Bromsgrove	6929	564	34928	6724	2710	2016	11274
ScR	Cowlairs St Rollox Barassie Inverurie Germiston (ii)	6084	—	28315	—	1145	—	3637
SR	Eastleigh Lancing Ashford	3771	388	11406	2896	561	302	4427
WR	Swindon Caerphilly	3518	153	12978	1368	1410	97	4574
	Total	34314	1312	219935	16608	11246	2710	34970

Notes:
(i) Excluding 90 out-station wagon repair shops, employing 4476 staff and 222 wagon repair sidings, 2658 staff.
(ii) Germiston wagon repair shops, owned by Ministry of Supply leased by RE in the early years after nationalization.

Nationalization on 1 January 1948 brought the opportunity – indeed the obligation – for further rationalization of the workshops, although the extent to which this could be carried out during the early years of British Railways was limited by the need to overtake the heavy back-log of repairs and new construction brought about by war conditions. It was, however, first necessary to establish what the future work-load was likely to be, both in repairs and new construction, and then to repeat the action taken by the four group Companies after 1923.

Reference has been made in previous chapters to the action taken by Riddles to establish Policy Committees, made up of representatives from

HQ and the Regions, to review practices and requirements in the various fields.

Within the first week of the RE's existence, Riddles established two such committees. One was required to examine the methods used by the former companies to decide when locomotives should be sent into works for repairs and to recommend one system for universal adoption in the future. The remit given to this committee, chaired by J. F. Harrison, then Assistant CME, E & NE Regions, was based on certain principles, namely:

(a) The decision as to whether a locomotive should be agreed for shop repairs or not would be made by the Regional Mechanical Engineer's department.

(b) Such a decision would be based only on the actual condition of each individual locomotive.

(c) The stock of locomotives would at all times be maintained in first-class mechanical condition.

(d) The expenditure incurred on the maintenance of locomotives would be the minimum consistent with the principle referred to at (c) above.

(e) The resources of all works in each Region and between the various Regions would be used to the best advantage.

This Committee recommended that a Central Shopping Bureau for controlling locomotive repairs should be set up at CME HQ in each Region, on lines similar to the organization established by the former LMS in their CME organization at Derby. Similar arrangements were established for the control of carriage and wagon repairs.

The second Committee – the Locomotive Works Organization Committee – was chaired by E. J. Larkin, Staff Assistant to the CME, LM Region, and included representatives of the CMEs of the Eastern, Southern, and Western Regions. The remit given to the Committee by Riddles, on 5 January 1948, commented on the fact that work to be undertaken at the main locomotive workshops was generally the same in all Regions but forms of organization and control differed as between Regions. He suggested that, having due regard to the size of the Works and other local conditions, it was probable that there was one form of organization which would produce the most efficient results and, if this was so, it was essential that it be applied in due course to the Works of all Regions. He therefore desired

that the Committee should examine and report in full detail upon the organization of the main Locomotive Works in all Regions, showing up in chart form the lines of responsibility and duties of the various Assistants and supervisory grades employed, with particular reference to:

(1) the organization for the control in progressing of locomotive repairs;

(2) the control of new manufacturing activities, e.g., new locomotives and boilers, and spare parts required for locomotive maintenance.

Fig. 13.2   The Mechanized Iron Foundry at St Rollox, before the Second World War (BRB)

The Works to which the investigation was to relate were those listed in Table 13.1.

The report presented by the Committee in December 1948 constituted a wide review of the organization at each of the Works concerned, including costs, output, and methods of control of new locomotive construction and locomotive repairs. It commented that there were strong general grounds for the introduction of tighter methods of control and co-ordination as between the various sections of the organization. A standardized, clearly defined organization would improve Works efficiency; the most economical manufacturing methods should be laid down in precise terms; means should be provided of collecting and analysing reliable production data to secure that operating efficiency could be progressively improved. The report recommended the adoption of a functional type of organization, which would make it possible to lay down clear lines of demarcation between the duties of the various managers and supervisors within a Works.

In September 1949 Riddles set up a further Committee, again under Larkin's chairmanship, with a similar remit, in relation to Carriage and Wagon Works. In its report dated December 1950 the Committee reiterated the view that a functional type organization should be adopted, as in the case of Locomotive Works. These two reports played a significant role in the decision on the management pattern to be adopted in the Works reorganizations which were to follow.

In one respect, Riddles brought about an early change in organization. All the group railways had locomotive and carriage and wagon engineering under one control at HQ and Workshops levels. Riddles felt that such an arrangement led to carriage and wagon engineering getting less attention than it deserved and he altered this policy by separating these functions in the Regions and at Works. Separation at Works level led in some cases – for example, Ashford – to two Works Managers in the one Works – an anomalous situation which was remedied later. The situation in regard to locomotive and carriage and wagon engineering provides an excellent illustration of the constant and confusing changes which occurred.

On Riddles' retirement, Bond, as Chief Officer (Mechanical Engineering), took charge of both locomotive and carriage and wagon engineering. In 1954, however, when Robson succeeded Pugson at BTC HQ, the two functions at HQ were again separated and remained so until Harrison was appointed Chief Mechanical Engineer in 1958, when they were once more brought under one control.

The first five years of nationalization was a period of tight control by the Railway Executive and this enabled a great deal to be done towards achieving a co-ordinated and uniform approach in mechanical engineering matters. By the end of those five years, every important aspect of locomotive and rolling stock maintenance and construction had been, or

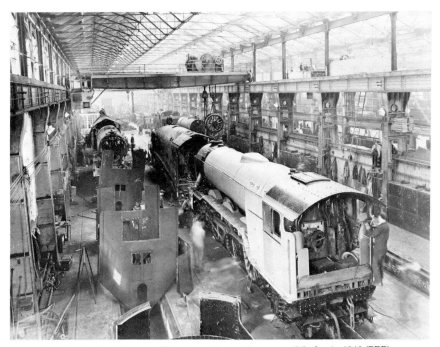

Fig. 13.3   The 'Crimpsoll' Erecting Shop at Doncaster Works, in 1948 (BRB)

was being, examined in detail. A uniform system for the organization and control of repairs to locomotives had been introduced and had been effective in reducing the number of locomotives under and awaiting repair from seven to five per cent of the total stock, and in tightening up on the time locomotives were out of service for repairs – important factors which contributed to the ability to secure a ten per cent reduction in locomotive repair costs, in workshops and at running sheds. The LMS system of individual costing of repairs in shops and sheds had been introduced for a representative selection of locomotives, to ascertain and record the levels of maintenance costs incurred by the various classes of locomotives.

Another benefit of the tight central control had been in relation to the management of the various Works. Following the reports of Larkin's two Committees, a standard pattern of organization was evolved for adoption at all main Works, as the opportunity occurred. Although at that stage the Works continued their primary task of maintaining the locomotives of the company to which they formerly belonged, they were also directed to undertake work, particularly in relation to new construction and the manufacture of components, on an inter-Regional basis. Production processes at the various Works were also submitted to close scrutiny and a standard system of manufacturing tolerances introduced in place of the many incompatible systems previously in use, in order to facilitate a greater degree of interchangeability of manufactured components. The rationalization methods adopted by the four group railways after 1923 were again being applied, this time on a national scale.

Regrettably, the Transport Act of 1953 was to make further progress in rationalization and standardization more difficult. Under the new organization, the BTC reserved certain functions to itself and further stated that the authority of the engineering officers of the BR Central Staff extended over these reserved functions. Thus, when he succeeded Riddles, Bond became responsible for, amongst other things, the standards and codes of practice to be observed in the design, manufacture, and maintenance of locomotives, carriages, and wagons and general mechanical engineering plant and equipment; the preparation and submission, jointly with other departments, of annual building programmes for locomotives and rolling stock; and the allocation and overall planning of the work to be done in the main railway workshops.

However, the outcome of the greater degree of autonomy given to Regional General Managers by the Act was to limit the effectiveness of efforts to improve co-ordination of the railway workshops, for the benefit of the railways as a whole. With design work still being undertaken in drawing offices now returned to Regional control, it was difficult to ensure that the rules were not breached and that Regions did not occupy themselves in design on projects which were not in accord with BR's overall plans. The advent of the Modernization Plan accentuated the difficulties of the situation, attended as it was by the introduction into service of a previously undreamt-of volume of new equipment. In these circumstances, firm control and co-ordination of design was essential and finally, after a number of instances of unilateral action by Regions had occurred, the Commission made it quite clear that their reserved rights in this context had to be rigidly respected. It was not, however, until some seven years later that the Centre was to regain effective control of the operation of the workshops.

Another of Riddles' Policy Committees was required to

Review and report upon the present arrangements for building new loco-motives and locomotive boilers in all Regions.
   Recommend, having regard to
   (a) the probable future demand for locomotives and locomotive boilers, and
   (b) the capacity of the Works at which new locomotives and locomotive boilers are at present built,
whether any changes should be made in present arrangements, with particular reference to economies or other advantages which might accrue from con-centrating new construction in a limited number of Works which would meet the requirements of all Regions.

The Committee, chaired by Bond and with all the Regions represented by their Mechanical and Electrical Engineers, closely examined the former company practices and noted, in their report issued in May 1952, that

(a) of the eighteen Main Locomotive Works, ten only were employed on the construction of new locomotives and ten also were used for the manufacture of locomotive boilers;

(b) building programme procedures of the main-line Companies varied widely but control of new building of locomotives and boilers, as exercised by the RE following nationalization, would enable the manufacturing capacity in all the Main Works to be considered as a whole, so that the facilities could be utilized in the general interests of all the Regions;

(c) the group Companies had, following the amalgamations, con-centrated activities at certain Works, which had been reduced in number, in the interests of economy and greater efficiency in production;

(d) they had also effected a significant reduction in the number of engine classes and indeed were planning on a further reduction in the number of classes for future building to meet their operating needs; and

(e) nationalization had provided still further opportunity for reducing the number of engine classes required by BR to twelve standard designs. Construction of these was rendered more economical in the matter of patterns, jigs, and tools required, by the introduction of inter-Regional assistance and concentration of manufacturing

Fig. 13.4   Assembling the frames of BR Standard Class 4 4–6–0 locomotive No. 75000 at Swindon Works, May 1951 (BRB)

resources at certain Works for the major component parts required on all designs.

The report stressed that the main function for which a Locomotive Works exists is, and always must be, the repair and maintenance of existing locomotives. What capacity is available for new construction can only be secondary in importance to the primary function of maintenance. Bearing this basic principle in mind, the Committee's findings and recommendations were as under:

(a) The average rate of renewal of locomotives between the amalgamations and nationalization was just over 2 per cent per annum. On this basis, the Committee considered that a locomotive stock position of about 19 000, with a maximum of 2·1 per cent renewal rate, was a reasonable forecast of the probable requirements to meet traffic conditions for some years to come.

(b) After taking account of maintenance requirements (average about 80 per cent of man-hours available in the Works), it was considered that the capacity for new locomotive construction was only marginally sufficient to meet the building of 400 new locomotives per annum. This figure was, however, likely to be affected by certain factors, namely

 (i) the new building capacity at Horwich was to be turned over to work on armoured fighting vehicles and new building at

Gorton was to be discontinued, after completion of the construction of the mechanical parts for the electric locomotives for the MSW line, the combined capacity of these two Works being 65 locomotives per annum; and

(ii) plans were being prepared for the construction of around 500 diesel shunting locomotives over the next few years, the mechanical parts being manufactured in railway shops. As these locomotives would form a part of the 400 new locomotives intake per annum, the number of steam locomotives, for construction within railway workshops, would be reduced by the amount of the intake of diesel shunting locomotives.

(c) After considering the higher cost of locomotives purchased from contractors compared with manufacture in railway shops (average £3733 per locomotive in 1947 and 1948), the conclusion was reached that the capacity on BR for construction of new locomotives in the foreseeable future should not, for some years to come, be reduced below the level then existing, when both Horwich and Gorton contributed to new locomotive output. The total capacity for new construction should therefore remain, although it might be desirable to effect further concentration of new building activity within the railway workshops.

(d) Annual requirements of new locomotive boilers were assessed at an average of 560 per annum, against an existing construction capacity of 730 per annum. Some of this capacity would disappear when Brighton Works on the SR was turned over to electrical multiple unit maintenance and it was suggested that a scheme for transferring boiler construction work from Stratford and Gorton to Darlington and Doncaster should be prepared and implemented.

(e) In regard to the future building of new locomotives and boilers, and in the light of the trend towards concentration of construction and maintenance resources, three possible policies emerged:

(i) to confine all locomotive building to one Works only;

(ii) to reduce still further by concentration of facilities the Works which should in future be allowed to undertake new construction; and

(iii) to continue erecting new locomotives and building new boilers at all Works then so employed.

(f) The first course was not considered to be a practical proposition. Only Crewe and Swindon had a sufficient level of staff to undertake work of this magnitude. At both Works there was currently a far greater proportion of maintenance activity than of new construction, and the constitution of the staff by grades for maintenance was very different from what it would have to be if new construction only were undertaken. A seriously unbalanced staffing situation would thereby emerge, which it would be impossible to resolve at a time of full employment and housing shortage. There would furthermore be problems in regard to floor space. The experience of the past, of considerable fluctuations in requirements for new locomotives from year to year, also militated against the proposal.

(g) With regard to the second and third options, the current level of capacity should be retained, but economies should be sought within the framework of the present structure. Detailed examination suggested that, by certain rearrangement within the Works, it should be possible and economical to absorb into Crewe Works the present capacity of Horwich engaged on new construction, and, into Darlington and Doncaster, that of Gorton. These proposals were to be regarded as a first stage for rationalizing locomotive construction. The recommendation would reduce by two the number of Works allowed to undertake new construction.

The fact that the report did not appear until May 1952 did not prevent rationalization proceeding whilst the investigation was in process. The Committee's recommendations were not, however, completely implemented before the situation was complicated by further developments.

Although the Modernization Plan of 1955 made no direct reference to the workshops, it was obvious that the introduction of new forms of traction would have a very considerable effect upon the type and volume of the work they would be called upon to do and on the equipment with which they would need to be provided.

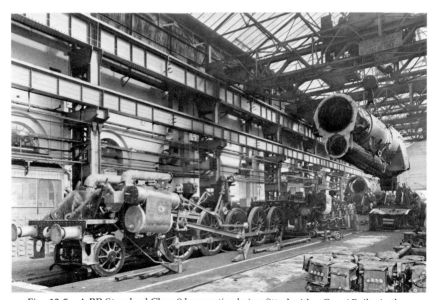

Fig. 13.5   A BR Standard Class 9 locomotive being fitted with a Crosti Boiler in the Erecting Shop, Crewe Works, 1955 (BRB)

With this in mind, the Commission, at a meeting of the British Transport Joint Consultative Committee on 20 January 1956, announced to the staff representatives what the general policy would be for the manufacture, supply and maintenance of equipment for British Railways during the ensuing four or five years. On 8 January 1956, this policy was notified to the principal trade associations. The policy was to be the basis of recommendations to be made by the General Staff in relation to future workshops capacity and an extract from it is worthy of inclusion here:

2. . . . the Commission are bound, in the light of their statutory obligation, to give over-riding consideration to the interests of the railway industry itself. Such consideration must also imply regard for the future of their present employees.
3. At the same time, the Commission desire to foster with outside industry a spirit of close co-operation for mutual benefit. The Commission will gain from the experience, resources and enterprise of industry. They will offer to industry a ready partnership in the development of new forms of railway equipment, and the facilities the railways afford for testing and proving them for use at home and abroad.
4. In the application of these broad principles, the Commission have decided that:
   (a) as a general rule, maintenance work will be carried out in British Railways workshops to the extent of their capacity in accordance with present policy. There will be consultation at all times with manufacturers to ensure that the maintenance of new equipment supplied by them is correctly performed:
   (b) the railway workshops will be used for the manufacture of equipment and components for which they are laid out and equipped, so long as they can do so on an economic basis. The Commission will purchase equipment from industry as their programmes require and complete locomotives when circumstances justify this course;
   (c) the Commission will rely in general on outside industry for the manufacture of diesel and electric power equipment.
5. It should be borne in mind that the greater part of the resources of British Railways locomotive workshops are devoted to repair and maintenance.
6. As regards the manufacture of equipment other than locomotives, for example, carriages and wagons, no major alteration is proposed in the policy at present followed for manufacture and maintenance.
7. The policy outlined above is regarded as firm for the next four or five years, subject, of course, to the intervention of unforeseen factors outside the control of the Commission. It will not necessarily be changed thereafter, but the Commission do not think it wise to commit themselves for a longer period.

The decision that the Commission would generally rely on outside industry for the manufacture of diesel and electric power equipment was wise in view of the industry's wealth of experience in this field, and the fact that volume production, taking into account their other contracts, could produce railway requirements at more economic prices. The industry did, however, strongly contest the policy decision that the railways would, as a general rule, build their own locomotives and rolling stock. Nevertheless, the Commission maintained that there was a positive cost advantage in their doing so, to the limit of their capacity to undertake the work. At the same time, it was accepted that the primary task of the railway workshops was the maintenance of locomotives, carriages, and wagons. It has been proved that it is uneconomical to maintain a surplus of capacity to encompass more than an average volume of new construction. It is not always practicable to regulate new construction to provide an even flow of work over a long period and this accounts for the fluctuations in orders placed upon private manufacturers. As a generality, there were very few years since the 1923 amalgamations when no orders for locomotives and rolling stock were placed with outside industry. Indeed, there have been times – as during the fulfilment of the Modernization Plan – when very heavy demands have been placed upon private builders. A major change in the expected work-load of the main workshops called for a fresh review of workshop capacity, to ensure that the facilities were adapted to the new circumstances.

The Mechanical Engineering Committee therefore reviewed the situation and produced a report in November 1956, outlining 'The anticipated effect on the Main Locomotive, Carriage and Wagon Works and carriage and wagon outdoor depots of the Modernization and Re-equipment Plan'.

The Plan itself suggested that, during the fifteen-year period up to 1970, the number of locomotives, passenger-carrying and non-passenger-carrying coaching vehicles to be constructed would be as under:

Locomotives: Electric	1100
Diesel	2500
Diesel shunting	1200
Total	4800

Coaching stock: Passenger-carrying (locomotive-hauled, electric, diesel)	24000
Non-passenger-carrying	7000
Total	31000

So far as wagons were concerned, the plan was to reduce the number of wagons required by increasing their average size and by achieving a reduction in round journey time. The Committee assumed overall reduction of about 30 per cent in wagon turn-round time and forecast that by, in this case 1974, when the assessed requirements would be reached, the stock of all classes of wagons would have fallen from 1 141 500 to approximately 752 000 of which some 297 000 would be newly built. In addition to new builds, it was estimated that, by 1970 there would still remain about 7500 steam locomotives, 12 000 passenger-carrying and 9000 non-passenger-carrying vehicles and (at 1974) 455 000 wagons in service for which Works maintenance facilities would be needed.

For the purposes of their investigation, the ME Committee had to proceed on the basis that the provisions of the Plan would be carried out as contemplated, and, therefore, that the changes in the activities of the Main Works would need to be adjusted over the same period as the Plan, namely 1955 to 1970. This span of fifteen years was, however, recognized as long enough in itself to produce its own changes, quite apart from what was planned.

The re-equipment would require from the outset that much of the existing capacity, either in railway shops, outside industry, or both, should be available for the construction of the new locomotives and rolling stock required. Capacity had also to be reserved for dealing with the enhanced rate of condemnations arising from the Plan. The need to ensure sufficient capacity for maintenance was, however, paramount. On the basis of these three major factors the railway workshops would

(a) continue to maintain *all* stock, whatever the type of motive power, although some repairing of wagons by private firms might continue;

(b) dispose of, by breaking up for sale, all condemned and withdrawn locomotives and rolling stock;

(c) build mechanical parts of new locomotives, together with most of the new passenger and non-passenger-carrying vehicles and wagons as complete units;

(d) manufacture component parts for the maintenance of all railway rolling stock and for store stock; and

(e) *not* manufacture diesel engines and transmissions or electric traction motors, which would be purchased from contractors.

Based on these assumptions and on the expectations that the Plan would be achieved within the specified time-scale, it was estimated that the stock to be maintained on completion of the Plan in 1970/74, compared with 1955, would be as set out in Table 13.3.

How easily such assumptions can be upset by subsequent events is demonstrated by the facts of the situation. First, the Plan itself was by no means achieved within the time-scale. Second, the stock estimates were based on a three-year moratorium on new orders for diesel main-line locomotives whilst experience with the initial builds was obtained in service. The later decision of the Commission to forgo this test period, essential though it was in the opinion of the responsible engineers, and press ahead with the elimination of steam resulted in all steam locomotives being withdrawn by 1968 – very different from 7500 of them being left in 1970.

Table 13.3   Estimated stock position, 1955 and 1970/1974

Rolling stock	Existing in 1955	New con-struction (To build)	Condem-nations (To with-draw)	Ultimate
Locomotives				*1970*
Steam	18000	330	10830	7500
Diesel main line	7	2500	—	2507
Diesel shunting	450	1650	—	2100
Electric	70	1100	—	1170
Total	18527	5580	10830	13277
Coaching stock				*1970*
Passenger-carrying				
Locomotive-hauled	37200	13700	27700	23200
Diesel multiple unit	300	4300	—	4600
Electric multiple unit	4800	6000	2400	8400
Total	42300	24000	30100	36200
Non-Passenger-Carrying	16000	7000	7000	16000
Total	58300	31000	37100	52200
Wagons				*1974*
Open merchandise	309700			200000
Covered merchandise	148000			140000
Mineral	606900			351000
Special	2300	297000	686500	2000
Cattle	12600			9000
Steel-carrying	47100			40000
Brake vans	14900			10000
Total	1141500			752000

The general policy of the Commission that, whilst railway workshops would not manufacture diesel engines, transmissions or electrical equipment, all other manufacturing activities would continue as necessary, is still in force. As a result, however, of the 1968 Transport Act – referred to later – 'other manufacturing activities' have considerably increased, compared with the commitment which could be foreseen at the time of the Committee's report, which made the point that, despite the estimated reduction in stock numbers it would be unwise to assume that works capacity could be proportionately reduced. One objective of the

Modernization Plan was a significant improvement in both passenger and freight traffic, which could only be achieved by a much more intense and therefore more onerous use of stock than had previously been the case. This would involve more frequent maintenance on a mileage basis. Furthermore, the new forms of motive power were more complicated than the steam locomotive and the addition of a large number of multiple unit power cars to existing carriage stocks would inevitably affect the total effort required in their maintenance and would result in the development of new activities in some of the Works.

Overall, it was anticipated that there would be little reduction in the volume of output of the carriage and wagon shops – indeed, to cope with the fitting of continuous brakes to wagons additional staff might well be required – but with the fall in steam locomotive stock some reduction in locomotive workshop capacity would be secured and some change would occur in the extent and nature of employment of workshops grades.

The committee reviewed the likely effect on each of the Works, bearing in mind the particular types of traction which might be expected to be introduced in their geographical situations. They also felt that the principle of considering the Works in Regional groups should be maintained, for the time being, as it was thought to be too early for a unified plan, embracing all Regions, to be formulated with any acceptable degree of precision. As the plan progressed, however, it might be that certain Works, irrespective of geographical location, should be further developed in relation to type of activity rather than to Regional self-sufficiency.

It was proposed that five main and five subsidiary Locomotive Works should be closed over a period of about seven years. Those recommended for closure were:

Main Works	Gorton	
	Stratford	} Eastern Region
	Bow	London Midland Region
	Ashford	
	Brighton	} Southern Region
Subsidiary Works	Rugby	London Midland Region
	Gateshead	North Eastern Region
	Inverness	Scottish Region
	Barry	
	Newton Abbot	} Western Region

Additionally, it was suggested that, whilst the Works retained would need to adjust some of their activities in phase with the plan, only a few would be likely to lose all steam maintenance by 1970.

In so far as carriages were concerned, it was the view that there would be no reduction in output of new vehicles from, and no drastic change in maintenance by, railway workshops. There would be likely to be a gradual reduction in output of new wagons from railway workshops and contractors' facilities in this respect would not be needed. So far as wagon repairs were concerned, whilst there would be a reduction in the volume of repairs carried out in cripple sidings, the additional staff and facilities needed to maintain, scrape and paint steel wagons, and to fit continuous brakes, would probably mean that no adjustment in the number of workshops would be called for, although there might be changes in work-load and type of work at individual Works.

Before this report could be considered by the BTC, however, it was overtaken by another report – this time by the Traffic Officers at HQ – on diesel and electric traction and passenger services of the future. This report purported to cover the period up to 1990, in which year it was assumed that steam traction would finally disappear. Any redeployment of workshop facilities would need to take into account the longer term traction policy and the report indicated the range of changed commitments the Works would have to meet in the future. The report was accepted by the BTC on 29 May 1957, but had no influence on the course of events, except perhaps further to complicate the difficult problem of attempting to adjust Works facilities to constantly changing estimates of long-term requirements. In its turn, it was superseded by a further report, entitled 'Modernization and Re-equipment of BR: Repair and Production Policy for Locomotives and Rolling Stock', prepared by a committee of the General Staff, chaired by the Secretary-General, Maj-Gen Ll. Wansbrough-Jones.

This report, dated February 1959, was a very comprehensive one. Its purpose and scope is well described in the first paragraph of the introduction:

> Under Section 25 of the Transport Act, 1953, the Commission are required, amongst other things, to provide efficient and economical railway services for Great Britain. As an integral part of the enterprise, the railway workshops must make their contribution to efficiency and economy, and it is the purpose of this report to indicate how that can be achieved in the modernized railway system. The report deals with the repair and production activities of British Railways at the main and subsidiary locomotive works, at main carriage and wagon works, at electric traction depots and at outstation wagon shops. Reference is also made to manufacture for British Railways by contractors of locomotives and rolling stock, and to repair work done by the private wagon repairing firms, also on behalf of British Railways.

There is in this report a brief reference to the fact that the possibility of centralizing control of the main workshops had been mentioned in the Explanatory Statement to the BTC (Organization) Scheme of 1954, wherein it is stated that 'it might be that some activities now controlled Regionally could with advantage be separated, and formed into Central Services, e.g., . . . work in the main Mechanical Engineering Workshops. . . .' This course had always been strongly pressed by the responsible officers of the BR Central Staff but, in February 1957, the Commission recorded a decision that

> The control of the main workshops will continue to be vested in the Regions. A review will be made by the General Staff of the possibility of segregating manufacturing and repair shops at some future date.

Regional influence in favour of the decentralization, enjoined by the 1953 Act and the re-organization which stemmed from it, was still strong, however, and it was not until the Commission was replaced by the Railways Board that the question of central control was raised again.

The General Staff report dealt with the eighteen Locomotive and nineteen C & W Works which were substantially those taken over from the four group Companies in 1948. So far as locomotives were concerned, the only change in Main Works was that Gorton, previously controlled by the ER, had now passed to the LMR, as a result of changes in Regional boundaries. At Horwich, there was a carriage shop which repaired both multiple-unit and hauled coaching stock, but this was in all respects an integral part of the Locomotive Works. With regard to out-station shops, seven had been closed, or converted to running maintenance depots – Leeds and Bristol on the LMR and Bristol (Bath Road), Newport, Old Oak Common, Tyseley, and Worcester on the WR.

There had, however, been some changes in functions over the intervening years since 1948, due to the change in forms of traction, and Tables

Fig. 13.6   Work in progress on the construction of Diesel Locomotives in
Derby Works, 1959 (BRB)

13.4 and 13.5 show the principal activities of the Locomotive and C& W Workshops at the end of 1957. Staffing details are also given.

Table 13.4   Principal Activities and Staff at Locomotive Works, as at 31 December 1957

Region	Works	Activities		No. of staff
		New construction of	Repair of	
ER/NER	Darlington North Road	D. shtg locos	Steam locos D. railcar engines	3543
	Doncaster	Elec. locos D. shtg locos	Steam locos	2695
	Stratford	—	Steam locos D. shtg locos D. railcar engines	1524
	Gateshead	—	Steam locos	235
	Total			7997
LMR	Crewe	Steam locos D. shtg locos	Steam locos D. shtg locos	6980
	Derby	D. main-line locos D. shtg locos	Steam locos D. main-line locos D. shtg locos D. railcar engines	3648
	Horwich*	D. shtg locos	Steam locos D. shtg locos	3202
	Gorton	—	Steam locos Elec. locos	1766
	Bow	—	Steam locos	228
	Rugby	—	Steam locos	65
	Total			15889
ScR	St Rollox	—	Steam locos	2079
	Cowlairs	—	Steam locos D. shtg locos D. railcar engines	1845
	Inverurie	—	Steam locos	435
	Inverness	—	Steam locos	84
	Kilmarnock	—	Steam locos	73
	Total			4516

Region	Works	Activities		No. of staff
		New construction of	Repair of	
SR	Eastleigh	—	Steam locos Elec. locos	1686
	Ashford	—	Steam locos	1332
	Brighton	—	Steam locos	290
	Total			3308
WR	Swindon	Steam locos D. main-line locos	Steam locos D. shtg locos D. railcar engines	5247
	Wolverhampton	—	Steam locos	564
	Caerphilly	—	Steam locos	597
	Barry	—	Steam locos	217
	Newton Abbot	—	Steam locos	116
	Total			6741
	Grand total			38451

* Excluding carriage shop: see Table 13.5

New construction: summary: steam locomotives at 2 Works, diesel main-line at 2, diesel shunting at 5, electric at 1.

Table 13.5   Principal Activities and Staff at Carriage and Wagon Works, as at 31 December 1957

Region	Works	Activities		No. of staff
		New Construction of	Repair of	
ER/NER	Doncaster	Elec. MU	Diesel MU Loco. hauled Wagons Containers	2255
	Stratford	—	Elec. MU Diesel MU Loco. hauled	1444
	Temple Mills	—	Wagons Containers	
	York	Elec. MU	Diesel MU Loco. hauled Wagons Containers	3008

Table 13.5   Principal Activities and Staff at Carriage and Wagon
Works, as at 31 December 1957

Region	Works	Activities		No. of staff
		New Construction of	Repair of	
	Shildon	Wagons	Wagons Containers	3090
	Faverdale	Wagons Containers	Wagons Containers	617
	Walker Gate	—	Elec. MU Loco. hauled Wagons Containers	539
	Total			10953
LMR	Derby	Diesel MU Wagons	Elec. MU Diesel MU Loco. hauled Wagons	5186
	Wolverton	Elec. MU Loco. hauled Wagons Containers	Elec. MU Diesel MU Loco. hauled Containers	3753
	Earlestown	Containers	Wagons Containers	1772
	Gorton and Dukinfield	—	Loco. hauled Wagons Containers	667
	Bromsgrove	—	Wagons Containers	359
	Horwich Carriage Shop	—	Elec. MU Diesel MU Loco. hauled	72
	Total			11809
ScR	Cowlairs	Containers	Diesel MU Loco. hauled Wagons Containers	1191
	St Rollox	Containers	Loco. hauled	894
	Barassie	—	Wagons Containers	702

Region	Works	Activities		No. of staff
		New Construction of	Repair of	
	Inverurie	—	Loco. hauled Wagons Containers	264
	Total			3051
SR	Eastleigh	Elec. MU Diesel MU Containers	Elec. MU Diesel MU Loco. hauled Wagons Containers	2026
	Lancing	Wagons	Elec. MU Loco. hauled	1844
	Ashford	Wagons	Wagons Containers	1001
	Total			4871
WR	Swindon	Diesel MU Loco. hauled Wagons Containers	Diesel MU Loco. hauled Wagons Containers	4346
	Total			4346
	Grand Total			35030

New construction: summary: electric multiple units at 4 Works, diesel multiple units at 3, loco.-hauled coaching stock at 2, wagons at 7, containers at 7.

In order to assess the likely workshops requirements, the report examined the nature and extent of the activities in which the railway shops might be engaged by the end of the examination period – 1990 – covering locomotive and rolling stock construction and repair, and other activities, such as the manufacture of rail chairs and baseplates, points and crossings, and wooden items, and the repair of a large variety of items, from rail breakdown cranes to platform barrows. The outcome of this assessment was that the railway workshops should maintain capacity to build in any one year about 250 locomotives (electric or diesel), 1350 coaching vehicles, 13000 wagons, and 2500 containers, subject to costs being competitive with those of outside industry. Any requirements above railway capacity would have to be obtained from industry.

This estimated requirement permitted a reduction in the then existing capacity within the railway workshops and the report recommended that the surplus should be eliminated over the next ten years, by a three-stage programme of closures, as under:

Stage I, Phase 1 (1959):	Locomotive works:	Brighton (SR)
		Gateshead (NER)
		Rugby (LMR)
		Barry (WR)
		Newton Abbot (WR)
		Inverness (ScR)
		Kilmarnock (ScR)
	Wagon works:	Dukinfield (LMR)
Stage I, Phase 2 (1960):	Locomotive works:	Bow (LMR)
		Caerphilly (WR)
		Ashford (SR)
		Stratford (ER) (Reduce by one-third)
	Wagon works:	York (NER)
Stage II (1961–3):	Locomotive works:	Cowlairs (ScR)
		Gorton (LMR) (Except electric)
	Carriage works:	Cowlairs (ScR)
		Gorton (LMR)
	Wagon works:	Barassie (ScR) Reduce by one-third)
Stage III (1964–8):	Locomotive works:	Wolverhampton (WR)
		Horwich (LMR) or Darlington (NER)
	Wagon works:	Eastleigh (SR)
		Gorton (LMR) or Bromsgrove (LMR)

New construction activities would be discontinued or reduced at several centres, namely

Locomotives:	Darlington (NER)
	Horwich (LMR)
Coaching vehicles:	Doncaster (ER)
	Ashford (SR)
Freight stock:	Faverdale (NER)
	Eastleigh (containers) (SR)
	Lancing (SR)
	Swindon (WR)

For the overhaul of electric stock, other than major coach body repairs, there were at that time twelve electric traction depots in operation, covering the suburban services around London, Manchester, Liverpool, and Newcastle, and the MSW cross-Pennine services.

Supplementing the larger workshops there were a total of 76 outstation wagon shops – distribution as below – where covered accommodation with a limited amount of equipment was provided for undertaking classified repairs:

Region	No. of depots	Staffing, including Supervisory
E/NER	19	1413
LMR	29	1354
ScR	14	714
SR	4	338
WR	10	932
Total	76	4751

In so far as manpower was concerned, it was estimated that a progressive reduction in staff numbers employed in workshops, including salaried staff, would be made, as under:

Stage	Period	Cumulative totals
I	1950–60	8425
II	1961–3	13345
III	1964–8	19700 = over 25 per cent of 1957 staff

Over the same period, railway outstation repair staff would be reduced by 50 per cent, spread over the three stages; railway staff engaged on wagon repairs in open sidings by 80 per cent in Stage I; and by private repairers on behalf of BR to 25 per cent by the end of Stage II.

In 1957 about 9000 men were employed by private firms in wagon repairing activities on behalf of BR, in small depots scattered around the country. The continuing reduction in the wagon fleet, however, made it likely that the use of private repairers would diminish and even be discontinued, except perhaps in areas where they had reasonably modern repair facilities and the railways did not. The extent to which private repairers should be used has in fact been a bone of contention up to the present time. In general, private owners' wagons are repaired by private wagon repairers and in the light of the present freight policy, that customers should be encouraged to provide their own wagons, this commitment is likely to increase. On the other hand, the search for economies, by reductions in staffing levels, over the past 20 years and more, has led to insistence by staff representatives that outstation repair of BR-owned wagons should be taken away from private repairers and allocated to the railway's own staff, before any question of redundancy can arise, and this factor has led to a reduced reliance by BR itself on the private repair organization.

Like its predecessor, submitted by the Traffic Officers, the General Staff report was based on the supposition that the ultimate displacement of all steam locomotives by electric and diesel traction might not be achieved until 1990. On this assumption, the report estimated that the ultimate stock required would be broadly as under:

Type of stock	Ultimate stock, as foreseen in report (As at 1990)		Relevant figures in M & E Committee report dated November 1956 (As at 1970)	
Locomotives	Electric	3900	Electric	1170
	Diesel main line	5300	Diesel main line	2507
	Diesel shunting	2100	Diesel shunting	2100
	Total	11300	Steam	7500
			Total	13277
Coaching stock vehicles:				
Passenger-carrying: Electric & diesel multiple unit	13000		13000	
Locomotive hauled	23200		23200	
Total	36200		36200	
Non-passenger-carrying	15000		16000	
Total coaching stock	51200		52200	
Wagons	802500		752000	
			(As at 1974)	
Containers	40200		Not quoted.	

The General Staff report dealt, too, with the question as to whether increased efficiency, and hence even lower unit costs, could be achieved by completely segregating new building from repairs or by concentrating it at fewer Works. After consideration of the advantages and disadvantages, the report endorsed the view expressed in the Mechanical and Electrical Engineering Policy Committee report dated May 1952 that complete segregation was not justified, but that the number of Works engaged in new building should be reduced, as opportunity occurred.

The proposals contained in the General Staff report were soundly based on the conditions then applying, but were founded on the false premise that steam operation would continue until 1990, whereas it had gone some 22 years earlier. Whilst they were being carried out, particularly in regard to the closure of subsidiary Works, the increasing rate at which steam locomotives were being replaced by diesel and electric traction made a further review of the proposals essential. Before the review could be undertaken, however, there were to be changes in organization and attitudes at the BTC which were to affect the future activities and control of the workshops.

In 1961, Dr Richard Beeching became Chairman of the BTC and later of the BRB. He appointed a number of new Board Members from outside the railway in February 1962, among them Sir Steuart Mitchell, formerly Director-General of Royal Ordnance Factories. One of Mitchell's first assignments was to make a case for placing the workshops under central management. He appreciated that the Works should be run for the benefit of BR as a whole and that this objective could best be achieved by removing them from the management of individual Regions. He knew, from the reports submitted since the publication of the Modernization Plan, that some reduction in workshop capacity was already in progress, by closing some Works completely and reducing the size of others over the ensuing six or seven years. Decisions which would have to be made in the future as to which Works should be closed and which retained would inevitably involve a significant degree of rationalization and redistribution of work-load, without regard to Regional boundaries or Regional prejudices. Central management would enable these decisions to be made more objectively, and was therefore an essential precursor to yet a further review of the earlier Workshops plan, which had been made in the context of Regional control, as ordained by the BTC in 1957.

Fig. 13.7   Diesel Locomotives being overhauled in Derby Works. Three classes of locomotives are in the picture: Class 08 shunting locomotive and Classes 25 and 45 main-line locomotives (BRB)

Fig. 13.8   Inter-City Mark II coaches nearing completion at Derby Litchurch Lane Works. Note the boards indicating the construction stage and the work to be carried out (BRB)

As a first step, therefore, the decision was taken, in June 1962, to bring the workshops under central control. In 14 years, the workshops had three different management organizations. For the first five years they had been controlled directly from RE HQ, through the functional line to the Regional Mechanical Engineering Departments, a simple organization which produced very good results and substantial economies in construction and maintenance costs, and, so far as was practicable in so short a period, rationalization of capacity. The Transport Act of 1953 resulted in decentralization of the management of the workshops to the Regions, thereby creating problems in the co-ordination of activities as between individual Regions and Works. The action taken in 1962 produced a further variation – centralized control, but under quite separate management – the Workshops Division. Although central control of the workshops was eminently desirable, and was beneficial from the point of view of inter-works co-ordination, perhaps even greater benefit might have accrued – particularly in present-day conditions of carrying out work for outside parties – if they had been placed under the control of the CM & EE at BR HQ, who would then have had under his own jurisdiction all aspects of design, construction, and works maintenance of locomotives and rolling stock.

Sir Steuart Mitchell's Workshops Plan, produced later in the year, was based on a number of fundamental principles, namely

(a) that the greatest economy was to be obtained by maintaining the

smallest number of Works, compatible with satisfying the needs of the operating department;
(b) that the shops to be retained should be those which were the most efficient and productive, subject to the requirement that geographical factors should be taken into account, to avoid excessive light running to and from the shops;
(c) that the main functions of the Works should be to carry out repairs, with an economic margin to be taken up by new construction; and
(d) that the predominant factor in deciding which shops to retain should be the requirement for proper service to the Regions.

The Plan was agreed by the Railways Sub-Commission of the BTC – the changeover to separate Boards, under the provisions of the 1962 Act, had not yet taken place – in August 1962, and was later approved by the Minister of Transport. It was announced to the Trades Unions on 19 September 1962.

Re-organization was based on an assessment of the probable workload five years ahead in 1967, distilled from estimates included in the previous reports to which reference has been made and from individual views specially sought in connection with the preparation of the Plan. The assessment of fleet size, adopted for planning purposes, was:

		Assumed fleet size, 1967
Locomotives:		
Diesel main line	3570	
Electric main line	358	
Diesel shunting	2011	
Steam	4000	
Total	9939	9939
Coaching stock:		
Locomotive-hauled passenger-carrying	15000	
Diesel multiple unit	2500	
Electric multiple unit	7500	
Non-passenger-carrying	8000	
Total	33000	33000
Wagons:		500000

Costs of typical heavy repairs at Works previously involved were compared and conclusions drawn as to which Works were in low, medium, and high cost categories. Special factors – the effect of in-

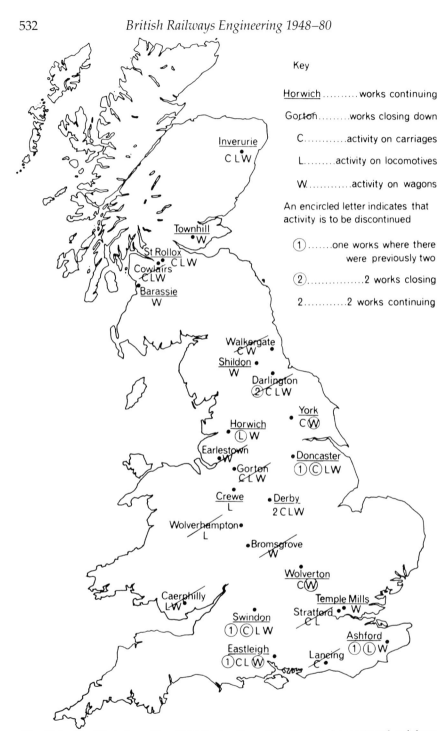

Key

Horwich ....works continuing

Gorton.........works closing down

C............activity on carriages

L.........activity on locomotives

W.............activity on wagons

An encircled letter indicates that
activity is to be discontinued

① ....one works where there
              were previously two

② ....2 works closing

2 ....2 works continuing

Fig. 13.9   The Workshops Plan, 1962: the location of the Works to be continued and those
to be closed

creased mileage to and from Works; repair times; operational problems arising from the geographical location of repair facilities, for example, the question of cross-London movement; and the general employment situation in the vicinity of the Works – were also taken into account in formulating proposals as to which Works should be retained.

The main features of the Plan were as follows:

(a) Of the 32 existing Works, only 16 should be retained, the activities of these to be drastically rationalized: see Fig. 13.9 and Table 13.6.

(b) The continuing Works were to be planned on the basis of double shift working wherever possible, to reduce overhead expenses by better utilization of capital equipment. Double shift working also constituted an element of insurance against a possible further reduction in work-load beyond 1967.

(c) There would be considerable modernization, including the provision of new plant and machine tools, overtaking deferred maintenance and general amenity improvements. This was one important respect in which the 1962 Plan differed from the earlier ones.

(d) Staff numbers were expected to be some 40 per cent below the 1962 establishment forecasts, namely:

	1962	1967
Salaried staff	7300	5800
Wages grades	58700	34200
Total	66000	40000

A second important difference between this Plan and its predecessors was that new and much more generous financial provisions were to be made for staff declared redundant.

Table 13.6   Workshops Plan, 1962: Summary of Proposals for Retention/Closure

Works	To be retained for	To close (in)
Ashford	Wagon repairs and new building	Loco Works (1962)
Barassie	Wagon repairs	—
Bromsgrove	—	Wagon Works (1964)
Caerphilly	—	Loco and Wagon Works (1963)
Crewe	Loco repairs and new building	—

13.6   Workshops Plan, 1962: Summary of Proposals for Retention/Closure

Works	To be retained for	To close (in)
Darlington	—	Loco Works (1965)
Faverdale	—	Wagon Works (1963)
Derby (separate Loco. and C & W Works)	Loco and carriage repairs and new building: wagon repairs	—
Doncaster	Loco, carriage and wagon repairs	—
Earlestown	—	Wagon Works (1964)
Eastleigh	Loco, carriage, and container repairs	Wagon Works (1963)
Cowlairs	—	Loco, Carriage and Wagon Works (1964)
St Rollox	Loco and carriage repairs: container building	—
Gorton	—	Loco, Carriage and Wagon Works (1963)
Horwich	Carriage and wagon repairs	Loco Works (1964)
Inverurie	Loco, carriage, and wagon repairs	—
Lancing	—	Carriage Works (1964)
Shildon	Wagon repairs and new building	—
Stratford	—	Loco and Carriage Works (1963)
Swindon	Loco, carriage, and wagon repairs	—
Temple Mills	Wagon repairs	—
Townhill	Wagon repairs	—
Walker Gate	—	Carriage and Wagon Works (1964)
Wolverhampton	—	Loco Works (1964)
Wolverton	Carriage and container repairs	Wagon Works (1964)
York	Carriage repairs and new building	Wagon Works (1963)

In the interim between the issue of the General Staff report in February 1959 and the publication of the new Plan in 1962, a number of Locomotive Works – Gateshead in the Eastern/North Eastern Regions; Bow and Rugby in the London Midland Region; Inverness in the Scottish Region; Brighton in the Southern Region; and Barry and Newton Abbot in the Western Region – had been closed.

At the same time as the Workshops Plan was being developed, studies were in progress of the likely future traffic situation and reports on the future reshaping of the system were being prepared, and scope was therefore allowed in the Plan for some flexibility in its implementation, bearing in mind that whilst reshaping of the railway system would inevitably reduce the size of the network, the reduction in miles run and the work-load of the workshops would not necessarily be proportionate.

The intention was that any further requirements, over and above the 1967 work-load assessment, would be placed with outside industry. The decision as to the Works to be retained, in order to meet the base work-load, took into account the factors of choice referred to above, that is, those Works which would give the most satisfactory service to the Regions, bearing in mind efficiency of operation and geographical accessibility, and also paying regard to the social and economic problems associated with conditions of local employment. In the latter context, effort was made to avoid closures in areas where the railway workshops

Fig. 13.10   Boiler repairs being carried out in the Old Works at Crewe, 1963 (BRB)

Fig. 13.11   The Erecting Shop at Swindon Works, May 1963, showing a steam locomotive
on the traverser, with a diesel locomotive on the left (BRB)

were a major source of employment and where a difficult unemployment problem would arise if this outlet was withdrawn. In past years, considerable local difficulties had been created owing to the closure of subsidiary workshops in relatively small towns, as, for example, when the Midland and Great Northern Joint Railway workshops at Melton Constable were closed by the LNER in 1936. The 1962 Plan largely succeeded in avoiding action which adversely influenced the employment situation in relatively small communities. In fact, the decision at that time to retain Inverurie was taken as much for social reasons as for any other. In due course, however, the retention of Inverurie could no longer be justified and these Works were closed in 1969, for purely economic reasons, causing high unemployment in a small community, with dubious immediate prospects of alternative work becoming available.

Following outline approval of the 1962 Plan, each Works which was to be retained developed its own individual plan for modernization and reorganization. By this means, the need for a large central planning team was avoided, and it also ensured that plans took full cognisance of local conditions, facilities and layouts.

Most of the Works concerned had been built in the nineteenth century and developed over the years to meet emerging needs – a piecemeal process which had in some cases resulted in badly sited activities in relation to the overall requirement. The Workshops Plan provided the opportunity to replan each Works to meet the needs of the present work-load in the most economical way. Shops have been enlarged and resited to secure improvement in vehicle flow through Works. Individual Works projects included the civil engineering works involved, including new buildings and improved heating, lighting, and staff amenities; alterations in shop layouts and repair arrangements to achieve maximum reductions in unit costs; and recommendations for modern machine tools and other plant and equipment.

The first scheme, for St Rollox, was authorized by the BR Board on 10 October 1963 and a submission covering all sixteen of the retained workshops was made to the Ministry on 8 May 1964, seeking authority for an expenditure of £17·6 million, over a period of three years. The other fifteen individual schemes were all authorized by the BR Board between May and October 1964. Individual schemes totalled £16·8 million – £800 000 below the authority level – and final cost was in fact rather less, at approximately £16 million. Completion of the Plan was achieved commendably near to the due date at the end of 1966.

Since nationalization, considerable expenditure had been incurred on new machine tools and plant – including, for example electrical repair facilities and diesel engine test plants – to meet requirements arising from the introduction of new forms of traction and new designs of rolling stock. The Workshops Plan accelerated this process. Requirements were co-ordinated at Workshops Division HQ, for bulk purchase, and included such items as wheel lathes, axle-turning and burnishing lathes, armature balancing machines, plug-board capstan lathes, lifting jacks, spray painting equipment, and welding equipment. Numerical control of machine tools, such as lathes and drilling and milling machines, with magnetic or punched tape operation, has been introduced in a number of appropriate instances, with resulting savings in staff.

Reference has been made to the staff reductions expected under the Plan. It was thought that around 15 per cent of these savings would be secured through natural wastage, but that the remaining redundancy problem would be sufficiently serious as to warrant especially generous

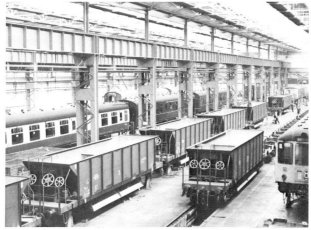

Fig. 13.12   Carriage and wagon work in progress at Crewe in the 1960s (BRB)

compensation terms; as long notice as possible of closure; and a special investigation, in conjunction with the Ministry of Labour and Local Authorities, to attempt to find alternative employment. Steps were taken to ensure that the staff would be kept fully informed of plans as they developed. The initial announcement to the Trades Unions was naturally met with considerable protest. Indeed, there was a one-day strike, to register the staff's hostility to the Plan. Nevertheless, it went forward to completion, with strict adherence to consultation procedures and, in the event, little real difficulty. Up to two-thirds of the staff made redundant found alternative employment without significant delay.

In the years following the implementation of the Plan some changes, both in the number of Works retained and in the nature of the work they were to perform, were necessary. Mention has already been made of the outright closure, for economic reasons, of the Inverurie Works in the north of Scotland. Because of changes in traffic movement patterns, and in the size of the total rolling stock fleet, Townhill became a maintenance depot under Regional control in July 1968 and Barassie Works were closed in 1971. At the same time, for broadly similar operational reasons, it has been found necessary to reinstate works repairs at Stratford and to effect changes in the functions of certain other Works.

When the Workshops Division was established in 1962 its first General Manager was H. O. Houchen, brought in from outside the railway, who

Fig. 13.13　Work in progress on the construction of the last steam locomotive to be
built in Horwich Works, 1967 (BRB)

set up his Headquarters at Derby. He became a Member of the BR Board in 1964 when Mitchell retired but remained as General Manager of the Workshops Division until mid-1966, when he became Chairman of the Workshops Committee of the Board, being succeeded as General Manager by Bond.

These changes were made at a time when the Division was facing, in particular, two problems. First, as has previously been stated, the separation of the workshops from Regional control was not a popular move in all quarters and inevitably errors of omission and commission by the new organization were bound to be highlighted by those who were aggrieved by the change in management. Second, the implementation of the 1962 Plan was in progress, and a reorganization of this magnitude was bound to cause problems. There were delays in the acceptance into and out-turn from shops of locomotives and other rolling stock, which inevitably the Regions attributed to lack of adequate planning in setting up the new organization.

In fact, accepting that some degree of difficulty and confusion must attend major reorganizations, the difficulties which did arise were attributable not to inadequate planning but to a change in attitude of mind on the part of the new workshops management when in 1962 it first became a central organization, isolated from the day-to-day running of the railway. Bond, first as Technical Adviser and later as General

Fig. 13.14   Locomotives under repair in the Erecting Shop, Crewe Works, late 1960s (BRB)

Fig. 13.15   Diesel locomotive repairs in progress, St Rollox Works, 1970 (BRB)

Manager of the Division, was most insistent on impressing upon the Division's officers and staff that they existed only to serve the needs of the railway, of which the Division was an integral part. This was confirmed, if confirmation was needed, by the fact that the General Manager of the Workshops Division was, together with HQ Chief Officers and Regional General Managers, a member of the Railway Management Committee. By dint of constant stressing of this point, together with some element of reorganization within the Production Section of the Division, this message finally got home and by 1968 any cause for disharmony between the workshops and their customers had been eradicated.

However, another possible threat to close relationships between the Regions and the workshops was implicit in the 1968 Transport Act. The 1962 Act permitted the BR workshops to manufacture and repair anything which was for BR's own use or for use by any of the other Boards which had previously formed part of the BTC. The workshops were not, however, permitted to undertake work for any other party, an irksome restriction preventing profitable use of temporary spare capacity to the mutual benefit of the railway and potential customers. Discussions had been going on for some time between the Railways Board and the Ministry of Transport with a view to removing the restrictions under which the workshops had hitherto operated and giving them complete freedom to accept work for outside parties. It was announced in the Queen's Speech at the opening of Parliament on 9 November 1965 that 'Legislation will be introduced to remove statutory limitations impeding the proper use of the manufacturing resources of the nationalized industries'.

This was a decision welcomed by the Workshops management. The production demands on the railway workshops, whether for maintenance or new construction, are always subject to quite wide fluctuations, within a general trend, which the removal of the statutory limitations would do much to eliminate. The additional powers which the Board would welcome and the manner in which they would be used can be summarized as:

(a) freedom to undertake outside work to fill periods of slack internal demand in machine shops, foundries, and similar manufacturing facilities;

(b) restriction to the manufacture of products of which the railway is a substantial user; and

(c) no requirement to enter the industrial field upon a wider scale, nor to provide additional capacity in property or manpower over and above that which is necessary for railway purposes.

This was undoubtedly a reasonable response from an organization the prime purpose of which was to provide an efficient and economic service to the railway. The proposed new powers, however, were politically controversial and met with opposition from the Confederation of British

Fig. 13.16   Working on the interior of a Mark III coach, Derby Litchurch
Lane Works, 1975 (BRB)

Fig. 13.17   Class 313 electric multiple units under construction at York Works, for
the GN Inner Suburban services (BRB)

Industry, which considered them to be against the public interest. In a
statement entitled 'The manufacturing powers of the nationalized industries', issued by the CBI in January 1966, it was suggested, *inter alia*, that,
in order to ensure fair competition with private enterprise, manufacturing by nationalized industries should be organized by means of companies operating under the Companies Acts, or, when only a part of a
nationalized industry competed with private firms, it should trade as a
separate entity, which the CBI regarded as essential for assessing its
performance against that of its competitors.

Presumably in deference to these views the case for and against constituting the Workshops Division as a separate wholly-owned subsidiary
company of the Railways Board was considered. Bond had serious misgivings at this emerging trend of events. He was convinced that it was in
no small measure due to the philosophy of separation being encouraged
rather than otherwise when the Workshops Division was formed that the
Regions had perforce to put up with a service which was not as good as it
should have been. The reputation of the Workshops suffered as a consequence. Bond made his views known, drawing attention to the serious
consequences for the railway if the Board of a separate company, though
wholly owned, got their priorities wrong and ever allowed activities
arising from the proposed new powers to take precedence over railway

Fig. 13.18 Work in progress on the construction of High Speed Trains, Crewe Works (BRB)

requirements, to meet which was the only purpose for which the Workshops existed.

In the event, a separate company was formed, as recorded in the British Railways Board's Annual Report for 1970, from which the following paragraphs are quoted:

> British Rail Engineering Ltd, the new company formed by the Board to manage their 14 main works in place of British Rail Workshops, began trading on 1 January 1970.
>
> Its establishment followed the grant to the Board, in the 1968 Transport Act, of powers to use the main works' spare capacity to manufacture for outside industry. The Company's object is to exploit the new opportunities to the full, while continuing to regard as its primary duty the provision of a construction and repair service to the railways. Much was achieved by the company – one of Britain's largest engineering concerns – during its first year.
>
> A commercial department was set up to obtain orders for railway rolling stock, containers, and general engineering.
>
> A joint company, BRE-Metro Ltd, was formed with Metro-Cammell Ltd to promote export sales of locomotives and rolling stock. The two partners believe that this combination of their marketing and production resources will provide opportunities for a substantial increase in sales.

BR Engineering also became a full member of the Locomotive and Allied Manufacturers' Association (now the Railway Industry Association). The object was twofold: to identify the company more closely with the railway supply industry, and to take advantage of the considerable commercial and technical information which the Association provides.

While proclaiming the company's primary duty to the provision of services to the railway, the increasing emphasis on outside activities will be noted.

Bond retired in July 1968, before the formation of BREL. He was succeeded as General Manager of the Workshops Division by A. E. Robson who, on 1 January 1970, became Managing Director of the new company, which then controlled 14 workshops (since reduced to 13 by the closure of Barassie). He was followed in turn first by S. Ridgway, previously CM & EE of the Western Region, and later by I. D. Gardiner, who was appointed to the company from outside the railway service. The company has prospered, so far as outside work is concerned, since 1970. In that year, work on this account amounted to £3.8 million in value. In 1979, orders worth over £50 million were obtained from outside customers, mainly in the export market. Orders received during the intervening years have included wagons for the Malayan Railways and for Sweden, coaches for the Northern Ireland Railway and Coras Iompair Eireann, iron ore tipplers for the British Steel Corporation, wagons for Yugoslavia and Bangladesh, passenger and freight vehicles for Tanzania, shunting locomotives and wagons for Kenya, electric multiple unit trains for Taiwan, and containers for a variety of customers at home and overseas.

Fig. 13.19   Wagons for the Kenya Railways under construction at
Ashford Works, BREL 1979 (BRB)

In the section of the British Railway Board's Annual Report for 1977 covering the activities of BREL it is noted that 'work for outside customers is becoming increasingly significant'. In this context it is instructive to compare the references to the Workshops in the BRB Annual Reports for 1968 and the later 1970s. In the former it is recorded that for locomotives '95 per cent of the scheduled repair target was met and the proportion of the diesel main line fleet under repair or awaiting repair was reduced from an average of 6·6 per cent in 1967 to an average of 5·3 per cent in 1968' and that 'A total of 14993 coaching vehicles was repaired – 99 per cent of the scheduled target. The average time in Works was reduced from 31·9 to 20·5 days over the year, largely because of the emphasis placed on the staged planning of repairs, the use of critical path analysis and the development of standard repair procedures'. The Annual Reports for the late 1970s do not quote comparative repair statistics, but tend to concentrate more on achievements in new construction. In a workshop organization providing a service to a railway, repairs are, in general, always more important than new construction. Reduction in the percentage of vehicles under repair and the time they are in the Works to the lowest possible level are key factors in judging the efficiency of railway workshops. It is in this relatively unglamorous field of heavy repairs and maintenance that the workshops, by whatever name they are known, will be required, in the future, to make their principal contribution to the prosperity of British Railways.

CHAPTER FOURTEEN

International Relationships

T HE Industrial Revolution created in Britain not only the need for
railways, but also the source of wealth with which to build them.
Britain was then in a position to provide the capital, the equipment,
and the engineering skills with which to develop railways throughout the
world. Indeed, equipment was exported on such a scale that there was,
for some years, an inability to meet in full the demands of both the export
and the home markets. This situation gave certain railway companies one
more reason for developing their own manufacturing workshops, which
have always been a feature so characteristic of railways in Britain and
have been described in Chapter Thirteen.

British railway engineers in the second half of the nineteenth century
enjoyed unchallenged prestige, and their services were sought widely
throughout the world. By 1848, Thomas Brassey had not only built
three-quarters of the French railway system then in existence, but had
moved on to Italy, Norway, Austria, and Canada. To Canada alone he
took over 3000 men, mainly navvies, but including also a number of
engineers. Immigrants apart, the railway builders dominated the world
travel market at that time.

As railway experience grew in other industrial countries, their
engineers began to make their own contributions to the technological
development of railways. Just as the names of Stephenson, Brunel,
Crampton, and Saxby became well known outside Britain, so did the
work of engineers in other countries become known to the railways of
Britain. Giffard's injector, Walschaerts' valve gear, Belpaire's firebox, and
the Westinghouse brake were part of the return flow of railway technology. Churchward is known to have taken much from French,
German, and American practice in establishing the high standards of
Great Western mechanical engineering after the turn of the century. It is
revealing to examine the patent lists, which were dominated by British
names for many years, and to note their increasingly international content towards the end of the nineteenth century.

It was not only the liberalism and individualism of the Victorian age
that created the interchange of ideas in the technology of railways.

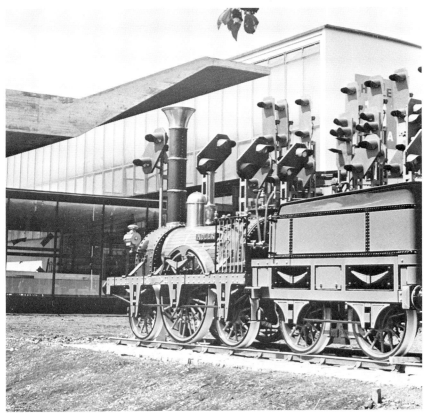

Fig. 14.1   *Der Adler*, built by Robert Stephenson to haul Germany's first train in 1835, against a background of more modern signalling equipment used by the German Federal Railways (German Federal Railways)

International transport, like all forms of communication, has a basic need for co-operation. In the case of railways, however, the co-operation must be of a very high degree. Aircraft, motor cars, and lorries move individually as units and must, in engineering aspects, be compatible with the airports or road systems of the countries in which they operate. For railways, the situation is more complicated. The traction unit on an international train may be required to take electric power from two, or more, different types of supply system. Also, on one train there may be vehicles belonging to several railway administrations. It is necessary, therefore, for track gauge, structure gauge, traction system, couplings, buffers, and brakes to be compatible. All require agreement and detailed codification.

The individualism of railways has created great variety in equipment. This has denied to their managements the cost advantages of long production runs but has accentuated the need for international co-ordination. This has been particularly the case in Europe, where an element of chauvinism has discouraged the emergence of one railway manufacturer capable of mass producing standard equipment to the extent that a handful of aircraft or automobile corporations produce on a global scale, or the Electro-motive Division of General Motors has come to dominate the American diesel locomotive market. The manufacturer of railway equipment has generally been compelled, therefore, to build in comparatively small batches to meet the requirements of individual railways. This diversity has both led to a continuing interest by engineers in the experience of their colleagues and to the need to keep under constant review the arrangements for inter-working between railway systems.

The pressures of competition have always been the cause of secrecy with regard to industrial techniques. In Britain, for example, the LMS and LNER kept their ideas on speeding up their respective Anglo-Scottish expresses very much to themselves, although they co-operated in air resistance tests and in building a locomotive testing plant. Gresley's team maintained a tight-lipped silence when designing the steam passages for the A4 class Pacifics, and the LNER's high pressure 4–6–2–2 locomotive No 10000 was known as the 'Hush hush' on account of the secrecy associated with its development.

British Railways are now one system and the railways of Europe are more concerned with co-ordination rather than competition, although commercial rivalry continues, for example, in the case of traffic between Italy and Northern Europe where a choice of routes exists. There is, however, one reason for certain railway administrations now being a little less free in providing the outflow of technical information which has always characterized the relations between railways. This is the growing realization that railway expertise is a saleable commodity throughout the world. Consultancy has become a source of revenue, and a number of national railway systems now have subsidiary companies engaging in the activity. Consideration will be given later in this chapter to the consultancy activities of British Railways. For the time being, it is important to note that the growth of a commercial attitude towards the increasing demand for railway skills has not diminished the degree of co-operation between railway engineers themselves, either in formal or informal situations.

These links between railway engineers have existed at all levels. In the nineteenth century there were directors of railway companies in Britain who served also as directors of other companies throughout the world. Sometimes, they brought their engineers together to consider common problems. Sir Edward Watkin, Chairman of the Manchester, Sheffield and Lincolnshire (later to become the Great Central) Company, had the wisdom, when extending the Company's main line South to London, not to ignore certain features of the Nord Railway in France, of which he was also a director. His dream of running through trains from Manchester to continental Europe through the Channel Tunnel was premature, but his foresight could not be faulted. Turning to a later age, Chapter Four has

Fig. 14.2   Links between the engineers of the British and Netherlands Railways have been close. After withdrawal of the electric passenger service between Manchester and Sheffield, the Netherlands Railways purchased the displaced CC locomotives. In this picture, BR No. 27000, now NS No. 1505 (See Fig. 3.1) stands outside Utrecht Station (A. H. Emerson)

already described how the British Transport Commission invited Dr F. Q. den Hollander, former President of the Netherlands Railways, to give part of his time to the work of the Technical Development and Research Committee, where his contribution was greatly valued.

The personal associations between senior engineers on an international basis have been numerous, but one of the most fruitful was that between Gresley and Bulleid of the LNER and Andre Chapélon of the P.O.-Midi Company and, later, French National Railways. The first of Gresley's 2–8–2 Class P2 locomotives was tested on the plant at Vitry-sur-Seine and Chapelon's work influenced the design of more than one type of British steam locomotive. These associations were not only at senior levels. International exchanges between engineers at much earlier stages in their careers have taken place since the days before the railway amalgamations took place in 1923. They were continued by the main-line railways of Britain, and by British Railways after nationalization in 1948.

The acute need for the co-ordination of the international aspects of railway working has already been emphasized. Railway engineering harmonization within Europe began in 1846, with the forming of the Association of Central European Railway Administrations. Thanks to this early work, it was possible to travel by train direct from Vienna to France via Germany in the early 1850s. By 1872, the European Timetable Conference was arranging train connections between the major cities of Europe, and it was soon extended to include a Through Carriage Conference to avoid change of carriage on inter-city journeys. Another major step forward was the creation in 1882 of the Conference for the Technical Unity of Railways, which still deals with the 'regulations with which railway tracks and vehicles must comply for running in international services'. This led to agreement on a gauge common to all the railways, although Russia, Ireland, and the Iberian Peninsula did not conform to the track gauge which was standard for the rest of Europe.

At this point it is necessary to refer to the attitude adopted by the railways in Britain to their European neighbours. It must be remembered that the British companies still had their own problems of co-ordination in the nineteenth century. In the year of 1846, when the Association of Central European Railway Administrations was formed, the British Government finally decided on the 'Stephenson' track gauge of 4 ft 8½ in between rails as the standard for the railways of Britain (5 ft 3 in for Ireland!). It was not, however, until 1892 that the Great Western tracks were totally converted from Brunel's 7 ft gauge to the British standard. The decision taken by the continental railways to adopt the Stephenson gauge reflected the initial influence of the British engineers rather than any anticipation of a fixed link between Britain and the mainland. Such a link was not contemplated except by a minority opinion represented by men like Sir Edward Watkin or the members of the Channel Tunnel Company. Train ferries did not provide a floating link between Britain and her neighbours until necessitated by the military demands of the First World War although the train ferry itself became a reality in 1850. The Companies with cross-Channel shipping interests were naturally concerned with the commercial and legal aspects of through traffic working, but for many years there was little occasion for British railway engineers to be formally linked with their European colleagues.

When the train ferries allowed the running of railway vehicles between Britain and and mainland Europe, the railways of Britain became directly involved in the regulations relating to rolling stock in international traffic. These regulations were first designed after the Franco-Prussian War of 1870. Following the First World War they were incorporated in the International Wagon Union (known as RIV) and International Carriage and Brake Van Union (RIC) on the initiative of the Italian Railways. After the Second World War, the EUROP wagon pool was created in order to reduce the empty running of freight wagons and now involves over 300000 vehicles. British Railways engineers are marginally involved in the work of the RIV and RIC, but the restricted British structure gauge has created conditions where BR membership of a wagon pool has not yet proved practicable.

To complete the picture, it is necessary to refer to the legislative base which requires to be harmonized if international rail transport is to function. Switzerland merits the title of 'the railway turntable of Europe' and it has initiated many of the organs of co-ordination, including the 1882 Conference of Technical Unity. It was at Berne in 1890 that the International Convention concerning the Carriage of Goods was signed, after negotiations which had begun in 1874. This was the first supranational legislation ever to be introduced. Another convention applicable to passengers and baggage was completed in 1923. The supervision of these two conventions is the task at government level of the Central Office for International Transport. At the railway level the work falls to the International Rail Transport Committee, created in 1902, and located in Berne. It is an indication of the comparative isolation of Britain from the international rail transport world in the first half of this century that she did not subscribe to these conventions until the 1950s.

While British railway engineers had little cause to be associated with the formal machinery of European railway co-ordination until comparatively recently, they played a greater part in less formal links. From the early need in continental Europe for technical standardization between railways emerged the will to exchange technical experience. In 1885 a rather unusual type of organization was born in Brussels, where it still has its headquarters. It was called the International Railway Congress Association (IRCA) and its unusual character was in its involvement of both governments and railways in the promotion of railway progress by means of periodical congresses and publications. The IRCA holds these congresses at approximately four-yearly intervals, the 1979 one having been held in Stockholm on the major theme of investment in railways. The Association includes in its membership 33 governments, 96 railway administrations, and 15 organizations associated with railways.

The railways of Britain have played a prominent role in IRCA. One well remembered congress held in Britain was in 1925, when the LNER played host to delegates at the centenary celebrations of the Stockton and Darlington railway and presented that most vivid pageant of a hundred years of locomotion. Subsequent congresses have been held in a variety of locations, ranging from Dublin to New Delhi. Since the creation of British Railways in 1948, two congresses, one in 1954 and the other in 1971, have been held in London.

In addition to the several bodies which were set up to deal with specific railway problems arising from the need for standardization, co-ordination, and the exchange of information, it became necessary to create an overall organization which could act on behalf of railways as a whole. A body of this type, with limited scope, was created through German initiative at the end of the nineteenth century. It was not, however, until after the First World War that the Conventions of Porta Rosa (1921) and

Genoa (1922) created the International Union of Railways (UIC), which has become the predominant railway association in the world.

The UIC, with headquarters in Paris, began its activities in 1922. At that time there were 51 member administrations in 30 countries. The four main-line groups made up the British membership and Sir Herbert Walker, General Manager of the Southern Railway, represented their interests as a Vice Chairman of the UIC Board of Management. Sir William Forbes, General Manager of the London, Brighton and South Coast Railway had already played a prominent role in establishing the UIC before the amalgamations of 1923.

The objectives of the UIC are:

1. To standardize and improve the equipment and operating methods of the Railways for the purpose of international traffic.

2. With the participation of organizations other than the UIC, to ensure co-ordination and unity of action of International Organizations which are parties to the agreement.

3. To arrange, under the conditions laid down in the Statutes for the Railways to be represented on external bodies for the purpose of examining joint questions concerning them.

The involvement of the engineers has been most directly associated with the achievement of the first objective, particularly in Europe, where all the railways are UIC members, except those of Albania and the USSR. Although European international railway matters form the main purpose of UIC activity, there are member railways in Asia, North America, and Africa. The UIC also maintains liaison with the East European Railway Organization (OSJD), the Association of American Railways (AAR), and the similar association in South America. It also has close links with a number of non-railway organizations and enjoys consultative status at the United Nations Economic Commission for Europe. There is hardly any area relating to railways where the UIC cannot seek advice, or be called upon to give advice.

After nationalization of the railways of Britain in 1948, the Chairman of the Railway Executive represented British Railways on the Board of Management of the UIC. Since the abolition of the Railway Executive it has been the practice of BR to be represented on the UIC Board by a Member of the British Transport Commission or its successor, the British Railways Board. The first and second Members were both civil engineers: J. C. L. (later Sir Landale) Train and John Ratter. They were succeeded by David McKenna and David Bowick. The BR representative has always been a Vice-President of UIC.

Until the 1960s the British Railways involvement in UIC activities amounted to little more than its commercial interest in the movement of international traffic and the engineering aspects of the train ferry operations based on the Dover and Harwich stations. Ideas were exchanged, however, and in the early 1950s both the UIC Board of Management and the Railway Executive were concerned about the future of the long-distance passenger business. It will be remembered that the RE Modernization Plan made provision for helicopter terminals at a number of main-line railway stations, although the proposals were to have no practical outcome. It was decided to link the principal continental cities with Trans-Europ Express services, designed to attract the business traveller from car and airline. On BR routes, the Blue Pullman trains were introduced in the same period with a similar objective.

John Ratter was elected President of the UIC for the years 1961–2. His period in office did much to involve British Railways more closely in UIC activities. He was international in outlook and his attitude did much to reconcile the approaches of different factions within the widely ranging membership of the UIC. He had the support of Sir Brian Robertson and formed a firm friendship with Louis Armand, Secretary General of the UIC. Armand had a distinguished background as a railway engineer and, between the two world wars, had become well known in Britain for his work on locomotive feed water treatment in France. After becoming Director General of the French National Railways he left the railway scene for a time before returning in his UIC role. The initiatives taken in the early 1960s not only led to the closer association of British Railways with UIC work: the world stature of the UIC itself was greatly enhanced.

The UIC General Secretariat in Paris is responsible for general co-ordination, implementing the Board of Management's decisions and representation on outside bodies. The Group of Nine EEC Railways form a restricted membership group within the UIC, and David Bowick, Vice-Chairman of British Railways, was elected to chair this group in 1978. There is no reason, however, for BR to be involved with some of the bodies participating in the work of the UIC. For example there is no direct BR interest in either the EUROP wagon pool or the Trans-Europe Express services. On the other hand, BR mechanical engineers are concerned directly with the work of the International Wagon and Carriage Unions (RIV and RIC).

British Railways is also closely concerned in the work of two companies which are in railway ownership. One is INTERFRIGO, which promotes the development of refrigerated traffic on its 24 member railways. BR is involved in the management of the Company, and its staff have worked at the Basle Headquarters. The other organization is INTERCONTAINER, a jointly owned subsidiary of 23 European railway administrations. BR played a prominent role in the development of the large container in Europe. It exhibited a Freightliner train in European traffic centres and assisted in the creation of INTERCONTAINER. In the new climate following publication in 1963 of the Plan for Reshaping British Railways, the BR aim was to rationalize its international freight by projecting the liner train concept into Europe, and at the same time concentrating the movement of train ferry wagons on a limited number of routes so as to increase wagon productivity. Erik Upmark, then General Manager of the Swedish Railways and President of the UIC in 1967–8, commented 'BR was well known for the inefficiency of its freight service. Almost overnight, it shot ahead into the front rank and became a revolutionary force in European rail freight.'

The international standard (ISO) recommendations for container design were strongly influenced by deep-sea shipping requirements and, although the UIC recommendations closely followed the standard, they were later supplemented by the acceptance of the 'T' type container, which was suitable only for land transits. This was a significant development as it indicated that the container was now an accepted form of road/rail combined transport in Europe (as with the Freightliner train in Britain) and no longer merely the land extension of a sea journey. The interest of the European mainland railways in BR Freightliner equipment, as distinct from the acceptance of the container concept, was first evident following the introduction of the experimental container service from London (Stratford) to Paris (La Chapelle) in 1968. The INTERCONTAINER Company leased 30 Freightliner wagons for their initial service in Europe, but later used wagons which were not constrained by the requirements of the BR loading gauge.

The British Railways Chief Mechanical and Electrical Engineer was very closely involved in these container and wagon developments. In particular, H. Wilcock, Rolling Stock Design Engineer, became very well known in European railway circles. In view of the BR interest in the expansion of container services, it was appropriate that John Ratter was appointed as the first Chairman of INTERCONTAINER and, on his retirement, was then succeeded by another Member of the British Railways Board, David McKenna.

The development of the large container was, therefore, one of the major advances pioneered by British Railways within the international community of railways. Containerization would have spread in any case in connection with the deep-sea trade but BR's contribution was two-fold. First, it advocated the container as the only practicable form of combined transport which could be used for road/rail transits on any European railway. Gauge restrictions prevent the piggy-back operation receiving the same universal acceptance. Second, it emphasized the growing significance of the container train, rather than the individual wagon, as the unit of rail movement. The move towards containerization marches ahead, and INTERCONTAINER is a growth area within European rail freight activity.

Although organizations like INTERCONTAINER, which have grown from initiatives within UIC, exemplify the dynamic character of international railway development, the real heart of UIC activity has always been its formal committee structure. The two most important elements of this structure, so far as BR engineers are concerned, are the Traction and Rolling Stock Committee and the Way and Works Committee. Before considering the work of these two engineering committees, however, it would be useful to refer to the task of the UIC Planning Committee. Although not an exclusively engineering body, the Planning Committee has been responsible for considering the shape and nature of the future European railway system. One of the major contributions made by the Committee was its report 'The Image of the Railways of the Future', which recommended the types of rail service to be provided in the light of European traffic forecasts. Known to a wider public was another document entitled 'The Master Plan for European Railways' Infrastructure'. This plan was intended to identify the most important international routes, and develop the ways in which their capacity could be improved. The main BR developments within the plan have been the up-grading by the civil engineers of the London–Bristol–South Wales and London–Edinburgh routes to permit of speeds up to 125 miles/h. As the Channel Tunnel (an essential component of the proposals) did not materialize as expected, the high-speed passenger network in North West Europe, which was being developed under the title 'Ouest Europolitain', did not come to fruition. As a result, progress was fragmented and all the new trunk lines now being developed are confined within national frontiers. This means that one objective of the 'Ouest Europolitain' project, namely the harmonization of the engineering practices of the railways involved, will not now be achieved in the near future. Figure 14.3 indicates the very high standards of passenger service which would have resulted from these proposals.

The Traction and Rolling Stock Committee, on which British Railways

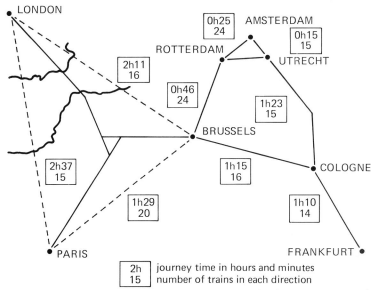

Fig. 14.3 The proposed 'Ouest Europolitain' high speed rail passenger network as designed in 1953 in anticipation of the building of the Channel Tunnel (UIC)

is represented by its Chief Mechanical and Electrical Engineer, seeks to reach international agreement concerning:

(a) Solutions to technical problems which occur during border crossings;

(b) The economic advantages of using labour-saving schemes in the development of traction units; and

(c) The formation of a common policy vis-a-vis the various organizations outside the railways such as the International Standards Organization (ISO), the United Nations Economic Commission for Europe (ECE), and the International Electrical Committee (IEC).

The Traction and Rolling Stock Committee – and it is not alone in this respect – faces the problem of balancing the claims of standardization and technological evolution. It has drawn up a standardization programme, which can progressively be implemented in five steps, i.e.,

(i) Standardization of quality and dimensions.

(ii) Compatibility of parts; for example, in brake equipment.

(iii) Interchangeability, using different assemblies for similar carriages or wagons.

(iv) Unification, as exemplified by the three types of standard UIC carriages which have been produced.

(v) Standardization of the characteristics of all rolling stock.

To look through the minutes of this Committee takes the reader's mind back to the British experience of standardization: to Churchward on the Great Western, to Stanier on the LMS, and to the Riddles team in the early days of the Railway Executive. On a European scale, the task of standardization is infinitely harder than on a national scale. While the fundamental elements of track gauge, loading gauge, and vehicle buffing/coupling were agreed in early days, only the track gauge has remained intact. The current loading gauge, for example, was agreed in 1938, but is now being exceeded in the building of the new lines linking Hanover with Wurzburg and Mannheim with Stuttgart on the German Federal Railways.

The working procedure followed by the Traction and Rolling Stock Committee – like that of the other main UIC Committees – is that their recommendations lead to the inclusion of specifications in the UIC Codes of Practice. Binding regulations follow unanimous agreement, but recommendations can be made by a simple majority decision. The situation of the British Railways engineer in these decisions has always been a difficult one. He has no wish to obstruct any course of action which would benefit the railway systems which are linked within a continental network, but cannot commit BR to some aspect of standardization which has no application on its isolated system. In practice, there is an understanding between the members of all the UIC Committees on the unique position of the BR representative in these discussions.

The civil and signal engineering counterpart to the Traction and Rolling

Stock Committee is the UIC Way and Works Committee. (It will be remembered that 'Way and Works' and 'Traction and Rolling Stock' appeared in the titles of the BR Chief Engineers for a period during the 1960s.) BR's Chief Civil Engineer and Chief Signal and Telecommunications Engineer are members of this Committee. Other civil engineering matters than those concerned with track or structure gauge, which are of main significance in international through train working, are the cross section and the angle of inclination of rails. Both affect wear and tear, with consequent effect on the period of useful life and the matter of wheel/rail dynamics with its direct bearing on safety and passenger comfort. Two major contemporary problems are bringing the civil engineers together from the different railways in joint consideration of their experience and research activities. One of these problems results from the increasing speeds and axle loads of today's trains. The other relates to the many bridges and tunnels which require reconstruction as they enter their second century of railway service. Dr J. E. Spindel, Development Engineer, BR Headquarters has chaired the UIC Sub-Committee on Bridges during recent years.

The signal engineers of the different railway systems also have a common interest in the problems raised by increasing train speeds. Signal engineering has, however, developed with strong national characteristics and the benefits of standardization can be expected in the case of individual components rather than with the systems themselves. The gap

Fig. 14.4 Collaboration between engineers on different railway systems allows vehicles like this train ferry wagon to circulate in Britain and mainland Europe (BRB)

which has existed between British Railways and other European admini-strations in level crossing protection methods has been due not to engineering preferences but to differences in public attitudes and the legislative background. The use of radio is one of those areas of common interest where it has been possible to make considerable progress through international engineering co-operation.

The efforts of the European railway engineers to develop standardiza-tion are pushed forward with two objectives in mind. The primary objec-tive is to facilitate the through working of trains and individual vehicles. In this area there are mandatory decisions required, for example, in respect of axle loads, signal aspects, and the inclination of rails. To assist through working there are also the desirable, but not mandatory, aspects of harmonization, which include the questions of gradients, track alignment, and the radii of curves. The secondary objective of stan-dardization is to create the situation in which costs can be lowered by long production runs and competitive tendering on a truly international scale. Joint purchasing and the placing of bulk orders has made some progress in such fields as rolling stock and signal cables, but is not yet on a significant scale. The constraints of the British Railways loading gauge complicate the BR interest in standard UIC rolling stock designs, but the standardization of components presents less difficulty. The problems are well known to BR as it was responsible for the chairmanship of the UIC Supplies Committee from 1973 to 1976, and this body is closely associated with the work of the two UIC engineering committees.

In addition to the permanent committees and their sub-committees, it is UIC practice to create special study groups for specific tasks. Con-tainerization of freight and the design of standard rolling stock involved other interests as well as those of engineering, so were suited to the multi-disciplinary approach. The BR involvement in the former has already been mentioned, and the design of components in the rolling stock design work was of particular interest to mechanical engineers. BR was closely concerned with the study of Optimum Passenger Comfort and the findings of this work were fed into the standard carriage designs.

Perhaps the best known of the UIC study groups is the one which has been concerned with the automatic coupling of freight wagons. While most non-European railways introduced the automatic central buffer coupling some years ago, wagons in Western and Central Europe are still manually coupled. This is in spite of the fact that the UIC has now developed an automatic coupler, which is acknowledged to be the most advanced design in existence. The new coupler is used in certain special cases, but has not been generally introduced because of the financial burden involved. The prospects of general introduction appear to recede year by year into the ever more distant future, and the year 2000 now seems to be the earliest possible date when the changeover could take place.

Fig. 14.5 Side (above) and frontal (below) aspects of the UIC Automatic Coupler, which still awaits general adoption on wagons in Central and Western Europe (SNCF)

The British Railways attitude to the automatic coupler is not in doubt. It will be remembered that the Railway Executive standardized the buckeye coupling on passenger carriages at an early date and then began the experiments which resulted in the Dowty type of automatic coupler for freight wagons. Since the Dowty coupler was developed, BR policy has reduced the need for wagon coupling by developing the train as the unit of freight movement and consequently reducing shunting operations. If, and when, the neighbouring mainland railways decide to adopt the automatic coupler, British Railways would fit the coupling to their wagons which circulate on the mainland. For dealing with foreign rolling stock, BR would provide 'match' wagons to achieve compatibility with their own equipment by fitting both manual and automatic couplings on these special vehicles. It is possible, however, that the mainland railways will increasingly accord with British practice in developing the proportion of train-load working within their freight operations. If so, the general introduction of the automatic coupler in Europe may recede even further into the future.

Much of the work of developing the European automatic coupler was carried out by the UIC Organization for Research and Development (ORE). Accommodated at the headquarters of the Netherlands Railways at Utrecht, ORE was established by the UIC Board of Management in 1950 for the purpose of:

1. The pooling of results of the research and experiments carried out by the different Railways and the distribution between its Members, of the necessary technical documentation.

2. The pooling of means of research.

3. The carrying out, on joint account, of certain investigations.

4. The examination, with a view to reduction in costs, of the rationalization of means of construction and of the possibility of dividing the work between the industries of the various countries.

In January 1980 42 railways were members of ORE. British Railways have been represented on the ORE Control Committee from the beginning. It has been customary for one representative to be the head of the BR Research Department and the other to be from one of the engineering departments. T. M. Herbert, Sydney Jones, K. H. Spring, and A. H. Wickens have shared the task with E. S. Cox, R. C. Bond, and M. C. Purbrick. The Control Committee decides the problems to be studied, which are generally very closely related to the work of the two UIC engineering committees. There has also been BR representation at the Utrecht headquarters, which is staffed by some 14 engineers. During the lifetime of ORE to date, over 70 engineers from 11 railways have had the opportunity of working together, so helping to create an international environment of technological research.

By the mid-1950s, British Railways experts were contributing to the co-operative research initiated through ORE, particularly in the fields of corrosion and protective coatings, bridge stress determination, and the stability, as well as the riding, of vehicles. ORE does not possess any laboratories of its own, but makes use mainly of the research facilities of its member railways; also of universities and public or private research institutes. The BR Railway Technical Centre at Derby has been involved in a number of projects, including the provision of an experimental section of concrete slab track at Radcliffe-on-Trent, near Nottingham, as part of an ORE proposal. The BR association with ORE has been a two-way process, as many of the reports produced by ORE have proved very useful to BR engineers. At the same time, it is only to be expected that British Railways, which has an internal research capacity on a unique scale within European railways, has the task of determining the right balance between its internal and external research activities.

Towards the end of the 1950s it had become apparent to the UIC that, in order to assist design and development work, a Laboratory was required where railway vehicles could be submitted to tests under all the climatic conditions likely to be experienced in actual service. A vehicle testing station was, therefore, built at Vienna Arsenal and is now controlled jointly by the Austrian Government and ORE. The principal purpose of the station was to carry out research into, and the testing of, carriage heating systems, but the work has been extended to include air-conditioning tests and the effects of widely different climatic conditions on freight vehicles and locomotives. A BR sleeping car went to Vienna for tests in 1964. Since that date a number of Mark II carriages, fitted with different types of heating and air conditioning equipment, have gone to the testing station. The results of these tests have shown that the equipment included in the BR vehicles was more than capable of coping with climatic conditions of a severity not experienced in Britain.

Early in 1979 another dimension was added to the research effort of the Nine EEC railways when the EEC Commission began to develop its interest in the efficiency of the railways and the competitive strength of the railway manufacturing industry in Europe. The aim of the exercise is to ensure that the railway research and development activities are carried out to further the interests of both railways and manufacturers. The work is in its early stages, but it is already evident that British Railways, with its scale of manufacturing capacity and sophisticated research facilities, will be particularly interested in developments.

In addition to the IRCA congresses, the meetings of the UIC Committees and the gatherings of other international railway bodies which bring together railway engineers from different countries, British Railways and/or the British Engineering Institutions have convened a number of conferences of international importance. The first of these events to take place after nationalization was the Joint Engineering Conference, held in London during 1951 (the year of the Festival of Britain). In the civil engineering section, papers were given by J. S. Campbell and H. B.

Everard. R. A. Riddles gave the mechanical engineering paper, while C. M. Cock and H. H. Dyer handled electrical and signal engineering respectively. Those who were present at this conference appreciated its essentially practical approach to post-war engineering problems, and this practical aspect seems to have characterized many successive conferences.

Reference has already been made to the conference on Railway Electrification at Industrial Frequency, held in 1960, and the opportunity which it gave for over 60 authors to present papers relating to the progress made since the choice of electrification systems was discussed at the London Congress of the IRCA in 1954. In 1966, the Euston Main Line Electrification Conference considered both in the lecture hall and on the ground how the many aspects of the electrification had been carried out, giving at the same time an outline of the lessons which had been learned. The Transportation Engineering Conference of 1968 was followed in 1969 by the conference on High Speed Freight Wagons, when some very useful discussion took place on the potential conflict between engineering sophistication in wagon design and the commercial ability to pay for it. Other conventions organized in the 1960s were devoted to Railway Braking (1962), Adhesion (1963), Automatic Railways (1964), Interaction between Vehicle and Track (1965), and Guided Land Transport (1966). All attracted distinguished participation on an international basis.

The 1972 Conference on the Passenger Environment brought together the engineers, industrial designers, and marketing men to consider methods of optimizing passenger comfort. In 1975, the 150th Anniversary of Passenger Railways was the opportunity for holding a conference on the theme 'Rail Engineering – The Way Ahead'. As on its centenary in 1925, the opening of the Stockton and Darlington Railway had given railway engineers another opportunity to exchange experience and ideas. Over 80 authors presented papers to delegates from more than 30 countries. 1979 witnessed the Symposium on Safe and Efficient Freight Transport by Rail and a further Symposium on Railway Braking.

The matters discussed at these conferences have been referred to in the appropriate chapter of this engineering story, and it is only necessary to emphasize the contribution which has been made by the conference and the technical visit to the international advance of rail technology since the 1950s. During this period there has also been a great increase in visits to British Railways for purposes which are specific and not associated with conferences. BR receives three or four official visits a week from other railway systems, and of these at least one will wish to see the Railway Technical Centre at Derby.

BR engineers have also had reason to visit other railway administrations. Sometimes, it has been for a specific purpose as, for example, when North American traction practice was examined after the Second World War, or when the French 25kV a.c. electrification installations were visited in the 1950s. Examples of well prepared exchange visits have been those in 1969 with the USSR Railways and, later, with the railways of Japan and China. In 1979, Premier Hua of China showed his country's interest in the Railway Technical Centre at Derby by including it as one of his two industrial visits while in Britain.

More recently, there has been a growth in another type of visit by BR engineers. This is the developing field of railway consultancy, where links are being made with the railway expertise of Britain long after the laying of rails across a continent by British navvies, or the former British managements in many countries, have been forgotten. Some of the well respected firms of consulting engineers had origins in the Victorian era, and engineers from the former railway companies were sometimes seconded to work with them. There was also a long tradition of railway consultancy as part of the aid given to developing countries. International collaboration in giving aid under United Nations auspices led to the creation of the Economic and Social Committee for Asia and the Far East (ECAFE), now associated with Asia and the Pacific and known as ESCAP. The British Railways leader in the Railway Sub-Commission of ECAFE was John Ratter, followed by R. C. Bond.

From the increasing realization that British railwaymen had many skills which could profitably be employed by many railways overseas, emerged

Fig. 14.6 Premier Hua and Chinese delegation inspect the Tubular Axle a.c. Induction Motor during a visit to the Railway Technical Centre, Derby in 1979 (BRB)

a recognized consultancy service. At first, this was offered through the United Kingdom Railway Advisory Service (UKRAS), established jointly by the Ministry of Transport and British Railways. Its work was carried out in different parts of the world and involved former Railway Inspecting Officers, and experts from Manufacturing industry. Brigadier C. A. Langley, a former Chief Inspecting Officer and S. B. Warder, lately Chief Electrical Engineer at BR Headquarters were very heavily involved in the activities of UKRAS.

As the scope and scale of railway consultancy had increased substantially, British Railways formed, in 1969, Transport Systems and Market Research Limited (TRANSMARK) as a wholly-owned subsidiary. Its main function was to provide consultancy for railway, and other transport projects in all parts of the world. A small team of permanent staff in London co-ordinate the projects and provide a permanent link with clients. For the larger projects, and also for those involving the application of specific engineering skills, teams of experts are seconded from the departments of British Railways, including visits by the Chief Engineers.

TRANSMARK is responsible for marketing throughout the world BR research and development, computer programming, staff training, patents, and licensing. The one exception is railway rolling stock, which is the province of British Rail Engineering Limited. In 1978, TRANSMARK was awarded the Queen's Award for Export Achievement. In the previous three years the consultancy's earnings in the export market had increased sixfold, and in 1978 itself 69 projects were being undertaken in 29 countries and states. Altogether, TRANSMARK has been active in over 60 countries, where projects have ranged from comparatively small studies to sharing in tasks involving several million pounds.

An earlier chapter has described how British Rail Engineering Limited (BREL) was created, and entered the international market as a supplier of

Fig. 14.7   Civil engineers working on a TRANSMARK project in Saudi Arabia (BRB)

railway rolling stock. In addition to its primary role of constructing and repairing British Railways' rolling stock and mechanical engineering equipment generally, BREL has had to undertake the task of building up an export potential and organizing a marketing activity. The export sales company, BRE-Metro Limited, jointly owned with Metro-Cammell, is unusual in being a selling partnership between a publicly owned railway and a firm in the private sector. Like TRANSMARK, it provides the opportunity for BR engineers to meet the many demands which have arisen following the new found, and worldwide, confidence in the future of railways.

Although the civil engineering aspects have been described in Chapter Nine, no consideration of international railway engineering relationships would be complete without some reference to the Channel Tunnel, potentially the world's most important international fixed link. The Tunnel has a history which goes back to the Napoleonic era. There can be few such apparently inevitable engineering projects, which have still failed to materialize. On more than one occasion, the Tunnel has been on the very brink of becoming a reality when some new turn of events has caused progress to cease. The problem has not only been in reaching agreement between two sovereign states – Britain and France – on political, financial, managerial, and engineering considerations. It has been also in synchronizing agreement, particularly that relating to political will and financial opportunity, in the two countries for sufficiently long to ensure that there can be a firm commitment to the completion of the project.

Serious consideration of the Tunnel did not begin until the 1860s, when the Channel Tunnel Company was founded. Military and political opinion in Britain contributed to a general lack of enthusiasm for the project, which lasted until after the Second World War. Reference has already been made to Sir Edward Watkin's interest, but neither his influence nor that of the Channel Tunnel Company was reflected in general railway attitudes in the first half of the twentieth century. The Southern Railway was lukewarm in its reaction to the concept during the 1930s, and referred to the compensation required if its cross-Channel ferries were to be put out of business. The British Transport Commission was too involved with its own problems to give much positive thought to a fixed link with mainland Europe, but the British Railways Board was later to give the project its strong support.

Between the two world wars there was sufficient interest in the Tunnel for several Bills seeking development of the project to be proposed, but lost, in the British House of Commons. In 1924, the Prime Minister (Ramsay MacDonald), along with the leaders of the other main political parties, decided not to support the Tunnel. Winston Churchill was quick to express a contrary view, but the British public as a whole was not yet reconciled to a fixed link with mainland Europe.

The real thrust began in 1957, when the Channel Tunnel Study Group was established by the British and French Governments. The Group included the Channel Tunnel Company (in which British Railways was to have a continuing involvement), the French equivalent (in which the French National Railways had a major share), the Suez Canal Company, and a consortium of bankers. The Group recommended, in 1960, that a twin bore rail tunnel should be constructed. There was every prospect of raising the £120 million then required in the international money market, and if work had started in 1960 it was expected that the engineers could have completed the task in 1965. The bankers wanted a guarantee, however, from the two Governments to protect their investment in the event of possible geological problems with the Channel sub-soil frustrating the efforts of the engineers. This guarantee had not been received when, in December 1960 a rival group was established and, by October 1961 submitted proposals to build a bridge instead of a tunnel. The British and French Ministers of Transport now had to re-examine the form of link between the two countries. Their conclusions, published in September 1963, clearly favoured the tunnel solution. In 1964, the British and French

Fig. 14.8   Mock-up of the end section of double-deck vehicle designed by BR to convey motor cars and their passengers through the Channel Tunnel (BRB)

Governments announced their joint decision that a rail tunnel project should be pursued.

BR and the French National Railways (SNCF) were naturally disappointed over the delay but, after satisfying themselves that further work on the Tunnel would have the support of their Governments, created a joint organization in 1966. John Ratter was Joint Chairman of the Railway Steering Group, with the Director General of SNCF as his opposite number and one of the authors jointly chaired the Railway Working Party. The Chief Engineers of both BR and SNCF devised the railway engineering requirements, generally at meetings in London or Paris, but sometimes on site. In these discussions the engineering practices of the two railways were subject to much detailed examination and, as a result, each side gained a deep appreciation of the other's approach to an engineering challenge of exceptional proportions.

It was agreed that BR and SNCF would specialize on particular features of the Tunnel and its rolling stock. BR, for example, was responsible for designing the vehicles for carrying road vehicles and produced two mock-ups. The second of these was a full-size representation of the ends of two double-deck car carriers, in order to demonstrate the method of vehicle coupling and the proposed weather-proof flexible connection between the vehicles.

The planning and evaluation of the Channel Tunnel project extended continuously over a period of 15 years, with separate evaluations made by the British and French Governments on no less than six occasions. There can be few projects where so many re-appraisals have been made. In 1972 the two Governments decided to proceed with the detailed studies, with a view to a final decision in 1973, which would allow the Tunnel to be in active use by the Winter of 1979–80. The project would be financed by private capital, with BR and SNCF as modest shareholders. It was to be a joint Anglo-French operation, with BR and SNCF operating the Tunnel as contractors for the Channel Tunnel Authority. The civil engineering features have already been described. Traction was to be provided by 6000 h.p. locomotives fed from both British and French electricity grids at 25 kV 50 cycles. Three types of train were proposed. Accompanied road vehicles would be ferried in a form of 'merry-go-round' operation between the Tunnel terminals with passengers free to leave their cars during the journey. Fast Inter-city services would link London with Paris, Brussels, and other European cities and through freight trains would serve the main traffic centres on both sides of the Tunnel. It is significant that all the railway equipment to be used in the Tunnel had to be tried and proved in arduous service. As in the Riddles era at the Railway Executive, reliability and simplicity were to be preferred to technological sophistication.

The work on the Channel Tunnel was, however, abandoned in January 1975 following a decision taken unilaterally by the British Government,

Fig. 14.9   Access tunnels to the Channel Tunnel workings, alongside the main
line between Folkestone and Dover (BRB)

and several months before receiving the report of the Channel Tunnel
Advisory Group, which (under the chairmanship of Sir Alec Cairncross, a
distinguished economist) it had commissioned to make a further evaluation of the project. This, the seventh major appraisal within some twenty
years, again confirmed the validity of the Tunnel's prospects in that it
would still be the cheapest method of conveying the anticipated level of
cross-Channel traffic. The Tunnel, as a concept, did not die following the
controversial decision taken early in 1975. By 1978 British Railways was
advocating a single-track 'no frills' rail-only tunnel, and later gained the
support of the SNCF. The new proposal involves no high-speed link
between Folkestone and London. The anticipated London–Paris journey
time for passengers is more likely to be slightly over 4 hours, compared
with 2½ hours under the earlier scheme. Neither will the single-bore
tunnel involve the big terminals at Cheriton and Sangatte, so necessary to
the 'rolling motorway' inherent in the more ambitious project. On the
other hand, the single-track tunnel will be constructed to the international UIC loading gauge and be capable of becoming part of later, and
higher capacity, developments. Train capacity would naturally be much
reduced under single-line conditions, but it is proposed to operate trains
on a 'tidal flow' basis, with 10 trains an hour in one direction followed by
10 an hour in the other. The return on the investment of £800 million at
1979 prices is expected to be of the order of 13 per cent.

Again, there are several rival schemes to the BR/SNCF proposal, including a more elaborate form of tunnel, a road/rail tube, and no less than
three bridge schemes. Two further appraisals of the Channel Tunnel
began in 1979. One was required by the British Minister of Transport and
once more involved Sir Alec Cairncross. The other was required by the

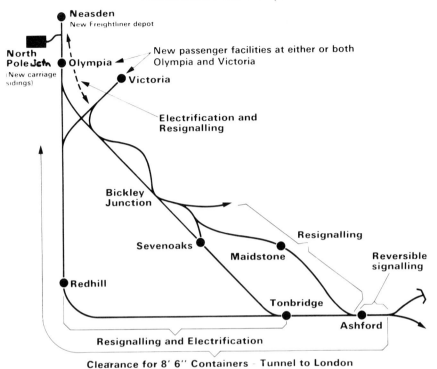

Fig. 14.10　Diagram showing the main engineering works which will have to be carried out between London and the Channel Tunnel under the BR proposal to construct a single bore tunnel (BRB)

EEC Commission. By 1980, therefore, ten major appraisals of the Tunnel will have been completed.

The situation has now taken on a new slant. The cross-Channel fixed link relates to one of Europe's major international routes and ranks, therefore, as an essential component in the EEC proposals for the future European transport infrastructure. Late in 1979 the EEC Commission sent to the Council of Ministers a 'Green Paper' seeking to set up special financial mechanisms which would assist in the completion of a number of selected projects. The cross-Channel link is a likely candidate for consideration, and 1980 begins with the prospects for the Tunnel again in the ascendant.

From what has already been outlined in this chapter, it will be appreciated that the international role of the British Railways engineers has grown significantly in the three decades since nationalization in 1948. At the beginning of this period, British Railways, apart from its commercial interest in international traffic associated mainly with its great shipping fleet, was very largely an isolated, island, railway system. By the end of the period, BR was engaged in overseas consultancy, exporting railway equipment made in its own workshops, taking a full part in UIC activities, prominent in the organization of international engineering conferences, and chairman administration of the Nine EEC Railways. That this situation has become more evident during the last decade has been due to a number of factors. These have included particularly the growth of research and development on BR, the thrust of containerization, the growth of ideas following new attitudes formed in the mid-1960s and the widening horizons which came with the accession of the United Kingdom to membership of the European Economic Community.

The deepening association between British Railways and the other European railway systems has also sharpened the interest in comparisons between the different systems. Earlier chapters have emphasized the importance attached to competition rather than co-ordination in British transport policies, except for a brief period after 1948 and, since 1968, in localized passenger traffic situations. The result has been seen in the spread of investment resources between the different forms of transport, particularly on the principal routes. The British attitude to the commercial nature of its railways is also apparent from the various measures taken in the pursuit of railway profitability. An indication of this attitude is the fact that revenue support provided to British Railways by 1979 was, in real terms, some 25 per cent less than that provided in 1976. This reduction was not in accordance with general trends in European railway finances, which reflect increasing levels of support to railways in recent years.

Comparisons between different railway systems are also affected by a number of other features in addition to government policies. The economic geography of a country, the ways in which rail marketing policies have free play in dealing with the mix of traffics available for transport, the part played by transit traffic in the rail economy, the extent of electrification, and national attitudes to pay and productivity are among the factors which have a bearing on the operational and financial performance of a railway. Also, the management and engineering skills available to a railway must be recognized as fulfilling a vital role.

In its booklet *Facts and Figures*, published in June 1978, British Railways, although recognizing the difficulties inherent in making this type of comparison, gave the following figures of total passenger kilometres and freight tonne kilometres per £ of support received from government in 1976, when the level of support received by BR was still relatively high compared with the following years:

Britain	101	Netherlands	62
Italy	97	West Germany	47
France	84	Austria	42
Switzerland	69	Belgium	27

There are other figures available, which indicate that the average British taxpayer contributes towards his railway system about one-third of that contributed by the average European taxpayer. In terms of investment per employee during the early 1970s, British Railways was attracting less than a third of the resources put into railways by its nearest mainland neighbours. BR investment also falls well behind the levels of mainland European railways when related to the number of train miles operated. In the January 1980 issue of the *International Railway Journal*, the British approach to investment in railways was described as 'timid'. The Journal compared capital spending for 1980 in different countries and the BR situation will be seen from the following comparison with neighbouring mainland networks:

	Capital Spending on Railways in £ million
West Germany	1219
France	740
Italy	476
Belgium	390
Britain	316
Netherlands	178

As it has been formally announced in Germany that the DB will receive during the 1980s a very substantially increased share of national transport investment compared with the 1970s (and 80 per cent of DB traffic is already electrically hauled compared with 42 per cent on BR), the gap between these two most comparable of European networks could further increase. More evidence of the disturbing investment situation on BR was produced in December 1979 in a report prepared jointly by Leeds University and British Railways in collaboration with nine other European Railways (*A Comparative Study of European Rail Performance*). Amongst a wealth of significant comparisons, the Study confirmed that the level of investment per train kilometre on BR was well below that of any of the other nine railways which took part in the work.

After taking account of the difficulties encountered in making international comparisons, the overall impression is clear. It is that British Railways engineers face constraints on both day-to-day and investment expenditure to a degree which is not approached by their colleagues in mainland Europe. 'A bow wave of investment which is still building up ahead of us' is how Sir Peter Parker described the situation in his commentary on the Board's activities for 1979.

CHAPTER FIFTEEN

Past, Present, and Future

E ARLIER chapters have given some indication of the unique manner in which political and economic forces have affected the course of railway engineering development in Britain. Chapters Three and Fourteen ended on sobering notes for the early 1980s by emphasizing the declining levels of financial support received by British Railways, particularly when compared with their neighbours on the European mainland. This is the time therefore, to consider the earlier engineering contribution, relate it to current conditions and give some attention to likely future developments.

It will be recalled that the headlong rush into the Railway Age produced some great engineers in Britain, but also left a legacy of problems for their successors to solve. The thrusting independence of Victorian industrial society resulted in too many railways being built in nineteenth-century Britain. The inevitable outcome of this over-investment was fierce competition, the impoverished state of many railway companies, and surplus railway capacity, particularly after the massive re-organizations of 1923 and 1948. As a result, the British Railways system was re-shaped during the 1960s on a scale which had not been experienced by any other major industry in Britain and has never been matched on any other major national railway network.

Statutory controls over railways were always necessary, but some outlived their usefulness. To take only two examples, legislation enacted in the earlier half of the nineteenth century saddled the railways of Britain until 1948 and 1954 respectively with the right of customers to run their own wagons, and the retention of the manually operated swinging gate at level crossings. Less direct forms of legislation have had much wider effect on railway development. Between the wars, the four main-line Companies were subject to the strictest statutory regulation in British railway history. This restricted their capacity to react to competition and the industrial depression of the 1930s. Standards of passenger service were enhanced by the spur of competition, but investment in badly needed productivity measures was sadly inadequate, with the LMS rationalization and Southern electrification schemes proving exceptions to the rule. On the coming of unification of the railways in 1948, BR inherited these problems. Unification also provided the opportunity to standardize on the best engineering practices, but these were delayed by opposing political attitudes and a succession of statutory re-organizations, which proved inimical to consistent technological development.

In earlier chapters it has also been explained how the years of investment famine lasted until the mid-1950s, with funds barely sufficient to overtake arrears in wartime maintenance, with nothing to spare for improving service quality and productivity. The flood of new equipment which then followed the Modernization Plan preceded the re-shaping of both attitudes and the physical network in the early 1960s. These events preceded the growth of more bi-partisan transport policies in the 1970s. Unfortunately, this period of comparative stability in political attitudes to British Railways has begun to merge with a time when much of the equipment obtained under the Modernization Plan is due for replacement, and there are other major demands on investment resources. Again, this pressure on investment funds coincides with low industrial activity, worsening railway finances, and severe restraints by the Government on public expenditure. It is a severe testing time for any industry, but particularly so for an undertaking like British Railways, with its high fixed costs which vary little with changes in the volume of traffic carried. In this situation, the engineer must continue with the severely practical approach which he has inherited. The aim of squeezing the maximum output from the minimum of equipment is as relative today as it ever has been in the engineering contribution to higher productivity and increased standards of railway service.

While 'Value for money' has been so characteristic of railway engineering in Britain since the 1920s, it has been equally important in the pursuit both of service quality and productivity. In the years preceding the Second World War, the British railway passenger service, in terms of speed and frequency, was hardly equalled anywhere in the world. The productivity of steam traction reached its peak, however, in the early 1950s. This was due partly to the lower demands on maintenance of the new British Railways standard locomotives and to the scrapping of the less efficient of the former Company types. It also reflected new operating patterns designed to achieve the maximum productivity of locomotives, and pioneered so effectively on the Great Eastern lines of the Eastern Region. By then, however, the twilight of steam had arrived, and far greater contributions to both rail traction productivity and service standards were made by its diesel and electric successors. Indeed, the diesel contribution was thought to be so marked in reducing traction costs by the end of the 1950s that the programme for the elimination of steam traction was compressed into a time span shorter than was considered prudent by engineering opinion. Acute maintenance problems resulted from the acceleration of the diesel programme, but the experience has been turned to very good account in the development of today's diesel equipment. The HST illustrates the extent to which high power diesel-electric drives have been developed in Britain.

Another example of the very valuable experience gained from an adverse situation relates to the electrical engineer. The clearance problems involved in adapting high-voltage a.c. electrification to the British loading gauge have been discussed in Chapter Seven. Here it is only necessary to emphasize the unique experience gained by the BR engineers, and the resulting increase in railway productivity which is now made possible by the lower costs of main-line electrification. Some significant further improvements have been made since July 1978, when the American engineer, W. D. Middleton wrote in *Traffic Quarterly*:

> . . . in Great Britain, which has been a world leader in the development of modern overhead catenary systems, improvements in catenary design have reduced the fixed installation costs of electrification per track-mile by close to 30 per cent.

Civil engineering progress, at least to the onlooker, has been less dramatic during the last thirty years than that experienced in mechanical engineering, but it should be remembered that the application of work study techniques to permanent way work was a major contributor to BR productivity in the 1950/60s. In the early days of railways, the weakness

Fig. 15.1   A High Speed Train running over a section of PACT track at
Duffield, North of Derby (BRB)

of the track delayed the development of the steam locomotive. During the early 1950s, arrears of track maintenance made it necessary to slacken the running times of passenger services. Those situations should be contrasted with, for example, the East Coast Main Line today, where an inter-city train can cruise at 100 miles/h over 90 per cent of the route and at 125 miles/h over 50 per cent of the miles, with a quieter and smoother ride than was possible thirty years earlier at much lower speeds. In addition, the real costs of maintaining the track to these high standards have been greatly reduced. In this example, both civil and mechanical engineering technology have made their individual contributions to higher productivity levels and better service to the passenger. The individual contributions have also been enhanced by the joint consideration of wheel/rail dynamics.

Reference has been made more than once to the railway productivity achievements of the signal engineer. It will be remembered that the 1948 signalling scene was still dominated by the mechanical control of points and semaphore signals, although some of the world's first signalling innovations appeared in Britain before the Second World War. By the end of the 1970s, multiple-aspect colour-light signalling, combined with the BR standard automatic warning system, represented a pinnacle in reliable, conventional signalling development. Solid state technology, electronics, and the micro-processor have now opened up new signalling opportunities. Developments described in earlier chapters like JOT, BRATO and the experimental introduction of Signal Repeating AWS on the Southern Region have indicated the approaching feasibility of the fully automated railway. That represents the ultimate engineering contribution to railway productivity if, and when, justifiable in social and financial terms.

Before being drawn into considerations of a future situation, it would be sensible to establish the contribution which has already been made to railway productivity in Britain. In the thirty years between 1948 and 1978, the number of staff on British Railways has fallen by 72 per cent, and is still declining. The carriage fleet has been halved and the number of wagons reduced by over 80 per cent. The locomotive fleet has declined by 82 per cent, but part of the replacement is in multiple unit sets, which are included in the carriage figures. In his Presidential Address to the Railway Division of the Institution of Mechanical Engineers on 1 October 1979, K. Taylor, Chief Mechanical and Electrical Engineer of British Railways, illustrated these changes in the composition of the locomotive and rolling stock fleets in Fig. 15.2.

Although remarkable advances have already been made, higher productivity remains a major contributor to the successful future of British Railways. There are several paths to higher productivity. One obvious course in a high fixed-cost industry like a railway is to increase the volume of traffic using it, and this has been a major cause of improved produc-

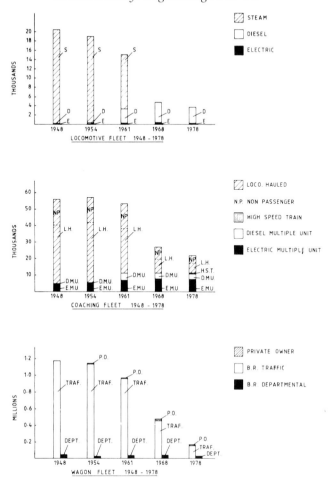

Fig. 15.2   Composition of locomotive and rolling stock fleets of
British Railways 1948 and 1978

tivity on railways in Eastern Europe, where it is national policy to make
the optimum use of railways. Railways in Western Europe, especially in
Britain, operate within more competitive transport policies and generally
work below full capacity. Due to coal production being less than half what
it was thirty years ago and to recent recession in the heavy industries, the
volume of traffic (measured in passenger miles + net ton miles) carried by
British Railways in 1978 was 27 per cent less than in 1948. Until there is a
revival in the country's industrial production, traffic volume can be
expected to make little contribution to BR productivity levels, although
passenger traffic is now higher than it was in 1962, when passenger route
mileage was cut by 30 per cent.

Another substantial contribution can be made towards improved productivity by a railway being allowed to concentrate on those activities to

which it is technically suited. As British Railways made great progress in this direction during its re-shaping activities during the 1960s, the opportunities from further re-shaping are limited, particularly if BR is required to retain its remaining unremunerative passenger services.

British Railways is left, therefore, with only two major opportunities for making further gains in productivity. One is the classical method of negotiation, with the aim of fewer people accomplishing the same task through the more effective use of existing equipment. British Railways and the trade unions involved have under discussion a number of proposals, which are vital to the future of the railway. Progress in this area, however, may be protracted and the results could fall short of requirements, at least in the short term.

The other opportunity is to be found in technological progress. The advance of technology, linked with its acceptance by those who work with it, has already made the greatest single contribution to the productivity of British Railways. For example, the single manning of locomotives was possible only with the arrival of diesel and electric traction, and many level crossings would still have to be manned if new signalling technology had not arrived on the scene. Signalling advances, more recently assisted by wider electronic developments, have drastically reduced the numbers of signalmen while improving the conditions of those who remain. Similarly, the introduction of continuous welded rail and machines for

Fig. 15.3   Modern signalling technology has made a great contribution to productivity. The control panel at London Bridge (BRB)

track maintenance have brought great economies in the civil engineering field. Meanwhile, radio and new train control systems have made it feasible to consider further reductions in train manning levels. It must, however, be emphasized that the great potential of technological innovation cannot be realized by engineers alone. It has to be matched by the willingness of men and women to accept it. Also, funds must be available to finance it.

If raising productivity levels is essential to the reducing of railway costs, improving the quality of service is equally essential to increasing the revenue received from rail customers. The engineer must, therefore, design, produce, and maintain equipment with both objectives in mind. It can be claimed that the engineers have provided equipment which allows a high quality service to be given by British Railways. Indeed, HST and APT are not intended to be a number of isolated prestige trains, but to represent a general high standard of service available to all passengers. The increasing patronage of HST in recent years speaks for its quality. Similarly, the new commuter trains on the Great Northern electric services have attracted more passengers. The fact that the advent of new trains makes, by contrast, the old ones seem less attractive than before, is not the fault of the engineer who produced the new trains. It relates to the wider areas of investment and its funding.

In discussing the raising of train service quality, however, the greatest single achievement of British Railways engineers since 1948 has not been in passenger travel. It has related to the closing of the gap between the relative efficiencies of the passenger and freight services. Although the unbraked wagon has only been eliminated from certain sections of the BR system, the freight service has been revolutionized by the development of the Freightliner, block train, and Speedlink services. The annual report of the British Railways Board for 1978 highlighted the fact that its freight and parcels activity had, for the first time, moved from a situation requiring Government financial support to a break-even point. The engineering contribution to this significant event has been of very great importance, and it is very disappointing that levels of industrial production will make the break-even situation harder to achieve in the early 1980s.

British Railways faces the 1980s, therefore, with the right types of equipment for operating high-quality passenger services, and for making a commercial success of its freight business. It now urgently needs the investment resources to replace the older passenger vehicles with HST, APT, and modern commuter stock. It would also welcome the national industrial revival which would swell its freight loadings, and strengthen the case for investing in rail freight. Track and signalling technology are also in an advanced stage, while the framework within which British Railways works is relatively stable when compared, for example, with earlier decades. Rarely have the candidates for investment been more promising, but the availability of funds could now prove to be the most serious obstacle to the technological progress of the railway as a whole.

The role which the railway will play in the future transport scene will, however, not only be determined by its success in improving productivity, raising standards of service, and receiving greater investment resources. Among the legislative, economic, social, and political factors which have played their parts since the dawn of railways, there is a comparative newcomer with a potentially significant impact. This is the question of the future availability of natural resources, particularly land and energy. In this area, the outlook for British Railways is good, although unlikely to carry as much weight in future investment decisions as the more immediate questions of productivity and finance.

As it is a guided system of transport, the railway is potentially a highly efficient user of land. One railway track, for example, can carry three times the tonnage carried on one lane of a motorway and tracks can be grouped closer together than motorway lanes. Rail's impact on the environment is also less intrusive than that of road or air. This environmental benefit was recognized in 1974 when the Railways Act provided for government funding to encourage industry to use rail freight, 98 per cent of which originates in private sidings. A policy followed by British Railways in recent years has been directed towards optimizing the use of the existing permanent way. At a time when high-speed trains have complicated line capacity problems, improved signalling and control systems have actually allowed some track facilities to be removed. It can be expected that further engineering contributions to optimizing the use of the railway network will come from train control, driver aids, and improved braking.

It is, however, the need to reduce the demand for energy which presents the major, and worldwide, natural resource problem. Transport happens to be the main growth sector in the consumption of oil and this will make it a particular target for conservation measures. Road transport accounts for about 80 per cent of the oil used in transport, and the proportion is increasing. This will attract a great deal of technological attention to the improvement of the efficiency of the road vehicle, especially as there is no forseeable suitable alternative to the use of oil in road (and air) transport.

The benefit to the railway is more likely to be on the basis that some degree of preferential consideration may be given to the development of the more energy-efficient forms of transport, of which rail is the foremost example. Any such consideration is likely to be more evident if rail can switch from oil to multi-fuel electric traction and, at the same time, show that it is capable of attracting traffic from the less energy-efficient (and oil-using) roads and airways. There will also be an incentive to governments to encourage the development of entirely new transport systems which would use less energy than existing systems. Reference will later be made to the examination of these possibilities which has been made by the engineers of the Research and Development Division of British Railways.

The implications of the energy situation for railways are threefold. Firstly, as a major and efficient carrier of fuels in bulk it can expect changes in the volume and pattern of rail movement, particularly if coal production expands. Secondly, as an economical user of energy in transport it should be in a position to attract freight and passengers from less energy-efficient users as the cost of energy rises in real terms. Thirdly, as a user of oil it will seek to become less dependent on oil. Measures are already being taken to conserve oil through greater operating efficiency and detailed improvements in traction. The opportunity in this direction which is so valuable to railways, however, is the facility to use electric traction generated from a number of energy sources.

As energy conservation will increasingly dominate transport development in the coming decades it justifies realistic appraisal of its effect on the railway engineering task. It is hardly necessary to consider the impact on the railway, for example, of the bicycle or the ship, which rank high in the energy-efficiency table. Their applications in transport within Britain are limited, although the coastwise ship carries much fuel in bulk. Similarly, the aircraft is an inefficient user of energy but would be difficult to replace for long passenger journeys, or over medium distances where no rail link currently exists, as is the position today with travel to Ireland or mainland Europe. Under identical conditions a train using steel wheels and steel rails may consume only one-fifth of the energy used by a rubber-tyred vehicle running on a modern road surface. The extent of this advantage is limited, however, by the railway's inability to provide a door-to-door service for the major part of Britain's freight and passenger traffic. The highly prized mobility given by the private car will ensure that its numbers will increase, even if oil supplies and road congestion restrict its use. Most of the freight traffic of the country will continue to move by road, at least for part of its journey. Where frequent stops are involved, the bus is actually more energy-efficient than the train.

The point being emphasized is that there are many areas where rail is not an effective substitute for road or air transport. On the other hand, there are the main routes between the major traffic centres where train, aircraft, bus, and car (lorry, in the case of freight) are interchangeable in many cases, at least over the trunk section of the route. This is the area in which some substitution can be expected to take place. It is to be expected, therefore, that a transport system, under pressure from the demands of land and energy conservation, will inevitably become more specialized in nature as rail, air, and road concentrate on those activities where each has a unique advantage. If so, then the co-ordination of transport at the national level in Britain will be increasingly determined by the technological ability of each form of transport to make the best use of land and energy. In these circumstances, technological considerations would make a greater impact than was ever made by the policy of transport integration ordained in 1947. The inevitable result of these developments would present the railway engineer with ever-increasing pressures to increase the carrying capacity of the main routes, and confirm the BR Research Division objective of the 1960s to devise ways of optimizing the use that could be made of the existing railway network in Britain. It would also involve the engineer in the further development of the interchange facilities required for transfer between different forms of transport. The Freightliner container terminals and the passenger stations at Gatwick Airport, Birmingham (International) and Bristol (Parkway) are examples of this trend towards inter-modal transfer.

The dilemma faced by the railway in the energy situation is that of how it should exploit its advantages. The engineer has already provided his management with a transport tool which, in its use of land and energy resources, can be several times as efficient as road transport. This advantage is lost when, for example, land and energy are used for the intermediate marshalling of rail freight in wagon loads. The representative energy comparisons by different forms of transport, as shown in HMSO Energy Papers, and quoted in the 1978 issue of *British Railways Board Facts and Figures*, are not a reliable basis for assessing potential energy savings but indicate that rail is not exploiting its inherent energy advantages. This will be appreciated from a study of Table 15.1

While a block train can convey a big tonnage of coal with less than a quarter of the energy consumption required by lorries to do the same job, the situation could well be reversed when a single wagon load has to weave its way through a number of marshalling yards. Again there is the

Fig. 15.4   Birmingham (International) serves the National Exhibition Centre and also acts as a rail/rail, road/rail and rail/air interchange point (BRB)

Table 15.1   General energy consumption comparisons

Passenger	Average load factor %	Average MJ/pass km
Inter-City electric train	45	1·0
Inter-City diesel train	45	0·9
Express coach	65	0·4
Scheduled aircraft	65	3·9
Car on motorway	2 passengers	1·6
Car rural	1·7 passengers	2·0
Commuter train	25	1·1
Underground train	14	1·6
Double-decker bus	25	0·8
Car	1·5 passengers	3·1

Freight	Range MJ/tonne km
Rail: bulk freight	0·4–1·2
general merchandise	0·5–1·7
Road: bulk materials	1·4–2·4
general merchandise	0·9–3·5

Note: MJ = MegaJoules

paradoxical situation in that the inter-city train is more energy-efficient than the bus or car, but under today's conditions the bus has the advantage on a passenger-mile, or even a seat-mile basis. The disparity arises because the comparison is not being made between like situations of speed, seating space, standards of facilities provided, and commercial attitudes to seat occupancy. Dr. A. H. Wickens, in his paper 'Transport has an Electric Future' given to the Institute of Fuel (now Institute of Energy) in 1976 showed that an APT uses only one-fifth of the energy of a bus on a typical inter-city route when operated at similar speeds and with the same space allocated to each passenger. Table 15.2 summarizes the result.

Table 15.2   Energy consumption of inter-city bus and APT in similar conditions

Vehicle (1 m²/seat)	System energy consumption (kJ/seat km)	Average speed (km/h)
Bus	550	60
APT	110	60

Note: kJ = kiloJoules

Comparisons of this type do not, however, lead to the conclusion that energy would necessarily be saved if trains reduced their speeds, and confined their amenity standards to levels appropriate to a bus. The result of the reduced speed and comfort of the train could well be a substantial transfer of patronage to air or private car, with less efficient use of energy. Consideration must always be given, therefore to the total transport energy account before allowing energy considerations to dominate the design and operation of inter-city passenger trains.

Fortunately for British Railways, the Mark III carriages, HST, and APT show how reduced weight and improved aerodynamics are able not only to reduce the demand for energy but also (through increased speed and comfort), to attract passengers from less energy-efficient competitors. The Mark III vehicle was, during the late 1970s, in terms of weight per seat, the lightest carriage on any inter-city service in Europe. APT is a further development in this direction and, compared with a conventional train at the same speed, represents an energy saving of 40 per cent per seat/km. Again, this has not been achieved by any sacrifice in safety standards: APT meets the UIC requirement that carriages should withstand an end loading strain of 200 tons.

The types of rail service to be provided by British Railways in the future will depend partly on their own long-term evaluation of commercial opportunities and partly on the social obligations which governments continue to place on them. In the background, however, will be the increasing tendency for all forms of transport to specialize on those types of service where they have particular advantages. The inter-city rail passenger service is an obvious candidate for expansion; HST and APT probably represent the most advanced contribution which engineers have ever made to raising the general level of inter-city performance on any railway.

Turning to commuter traffic, the major flows are increasingly carried by electric traction. The electric multiple units now on the Great Northern lines will be further developed as the Class 317 on the Moorgate–Bedford services, but the main problem will be in funding the investment required on the Southern Region services. Some diesel replacements will also be required irrespective of further electrification. Reference has already been made to the Class 210 and Leyland Experimental Vehicle (LEV) developments. In connection with the latter, the engineer will have some responsibility for determining whether, on the low density passenger services, the future lies with train or bus. The cost and energy advantages are with the bus on short-distance services with frequent stops, but increasing problems with oil supplies could encourage the development of lightweight electric trains as adopted in the example of the Tyne and Wear Metro. Whatever the outcome, the LEV will make a valuable contribution to the development of lightweight vehicle technology.

It could well be, however, that it will be in the carriage of freight by rail

Fig. 15.5   The BR standard Mark III Second Class carriage combines high standards of comfort with low weight per seat (BRB)

that the future will see the greatest changes. The potential of the freight train to achieve low cost and energy-efficient transport has been shown by the success of the block train. The problem has been in finding enough situations where this enormous rail potential can be exploited in a country where distances are short. In the future, the lorry is likely to find its ubiquity restricted by environmental considerations and its fuel will be less plentiful as well as more expensive. There is already a growth in the concept of transfer centres between the large line haul vehicle and the smaller lorry for local work. Whenever the transfer of loads is involved, trunk haul by rail again becomes a suitable candidate for consideration and the use of combined rail/road transport is likely to grow. After all, there seems to be something odd in engineering terms to observe on the motorways large lorries, each with its own driver, running head to tail.

The longer term prospects for the railway, subject to the availability of investment funds, look very promising. There will be a number of factors, some internal and others external to the railway, which will play their part in shaping the future. The history of transport shows how technological development has swung the balance of advantage from one form of transport to another. The steam locomotive ended the canal era in Britain and the internal combustion engine allowed the roads to take over a large part of the country's transport. The jet engine deepened the penetration of the aircraft into surface transport markets. These more dramatic changes tend to obscure the changes which affected the pace of mutation, like the introduction of electric traction to rail commuter services, which halted the expansion of tramways in many cities. In the absence of a further and breathtaking stage in the technological leapfrog which has characterized transport in the past, it is likely that success will follow the dedication of engineers to increasing the efficiency of their particular form of transport. Where is this dedication likely to lead the railway engineer?

Thinking first of railway civil engineering, one continuing objective will be permanent way which is smooth, have fewer sharp curves and with a minimum number of junctions, limited, wherever possible, to straight sections of line. Over the years there have been many changes which have brought nearer the achievement of this objective, and these have been described in Chapter Nine. Studies have shown that continuously welded rail (CWR) reduces rolling resistance by 5 per cent compared with jointed track, so adding the bonus of energy saving to the advantages of CWR in reducing maintenance costs and enhancing passenger comfort. Junctions have been progressively reduced in number through the re-shaping of the BR network, and the more effective use of track has enabled track mileage to be reduced. The increasing use of the continuous automatic brake on freight trains has allowed better use to be made of the mileage available, which can be expected to be further rationalized by major service and/or signalling changes.

Some of the most restrictive curves have been eased, and a few eliminated. The re-alignment of track can still, however, be justified in a number of cases in order to shorten journey times. Re-alignment can also make a contribution to energy conservation, by reducing the energy

Fig. 15.6 The potential of the freight train in achieving low cost, and energy efficient, transport is exemplified by this block train of iron ore (BRB)

required to steer the rail vehicle on curves. APT is already energy-efficient when compared with a conventional train, but about one-third of its demand for energy when running on the West Coast Main Line is used in negotiating the curves on that route. Even if the task were physically possible, it is unlikely, however, that any contemplated energy situation would ever justify re-alignment on this particular scale.

Chapter Nine has already made mention of the many sophisticated machines and procedures used by the civil engineer in today's maintenance of the track. D. S. Currie, Civil Engineer (Permanent Way) at British Railways Headquarters made the following comments in his Presidential Address to the Permanent Way Institution on 28 January 1978 in relation to track maintenance:

> In recent years the machines have become larger, more sophisticated and extremely costly. Outputs have increased considerably, but I feel we are at a stage of asking how much further can we go with complex machinery. The lengths of time we can use the large machines on running lines are limited, and it may be that we should be looking at smaller, simpler demountable machines for certain operations. We will always require tampers, ballast cleaners, and relaying equipment, but I feel that there is considerable scope for further mechanization of many of the labour intensive tasks with which we are still involved. . . . On our main trunk routes we are rapidly approaching the time when relaying systems will change, and instead of complete renewals we will be involved in re-railing. This calls for a new type of machine for the rail changing operation, and again this is being examined currently. . . . We will continue to mechanize work wherever possible if there are economic and social advantages in so doing.

The Channel Tunnel may still prove to be the most significant civil engineering development in Europe this century. In its modified form as a rail tunnel only, it will be difficult to be overlooked by any government, particularly if supported by private sources of investment. In the Sir Seymour Biscoe Tritton Memorial Lecture, given by Sir Peter Parker, Chairman, British Railways Board to the Institution of Mechanical Engineers on 27 February 1979 he pointed out that a passenger could travel from London to Paris by train for less than a quarter of the fuel required by air. After referring to the problem of dealing with a volume of traffic across the English Channel which could more than double by 1990, Sir Peter went on to say:

> I do not believe that for the day after tomorrow it is unrealistic to predict a network of high speed, air-conditioned, electric train services linking London with the main centres of Western Europe. And in freight the link will add a vital arm, for the whole of the UK, to our emerging strategy, with bulk train load and Freightliner services providing a core to the movement of goods across Europe.

British Railways is also considering the feasibility of another tunnel project. This would be a twin bored tunnel, which would allow trains now terminating in London at Euston, King's Cross, or St Pancras to run through to destinations in Kent and Sussex on the Southern Region. It would give some 8 million people living south of the Thames direct access to inter-city routes. It is anticipated that thirty trains an hour could be run in either direction and use dual current traction suited both to the standard a.c. and to the Southern d.c. systems. The proposed transformation of main-line London termini into semi-through stations on North–South routes could have a very significant effect on the use made of inter-city services and on travel patterns generally. The experience of the through running made possible in a densely populated area following the building of the Brussels Junction Railway, has proved to be very encouraging and could well be repeated on an even larger scale in Britain.

Chapter Ten has already explained how the signal engineers have now equipped nearly a half of British Railways' single track miles with modern electrical signalling, while the number of signalboxes has been reduced from 10000 to under 2400 in less than two decades. In his Presidential Address to the Institution of Railway Signal Engineers on 25 April 1979, K. E. Hodgson, Signal Engineer (New Works) at BR Headquarters explained that, by the end of 1978, 12000 single track miles of time-expired mechanical, along with 3500 of earlier electrical, signalling needed replacement. He illustrated the situation in Fig. 15.7. Of the 12000 miles equipped with mechanical signalling, 5500 did not have levels of traffic sufficiently high to justify the introduction of continuous Multiple Aspect Signalling (MAS) with centralized control. The future signalling systems on these comparatively little used lines remains to be determined. Meanwhile they present the signal engineers with ever-increasing replacement and maintenance problems.

ANALYSIS OF TYPES

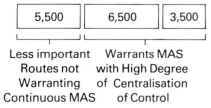

22,000 Single Track Miles		
53%	16%	31%
12,000	3,500	6,500
Mechanical	Earlier Electrical	Modern Electrical

FORM OF REPLACEMENT OF MECHANICAL AND EARLIER ELECTRICAL SIGNALLING

5,500	6,500	3,500
Less important Routes not Warranting Continuous MAS	Warrants MAS with High Degree of Centralisation of Control	

Fig. 15.7   Types of Signalling on British Railways (IRSE)

The situation on the lightly used BR lines emphasizes the urgency of the need to replace much out-dated signalling equipment with less expensive systems, while maintaining safety standards. Hodgson referred in his paper to the development by BR on single lines of a microprocessor interface between radio and the existing key token instruments, which avoids the high cost of renewing existing aerial wires by cables. Other applications of advanced technology are likely to be used in replacing the signalling systems on lightly used lines, if they are to have a continuing role within the BR route system.

Another very pressing problem confronting the signal engineer as a result of reduced investment resources is that of the mechanical interlocking frame, particularly where there is no early possibility of replacement by MAS. By the year 2000 around 90 per cent of these frames will have seen a century of service. In order to replace all of them by that date it would be necessary to increase by 50 per cent the 1979–80 rate of investment in BR signalling. Replacement parts for these old interlocking systems were becoming almost impossible to obtain during the 1970s. It seems, therefore, that the signal engineer, who has become increasingly involved in the technology of solid-state electronics, will have to re-learn the craft of the blacksmith. Otherwise, these nineteenth-century interlocking frames will be without the spare parts essential to their continued operation. It is impossible to think of the automobile or aircraft engineer maintaining a public transport service with moving parts even half the age of some railway signalling equipment. The situation well illustrates, however, the very real difficulties encountered by railway engineers when, due to under-investment, the equipment is likely to outlive the production of its spare parts by many years.

It has already been explained that control systems have now opened up the possibility of a fully automated railway if, and when, such a railway can be justified in financial and social terms. In the same Presidential Address Hodgson went on to discuss the limited opportunities available today for Automatic Train Operation (ATO), which he saw as being in 'mass transit, selected urban areas or new lines carrying dedicated rolling stock.' He saw the needs of speeds up to 125 miles/h being met over the high-speed routes by signalling designed originally for 100 miles/h, but with the two additional features which have already been described: i.e., the flashing yellow aspect at certain junctions and the Transponder used with the APT. These will provide a breathing space while further high-speed opportunities on BR tracks are explored.

The same Presidential Address to the IRSE also touched on the future of level crossing protection, and included the following comment:

> To achieve the full benefits of modern signalling and operations it is essential to eliminate level crossings entirely, or to protect them by train operated systems. . . .

The Department of Transport and the British Railways Board, in a recent report, recommended simplified, less costly methods of protection for level crossings. This could ease the restrictions on railway operations considerably by increasing the percentage of train operated crossings on the BR network from 19 per cent to 60 per cent. The methods recommended would also help to reduce the operational costs on lightly used lines. If the recommendations are accepted, the conversion work will take 10 years to complete.

Fortunately, and as recorded in Chapter Twelve, most of the report's recommendations have been agreed. It is to be hoped that financial resources will allow of implementation.

It was, however, when making reference to the Computer Train Describer as the key to many other systems that Hodgson touched on some of the key issues in the purpose of technological change. He said:

It is difficult to withstand the pressure to use the latest fashion in technology, but it is the responsibility of the profession to apply only what is appropriate to the situation present and future. . . .

Some of the systems shown [in Fig. 15.8] are entirely dependent on the Train Describer and other are enhanced by the information derived from it. . . .

All of the systems shown are capable of integration into the existing signal and telecommunications systems.

Perhaps Fig. 15.8 illustrates particularly well the kind of technological advance which the signal and telecommunications engineer can offer British Railways, if such systems can be justified. It shows the extent of

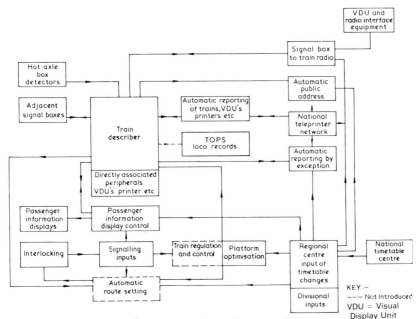

Fig. 15.8   Train Describer and associated systems

the number of systems which can be associated with the modern train describer, including a range of activities from the timetable input to the regulation of out of course working.

A high-capacity, high-speed system as outlined can remotely control large signalling installations as well as providing numerous additional indications. The processing power now available is relatively simple to apply to a system that works with regularity to a pre-determined sequence (as on many rapid transit railways), but is more complex on a main line railway. While there is a common trend towards ever-increasing automation, British Railways is faced with long established systems, where innovation runs up against the problems of both compatibility and finance. There are many fields where further technological development could rapidly change the situation but the point is again made that the BR signal engineer is very conscious of the financial implications before recommending change, however commendable it may be in engineering terms.

Turning to the area of mechanical and electrical engineering, reference has already been made to the increasing need to design traction equipment and rolling stock with a view to achieving energy efficiency, particularly for high-speed running with its greater demands on the use of energy. Changes in construction materials, particularly the replacement of steel by lighter alloys, will allow for weight reduction in vehicles, provided that the cost premium is acceptable. HST and APT design and construction have taken particular account of considerations of mass, as well as of aerodynamics. The inter-city train represents, however, only part of the passenger and freight equipment design activities of BR, where mechanical engineering development ranges from lightweight vehicle technology to improved braking systems. It must also be remembered that the mechanical and electrical engineer is not only concerned with traction and rolling stock. Other machinery, including the example of cranes at Freightliner terminals, forms an important area of his responsibility.

The foreseeable future appears to offer no reasonable alternative to diesel and electric traction on railways. The results of further diesel engine development do not, at the present stage, offer dramatic improvements on the equipment installed in the railcars and locomotives which have been described in Chapter Six. The next-generation design of diesel-electric freight locomotive does, however, include some features of interest. This is the Class 58, designed at Derby, with a basic layout re-arranged from the earlier Class 47 and Class 56 practice with the objectives of easy maintenance and lower production costs. The Class 58 will be of low cost and rugged construction, have a power output between 3500 and 4000 h.p. and be capable of adaptation for export purposes. Much of the structure, bogies, and components will be suitable for use on the new electric freight locomotives which will follow the Class 58 on the

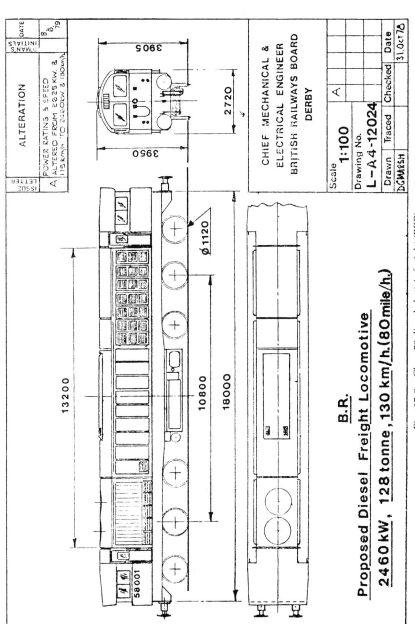

CHIEF MECHANICAL &
ELECTRICAL ENGINEER
BRITISH RAILWAYS BOARD
DERBY

Scale **1:100**

Drawing No.
L-A4-12024

	A		
Drawn	Traced	Checked	Date
DGMARSH			31.0cт76

ISSUE LETTER	ALTERATION	D'MAN'S INITIALS	DATE
A	POWER RATING & SPEED ALTERED FROM 2625 KW & 115 km/h TO 2460KW & 130 km/h		8.6.79

3905

2720

3950

Ø 1120

13200

10800

18000

58001

B.R.

Proposed Diesel Freight Locomotive

2460 kW , 128 tonne , 130 km/h.(80 mile/h.)

Fig. 15.9   Class 58 diesel electric freight (BRB)

designers' drawing boards. It is proposed to use a twelve-cylinder engine and the electrical equipment will essentially be similar to that of the Class 56. It is intended that production should begin in 1982.

Compared with the diesel, electric traction offers more development opportunities. These arise both at the generating station and on the train, as well as with ever-improving overhead equipment. The opportunities for the gas turbine, due to the variable demands of rail traction, are small and it does not emerge as a satisfactory alternative to the diesel. Neither is there any prospect of the steam locomotive returning to British Railways, although the energy situation has kindled some interest in its further development.

British Railways' engineers have also examined a number of other future traction possibilities, which could either have general application or be used in specific circumstances. These have included various forms of heat engines, the linear induction motor, operation in evacuated tubes, and hybrid power systems. Although there are weight and control system penalties in having two power sources in one locomotive, the electro-diesel hybrid has proved useful on the Southern Region of BR. A more powerful application of the hybrid, with a 1200 h.p. diesel engine included in an electric locomotive, has been considered for working on the non-electrified spurs connected to an electrified main line.

Energy storage systems based both on the flywheel and the battery have also been used for traction purposes. Early Southern electric loco-motives used flywheels to provide power when passing over gaps in the

Fig. 15.10   MAGLEV vehicle negotiates a curve on test track at Railway Technical Centre, Derby (BRB)

conductor rails, and a battery-operated railcar was tested alongside its diesel equivalent in the Scottish Region. Since then the sodium–sulphur battery has been subject to intensive development work at the Railway Technical Centre in Derby, and elsewhere. The fuel cell appears to be less promising as a transport application.

The BR Research and Development Division has also studied the comparative advantages of Magnetic suspension (MAGLEV) and the conventional wheel-on-rail system in the transport of passengers at speeds higher than those currently used. An experimental MAGLEV system was installed at Derby to enable a study, commissioned by the Department of Transport, to be made. This study embraced both attraction and repulsion systems, and the Division reported in January 1978. The findings of the study were that, for speeds of 125 to 185 miles/h the wheel-on-rail system had the overall advantage. For speeds between 250 and 310 miles/h there was less difference between the systems, although wheel-on-rail still seemed to offer more advantages. In this higher speed band, however, the linear induction motor (where the power system does not have to be carried with the vehicle) began to come into its own as a form of traction.

As the commercial case for surface travel in Britain at speeds in excess of 200 miles/h has not yet effectively been made, it can be expected that evolution of the wheel-on-rail system will continue in the foreseeable future. As the design life of APT will continue beyond the year 2000, the high-speed potential of wheel-on-rail may well be stretched appreciably during that period. It would be logical, as a first stage, to consider installing the signalling and control systems which would allow APT to exploit its existing speed potential of 155 miles/h. It is at present restricted to 125 miles/h, although it has been run at 160 miles/h in trials on the West Coast Main Line. One overwhelming advantage in stretching the existing system to its limit, rather than embarking on new systems which are not compatible with that currently employed is that use can continue to be made of track and terminals shared with other trains.

As electrification is technically the most suitable form of traction for high density railway services, while the energy and economic advantages are also moving in its favour, it can be expected to expand. This is especially the case in Britain, where only one-fifth of the railway route system is electrified. Chapter Seven has shown how the real costs of electrification have been reduced, thereby strengthening the arguments in favour of expansion. In effect, the energy situation is an additional bonus to associate with the improving financial case for electric traction in Britain. The better financial case follows not only the technical improvements in railway electrification practice, but also the increasing efficiency of electricity generation. It has been unfortunate for the cause of railway electrification in Britain during recent years that the discounted cash flow (DCF) approach has made the investment appear to be unattractive by minimizing revenue and maximizing expenses in the early years, which are significant to the calculations. Indeed, it is interesting to speculate how the course of early railway building in Britain would have been shaped by the DCF approach. It is encouraging to know that other financial, as well as wider, criteria may now play a role in future electrification decisions.

In November 1977, as a result of its consideration of the specific recommendations of a Select Committee on Nationalized Industries, the Government announced its intention 'to review with the (British Railways) Board the general case for further main line electrification on the basis of the up-to-date appreciation which it expects to receive shortly from the Board.'

The Board published in May 1978 a discussion paper 'Railway Electrification'. This document summarized briefly the technical and social advantages of electric over diesel traction, touched on the better quality of the electric service and mentioned the increasing lead in these areas which electric traction would take in the coming years. A chart produced in the paper compared electric and diesel traction costs and is reproduced as Fig. 15.11. The electrification costs have been divided between installation and traction, which shows the great advantage of the electric power unit in maintenance costs, which are less than a quarter of those of the diesel unit.

Even under today's conditions, the primary energy cost of electric traction is lower than that of diesel, and the energy advantages in favour

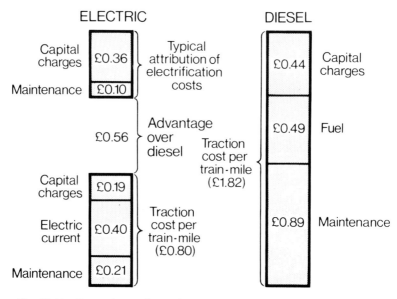

Fig. 15.11   Comparisons of typical inter-city passenger train traction costs (BRB)

of electrification should progressively improve. The financial problems of electrification generally lie not so much in traction matters as in justifying the expenditure required in altering signalling, telecommunication, and civil engineering works, along with the interruption to traffic working while electrification works are in progress.

In May 1978 the Secretary of State for Transport, in agreement with the British Railways Board, commissioned a review of the case for a programme of main-line electrification, to be carried out by a joint Department of Transport/British Railways Steering Group. The Group included representatives of the Treasury and the Department of Energy and was required:

> To review the case for a programme of main line electrification, to analyse the various relevant considerations and formulate the issues for decision.

Over forty bodies were invited to submit evidence to the Steering Group. One important feature to emerge from comparing the submissions is the confidence of the manufacturing industry in its ability to complete the electrification required within a relatively short time scale. The British Railways view was that the pace of progress would be limited to 250 route miles of electrification a year. The reason for the difference is that electrification itself can proceed at a faster rate than the associated works, particularly signalling, but that the real limiting factor is the extent of operational disruption to existing train services which can be tolerated on the densely occupied BR system while the work proceeds. It is likely that new installation methods will lessen the difficulty. The search still continues, in an atmosphere of optimism, to reduce the capital and maintenance costs of electrification, as well as shortening the time scale for carrying out the work.

The work of the Group resulted in the document 'Review of Main Line Electrification: Interim Report', which was published in September, 1979. This interim report looked at five different extents of electrification. These options were:

Option 1 The base situation, including lines already electrified plus schemes in hand, or which would have started by 1981, according to the British Railways Board's 1978 Corporate Review. The option includes St Pancras to Bedford, and a number of extensions to the existing East Anglia, West Coast Main Line, and Strathclyde schemes.

Option 2 A modest extension of electrification, including the East Coast Main Line to Newcastle, the Midland Main Line to Leeds, Birmingham to York, Edinburgh to Glasgow, and Edinburgh to Carstairs.

Option 3 A medium proposal with emphasis on electrifying passenger services including all the main inter-city routes. These include, in addition to those in Option 2, London to Bristol, South Wales and Plymouth; Birmingham to Taunton, and Newcastle to Edinburgh.

Option 4 An alternative medium proposal, embracing the same main routes as Option 3, but with emphasis on including more freight flows within the electrified network. Additional routes include Doncaster to Grimsby; Didcot to Coventry, and Manchester to Sheffield (Hope Valley).

Option 5 The largest option including Plymouth to Penzance; Crewe to Holyhead; Edinburgh to Aberdeen, and Doncaster to Hull.

Table 15.3 shows the electrified route and track mileages included in each of the options, and Table 15.4 indicates the effect on the proportion of loaded train miles which would be hauled electrically.

Table 15.3   Electrified mileage in each option

Option	Route miles	Percentage of network	Single track miles	Percentage of network
1	2580	23	6420	29
2	3450	31	8850	40
3	4510	41	11350	51
4	4890	44	12150	55
5	5810	52	14000	63
Total BR network at end of 1978	11123		22138	

The methods of financial appraisal used in the review are of particular interest, although they deal only with the relative costs under the different options and are, therefore, less comprehensive than those expected to be included in the final report, which will also cover the revenue aspects. In this first phase of the study a simple mathematical model was used to compare the costs of alternative methods of providing the same standard of service. This established whether the savings in operating costs and in the capital costs of electric rolling stock would cover the additional costs of providing and maintaining the electrification infrastructure. Table 15.5 summarizes the relatively modest cost advantages under current conditions of the other options over the base situation in Option 1.

At the same time it was recognized that, during the implementation of a major programme of electrification, there will be important changes in the costs of fuel, labour, and materials, in technical and market conditions, as

Table 15.4   Summary of loaded train miles

Type of Service	Total annual mileage (all traction types)	Percentage Hauled Electrically				
	Millions	OPTIONS				
		1	2	3	4	5
PASSENGER						
Inter-city	67	35	58	84	86	93
London & South East	78	86	87	90	91	91
Passenger Transport Executive	33	46	53	61	68	83
Other	23	2	9	28	19	45
TOTAL Passenger	201	53	63	76	77	85
FREIGHT	33	15	28	40	49	55
PARCELS	12	31	58	84	86	93
DEPARTMENTAL	13	31	58	84	86	93
GRAND TOTAL	259	45	56	69	71	79

Table 15.5   Summary of annual costs at 1978 relative cost levels
(£ million at 1978 money values)

Type of Service	Assessed costs of Option 1	Cost Advantage over Option 1			
		Option 2	Option 3	Option 4	Option 5
Passenger	526	14	32	34	45
Freight	153	6	12	17	20
Parcels	33	3	7	7	8
Departmental	29	0	1	1	1
Total Operations	740	23	52	58	74
Infrastructure	0	−20	−41	−47	−62
Total	740	3	11	11	12

well as the transitional traffic conditions which could not be dealt with in any simple comparison relative to the situation in 1978.

The electrification options considered in the interim report would increase the proportion of electrified mileage in the BR route network from 23 per cent in the base situation to between 31 per cent and 52 per cent, according to the option selected. If 52 per cent of the network were to be electrified, 85 per cent of passenger train mileage and 79 per cent of all loaded train miles would be electrically operated. The net additional investment involved, at 1978 price levels, would be between £160 million and £500 million. The respective savings in annual costs would be between £3 million and £12 million under the situation as it was in 1978. Changes due to energy price increases, along with staff cost escalation in real terms by the year 2000 could raise the cost advantage of electrification to between £11 million and £59 million, according to the option adopted and staff productivity changes over the period. To these savings must be added any revenue increases as well as the less quantifiable benefits relating to the environment and oil conservation.

With about 80 per cent of the train mileage electrically operated (i.e., the largest option), the direct oil saving to British Railways would approximate 120 million gallons a year, which is equivalent to around one half per cent of Britain's oil consumption. To this should be added, however, the potentially greater savings related to traffic extracted from less energy-efficient carriers than rail and the security of having one national transport system which does not depend on oil alone.

The wider benefits from electrification are for consideration in a final report. It should be pointed out that the options selected do not reflect the precise electrification schemes which would be the most favourable to BR in financial terms, and the actual programmes which finally emerge may differ from the patterns in the options. British Railways will have their own priorities, and the extension of existing schemes into more economic electrification groupings is expected to head their priority list.

It will, indeed, be a cause for surprise if the case for substantial development in main-line electrification does not emerge in the final report to the Minister of Transport and the Chairman of the British Railways Board. There may be more reason for doubt regarding the implementation of any recommendations, and much will depend on decisions reached by the Government in the light of the national economic situation in the early 1980s. The claims of BR on national investment resources will be very strong during the 1980s, including not only main-line electrification but also the replacement of out-dated commuter carriage fleets, a rail-only Channel Tunnel and new APT train sets.

These investment demands also present a serious challenge to the engineers themselves, as the pressure on design and construction reaches a peak in the 1980s as it did in the 1950s. It will be remembered that the Modernization Plan of 1955 satisfied the appetite of a railway

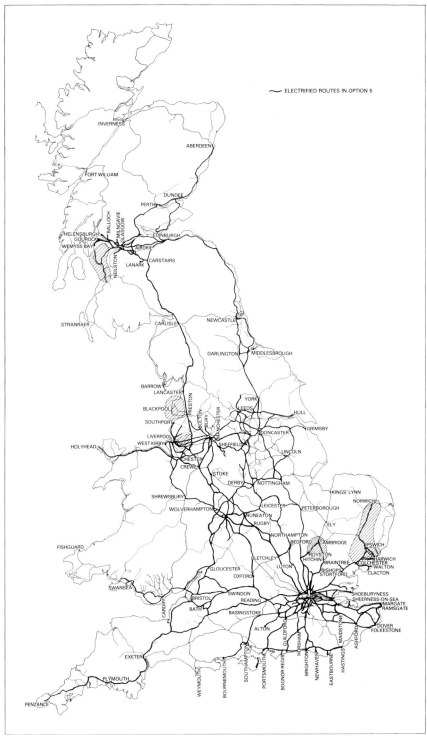

Fig. 15.12 The electrified routes in Option 5. The cross-hatched areas include the lines where British Railways has completed all the detailed planning work necessary for electrification

ELECTRIFIED ROUTES IN OPTION 5

system, which had been starved of investment for many years, but proved difficult to digest. British Railways was unaccustomed at that time to investment planning on the scale required by the Plan, and had to take urgent measures to augment its resources in terms of the engineers who could carry out the task. Fortunately, the investment planning skills and the resources of engineers should not present the problems which were experienced in the 1950s, when a massive investment scheme exceeded the scale of expectation.

At the time of nationalization, British Railways became the employer of the largest number of engineering apprentices in the country, and these were concentrated mainly in the Mechanical and Electrical Engineering Departments. The former LMS Company had initiated its Progressive System of Workshop Training in the 1930s and in 1947 the Derby Works Training School was opened. Within British Railways these Works Training Schools were established at all main works, and the British Transport Commission recommended that the example should be followed throughout its activities. The BR approach to engineering training enjoyed high standing within the engineering industry.

In the days of the former Companies it was customary for the apprentice destined to become a professional engineer in the department of the Chief Mechanical Engineer to enter as a pupil, or premium apprentice. The emphasis was on a practical training, coupled with a requirement on the individual to meet the required academic standards. This training would begin in the workshops and motive power depots. It would then include the drawing office and involve experience in plant engineering and production planning. The intention was to produce a professional engineer who could handle both professional and managerial problems with equal facility.

Training must comply with the requirements of the particular Chartered Institution in order to ensure that professional standards are achieved. At the same time, increasing specialization and the wider variety of experience required by today's engineers gives further emphasis to the importance of their training. Again, in January 1980 the Committee of Inquiry into the Engineering Profession, under the chairmanship of Sir Montague Finniston, made wide-ranging recommendations which may make their own impact on the education and training of the engineer.

In the late 1960s, the Chief Mechanical and Electrical Engineer of British Railways (at that time T. C. B. Miller) instituted a review of the methods then in force relating to the career development of the Chartered Engineer. A Central Engineering Training Group (CETG) was created, initially for mechanical and electrical engineers, but later extended to bring in also the civil and signal and telecommunications engineers. This Group, through its Executive Member (initially C. F. Rose, who was succeeded by R. H. N. Hardy), assists in the recruitment, as well as the organization of training and development, of potential Chartered Engineers in all the engineering departments of British Railways. The objective is that of ensuring a satisfactory succession of professional engineers for the future.

The 'Designated Engineer' (as he or she is termed at this stage) is most likely to be a sandwich course entrant, who will spend three years at university between two separate years of carefully planned practical training. Other entrants to the scheme could be direct appointments from industry, graduate entrants direct from university, engineering apprentices, or technician engineers. Whatever the entry level, it is almost invariably the case that a University Degree is an essential step to becoming a Chartered Engineer. The Technician Engineer and Technician have now become established qualifications of the important level in the engineering organization immediately below that of a Chartered Engineer.

The actual course of training to be followed is tailored to the background of the individual. For example, the well qualified entrant from outside industry may require to have little more than a course of induction to British Railways, while the engineering apprentice will need to have practical experience widened by new knowledge of a type which could not be gained on the shop floor. In the case of the mechanical and electrical engineers, the Works Training Schools and workshops of British Rail Engineering Ltd (BREL) play a prominent role in objective training. Other roles are played by the Railway Technical Centre at Derby, Regional Headquarters, the local maintenance depot, the polytechnic, and the university. The civil engineering department has its own school at Watford where special courses are run to supplement the training given at Regional Headquarters and at more local levels.

At any one time there are approximately 1200 men and women who are preparing to become Chartered Engineers on British Railways. As the scheme for training Designated Engineers has a very good reputation within the engineering industry, it attracts many candidates. By the same token, any good training scheme suffers losses to other employers. A high, and sustained, level of railway investment would, however, increase the opportunities for the young engineer within British Railways itself. The resources in trained engineers are, therefore, potentially much more favourable than in the situation of the 1950s.

The quality of technological contribution to the future of British Railways has been considerably strengthened during the last decade by a body of professional engineers equipped with both the practical and academic skills. Particular attention has been given to the right balance between these two forms of achievement, so that original thinking will be related to practical application. The specialist who is encouraged to achieve a higher degree is also expected to maintain his contact at shop floor level.

Fig. 15.13 In addition to the programmed training of the engineers themselves, it is necessary to train all railway staff who may be involved with changing technology. Here, the characteristics of the first Brush type 1 250 h.p. diesel electric locomotive to be delivered to the Eastern Region of BR are being explained to enginemen at Stratford Depot in East London (BRB)

From what has been outlined in this, and earlier, chapters it is evident that British Railways' engineers have the training, the experience, and the ability to develop the railway in whatever form the future may require. It is also clear that they have a formidable technological base from which to produce new equipment and no lack of schemes on which to deploy it. Perhaps, this is the appropriate stage, therefore, in this chronicle of some thirty years of railway engineering history to emphasize that technology alone cannot progressively improve the performance and public image of a great railway. There is good reason to realize that technological development is now racing ever further ahead of the capacity for political and social development to keep pace with it. Indeed, the advent of the micro-processor alone makes the point.

Railway history provides many examples of what happens when technological advance is out of phase with its surroundings. The story of the road/rail transfer of containers during the last two decades indicates that new developments often find themselves in conflict with those responsible for working with them. Progress in the respective areas of industrial relations and technological development require to be dove-tailed.

Also, the march of progress suffers when engineering development outstrips legislative and commercial practice. When the engineers of the Cambrian Railways built wagons with continuous brakes in the 1890s, they would have been disappointed to know that wagons without continuous brakes would still be running on the railways of Britain in the 1980s. They were not to know that the statutory right of the customer to put his own wagon on the rails would endure for a century. Neither were the designers of the new BR horse-box in the early 1950s to forecast that the railway would shortly be in a statutory position which would allow it to discard this unprofitable rail traffic.

Coming closer to the present day, HST, APT, and the new high-density electric multiple unit make an odd contrast with the out-dated commuter train which may be standing at an adjacent platform. Also, today's signalbox, with its associated systems based on electronic engineering, is hardly matched in sophistication by the ticket issuing and seat reservation systems in general use, or by the nineteenth-century interlocking frame which may be its immediate neighbour.

The evidence, therefore, suggests that advances in engineering have tended to outpace those in several other areas of railway activity, as well as outstripping the capacity of the railway's investment resources to implement new engineering design. The reasons for this situation are sufficiently complicated and far reaching to justify their own narrative. It is, however, an appropriate note on which to end this story of three decades of railway engineering development in Britain.

Bibliography

Railway Companies', British Transport Commission's, and British Railways Board's annual and other reports, publications and documents

British Railways Electrification Conference, London, 1960: Railway Electrification at Industrial Frequency: proceedings

Proceedings of
> The Institution of Civil Engineers;
> The Institution of Mechanical Engineers;
> The Institution of Electrical Engineers;
> The Institution of Locomotive Engineers;
> The Institution of Railway Signal Engineers;
> The Chartered Institute of Transport;
> The Newcomen Society;
> The Permanent Way Institution;
> The Railway Study Association.

Euston Main Line Electrification: Technical Conference, October 1966: (organized by BRB and Institutions of Civil, Mechanical, Electrical, Locomotive, and Railway Signal Engineers)

Transportation Engineering Conference: April 1968: Proceedings: (organized by Institution of Civil Engineers)

International Engineering Conference: 150th Anniversary of Passenger Railways: September 1975: Proceedings: (sponsored by Institutions of Civil, Mechanical, Electrical, and Railway Signal Engineers: organized by Institution of Mechanical Engineers)

Safe and Efficient Freight Transport by Rail: Symposium, March 1979: Institution of Mechanical Engineers and the Private Wagon Federation

Bulletins of the International Railway Congress Association

International Union of Railways: Reports on 'Optimum Passenger Comfort': 1969 and 1972

Fourth International Symposium on Railroad Cybernetics: Freight Traffic Management and Operation: April 1974: (organized by Association of American Railroads, International Union of Railways and International Railway Congress Association)

The Railway Gazette
The Railway Gazette International
Railway Magazine
Modern Railways
Railway World
Railpower (Published by Railway Industry Association of Great Britain)
The Railway Engineering Journal
Railway Engineer
Railway Engineering International
Railnews

Engineering
Modern Transport
Railway Directory and Yearbook
Report of the Railway Electrification Committee, 1927: Ministry of Transport
Report of the Committee on Main Line Electrification, 1931: Ministry of Transport
Railway (Standardisation of Electrification) Order, 1932: (SR&O 1932 No. 827)
Capital Investment in 1948: HMSO
Chief Inspecting Officer of Railways' Annual Reports on Railway Accidents and
    Reports on Individual Accidents
Acts of Parliament, Consultative Documents and White Papers on Transport
    Policy: HMSO: 1948 to 1979
*Requirements for Passenger Lines and Recommendations for Goods Lines, in regard to
    Railway Construction and Operation*: HMSO (1950)
The British Transport Commission: *Proposals for the Railways*: HMSO 1956
BR: Re-Appraisal of the Plan for the Modernisation and Re-equipment of BR:
    White Paper: HMSO July 1959
Railway Accidents: Failures of Multiple-Unit Electric Trains on BR: Final Report:
    Ministry of Transport, March 1962
Railway Electrification on the Overhead System: Requirements for Clearances:
    Ministry of Transport, 1967
Report of the Public Inquiry into the Accident at Hixon Level Crossing: 1968
Level Crossing Protection: HMSO 1957
Level Crossing Protection: HMSO 1978
Review of Main Line Electrification: Interim Report: HMSO 1979
The Flying Scotsman: The World's Most Famous Express: LNER Publicity (1925)
Clearing the Lines: The Railways ask for a Square Deal: The Railway Companies'
    Association (1938)
Report of the LNER Post-War Development Committee (1943)
BR in Peace and War: (1944)
It can now be revealed: more about BR in Peace and War: (1945) British Railways Press
    Office
Forward: the LNER Development Programme: (1946)
The Railway Executive International: (Issued by Industrial Relations Publicity: 1971/
    72)
British Railway Track: Permanent Way Institution (1971 and 1979)
Railway Electrification: the Case for a Continuous Programme: Aims of Industry Pres-
    sure Group: (1973)
The Case for Electrification of the Railways: British Electrical Development Association
    Inc. (*c*.1935)
BICC Co Ltd. Construction Bulletins
*Overhead Traction Equipment for the Electrification of the Liverpool–Shenfield
    Section*: BICC Co Ltd (*c*.1949)
Railway Electrification: BICC Co Ltd (1953)
'Manchester–Glossop Railway Electrification': E. H. Croft: Reprint from *GEC
    Journal* (July 1954)
Main Line and Suburban Resignalling Eastern Region, British Railways: GEC – General
    Signal Ltd (1979)
Electric Locomotive Equipment for the MSW line of BR: Metropolitan – Vickers Electric
    Co Ltd (1955)
Chesapeake and Ohio Railroad report re 'Railvan' (*c*.1955)
Pressed Steel Co. pamphlet re 'Roadrailer' (*c*.1960)
'NER Electrification: Equipment of the Shildon–Newport Mineral Branch': Reprint
    from *The Tramway and Railway World*, June 1916, and issued by Siemens Bros
    Dynamo Works Ltd

BR Motive Power: combined volume, 1979: Ian Allan
BR After Beeching: G. Freeman Allen (1966)
The Locomotive Exchanges: C. J. Allen (1949)
New Light on the Locomotive Exchanges: C. J. Allen (1950)
The Great Eastern Railway: C. J. Allen (c.1950)
Great Northern: C. J. Allen (c.1961)
The Deltics: a Symposium: C. J. Allen, G. F. Fiennes, R. Ford, B. A. Haresnape, B. Perren (1972)
The Organisation of BR: M. R. Bonavia (1971)
The Birth of British Rail: M. R. Bonavia (1979)
A Lifetime with Locomotives: R. C. Bond (1975)
150 years of Uninterrupted Progress in Railway Engineering: R. C. Bond and O. S. Nock (1975)
Nigel Gresley: Locomotive Engineer: F. A. S. Brown (1961)
Locomotive Panorama: Vols I & II: E. S. Cox (1965/66)
B.R. Standard Locomotives: E. S. Cox (1966)
Electric Traction: A. T. Dover (1929)
British Transport: H. J. Dyos & D. H. Aldcroft (1969)
History of Railways in Britain: Frank Fernyhough (1975)
The Transport Problem: C. D. Foster (1963)
Railways To-morrow: Rolt Hammond (1963)
Modern Methods of Railway Operation: Rolt Hammond (1967)
Steam in the Blood: R. H. N. Hardy (1971)
The Electric Railway that Never Was: York–Newcastle, 1919: R. A. S. Hennessey (1970)
The Train that Ran Away: S. Joy (1973)
BR Signalling: G. M. Kitchenside and A. Williams (1978)
Bulleid: Last Giant of Steam: S. Day-Lewis (1964)
British Electric Traction: H. W. A. Linnecar (1947)
Off the Rails: Richard Marsh (1978)
The Guinness Book of Rail Facts and Feats: John Marshall (1975)
The Railway-Lover's Companion: Ed. Bryan Morgan (1963)
Civil Engineering: Railways: Bryan Morgan (1971)
Fifty Years of Railway Signalling: O. S. Nock (1962)
BR in Transition: O. S. Nock (1963)
Southern Steam: O. S. Nock (1966)
Historic Railway Disasters: O. S. Nock (1966)
Britain's New Railway: O. S. Nock (1966)
The Railway Enthusiast's Encyclopaedia: O. S. Nock (1968)
Electric Euston to Glasgow: O. S. Nock (1974)
The Railways and the Nation: A. J. Pearson (1964)
The Rail Problem: R. W. S. Pryke & J. S. Dodgson (1975)
The Last Steam Locomotive Engineer: H. C. B. Rogers (1970)
Red for Danger: L. T. C. Rolt (1976)
Electrification of Railways: H. F. Treuman (1920)
Railway Wonders of the World: Vols I & II: Ed. Clarence Winchester (c.1936)

Appendices

YEAR	Head of Civil Engineering Dept.	Eastern Region	North Eastern Region	London Midland Region	Scottish Region	Southern Region	Western Region
1948	J. C. L. Train	J. I. Campbell	J. Taylor Thompson	W. K. Wallace	W. Y. Sandeman	V. A. M. Robertson	A. S. Quartermaine
1949	,,	,,	,,	J. Briggs	,,	,,	,,
1950	,,	,,	A. Dean	J. Taylor Thompson	,,	,,	,,
1951	,,	,,	,,	,,	I. R. Frazer	F. E. Campion	M. G. R. Smith
1952	J. Ratter	,,	,,	,,	,,	,,	,,
1953	,,	,,	,,	,,	M. G. Maycock	,,	,,
1954	C. W. King	A. K. Terris	,,	,,	,,	,,	,,
1955	,,	,,	,,	,,	,,	,,	,,
1956	,,	,,	,,	,,	,,	,,	,,
1957	,,	,,	,,	A. N. Butland	,,	A. H. Cantrell	,,
1958	,,	,,	E. L. Trifitt	,,	H. C. Orchard	,,	,,
1959	,,	,,	,,	,,	,,	,,	,,
1960	A. N. Butland	,,	,,	W. F. Beatty	,,	,,	,,
1961	,,	,,	,,	,,	,,	,,	,,
1962	,,	,,	,,	,,	A. Paterson	,,	F. R. L. Barnwell
1963	A. Paterson	,,	,,	,,	,,	,,	,,
1964	,,	,,	,,	,,	I. M. Campbell	,,	,,
1965	,,	R. E. Evans	H. Ormiston	,,	,,	,,	,,
1966	A. W. McMurdo	,,	A. W. McMurdo	,,	,,	,,	,,
		Eastern Region A. W. McMurdo					
1967	,,		,,	,,	M. C. Purbrick	R. E. Evans	,,
1968	,,		,,	,,	,,	,,	,,
1969	,,		,,	,,	,,	,,	,,
1970	,,		,,	,,	,,	,,	,,
1971	,,		,,	M. C. Purbrick	D. S. Currie		L. J. Soane

YEAR	Head of Civil Engineering Dept.	Eastern Region	London Midland Region	Scottish Region	Southern Region	Western Region
1972	A. W. McMurdo	H. Ormiston	M. C. Purbrick	D. S. Currie	R. E. Evans	L. J. Soane
1973	"	"	"	"	"	"
1974	M. C. Purbrick	"	R. J. Coon	G. B. Craig	J. B. Manson	"
1975	"	P. B. Davis	"	"	"	P. Rees
1976	"	"	"	"	"	"
1977	"	"	"	"	"	"
1978	"	"	"	"	F. Proctor	"
1979	"	"	"	"	"	"

N.B. During the period 1965–69 A. N. Butland was head of the Civil Engineering and the Signal & Telecommunications Engineering Departments at BR Board HQ and was designated Chief Engineer, Way & Works.

BRITISH RAILWAYS HEADQUARTERS
MECHANICAL AND ELECTRICAL ENGINEERING

YEAR	Member of Railway Executive for M & E Engineering	Chief Officer: Loco Construction & Maintenance	Chief Electrical Engineer	Chief Officer Carriage and Wagon Engineering	Chief Engineer Traction and Rolling Stock
1948	R. A. Riddles	R. C. Bond	C. M. Cock	E. Pugson	—
1949	"	"	"	"	—
1950	"	"	S. B. Warder	"	—
1951	"	"	"	"	—
1952					—
		Chief Mechanical Engineer	*Chief Electrical Engineer*	*Carriage & Wagon Engineer*	
1953		R. C. Bond	S. B. Warder	A. E. Robson	—
1954		"	"	"	—
1955		"	"	"	—
1956		"	"	"	—
1957		"	"	"	—
1958		"	"	"	—
1959		J. F. Harrison	"		—
1960		"	"		—
1961		"	"		—
1962		"	"		—
1963		"	"		—
1964					J. F. Harrison
1965					A. E. Robson
1966					"
1967					—
1968					T. C. B. Miller

YEAR	Chief Mechanical and Electrical Engineer
1969	T. C. B. Miller
1970	"
1971	G. S. W. Calder
1972	"
1973	"
1974	"
1975	"
1976	"
1977	K. Taylor
1978	"
1979	"
1980	

BRITISH RAILWAYS
REGIONAL CHIEF MECHANICAL AND ELECTRICAL ENGINEERS

YEAR	Eastern Region	North Eastern Region	London Midland Region	Southern Region	Scottish Region	Western Region
1948	A. H. Peppercorn	Joint with Eastern Region	H. G. Ivatt	O. V. Bulleid	G. S. Bellamy	F. W. Hawksworth
1949	J. F. Harrison		,,	,,	,,	,,
1950	,,		,,	,,	,,	K. J. Cook
1951	K. J. Cook		J. F. Harrison	H. H. Swift	,,	,,
1952	,,		,,	,,	M. S. Hatchell	R. A. Smeddle
1953	,,		,,	,,		,,
1954	,,		,,	,,		,,
1955	,,		,,	,,		,,
1956	,,		,,	,,		,,
1957	,,		,,	W. J. A. Sykes		,,
1958	,,		,,	,,		,,
1959	K. J. Cook / T. C. B. Miller	M. C. Burrows	A. E. Robson	,,	,,	,,
1960	,,	,,	,,	,,	J. J. Finlayson	R. A. Smeddle
1961	,,	,,	,,	,,	C. T. Roberts	T. Matthewson-Dick
1962	C. Scutt	,,	,,	,,		,,
1963	,,	,,	,,	,,	,,	S. Ridgway
1964	,,	,,	,,	,,	,,	,,
1965	,,	J. Sinclair	,,	,,	,,	,,
1966	,,	,,	A. H. Emerson	,,	G. S. W. Calder	,,
1967	,,		,,	,,	,,	,,
1968	,,		,,	,,	,,	,,
1969	,,		,,	,,	,,	,,

YEAR	Eastern Region	North Eastern Region	London Midland Region	Southern Region	Scottish Region	Western Region
1970	C. Scutt		A. H. Emerson	C. M. Maguire	G. S. W. Calder	S. Ridgway
1971	,,	N. E. Region merged with Eastern Region 1–1–67	K. Taylor	,,	F. G. Clements	,,
1972	,,		F. G. Clements	,,	M. V. Casey	S. R. D. Power
1973	,,		,,	,,	,,	,,
1974	,,		,,	,,	,,	,,
1975	,,		,,	,,	,,	,,
1976	,,		,,	,,	,,	,,
1977	M. V. Casey		,,	,,	G. H. Passey	,,
1978	,,		,,	,,	,,	,,
1979	J. A. Sourbut		,,	,,	,,	,,
1980	,,		,,	,,	,,	,,

BRITISH RAILWAYS HEADQUARTERS
SIGNAL AND TELECOMMUNICATIONS ENGINEERING

YEARS	NAME	DESIGNATION
1948–52	H. H. Dyer	Chief Officer, Signal and Telecommunications Engineering
1952–59	J. H. Fraser	Chief Signal Engineering Officer
1959–67	A. W. Woodbridge	Chief S & T Engineer
1967–74	J. F. H. Tyler	Chief S & T Engineer
1975–80	A. A. Cardani	Chief S & T Engineer

Regional Chief Signal and Telecommunications Engineers

YEAR	Eastern Region	North Eastern Region	London Midland Region	Southern Region	Scottish Region	Western Region
1948	A. M. Moss	J. H. Fraser	W. Wood	L. J. Boucher	W. Bryson	A. W. Woodbridge
1949	„	„	L. S. Williams	„	„	„
1950	„	„	„	„	„	„
1951	„	„	„	„	„	„
1952	„	A. F. Wigram	„	„	„	„
1953	„	„	„	„	„	„
1954	„	„	„	„	„	„
1955	„	„	„	„	L. J. M. Knotts	„
1956	R. A. Green	„	L. S. Williams	„	„	„
1957	„	„	E. G. Brentnall	„	„	A. A. Cardani
1958	„	„	„	„	„	„
1959	„	„	„	J. F. H. Tyler	„	„
1960	„	„	„	„	L. J. M. Knotts / H. O. Baldwin	„
1961	„	„	„	„	„	„
1962	„	„	„	„	„	„
1963	„	„	„	„	„	„
1964	„	„	„	„	„	„

YEAR	Eastern Region	North Eastern Region	London Midland Region	Southern Region	Scottish Region	Western Region
1965	R. A. Green	A. F. Wigram	E. G. Brentnall	J. F. H. Tyler	H. O. Baldwin	A. A. Cardani
1966	„	„	„	„	„	„
1967	„		„	A. W. Damon	„	„
1968	„		A. A. Cardani	„	„	M. E. Leach
1969	„		„	„	D. S. Jewell	„
1970	H. O. Baldwin		„	„	„	„
1971	„	Merged with Eastern Region	„	„	„	„
1972	„		„	A. W. Damon / K. E. Hodgson	„	„
1973	„		R. Peat	„	„	„
1974	„		„	„	„	A. R. Brown
1975	M. E. Leach		F. W. G. Smith	R. Peat	„	„
1976	„		„	„	„	„
1977	„		A. R. Brown	„	„	F. Kerr
1978	„		„	W. H. Whitehouse	„	„
1979	„		„	„	„	„
1980	„		„		C. Hale	„

BRITISH RAILWAYS: HQ AND REGIONS
CHIEF OFFICER (MOTIVE POWER: BR HQ) AND REGIONAL MOTIVE POWER SUPERINTENDENTS

YEAR	British Railways HQ	Eastern Region	North Eastern Region	London Midland Region	Southern Region	Scottish Region	Western Region
1948	H. Rudgard	L. P. Parker	F. H. Petty	S. W. Abraham	T. E. Chrimes	R. F. Harvey	W. N. Pellow
1949	"	"	"	"	"	"	"
1950	"	"	"	"	"	E. D. Trask	"
1951	R. F. Harvey	"	"	"	"	"	"
1952	"	"	"	"	"	"	"
1953	"	"	"	"	"	"	"
1954	"	E. D. Trask	"	S. T. Clayton	"	C. R. Campbell	"
1955	S. T. Clayton	"	"	"	"	"	"
1956	"	"	"	"	"	"	H. E. A. White
1957	"	"	"	"	"	"	"
1958							
1959							

BRITISH RAILWAYS
REGIONAL CARRIAGE AND WAGON ENGINEERS

YEAR	Eastern Region	North Eastern Region	London Midland Region	Southern Region	Scottish Region	Western Region
1948	–		–	–	–	–
1949	–		–	–	–	–
1950	A. E. Robson		–	F. Munns	E. A. Milne	H. Randle
1951	,,	Joint with Eastern Region	–	,,	,,	,,
1952	,,		H. Randle	,,	,,	C. T. Roberts
1953	L. Reeves		,,	,,	J. Blair	,,
1954	,,		,,	,,	,,	,,
1955	,,		,,	,,	,,	,,
1956	,,		,,	,,	,,	,,
1957	,,		,,	,,	,,	,,
1958	,,		,,	,,	–	–

After 1957–58, all Regional Carriage and Wagon Engineers were responsible to the Regional Chief Mechanical and Electrical Engineers.

BRITISH RAILWAYS WORKSHOPS
LATER BRITISH RAIL ENGINEERING LTD

General Managers/Managing Directors

1963–65	H. O. Houchen
1965–68	R. C. Bond
1968–73	A. E. Robson
1973–76	S. Ridgway
1976—	I. D. Gardiner

BRITISH RAILWAYS RESEARCH
Head of Research: British Railways

1948–53	T. M. Herbert
1953–64	C. C. Inglis
1964–65	S. Jones
1965–70	S. F. Smith
1970–79	K. H. Spring
1979–	A. H. Wickens

INDEX OF BRITISH RAILWAYS ENGINEERS SINCE 1948 WHO HAVE BEEN HEADS OF DEPARTMENTS, TOGETHER WITH OTHERS REFERRED TO IN THE TEXT.

This index does not include engineers who had left the railway service before nationalization on 1 January 1948. Where their names appear in the text, they are incorporated in the General Index. The General Index also includes the names of those who were not engineers or not railway employees.

The Council of Engineering Institutions (CEI) was founded in 1966 and Corporate Members of Chartered Institutions, including The Institutions of Civil, Mechanical, and Electrical Engineers, were thereafter empowered to adopt the designation Chartered Engineer (CEng). Following later reorganizations within the Member Institutions, Members were redesignated Fellows and Associate Members became Members. In 1969 the Institution of Locomotive Engineers amalgamated with the Institution of Mechanical Engineers forming the Railway Division (RD).

Index